FLUID DYNAMICS OF MULTIPHASE SYSTEMS

A Blaisdell Book in the Pure and Applied Sciences

CONSULTING EDITOR

Leon Lapidus, *Princeton University*

Fluid Dynamics
of Multiphase Systems

S. L. Soo

UNIVERSITY OF ILLINOIS, URBANA

BLAISDELL PUBLISHING COMPANY

A Division of Ginn and Company

WALTHAM, MASSACHUSETTS · TORONTO · LONDON

TO MY WIFE, HERMIA G. SOO

Preface

Multiphase systems consist of mixtures of solid particles, liquid droplets, or bubbles in fluids. Studies on the dynamics of multiphase systems encompass broad lines of disciplines in engineering and sciences. Cutting across various lines of application, the present volume covers basic concepts and phenomena of particulate clouds of multiphase systems. It is intended as a research reference and for a second year graduate course.

The topics of studies in various professional disciplines reported in their respective journals as well as journals of applied physics, mechanics, and mathematics can be outlined approximately as follows:

The first group of disciplines consists of chemical, fuels, food, agricultural engineering, pulp and paper, colloidal chemistry, and soil physics. Each concerns a number of the topics such as transfer lines, pneumatic conveyors, fluidization, batch settling, packed beds, heterogeneous reactors, spray driers, extraction, absorption, evaporation, and vortex collection.

In the group including meteorology, geophysics, electrical, sanitary and hydraulic engineering, photoreproduction and rheology, we have topics such as sedimentation, porous media, transport and dispersion, nuclear fallout, control of air and water pollution, droplet charging and coalescence, electrostatic precipitation, and xerography.

In the group consisting of mechanical, nuclear and vacuum engineering, acoustics, and medical sciences our concern is with combustion, boiling, atomization, cavitation, cryopumping, reactor coolant and fuel feeding, attenuation and dispersion of sound, underwater detection, flow and coagulation of blood.

In the general realm of aerospace engineering and sciences, topics include satellite drag, spacecraft-ionosphere interaction, colloidal propulsion, control of radiowave attenuation, ablation, metalized propellant rockets, MHD generators, and accelerators.

Naturally, it will be easy to point out further crosslisting of applications and purposes. An interesting phenomenon arising from the fact that basic concepts of multiphase systems serve such a large variety of fields of study and application is that researchers in one field tend to be unaware of current developments in other fields, and, in a few instances, even in the same field. What appears to be the "information explosion" is, at least in part, compounded by a substantial amount of independent or related efforts. Because much remains to be explored, progress is best served through a review at this stage.

Studies of multiphase systems are still going through stages of development including recognition of basic phenomena, development of instrumentation, mathematical representation, and methods of solution. The present volume cuts across various lines of discipline to regroup the basic concepts under a few essential topics. Crossreference to publications in various fields under a given topic, even merely by citing their availability, is also intended to indicate pertinent journals in which information not yet published will eventually be found. The older as well as the more recent references are included here so that the reader may more easily locate information from libraries accessible to him; a study of the earlier literature also illustrates various thinking procedures in the course of the development of ideas and is almost the only way to begin any kind of research. The bibliography is aimed at comprehensiveness in terms of ideas but not exhaustiveness in data presentation—a feature which is left to handbooks. Treatment of all topics with equal sophistication is not feasible at present. However, completeness of basic concepts and physical understanding is aimed at and gaps have been filled in whenever possible. Qualitative descriptions are furnished where rigorous formulation is not available; experimental details are included where they contribute to the understanding of the basic phenomena. Although various side issues are covered as literature surveys, the details of the main issue, fluid dynamics of multiphase systems, are self-contained within this book. The reader will no doubt find that a great deal of research remains to be done in this field of study. However, it is believed that based on the information provided a rational method of approach toward research, development, and design can be formulated.

Since the primary concern is with particulate clouds, the order of presentation is, after an overall introduction in Chapter 1: Chapters 2 and 3 survey basic information on single particles without derivation except the case of a single particle in a random-flow field; the rest of the chapters cover basic aspects of particulate clouds.

Needless to say, a great deal of ground is covered on various aspects of particulate systems. In order to assist the reader in gaining a perspective of some of the basic methods of approach to various problems, a summary of basic concepts is given at the end of each chapter (except Chapter 1). All these primary concepts together form the basic links of the development to the present stage of understanding. Authors and approximate dates of introduction are included for the sake of historical interest.

Many papers presented at recent meetings, preprints, and recent theses were referred to; information regarding their eventual location in journals will be welcome for later revisions.

The author wishes to take this opportunity to acknowledge the important contributions of a number of his thesis advisees, who carried out their graduate research on various topics in this field. Thanks are due to Professors L. Lapidus and W. R. Schowalter for reading the manuscript and contributing their worthy suggestions.

The author wishes to thank Mrs. M. W. Wolf and Mrs. C. H. Cummings who typed the manuscript and assisted in preparing the line drawings with great precision. Shirley and Lydia Soo assisted in arranging bibliography and index cards.

S. L. Soo

Urbana, Illinois

Contents

SYMBOLS

In this text over five hundred different physical quantities are included in various formulations. Use of the same letters or symbols for different entities or concepts has been unavoidable. Choice of notation was also affected by the desire to retain commonly used notations familiar in each field of study, while at the same time avoiding ambiguity by making a single choice where two or more symbols for the same quantity are known to exist in the literature.

Unless otherwise defined in the text, the following symbols, with their meaning, are understood:

a radius of a particle (bubble, or droplet)

C_D drag coefficient

C_f friction factor

c specific heat at constant pressure of the fluid phase

c_p specific heat at constant pressure of the particulate phase

D diffusivity

e electronic charge

F time constant of particle-fluid momentum transfer

F_p time constant of particle-particle momentum transfer

$\mathscr{F}$ force

$\mathscr{F}_E$ energy source

f distribution function

G time constant of particle-fluid heat transfer

G_p time constant of particle-particle heat transfer

h heat-transfer coefficient

i $\sqrt{-1}$

J flux density

j j-factor of heat transfer

k Boltzmann constant; mass transfer coefficient; or rate constant

L length

l_1 Lagrangian scale of turbulence

M total mass

$\mathscr{M}$ molecular weight

m mass of a particle

N total number of particles

N_{Re} Reynolds number

N_{Sl} Strouhal number

N_{Nu} Nusselt number

N_{Pr} Prandtl number

N_M Mach number

N_{Kn} Knudsen number

N_{Sh} Sherwood number

N_{Pe} Peclet number ($N_{Pr} N_{Re}$)

N_{Sc} Schmidt number

N_{Fr} Froude number

N_{We} Weber number

N_{Ja} Jakob number

N_{ev}	Electroviscous number
N_{Im}	Impact number
N_{RC}	Radiative conductivity number
N_m	gas-particle momentum number
N_{et}	electrothermal number
N_{es}	electrosurface number
$(N_{Re})_e$	electric Reynolds number
n	number density
P	static pressure
Q	total electric charge
q	electric charge per particle
R	radius of tube
$\bar{R}$	gas constant
$\mathscr{R}$	Lagrangian correlation
$\mathscr{R}_E$	Eulerian correlation
r	radius
S	entropy
T	absolute temperature
t	time
U_i	ith component of velocity
U, V, W	mean velocities
u, v, w	velocities
$\mathscr{V}$	total volume
v	particle volume
x, y, z	Cartesian coordinates
x_i	ith coordinate
Γ	flux; or rate of generation
γ	ratio of specific heats
Δ_{ij}	deformation tensor
δ	a small dimension
ϵ	fraction void
ϵ_o	permittivity of free space

η	fraction impaction
Θ	dilatation tensor
Θ	dimensionless temperature
θ	polar angle or angle
κ	thermal conductivity of a single-phase fluid or when treating a mixture as a single phase
$\bar{\kappa}$	thermal conductivity of the fluid material in a multiphase system
$\bar{\kappa}_p$	thermal conductivity of the material constituting the particles in a multiphase system
κ_{fm}	thermal conductivity of the fluid phase in a multiphase system
κ_m	thermal conductivity of a mixture
$\kappa_m^{(q)}$	thermal conductivity of component (q) in a mixture
κ_{pm}	thermal conductivity of the particulate phase in a multiphase system
Λ	mean free path, or wavelength
λ	Lagrangian microscale
λ_E	Eulerian microscale
μ	viscosity of a single-phase fluid or when treating a mixture as a single phase; abbreviation for micron, microns
$\bar{\mu}$	viscosity of the fluid material in a multiphase system
$\bar{\mu}_p$	viscosity of the material constituting the particles in a multiphase system
μ_{fm}	viscosity of the fluid phase in a multiphase system

μ_{pm} viscosity of the particulate phase in a multiphase system

μ_m viscosity of a mixture

$\mu_m^{(q)}$ viscosity of component (q) in a mixture

$\bar{\nu}$ kinematic viscosity of the fluid material in a multiphase system

ν frequency

ρ density of a single-phase fluid, or when treating a mixture on a single phase, or density of the fluid phase in a multiphase system

ρ_p density of the particulate phase in a multiphase system

ρ_m density of the mixture

$\bar{\rho}$ density of the fluid material in a multiphase system

$\overline{\rho_p}$ density of the material constituting the particulate phase in a multiphase system

σ surface tension, or normal stress

τ time, or shear stress

Φ impaction parameter for non-Stokesian behavior

ϕ volume fraction solid (of particulate phase)

φ angle or azimuthal angle

φ thermionic work function

Ψ Inertia parameter for impaction

ψ stream function

Ω solid angle

ω circular frequency

Unsubscripted Quantity for Fluid Phase of a Multiphase System

Bold face vectorial quantity

$\langle \ \rangle$ average of a quantity

$(\overline{\ })$ material property or mean value

$(\tilde{\ })$ Fourier transform of a function

$(\dot{\ })$ time rate

$(\ddot{\ })$ second derivative with respect to time

Subscripts

ij tensor

p particulate phase of a multiphase system

w at the wall

o reference value

f fluctuating quantity

Superscripts

$*$ dimensionless, reduced, or characteristic quantities

$+$ dimensionless quantities

(s) interaction parameter of s particulate phase with the fluid phase or the component of a mixture

(sr) interaction parameter of s particulate phase by the r particulate phase

(f) the fluid component

FLUID DYNAMICS OF MULTIPHASE SYSTEMS

1 | Introduction

1.1 Scope

A multiphase system consists of a fluid phase or fluid medium and a particulate phase of any number of chemical components. When the fluid medium is a gas, the particulate phase may consist of solid particles or liquid droplets or both. When the fluid medium is a liquid, the particulate phase may consist of solid particles, gas bubbles, or liquid droplets immisible to the fluid phase.

The dynamics of multiphase systems include momentum, energy, mass, and charge transfers between the phases, whether or not the process is influenced by the presence of a potential field.

There are many multiphase systems among engineering equipment and processes. Here are a few examples:

1. Gas-solid particle systems: pneumatic conveyors, dust collectors, fluidized beds, heterogeneous reactors, metallized propellant rockets; aerodynamic ablation, xerography; cosmic dusts, nuclear fallout problems.

2. Gas-liquid droplet systems: atomizers, scrubbers, dryers, absorbers, combustors; agglomeration, air pollution; gas cooling, evaporation, cryopumping.

3. Liquid-gas bubble systems: absorbers, evaporators, scrubbers, air lift pump; cavitation, flotation, aeration.

4. Liquid-liquid droplet systems: extraction, homogenizing, emulsifying.

5. Liquid-solid particle systems: fluidized beds, flotation, sedimentation.

Following the usual method of approach in dealing with mixtures, we shall attempt to express their properties in terms of those of the components.

1

Recapitulation is made next on the elementary properties of fluid media, solid materials, particulate matter, and dynamics of single-phase fluids.

1.2 Basic and Related Subject Matter

Studies of dynamics of multiphase systems have followed two methods of approach:

1. Treating the dynamics of single particles and then trying to extend to a multiple particle system in an analogous manner as in molecular (kinetic) theory.
2. Modifying the continuum mechanics of single-phase fluids in such a way as to account for the presence of particles.

Dynamics behaviors of single particles (solid particles, liquid droplets, or gas bubbles) have been studied extensively and are covered thoroughly in a number of books [D2, F36, G38], and, in general, utilize methods of particle mechanics. Extension to a multiple particle system from dynamics of single particles has not been particularly successful except in isolated cases. However, qualified analogies to molecular theory and free molecule flow [P2] were shown to be very useful in determining pertinent parameters of interaction among particles, and interaction of particles with a boundary.

Computations for transport processes based on kinetic theory (represented by the Boltzmann transport equation) [P2] calls for knowledge of molecular interaction. The details are complex for certain gases [H44] and unknown for most liquids [F22]. Continuum mechanics [S13], through the introduction of pertinent phenomenological relations, effectively replace the phase space (position and momentum coordinates) of the Boltzmann transport equation with configuration space (position coordinates) and transport properties; the latter can be experimentally determined. This is the rationale of the method of approach in item (2). This method of approach is relatively recent in dealing with multiphase systems.

Perturbation of gas dynamic relations [S25] as well as those of potential motion by the presence of the particulate phase gives rise to interesting flow and thermodynamic behaviors of multiphase systems.

Both laminar- and turbulent-flow regimes will be dealt with, although most of the practical multiphase systems are turbulent. This is because the laminar flow system lends itself to rigorous mathematical solution; a feasible method can be extended to a corresponding turbulent-flow system with minimal logical empiricism. Statistical theory of turbulence [H41] concerns statistical properties of random motion of groups of molecules and is significant to the problems of diffusion and transport. Its development took hints from statistical mechanics and kinetic theory, but the ergodity assumption in the latter two methods had to be dropped.

Dynamics of multiphase systems, of course, include heat and mass transfer [K23]. Radiation [C14], while insignificant in most cases of fluid flow, is a principal mode of energy exchange. When dealing with reactive (including ionization) systems, chemical kinetics [H38] method will be extended to account for the changes. Rate processes also include electron and ion dynamics [F21].

Further, we rely on thermodynamics [S51] for the basic relations between properties, dissipation and irreversibility, and asymptotic or equilibrium states. Other related subjects are properties of solids, electron states, and conductivity [M1]. Electric-charge phenomena and electrodynamics [J1] are involved in many systems with charge collection, emission, and surface interaction.

It is seen that studies of dynamics of multiphase systems cut across a large number of basic fields. Most of the references just cited are typical texts rather than specific references, which provide background information for this presentation. Due to its broadness, no attempt will be made toward review of all the basic relations.

1.3 Size and Size Distribution of Particulate Phase

The shapes of particulate matter encountered in multiphase systems are, in general, nonspherical. The spherical shape is a special case or an idealization of irregular shapes.

Among solid particles, smallest balls for ball bearings are $\frac{1}{32}$ inch (7.94×10^{-4} m) in diameter, with size and sphericity accurate to within fractions of 10^{-4} inch produced by grinding. In general, below 1 mm size only particles of glass (which might be viewed as a liquid with extremely long relaxation time) produced by spray method are spherical. Catalysts of millimeter sizes are usually formed into spheres from fine powders. Pulverized solids retain the basic shapes of their crystals.

Small liquid droplets usually attain spherical shape due to surface tension. When gravity or other field effects are significant, they attain shapes of smallest resistance (i.e., falling rain drops), or minimum potential (charged droplets).

Gas bubbles would retain spherical shape due to surface tension until perturbed by gravity or other field forces. Foams or large bubbles are further exceptions.

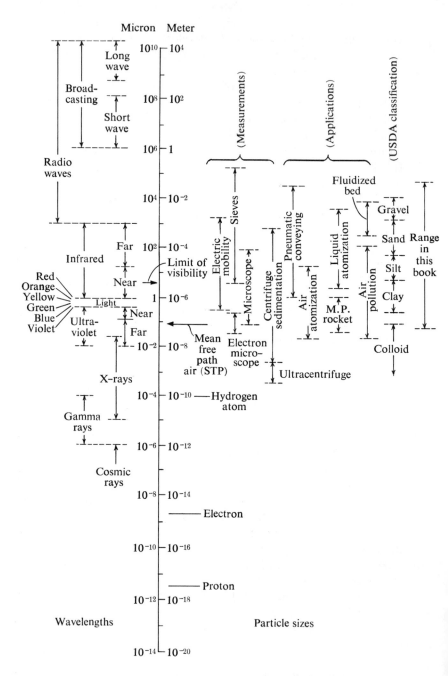

Figure 1.1 Magnitudes of particle sizes in multiphase systems in relation to other physical quantities.

The ranges of particle sizes and their measurements and classification under consideration of the present book are shown in Fig. 1.1, together with the magnitudes of other reference or significant physical quantities. A particle appears as transparent to wavelengths greater than its size.

Measurement—For solid particles above 10 μ in size, measurement can be accomplished by sieving [D2]. Use of the centrifuge and ultra centrifuge covers a wide range from below 10^{-3} μ to above 10^2 μ. For solid particles or liquid droplets from 10 μ to 0.5 μ, optical microscope can be used for measurement and counting; from 0.5 to 0.1 μ calls for the electron microscope [F36]. Size determination by measurement of mobility in an electric field is useful down to 0.1 μ in a gas or electrolyte (see Chap. 10). Measurement of the size of liquid droplets or gas bubbles will, in general, need an optical method with photographic recording followed by measurement and counting. Particle size distribution in a particle cloud can be determined from forward-scattered light (see Chap. 5).

When sieving is applicable, ASTM Standard gives sieves graded as shown in Table 1.1 according to sieve number and size of opening and tolerance. This U.S. Sieve Series was specified by the National Bureau of Standards [D2]. It is obvious that if a batch of powder passes through the No. 70 sieve but is retained by the No. 80 sieve, the sizes are within the range of 177 to 210 μ including some sticks, if any, larger than 210 μ, and smaller powders sticking to the sieve. Agglomeration of powder is also influenced by the humidity, electric charge, and surface behavior.

Distribution in Particle Size—The idea of distribution in particle size can be seen in the following manner: Imagine a stack of the series of sieves specified in Table 1.1 with the sieve of largest opening on top; shake a 1-Kg sample of solid particles through them, and weigh the final content of each sieve. We may get a diagram (histogram) as shown in Fig. 1.2. This diagram gives, for instance, 0.05 Kg of particles between the size range 3360 μ and 4000 μ. In terms of a mass distribution function $f_M(b)$ and

$$\mathrm{d}\left(\frac{M}{M_o}\right) = f_M(b)\,\mathrm{d}b, \tag{1.1}$$

where dM is the mass of particles within given size range b and $b + \mathrm{d}b$ for total mass M_0 of the sample of particles measured. The normalizing condition is given by

$$1 = \int_0^\infty f_M(b)\,\mathrm{d}b. \tag{1.2}$$

Over a finite-size range b_1 and b_2,

$$\frac{M}{M_o} = \int_{b_1}^{b_2} f_M(b)\,\mathrm{d}b, \tag{1.3}$$

Table 1.1

Nominal Dimensions, Permissible Variations for Woven Wire Cloth of Standard Sieves, U.S. Series ASTM Standard

Size, μ	Sieve No.	Permissible Variations in Openings Avg. $\pm \%$	Max. $\pm \%$	Size, μ	Sieve No.	Permissible Variations in Openings Avg. $\pm \%$	Max. $\pm \%$
5660	$3\frac{1}{2}$	3	10	420	40	5	25
4760	4	3	10	350	45	5	25
4000	5	3	10	297	50	5	25
3360	6	3	10	250	60	5	25
2830	7	3	10	210	70	5	25
2380	8	3	10	177	80	6	40
2000	10	3	10	149	100	6	40
1680	12	3	10	125	120	6	40
1410	14	3	10	105	140	6	40
1190	16	3	10	88	170	6	40
1000	18	5	15	74	200	7	60
840	20	5	15	62	230	7	90
710	25	5	15	53	270	7	90
590	30	5	15	44	325	7	90
500	35	5	15	37	400	7	90

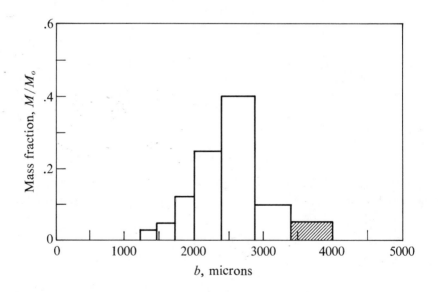

Figure 1.2 Typical finite mass distribution of sieve ranges.

given by the height of the shaded area in Fig. 1.2 for the range 3360–4000 μ. A continuous curve such as shown in Fig. 1.3 may be obtained when sufficiently narrow intervals are taken. The mass-distribution function gives the fraction of mass over a given size range.

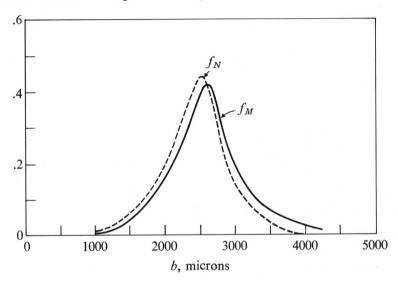

Figure 1.3 Typical continuous-distribution functions f_N and f_M for a given sample.

When a microscope is used for the determination of particle-size distribution, the results are given in terms of size b and number of particles N within a given size range. In terms of number-distribution function f_N, we have the fraction of particles (N/N_o), for total N_o particles counted

$$\mathrm{d}\left(\frac{N}{N_o}\right) = f_N(b)\,\mathrm{d}b, \tag{1.4}$$

with the normalizing condition

$$1 = \int_0^\infty f_N(b)\,\mathrm{d}b. \tag{1.5}$$

Since, for mass $m(b)$ of a particle of size b

$$M_o\,\mathrm{d}\left(\frac{M}{M_o}\right) = N_o m(b)\,\mathrm{d}\left(\frac{N}{N_o}\right), \tag{1.6}$$

the relation between the number-distribution function and mass-distribution function is therefore

$$f_M(b) = \frac{N_o m(b)}{M_o} f_N(b) = \frac{m(b)}{m_o} f_N(b), \tag{1.7}$$

where m_o is the average mass of a particle based on total number of particles.

As an example, we consider the case of spherical particles of material density $\bar{\rho}_p$ and we denote the radius of particles as a, then

$$m(a) = \frac{4\pi}{3} a^3 \bar{\rho}_p. \tag{1.8}$$

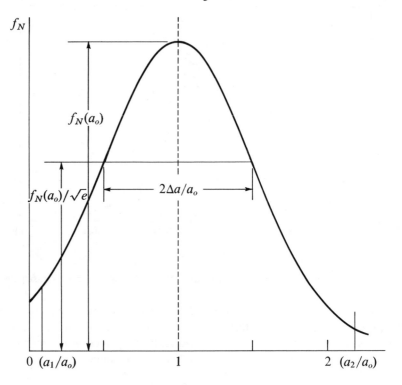

Figure 1.4 Relations between quantities in a normal distribution.

We further take the case in which the curve of number distribution can be fitted with a normal distribution function, or

$$f_N(a) = A_N \exp\left[-\frac{(a - a_o)^2}{2(\Delta a)^2}\right], \tag{1.9}$$

between radii a_1 and a_2, where a_o is the mean radius and $(\Delta a)^2$ is the mean square deviation (Fig. 1.4), and A_N is the normalizing constant, or

$$(\Delta a)^2 = \langle (a - a_0)^2 \rangle, \tag{1.10}$$

$2(\Delta a)$ is the width of the distribution curve at $f = f(a_o)/\sqrt{e}$.

The normalizing condition gives

$$1 = \int_{a_1}^{a_2} f_N(a) \, da, \tag{1.11}$$

or

$$\frac{1}{A_N} = \sqrt{2} \, \Delta a \int_{a_1}^{a_2} \exp\left[-\frac{(a - a_o)^2}{2(\Delta a)^2}\right] d\left[\frac{a - a_o}{\sqrt{2} \, \Delta a}\right]$$

$$= \sqrt{2} \, \Delta a \int_{(a_1 - a_o)/\sqrt{2}\Delta a}^{(a_2 - a_o)/\sqrt{2}\Delta a} \exp(-x^2) \, dx$$

$$= \sqrt{2} \, \Delta a \frac{\sqrt{\pi}}{2}\left[\operatorname{erf}\left(\frac{a_2 - a_o}{\sqrt{2} \, \Delta a}\right) + \operatorname{erf}\left(\frac{a_o - a_1}{\sqrt{2} \, \Delta a}\right)\right], \tag{1.12}$$

which gives the normalizing constant A_N. The mass distribution is now

$$f_M = A_M \frac{4\pi}{3} \bar{\rho}_p a^3 \exp\left[-\frac{(a - a_o)^2}{2(\Delta a)^2}\right]. \tag{1.13}$$

Expressing a^3 in terms of

$$a^3 = (a - a_o)^3 + 3a_o(a - a_o)^2 + 3a_o^2(a - a_o) + a_o^3, \tag{1.14}$$

the normalizing constant A_M based on mass is given by

$$\frac{1}{A_M} = \frac{4\pi}{3} \bar{\rho}_p 4(\Delta a)^4 \int_{(a_1 - a_o)/\sqrt{2}\Delta a}^{(a_2 - a_o)/\sqrt{2}\Delta a}$$

$$\times \left[x^3 + 3 \frac{a_o}{\sqrt{2} \, \Delta a} x^2 + 3 \frac{a_o^2}{2(\Delta a)^2} x + \left(\frac{a_o}{\sqrt{2}\Delta a}\right)^3\right] e^{-x^2} \, dx \tag{1.15}$$

$$= \frac{4\pi}{3} \bar{\rho}_p 4(\Delta a)^4 \left\{\left(\frac{a_o}{\sqrt{2} \, \Delta a}\right) \frac{\sqrt{\pi}}{2}\left[\frac{3}{2} + \frac{a_o^2}{2(\Delta a)^2}\right] \operatorname{erf}(x)\right.$$

$$\left. - \frac{1}{2}\left[1 + \frac{3a_o^2}{2(\Delta a)^2} + \frac{3a_o}{\sqrt{2}(\Delta a)} x + x^2\right] e^{-x^2}\right\} \Bigg|_{(a_1 - a_o)/\sqrt{2}(\Delta a)}^{(a_2 - a_o)/\sqrt{2}(\Delta a)}. \tag{1.16}$$

It is seen that for the case of very narrow size distribution or $\Delta a / a_o \ll 1$, the above limits of integration can be replaced by $+\infty$ and $-\infty$; in that case,

$$A_N \sim \frac{1}{\sqrt{2\pi} \, \Delta a} \tag{1.17}$$

and

$$\frac{1}{A_M} \sim \frac{4(2\pi)^{3/2}}{3} \bar{\rho}_p \left(\frac{a_o}{\Delta a}\right)\left[\frac{3}{2} + \frac{a_o^2}{2(\Delta a)^2}\right](\Delta a)^4, \tag{1.18}$$

or

$$f_M = \frac{1}{2\sqrt{2\pi}}\left(\frac{a_o}{\Delta a}\right)^3 \frac{1}{a_o}\left(\frac{a}{a_o}\right)^3 \left[\frac{3}{2} + \frac{a_o^2}{2(\Delta a)^2}\right]^{-1} \exp\left[-\frac{1}{2}\left(\frac{a - a_o}{\Delta a}\right)^2\right]. \quad (1.19)$$

The fraction of particles with radius less than a is given by

$$\frac{N_{(<a)}}{N_o} = \int_{a_1}^{a} f_N(a)\, \mathrm{d}a. \quad (1.20)$$

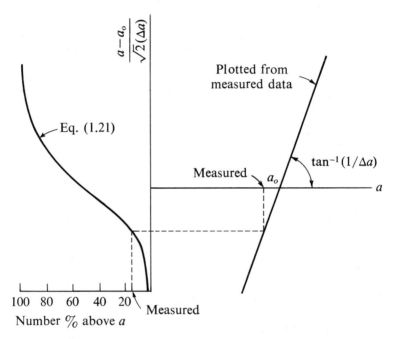

Figure 1.5 Determination of mean size (a_o) and mean deviation (Δa) of normal distribution from measured data.

For narrow size range or small deviation in a sample,

$$\frac{N_{(<a)}}{N_o} \cong \frac{1}{2}\left[1 + \mathrm{erf}\left(\frac{a - a_o}{\sqrt{2}\,\Delta a}\right)\right]. \quad (1.21)$$

A diagram can be plotted with the measured cumulative number of particles up to radius a along an ordinate of $\frac{1}{2}\{1 + \mathrm{erf}\,[(a - a_o)/\sqrt{2}\,\Delta a]\}$ corresponding to a linear scale of $(a - a_o)/\sqrt{2}(\Delta a)$ vs. a linear abscissa of a. If the resultant point can be approximated by a straight line, the intercept along the abscissa gives a_o, and the slope gives $1/(\Delta a)$ (Fig. 1.5).

The task of curve fitting to determine the size distribution is made easier by assuming a log-normal distribution or [F36],

$$f_N = A_N a^\nu \exp\left\{-\frac{(\log a - \log a_o')^2}{2[(\ln \Delta a')]^2}\right\},$$ (1.22)

where ν is a constant to be determined for a given sample: $\log a_o' = \langle\log a\rangle$, and $[\log(\Delta a')]^2 = \langle(\log a - \log a_o')^2\rangle$.

Various forms of distributions were suggested. A general discussion of theory and applications was presented by Cadle [C1]. Bimodel or multimodel distributions were discussed by Dallavalle, Orr, and Blocker [D4].

Equivalent Mean Diameters—Instinctively, attempts were made to find an equivalent sphere for irregular-shaped particulate matter. This technique does not always work, as when dealing with lint or fibrous dust particles. Depending on the transport phenomena involved for given f_N, the mean diameters have been defined according to:

$$\text{Mean diameter (length)} = 2a_o^{(l)} = \frac{\int 2a f_N \, da}{\int f_N \, da}$$ (1.23)

$$\text{Mean volume diameter} = 2a_o^{(v)} = \left[\frac{\int (2a)^3 f_N \, da}{\int f_N \, da}\right]^{1/3}$$ (1.24)

$$\text{Mean surface diameter} = 2a_o^{(s)} = \left[\frac{\int (2a)^2 f_N \, da}{\int f_N \, da}\right]^{1/2}$$ (1.25)

$$\text{Mean volume-surface diameter} = 2a_o^{(vs)} = \left[\frac{\int (2a)^3 f_N \, da}{\int (2a)^2 f_N \, da}\right]$$ (1.26)

$$\text{Weight mean diameter} = 2a_o^{(W)} = \frac{\int (2a)^4 f_N \, da}{\int (2a)^3 f_N \, da} = \frac{\int 2a f_M \, da}{\int f_M \, da}.$$ (1.27)

These relations are presented because the need of classification of the mean diameter and the size or mass spectrum obtained by various means. For instance, when dealing with momentum transport of small particles at low relative velocity to fluid (Sec. 2.1), the mean diameter based on length will be pertinent (Sec. 8.3). The mean volume diameter is pertinent to the determination of fraction void (Sec. 5.1). The mean surface diameter is pertinent to heat and mass transfer and reaction at the fluid-particle interface (Sec. 5.1 and 9.6). The mean volume-surface diameter is related to rate processes affected by volume to surface ratio. The weight mean diameter is generally applicable to the weighing of sieved samples discussed in the above.

For irregular shape,

$$2a_{\text{normal}} = \left[\frac{6 \times \text{volume of particle}}{\pi} \right]^{1/3}. \tag{1.28}$$

Mean diameters based on drag and surface area, are in general different.

1.4 Methods of Determination of Sizes

General references on this topic are the volumes by Martin [M14], and Orr and Dallavalle [O6].

In his survey, Browning made a complete outline of methods of determination of size of particles [B64]. Various methods were categorized as suggested by Sinclair [S36], and Manson, Ferrié, and Kling [M5], according to mechanical, physicochemical, optical, and electrical methods. The basic principles of various methods are clarified in later chapters.

Mechanical—In this category, methods include preparation of slides for microscope with a suitable coating, and those utilizing variation in drag force (Chap. 2) according to size and from measurement of mass flow.

(a) Preparation of microscope slides includes the low-speed collection of particles or droplets on slides coated with suitable material, depending on the materials of the particles. Coating may consist of mineral oil [F37], magnesia [B70], or soot [L27]. Jet impaction or dynamic collection on coated surfaces produces impressions depending on particle size [R5]. The amount of particles of different sizes can be selected by using different jet velocities. The cascade impactor makes possible study of dynamics of droplets [G17]. Collection at high temperature was recently done by Brown and McArty [B63].

(b) Sedimentation, elutriation (Chap. 9), and centrifugal separation (Chap. 8) make use of the time of fall and variation in terminal velocity in a gravitational field, and the last of the three methods makes use of a centrifugal field.

All of them utilize the drag force, relative velocity, and particle-size relations. Sedimentation determines particle size by the settling time over, say, an 88-in. fall [S26]. Elutriation is a process where a column of air is moved vertically upward through a suspension to remove all particles below a certain size. Increasing the velocity lifts off the next larger size range [R28]. Both cyclone [N7] and centrifuge were used to separate particles of different sizes.

(c) Flow processes of sprays (Chap. 8) were used for measuring particle size by what amounts to comparing momentum at different points of the spray, or by measuring mass-flow rate. The first method assumes the same velocity of all particles; thus equal-sized particles have the same momentum at an equal distance [H4]. (This is shown, however, not to be the case in Chap. 8.) The latter procedure uses collectors of glass-wool filter [L7]. More dynamic measurements are included in Chap. 4.

Physicochemical—This category includes freezing of liquid to solid for subsequent sieving, measurement of evaporation, thermal precipitation, and gas adsorption on particle surface. The freezing method can be used, for instance, for hydrocarbon spray into a liquid nitrogen bath [C23]. The droplet-evaporation method depends on deducing the concentration of free water from measurement of humidity of air [H12]. The gas-adsorption method presumes formation of a monolayer of gas on each particle in determining the surface area [K12]; this idea is nearly valid only at very low pressures.

Optical—A photographic method for measuring both size and velocity of a particle (solid, liquid droplet, or gas bubble) can be used for particle sizes between 15 and 500 μ. This utilizes a high-speed motion picture camera, or successive exposures [Y3]. This method is useful for studying breakup of droplets [L28]. For particles down to 0.5 μ, photography in combination with microscopy can be used [H29].

Diffraction of light occurs for particles whose size is of the order of the wavelength of light striking it. The angular distribution of the intensity and the degree of polarization of the scattered light are a function of the particle size, the index of refraction of the particle (transparent material), and the wavelength of the incident light [J17]. Special equipment is available for measuring the angular distribution and polarization of the scattered light [G48]. The basic principle governing the diffraction method is given in Chap. 5.

Electrical—Electrical measurements utilize the measurement of charge, mobility, capacitance, and resistance for determining particle size. Electrical pulses, created by drops touching a probe wire, bear in certain cases the empirical relation of the 1.6 power of the particle diameter [G11]. An improvement is the Coulter counter [U3], which utilizes the measurement of change of resistance. Another method analyzes the current voltage characteristics of a parallel plate capacitor through which the aerosol is passed [D6]. For measuring a liquid droplet, the heat removed from a heated resistance wire changes the resistance and is proportional to the droplet size [V17, G29]. Further details and implications are treated in Chap. 10.

2 | Transport Processes of a Rigid Particle

Preparatory to the treatment of multiphase systems, transport phenomena of a rigid single particle are treated first. Transport processes of a single particle in steady motion are reviewed, but derivations are relegated to other basic texts on fluid mechanics, heat and mass transfer.

Major concerns of this chapter are transport processes of a single particle suspended by a turbulent fluid stream. It is well known that no established and completely satisfactory procedure is available for treating this subject. The coverage here is intended to demonstrate the physical facts that need to be accounted for, to summarize the understanding at this stage, and to provoke thinking. However, it might be pointed out first of all that this single-particle problem is *not* a stumbling block to the study of multiparticle systems. Its discussion also serves to demonstrate the need for a different method of approach. It will be shown in Chaps. 4 through 9 that much has been accomplished toward dealing with the dynamics of a multiphase system with qualified continuum generalization.

Brownian motion of a particle is treated to complete the ranges of motion due to the drag of a fluid in continuum, slip, and free molecule flow, and motion of the particle itself due to thermal excitation.

2.1 Drag Coefficient of a Sphere

Studies of the magnitude of drag force on spheres in steady motion of a viscous fluid began with Newton's experiments in 1710, which gave

$$\mathscr{F} = 0.22\pi a^2 \bar{\rho} v^2 \tag{2.1}$$

15

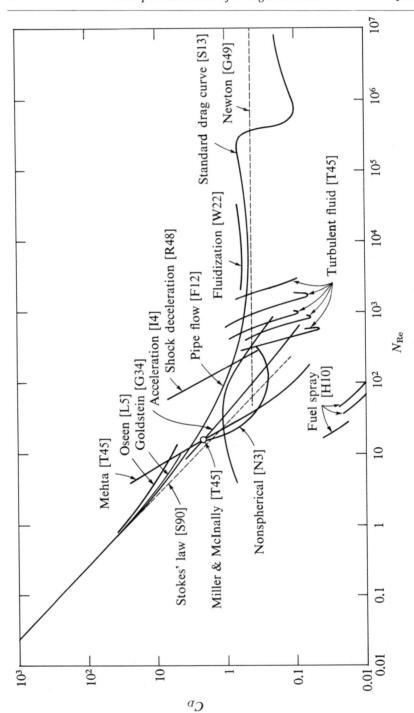

Figure 2.1 Drag coefficient of a sphere.

at high relative velocity v, where $\mathscr{F}$ is the force exerted on the sphere, a the radius, and $\bar{\rho}$ the density of the fluid material. This relation accounts for mainly the inertia effect [G49, H51].

At very low relative velocities, Stokes in 1850 suggested that the inertial effects are so small that they can be neglected from the Navier-Stokes equations. His asymptotic approximation thus obtained gives a symmetric flow field about a sphere. The resulting drag force is:

$$\mathscr{F} = 6\pi\bar{\mu}av, \tag{2.2}$$

where $\bar{\mu}$ is the viscosity of the fluid material, and $\mathscr{F}$ consists of two-thirds of shear force (friction drag) and one-third of pressure forces (form drag) [L5, S91]. Drag characteristics can also be expressed in terms of terminal velocity of free fall of a body in a fluid.

With the definition of the drag coefficient, C_D,

$$C_D = \frac{\mathscr{F}}{(\pi a^2)(\frac{1}{2}\bar{\rho}v^2)}, \tag{2.3}$$

we get, for the Newton's relation,

$$C_D = 0.44,$$

and for the Stokes' law regime,

$$C_D = \frac{24}{(2av\bar{\rho}/\bar{\mu})} = \frac{24}{N_{\text{Re}}}, \tag{2.4}$$

where

$$N_{\text{Re}} = (2a)v\frac{\bar{\rho}}{\bar{\mu}}$$

is the Reynolds number for a sphere based on its diameter.

Subsequent experiments yielded a so-called standard drag curve [S13], applicable to a single solid sphere moving at constant velocity in a still, isothermal, incompressible fluid, which is infinite in extent. The diagram in Fig. 2.1 shows that, by comparison to the standard drag curve, the Stokes' regime applies to $N_{\text{Re}} \leq 1$ nearly and the Newton's regime holds nearly for [G49] $700 \leq N_{\text{Re}} \leq 2 \times 10^5$. Beyond $N_{\text{Re}} \sim 10^5$ (upper critical Reynolds number), a sharp reduction in drag coefficient occurs due to transition from laminar to turbulent boundary layers over the body.

It is seen that above $N_{\text{Re}} \sim 1$, analytical description of the flow field becomes more difficult. Inertial forces become significant, and separation of boundary layers occur at $N_{\text{Re}} \sim 10$; the streamlines curl up to form a stationary vortex ring at the rear of the sphere. A further increase of N_{Re} leads to growth of the vortex in size and strength. At $N_{\text{Re}} \sim 100$, the vortex system extends to about 1 diameter behind the sphere [T3]. The contribution of inertial forces continues to increase at $N_{Re} \sim 150$; the vortex system begins to oscillate. In a laminar stream at about $N_{Re} \sim 500$, the vortex system leaves the body and forms a wake [T45]. This Reynolds number is called the lower critical Reynolds number. The vortex rings continue to form and shed from the sphere, giving rise to a periodic flow field and instantaneous drag force. The line of boundary-layer separation on the sphere also varies giving rise also to a transverse fluctuating force.

Analytical studies of flow beyond the Stokes'-law regime mostly extend from Oseen's approximation which includes inertial terms only in the flow field away from the body. His relation

$$C_D = \frac{24}{N_{Re}} (1 + \tfrac{3}{16}N_{Re}) \qquad (2.5)$$

is applicable to $N_{Re} < 5$ [S13]. Drag coefficient derived by Goldstein [G34] includes a series expansion as in Eq. (2.5) with higher orders of N_{Re}, which agrees quite well with the appropriate experimental data for $N_{Re} < 1$. The limitations of the Oseen approximation were illustrated by Pearcy and McHugh [P5]. Proudman and Pearson [P32] treated the problem by matching different series expansions for flow regimes near and away from the sphere or cylinder; good agreement with experiment was obtained for $N_{Re} < 4$. They extended Oseen's relation to:

$$C_D = \frac{24}{N_{Re}} [1 + \tfrac{3}{16}N_{Re} + \tfrac{9}{160}(N_{Re})^2 \ln (\tfrac{1}{2}N_{Re}) + 0(N_{Re}^2)]. \qquad (2.6)$$

Attempts to account for the vortex formation led to Kawajuti's analytical determination of a lower critical Reynolds number of 51 [K8]. Jenson [J8] computed stream functions; vorticity, pressure, and velocity distribution; and drag coefficients with the relaxation method. The drag coefficients found were:

N_{Re}	C_D		
5	8.03	(second order)	7.95 (fourth order)
10	4.84		
20	2.946		
40	1.861		

He found the first formation of wake at $N_{Re} = 17$.

The velocity distribution in the boundary layer near a sphere prior to separation was calculated by Froessling [S13] as shown in Fig. 2.2. In Fig. 2.2, v is the distributed velocity, v_o is the free stream velocity. The dimensionless radial coordinate is given by $(y/a)\sqrt{v_0 a \bar{\rho}/\bar{\mu}}$, where y is measured radially from the surface of the sphere. This result does not contribute to the prediction of drag coefficient, but has significant implication when dealing

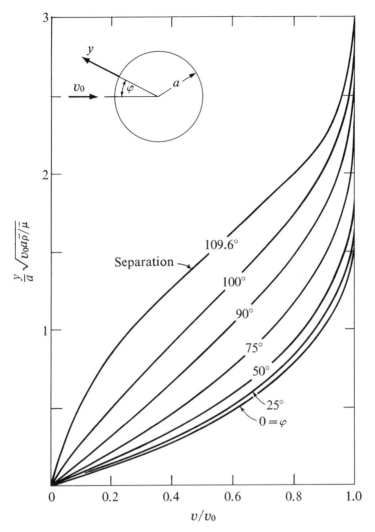

Figure 2.2 Velocity distribution in the boundary layer near a sphere [S13].

with a cloud of particles (Chap. 6). Wakes of a free sphere supported by a magnetic field at a Mach number of 16 were studied by Vas, Murman, and Bogdonoff [V8].

The magnitude of drag coefficient of particles in a multiphase system is modified by a number of complications. Particles are to be found in moving, accelerating, turbulent fluid stream, whose temperature is in general different from the particles, presence of a wall, and dense particle clouds.

The turbulent intensity encountered in a practical situation may amount to a few per cent of the stream velocity [L22]. The corresponding turbulence intensity of the particle flow field is higher by the ratio of the stream velocity to the relative velocity between the particle and the gas. The scale of turbulence, however, is unaltered. Further, turbulence may be generated by relative motion of particle to gas. Turbulence leads to a marked decrease in the magnitude of the drag coefficient due to lowering of the upper critical Reynolds number, with a rearward shift in the separation ring on the sphere [H50]. Such a transition has not been observed for $N_{Re} < 400$ at 40 per cent intensity [T45]. At lower turbulence intensities, transition would not occur, but a slight increase in drag in low Reynolds number range was noted [G13] through increased dissipation in the wake region. The effect of scale of turbulence is not determined; a known fact is that large-scale free-stream turbulence can feed energy into small scale vortices in the particle wake [K25]. The upper critical Reynolds number was shown to vary with the intensity of turbulence, the characteristic length (such as grid size) of the turbulence-producing mechanism, and the diameter of the sphere [G34].

The effect of free-stream turbulence becomes less significant with decreasing Reynolds numbers. Available data for spherical particles in turbulent, flowing systems at particle Reynolds numbers of 20 to 100 [B72, F12, H10, I4, L19, L38, N3, R48, T45, W22, Z5] range from a factor of 3 above standard drag curve to a factor of 100 below the standard curve (Fig. 2.1). Predominantly, these data show decrease in drag coefficient due to turbulence. Most of these measurements were plagued by inaccuracies of one form or another, such that the results were not applicable to the definition of steady (including turbulence) incompressible motion in an infinite fluid medium.

(a) When small particles were used accurate measurements of particle diameter and checks on their spherisity are difficult to make.

(b) In experiments with large numbers of particles per unit volume (low-fraction void), the interaction of the boundary layer (Fig. 2.2) of adjacent particles plays an important part and the wakes may actually disappear, thus altering the drag coefficient (Secs. 5.1, 6.3).

(c) Experiments with acceleration or deceleration of particles are influenced by effects discussed in Sec. 2.3 [I4, F12, R48, L19]. Where these experiments were carried out in a gas, the pressure gradient, temperature gradient, and local density and viscosity have to be carefully accounted for.

(d) Experiments with evaporating droplets are further influenced by the vaporation rate and combustion effects [C45].

Further understanding of the flow phenomena around spheres was developed via experiments carried out with cylinders [P32, A3].

When applied to a nonspherical or irregularly shaped solid particle, uniform motion and consistent orientation of such a particle cannot be assured without constraint [F10]. Drag coefficient of constrained rods, plates, etc., are given in various handbooks, but these situations are not always interesting to multi-phase systems.

Free motion of cylinders in a fluid involves both translation and oscillation or rotation. Based on inertia in potential motion, Kirchhoff, Kelvin, Tait, and Greenhill [L5] studied the case of small oscillation. Experimenting with freely falling cylindrical particles and disks in water, Marchildon, Clamen, and Gauvin [M11, M10] presented experimental results and correlations and noted the effect of secondary motion on the drag coefficient. Marchildon [M9] showed that oscillation never occurs at Reynolds number based on diameter below 80, and always occurs at above 300. Extending the work of Rayleigh [S94], he showed that the period of oscillation τ is given by

$$\tau = 40.9 \left[\frac{I}{\bar{\rho}(2a)L^2u^2} \right]^{\frac{1}{2}} = \frac{1}{v'}, \qquad (2.7)$$

where

$$I = \left(\frac{\pi}{16} \right) \bar{\rho}_p L(2a)^2 \left[\frac{L^2}{3} + a^2 \right].$$

The Strouhal number based on length L and radius a is thus

$$(N'_{St})_{a,L} = \frac{v'(2aL)^{\frac{1}{2}}}{v} = \frac{(\bar{\rho}/\bar{\rho}_p)^{\frac{1}{2}}}{10.5}. \qquad (2.8)$$

The drag coefficients were measured for different $\bar{\rho}/\bar{\rho}_p$ and $L/2a$. Schmiedel [S15] studied the motion of disks; bluff bodies were studied by Fage and Johansen [F1]. The Stokesian (small Reynolds number) resistance of an arbitrary particle was studied by Brenner [B57], who treated the hydro-dynamic force and torque experienced by a rigid particle of arbitrary shape translating and spinning in a fluid at rest at infinity. Extensive treatment of flow over bodies at low Reynolds numbers is given in the book by Happel and Brenner [H11]. Drag measurements on freely falling cylinders and cones were reported recently by Jayaweera and Mason [J15].

Lapple and Shepherd [L19] presented the effect of acceleration and decelera-tion on the drag coefficient; later studies were reported by Hughes and Gilliland [H65], and Torobin and Gauvin [T45]. Unsteady boundary layers over vibrating spheres were studied by Yeh and Yang [Y2]. A thorough review and extensive study was made by Marchildon [M9] on the effects of shape, turbulence, and acceleration on the drag coefficient and motion of cylinders and flakes.

When the particles are small compared to mean free path of the fluid, molecular slip occurs, resulting in lower drag. Theoretical solution of the Stokes flow problem with slip boundary conditions was given by Basset [B21].

Millikan approximated Basset's results into the free-molecule flow range [E15] giving a useful semiempirical relation for drag, with the empirical constants determined from oil-drop experiments [M35]. The drag coefficient can be expressed in the form [D28, D37]:

$$C_D = 4\sqrt{\pi}\,\frac{\Lambda}{a}\left[f'\left(1 - \frac{\Lambda}{2a}\right) + \frac{\Lambda}{a}\right]\left(\frac{v}{\sqrt{2\bar{R}T}}\right)^{-1},\qquad (2.9)$$

where Λ is the mean free path, f' is the velocity slip coefficient, $v/\sqrt{2\bar{R}T}$ is molecular speed ratio, $\bar{R}$ is the gas constant, and T is the temperature. The effects of multiple scattering were studied by Baker and Charwat [B7] and Liu, Pang, and Jew [L52].

The effect of permeability of a porous sphere in slow motion in a viscous liquid was studied by Joseph and Tao [J21]. It was shown that the drag force on a permeable sphere corresponds to an impermeable sphere of reduced radius a_e, and

$$a_e = \frac{a}{[1 + (k/2a^2)]},\qquad (2.10)$$

where k is the permeability (Sec. 9.8).

2.2 Heat and Mass Transfer from a Sphere

When a rigid sphere at a given temperature is submerged in a completely quiescent fluid at another temperature, the rate of heat transfer due to conduction alone as given by the Nusselt number, based on its diameter $2a$, is readily shown to be

$$N_{\text{Nu}} = \frac{2a\,h}{\bar{\kappa}} = 2,\qquad (2.11)$$

where h is the heat transfer coefficient and $\bar{\kappa}$ is the thermal conductivity of the fluid.

When relative motion of the fluid to the sphere exists, the local heat-transfer coefficient depends on the local velocity and temperature profiles, and flow separation. All the variables affecting the flow field—such as turbulence, rarefaction, variable fluid properties, and radiation—also affect the heat transfer. The overall rate of heat transfer depends on the flow field, and the location and existence of separated flow regions [I2, M19].

Theoretical solutions are available only for Reynolds numbers where Stokes' law applies to the flow field. Almost all solutions are given in the series expansion form:

$$N_{\text{Nu}} = 2 + (\tfrac{1}{2})N_{\text{Re}}N_{\text{Pr}} + \tfrac{1}{6}(N_{\text{Re}}N_{\text{Pr}})^2 + \cdots,\qquad (2.12)$$

where N_{Pr} is the Prandtl number of the fluid; $N_{Pr} = c\bar{\mu}/\bar{\kappa}$, where c is the specific heat of the fluid at constant pressure [K41, B56, F24]. Taylor [T13] further applied double series expansion from the surface and the infinity and subsequent matching. All differences are in the higher-order terms of the series expansion in Eq. (2.12). Figure 2.3 shows this asymptotic relation.

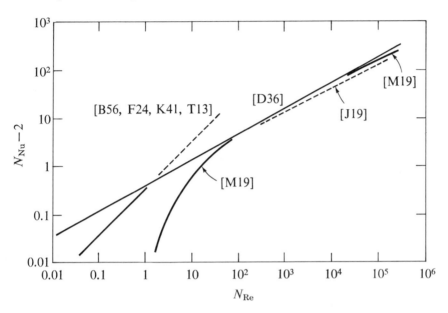

Figure 2.3 Heat transfer from a rigid sphere ($N_{Pr} = 0.72$).

Experimental determinations were made for high Reynolds numbers. Various correlations were suggested [M19, Y5]. The best fit appears to be that proposed by Drake [D36]:

$$N_{Nu} = 2 + 0.459 N_{Re}^{0.55} N_{Pr}^{0.33}, \tag{2.13}$$

for $1 < N_{Re} < 70{,}000$ and $0.6 < N_{Pr} < 400$. Figure 2.3 is plotted with $N_{Nu} - 2$ as ordinate to insure that correct asymptotic limit at $N_{Re} = 0$ is maintained. These data correlations are applicable to a single particle immersed in an incompressible fluid of infinite extent in the limit of very small temperature difference.

Data on particle clouds encounter similar complications as in the case of drag coefficient. Data based on clouds were obtained by Johnstone, Pigford, and Chapin [J19], Joukovski, Gander, and Holcomb [Z5]. Even data from fluidized beds do not deviate significantly from those obtained with transport in one direction. Levels of turbulence were not recorded.

The effect of turbulence was covered by van der Hegge Zijnen [V2] (for cylinders) over Reynolds numbers from 600 to 26,000 and by Loyzanski and Schwab [M19] to 10^5. It was found that turbulence was most effective in increasing heat-transfer rate when the scale of turbulence was 1.5 times particle diameter nearly [V2]. The effect of radiation on heat transfer will be treated with clouds of particles.

Rarefaction effects are expected for small particles in a gas. Imperfect accommodation and temperature jump reduce the heat transfer rate. Drake and Backer [D37], and Kavanau [K7] estimated the temperature jump with Oseen approximation for the flow field, for the supersonic and the subsonic ranges. Their relation with the modification of Sauer [S4] is given as

$$N_{\text{Nu}} = N_{\text{Nu}}^o \left[1 + 3.42 \, \frac{N_{\text{M}}}{N_{\text{Re}} N_{\text{Pr}}} \, N_{\text{Nu}}^o \right], \tag{2.14}$$

for an accommodation coefficient of nearly 0.8. In Eq. (2.14), N_{M} is the Mach number of the flow stream, while N_{Nu}^o is the Nusselt number based on Fig. 2.3, which is for $N_{\text{M}} = 0$. It is seen that $N_{\text{M}}/N_{\text{Re}}$ is related to the Knudsen number, N_{Kn}

$$N_{\text{Kn}} = \frac{\Lambda}{2a} = \sqrt{\frac{\gamma \pi}{2}} \frac{N_{\text{M}}}{N_{\text{Re}}}, \tag{2.15}$$

where Λ is the mean free path and γ is the ratio of specific heats of the gas. Some further understanding on slip and free molecule flow was developed from a study made by Baldwin, Sandborn, and Laurence on cylinders [B10], and study by Stalder and Jukoff [S79].

Analogous to heat transfer, mass transfer to or from a sphere placed in a stagnant fluid is given by Langmuir [L14]:

$$\frac{2ak_c}{D} = \frac{2ak_G RT}{D} = 2, \tag{2.16}$$

where D is the diffusivity, k_c is the mass-transfer coefficient given in (number of moles)/(unit area)(unit time)(concentration in number of moles/unit volume), and k_G is that in (number of moles)/(unit area)(unit time)(atmospheres) such that the rate of mass transfer $\dot{N}_A$ (number of moles/area, time) is given by

$$\dot{N}_A = k_c(C_i - C) = k_G(P - P_i), \tag{2.17}$$

where C is the concentration, P is the partial pressure of diffusing gas in atmospheres, and subscripts i denote equilibrium values based on the temperature of the system. When relative motion exists in the realm of rigid

532 So61f
C. 1

spheres, Powell measured the evaporation of water from wet surfaces of solid spheres up to 6 in. in diameter. Vyrubov absorbed ammonia from air using spheres coated with phosphoric acid [S31]. Froessling found that his data on evaporation of small drops of various liquids and solid spheres of naphthalene could be correlated by [S31]:

$$N_{Sh} = \frac{2ak_c}{D} = 2.0\left[1 + 0.276N_{Re}^{1/2}\left(\frac{\bar{\mu}}{\bar{\rho}D}\right)^{1/3}\right]. \quad (2.18)$$

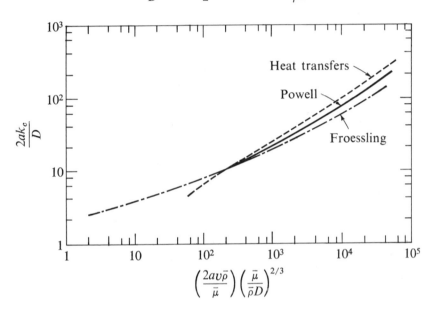

Figure 2.4 Mass transfer from single spheres [S31].

Correlations from various results are included in Fig. 2.4. Further extensions to higher Peclet numbers ($N_{Pr} N_{Re}$) were made by Jones and Smith [J20]. $\bar{\mu}/\bar{\rho}D$ has been denoted as the Schmidt number N_{Sc}.

When applied to mass transfer from a rigid sphere, similar considerations [K41, B56, F24, T13, F31] give the Sherwood number

$$N_{Sh} = \frac{2ak_c}{D} = 2 + 0.978(N_{Re}N_{Pr})^{1/3}. \quad (2.19)$$

The nature of the problem is analogous to heat transfer. The case including internal circulation of liquid droplets will be treated in the next chapter.

Melting ablation of decelerating spherical bodies at the condition of space reentry into planetary atmosphere was studied by Ostrach and McConnel [O7]. They considered the heat transfer to and flow of a melt layer on the surface of a glasslike spherical body.

Another aspect of gas-solid mass transfer is by adsorption, an available treatise on this subject is one by Brunauer [B69]. A major application is in the use of silica-gel in chromatography.

2.3 Momentum Transfer in a Nonuniform Fluid

Other factors which influence the motion and drag coefficient of a solid particle are velocity gradient, pressure gradient, and temperature gradient, nonuniform radiation, and concentration gradient.

Velocity gradient—Flow over a sphere in a tube of finite radius was treated by Brenner and Happel [B60] and Wakiya [W1].

Rotation of a solid particle may arise due to the presence of a velocity gradient in the fluid such as the shear layer near a wall. At low Reynolds numbers, rotation causes fluid entrainment, adding to the velocity on the one side of the body and lowering the velocity on the other side. The phenomenon, known as the Magnus effect, tends to move the particle toward the region of higher velocity [G34]. This and earlier results of Jeffery [J6] based on Einstein's result [E6] of excess dissipation proportional to the square of vorticity of incident particles would suggest that particles tend to migrate to the center of the pipe in Poiseuille flow. However, Segré and Silberberg [S20] showed, via accurate experiments, that particles tend to concentrate at a radius nearly 0.6 of pipe radius from the axis. They performed experiments in a glass tube of 11.2 ± 0.2 mm internal diameter, with polymethylmetha-crylate spheres of diameters in close range of 0.32, 0.8, 1.21, and 1.71 mm in a media of equal density prepared by mixing glycerine, 1,3-butanediol and water in various proportions. The particle concentration ranges from 0.33 to 4 particles per cubic centimeter. Concentration distributions were determined by optical scanning.

Robinow and Keller [R25], applying this concept to compute the force on a rotating sphere, give the lift force $\mathscr{F}_L$ is given by

$$\mathscr{F}_L = \pi a^3 \bar{\rho} \boldsymbol{\omega} \times \mathbf{v}[1 + 0(N_{Re})], \tag{2.20}$$

where $\mathbf{v}$ is the fluid velocity, $\boldsymbol{\omega}$ the angular velocity of the sphere. The torque is given by

$$\mathscr{L} = -8\pi\bar{\mu}a^3\boldsymbol{\omega}[1 + 0(N_{Re})]. \tag{2.21}$$

They give the equations of motion as:

and

$$
\left.
\begin{aligned}
m \frac{d\mathbf{v}}{dt} &= -6\pi\bar{\mu}a[1 + \tfrac{3}{8}N_{\mathrm{Re}}]\mathbf{v} + \pi a^3 \bar{\rho}\boldsymbol{\omega} \times \mathbf{v} \\[2mm]
I \frac{d\boldsymbol{\omega}}{dt} &= -8\pi\bar{\mu}a^3\boldsymbol{\omega},
\end{aligned}
\right\}
\tag{2.22}
$$

where m and I are the mass and the moment of inertia of the sphere respectively.

At high particle Reynolds numbers, the rotational shift of the separation point causes a force in the opposite direction [H51]. This force arises due to spin of a small particle when the particle diameter is smaller than the characteristic length of turbulent eddies or the thickness of a shear layer [S69]. The effect of velocity gradient on a sphere was computed by Zierep [Z6], that on a cylinder by Tsien [T55] and Lighthill [L43]. Saffman [S2] computed the lift force $\mathscr{F}_L$ acting on a sphere by a viscous liquid at low velocity u in simple shear du/dy parallel to streamlines and gave

$$
\mathscr{F}_L \sim K\bar{\mu}u\left(\frac{du}{dy}\right)^{1/2} \frac{a^2}{\bar{\nu}^{1/2}}
\tag{2.23}
$$

normal to the flow direction; $K = 81.2$ was obtained from numerical integration for $u/(\bar{\nu}\, du/dy)^{1/2} \ll 1$. The terminal transverse velocity v_p of the particle is given by

$$
v_p \sim Ku\left(\frac{du}{dy}\right)^{1/2} \frac{a}{6\pi\bar{\nu}^{1/2}}.
\tag{2.24}
$$

Saffman showed that unless the rotating speed is very much greater than the rate of shear and for a freely rotating particle $\omega = \tfrac{1}{2}(du/dy)$, the lift force due to particle rotation is less by an order of magnitude than that due to the shear when Reynolds number is small. The dependence on viscosity is such that the drift velocity should be proportional to $N_{\mathrm{Re}}^{2/3}$ if u is independent of $\bar{\nu}$. Segré and Silberberg found that a reasonable correlation existed for their experimental data if the transverse velocity was assumed to be linearly proportional to N_{Re}. An experimental effort toward determining the Magnus effect by measuring the lift, drag, and rotating speed of small spheres (0.061 to 0.126 in. diameter) in the shear region of Poiseuille flow was made by Eichhorn and Small [E4]. They obtained a relation for the lift coefficient C_L on the sphere as

$$
C_L \sim 7 \times 10^4 \left[\frac{2a}{u}\frac{du}{dy}\frac{a}{R}\frac{1}{(N_{\mathrm{Re}})_p}\right]^2,
$$

where u is the velocity, R is the tube radius, with $(N_{Re})_p = 2au\bar{\rho}/\bar{\mu}$ ranging from 75 to 230 and $(2a/R)(du/dy)$ ranging from 0.4 to 1 in their experiments. It is seen that following Saffman (Eq. 2.23), we should get

$$C_L = \frac{2K}{\pi}\left[\frac{(2a/u)(du/dy)}{(N_{Re})_p}\right]^{\frac{1}{2}},$$

a trend which is believed to be more reliable at low Reynolds numbers.

The above relations show that the magnitude of lift force to drag force is given by

$$\frac{|\mathscr{F}_L|}{|\mathscr{F}|} = \frac{1}{6}\frac{a^2\omega}{\bar{\nu}}$$

from Eqs. (2.20) and (2.2) and

$$\frac{|\mathscr{F}_L|}{|\mathscr{F}|} = \frac{K}{6\pi}\left[\frac{a^2(du/dy)}{\bar{\nu}}\right]^{\frac{1}{2}}$$

for Eqs. (2.23) and (2.2). Hence for small particles, the lift force due to its passage through a shear layer can be neglected when the characteristic Reynolds number $a^2\omega/\bar{\nu}$ or $a^2(du/dy)/\bar{\nu}$ are small.

Particles of Arbitrary Shape—Brenner [B58] studied the effect of boundaries on the Stokes resistance of an arbitrary particle. For a particle rotating near a boundary, he gives the drag force $\mathscr{F}$ as

$$\frac{\mathscr{F}}{\mathscr{F}_\infty} = \left[1 - k\left(\frac{\mathscr{F}_\infty}{6\pi\bar{\mu}vl}\right) + 0\left(\frac{c}{l}\right)^3\right]^{-1}, \tag{2.25}$$

where c and l are characteristic particle and wall dimensions, v is the particle velocity, and $\mathscr{F}_\infty = 6\pi\bar{\mu}cv$; k is a constant independent of the shape of the particle but dependent on the geometry of the system; it has the value of $\sim\frac{3}{8}$ for a particle moving along a free surface with l as the distance from the surface, and 2.1044 for a particle moving along a circular cylinder with l as the radius of the cylinder. For a rotating particle Brenner obtained the moment $\mathscr{L}$ acting on the particle as

$$\frac{\mathscr{L}}{\mathscr{L}_\infty} = \left[1 - K\left(\frac{c}{l}\right)^3 + \cdots\right]^{-1}, \tag{2.26}$$

where without the wall $\mathscr{L}_\infty = 8\pi\bar{\mu}c^3\omega$, ω is the angular velocity, and $K = \frac{1}{8}$ for the axis being perpendicular to a solid plane.

Pressure Gradient—The pressure gradient in the fluid will lead to a force acting on the particle besides fluid resistance. For a particle of radius a in a pressure gradient $\partial P/\partial x$ as shown in Fig. 2.5,

$$d\mathscr{F} = -a\cos\theta\,\frac{\partial P}{\partial x}\,2\pi a\sin\theta\,a\,d\theta\cos\theta.$$

Integration gives

$$\mathscr{F} = -\frac{\partial P}{\partial x} 2\pi a^3 \int_0^\pi \cos^2 \theta \sin \theta \, d\theta$$

$$= -\frac{\partial P}{\partial x} \frac{4\pi a^3}{3}, \tag{2.27}$$

the force in the opposite direction of the pressure gradient [T15].

Temperature Gradient—Temperature gradient in a fluid may contribute significantly to the variation in viscosity of the fluid. This variation may also

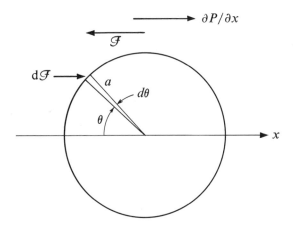

Figure 2.5 Force on a sphere due to pressure gradient.

arise due to heat transfer and the corresponding temperature distribution. Any variation of viscosity alters the velocity profiles and the drag coefficient. The effect under such a circumstance is usually minor [H51]. However, when applied to passage of a solid particle through a shock wave, the viscosity increases sharply in the shock thickness [S25]. This increase, the additional force due to sharp pressure gradient, and high rate of deceleration (Basset term in Sec. 2.4) are possible sources of the high drag coefficient of particles in a shock tube as obtained by Rudinger [R48].

The forces acting on a particle due to temperature gradient in a gas (thermophoresis) and nonuniform radiation (photophoresis) are called radiometric forces. For $a \ll \Lambda$, that is, in the free-molecule flow range, this arises from collision by gas molecules with different mean velocities from opposite directions and is given [C11] by:

$$\mathscr{F}_{\text{Ti}} = -\frac{\pi P \Lambda a^2}{2T} \frac{\partial T}{\partial x_i} = -\frac{\pi \bar{\rho} \Lambda a^2 \bar{R}}{2} \frac{\partial T}{\partial x_i} \tag{2.28}$$

for an accommodation coefficient α of 1; P is the pressure, $\bar{R}$ is the gas constant of the gaseous phase.

Nonuniform radiation gives rise to a temperature gradient inside the particle or $\partial T_p / \partial x_i$. For $a \ll \Lambda$, it was shown [R45] that:

$$\mathscr{F}_{\mathrm{Ti}} = - \frac{\pi \alpha P a^3}{3T} \frac{\partial T_p}{\partial x_i}, \tag{2.29}$$

due to greater momentum of gas molecules leaving the hotter side of the particle.

For the case $a \gg \Lambda$, the maximum velocity in this case rises to a maximum at distance Λ from the surface, and then decreases with distance. The force is directed toward the lower temperature. Hydrodynamic considerations by Hettner lead to [H35]

$$\mathscr{F}_{\mathrm{Ti}} = - \frac{3\pi \bar{\mu}^2 a \bar{R}}{P} \frac{\partial T_p}{\partial x_i}, \tag{2.30}$$

where $\bar{R}$ is the gas constant of the gas phase. An empirical relation suggested by Hettner for the range $a \gg \Lambda$ to $a \ll \Lambda$ is

$$\mathscr{F}_{\mathrm{Ti}} = - \frac{\pi a^2 \bar{\mu} \sqrt{\alpha \bar{R}/T}}{(P/P_0) + (P_0/P)} \frac{\partial T_p}{\partial x_i}, \tag{2.31}$$

where $P_0 = (3\bar{\mu}/a)\sqrt{\bar{R}T/\alpha}$.

To determine the temperature gradient inside a spherical particle, for $a \gg \Lambda$, Epstein [E16] gives

$$\frac{\partial T_p}{\partial x_i} = \frac{3\bar{\kappa}}{2\bar{\kappa} + \bar{\kappa}_p} \frac{\partial T}{\partial x_i}, \tag{2.32}$$

where $\bar{\kappa}$ is the thermal conductivity of the gas and $\bar{\kappa}_p$ is that of the solid material. The relations given by Epstein were checked for a of 0.4 to 1.6 μ by Rosenblatt and La Mer [R35].

When a small particle or droplet is in a concentration gradient of a vapor, such as having its surface wetted by a volatile liquid or condensation of a supersaturated vapor on a droplet, a relative motion, known as Stephan flow, of the vapor and the droplet was found [F35]. For a spherical droplet or particle, the velocity of relative motion is given by

$$v = \frac{D(C_s - C_\infty) a \mathscr{M}}{C r^2 \mathscr{M}'}, \tag{2.33}$$

where D is the diffusivity of the gas in the gas-vapor mixture, $\mathscr{M}$ is the molecular weight of the gas, $\mathscr{M}'$ that of the vapor; r is measured from the center of the droplet; C_s is the concentration of the vapor at $r = a$, C_∞ is that at $r = \infty$, C is the concentration of the gas. This phenomenon is called diffusion phoresis. Thus an evaporating wall will tend to drive a droplet away.

For $a \ll \Lambda$, Waldmann [W2] gave the terminal velocity v of an aerosol due to concentration gradient in a binary mixture of components 1 and 2 as:

$$v = \frac{(\sqrt{\mathscr{M}_1/\mathscr{M}_2}\, \delta_1 - \delta_2)\, D\ \text{grad}\ C_1}{(C_1\sqrt{\mathscr{M}_1/\mathscr{M}_2}\, \delta_1 + C_2\delta_2)} , \tag{2.34}$$

where $\delta = 1 + (\pi\alpha/8)$.

It is noted that in air at room condition, for instance, the effects of temperature and concentration gradients on the motion of a particle become significant only when its radius is in the submicron range.

2.4 Motion of a Particle Suspended in a Turbulent Stream

A simplified situation of a dilute gas-solid turbulent suspension is the case of motion of a single particle in a turbulent stream.

If the particle is large compared to the scale of turbulence, the main effect of the turbulence will be on the drag coefficient (Sec. 2.1) and the particle will follow the slower large-scale turbulent motion of the fluid. If the particle is small compared to the smallest scale of the turbulence, it will respond to all the turbulence components of the fluid. Under the latter circumstance, the flow resistance of the particle will be viscous with respect to the ambient fluid.

The presence of the particle will contribute to dissipation due to the lag of motion between the particle and the fluid. If sufficient number of solid particles are present, since such a lag increases with increasing wave number of the turbulence, the energy spectrum of the fluid turbulence will be modified, especially in the high wave-number range. However, only motion of a single particle will be considered here.

The motion of a small particle suspended in a turbulent fluid was formulated by Tchen [T15]. Tchen's studies will be considered, but clarifications by Hinze [H41], Corrsin and Lumley [C43, L59], and Soo [S52] will be incorporated in steps. The simplifying assumptions made by Tchen will be introduced as the need arises in various stages of formulation and solution.

Recognizing that the solid particle, due to its inertia, does not necessarily follow the streamline of the fluid, the rates of change bear the distinction that:

$$\frac{\mathrm{d}}{\mathrm{d}t_p} = \frac{\partial}{\partial t} + U_{pi}\frac{\partial}{\partial x_i} \tag{2.35}$$

for the solid particle; t is the time, U_{pi} the ith component of the velocity of the particle, x_i the ith component of the space coordinate;

$$\frac{d}{dt} = \frac{\partial}{\partial t} + U_i \frac{\partial}{\partial x_i} \tag{2.36}$$

for the fluid and U_i the ith component of the velocity of the fluid. This recognition is not particular to turbulence, but states the general nature of a multiphase system in that the particle lines (paths) and streamlines of the fluid do not necessarily coincide [S52].

For the formulation of the equation of motion, the assumptions made by Tchen are:

1. The particle is spherical and is so small that its relative motion to the fluid gives rise to resistance according to Stokes' law.
2. The particle is small when compared to the smallest wavelength of the turbulence; the effect of particle motion due to shear flow (Eq. 2.22) is neglected.

The desirability of treating a spherical particle has been explained above; that is, the orientation need not be concerned with here. Its smallness is not necessary for the general formulation in that the wavelength smaller than the particle contributes to a modification of the drag coefficient. This arbitrary smallness, however, makes the Magnus effect negligible under turbulent shear. Following the path of the solid particle, the general equation of motion based on the effects treated by Basset, Boussinesq, and Oseen is given by

$$\frac{4\pi}{3} a^3 \bar{\rho}_p \frac{dU_p}{dt_p} = \frac{4\pi}{3} a^3 \bar{\rho}_p F(\mathbf{U} - \mathbf{U}_p) - \frac{4\pi}{3} a^3 \frac{\partial P}{\partial r}$$

$$+ \frac{1}{2} \frac{4\pi}{3} a^3 \bar{\rho} \frac{d}{dt_p} (\mathbf{U} - \mathbf{U}_p)$$

$$+ 6a^2 \sqrt{\pi \bar{\rho}\bar{\mu}} \int_{t_{po}}^{t_p} d\tau \frac{(d/d\tau)(\mathbf{U} - \mathbf{U}_p)}{\sqrt{t_p - \tau}} + \mathscr{F}_e, \tag{2.37}$$

where $\mathbf{U}$, $\mathbf{U}_p$ are velocities of the fluid and the solid particle, ($\mathbf{U}$ is the mean velocity of the fluid encountered by the particle, not the distributed fluid velocity around the particle), $\bar{\rho}$, $\bar{\rho}_p$ are the densities of the fluid and solid material, $\mathscr{F}_e$ is the external force due to potential field, and F is the time constant for momentum transfer* due to drag force, or

$$F = \tfrac{3}{8} C_D \frac{\bar{\rho}}{\bar{\rho}_p} a^{-1} |\mathbf{U} - \mathbf{U}_p|, \; \sec^{-1} \tag{2.38}$$

and the drag coefficient C_D is given by: $C_D = C_D(N_{\text{Re}})$, and the Reynolds number N_{Re} is given after Eq. (2.4). Thus for the Stokes' law regime, $F = 9\bar{\mu}/2a^2\bar{\rho}_p$, and the viscous resistance is given by

$$(4\pi/3) \, a^3\bar{\rho}_p F(\mathbf{U} - \mathbf{U}_p) = 6\pi\bar{\mu}a(\mathbf{U} - \mathbf{U}_p) \tag{2.39}$$

as given by the Stokes' law. The second term of Eq. (2.37) is due to pressure gradient in the fluid surrounding the particle. The third term is the force to accelerate the apparent mass of the particle relative to the fluid. The fourth term, due to Basset, takes into account the effect of the deviation in the flow pattern from steady state.

It is seen that the terms due to pressure gradient, apparent mass, and the Basset force become important only if the density of the fluid has similar or higher order of magnitude than that of the solid particle. The Basset term constitutes an instantaneous flow resistance. It becomes substantial when the solid particle is accelerated at high rate, the observed drag force becomes many times that due to steady state drag coefficient. This was shown by Hughes and Gilliland [H65].

Corrsin and Lumley [C43] suggested that the ith component of the pressure gradient may be expressed as:

$$-\frac{\partial P}{\partial x_i} = \bar{\rho}\frac{dU_i}{dt} - \bar{\mu}\frac{\partial^2 U_i}{\partial x_j \, \partial x_j}, \tag{2.40}$$

according to the Navier-Stokes equation as applied to a single-phase fluid. This introduces the assumption that:

3. The flow field is not perturbed by the presence of the solid particle. (A modification of this approximation has to be made when dealing with a cloud of solid particles, see Chap. 6.)

Substitution of Eqs. (2.39) and (2.40) into Eq. (2.37) and rearranging gives:

$$\frac{dU_{pi}}{dt_p} = \frac{3\bar{\rho}}{2\bar{\rho}_p + \bar{\rho}}\left[\frac{dU_i}{dt} - \frac{2}{3}\bar{\nu}\frac{\partial^2 U_i}{\partial x_j \, \partial x_j}\right]$$

$$+ \frac{2}{\bar{\rho}_p + \bar{\rho}}\left[\frac{9\bar{\mu}}{2a^2}(U_i - U_{pi}) + \bar{\rho}(U_k - U_{pk})\frac{\partial U_i}{\partial x_k}\right]$$

$$+ \frac{9}{(2\bar{\rho}_p + \bar{\rho})a}\sqrt{\frac{\bar{\rho}\bar{\mu}}{\pi}}\int_{t_{po}}^{t_p} d\tau \frac{\dfrac{d}{d\tau}(U_i - U_{pi})}{\sqrt{t_p - \tau}}, \tag{2.41}$$

* Note that F has the dimension of [time]$^{-1}$ and is therefore not a constant in the usual sense. We use the term "time constant" following the convention which has been used in the formulation of relaxation processes or processes with the general characteristics of exponential decay according to $e^{-t/\tau} = e^{-Ft}$, where τ is called the relaxation time and $F = 1/\tau$ is called the time constant. The latter term is also extensively used in control engineering. A more logical terminology for F would be "inverse relaxation time." However, like many cases in languages, deference tends to be given to existing terminology and simplicity of usage. Therefore, all subsequent usage of the term "time constant" for various transport processes implies the above understanding.

where $\bar{\nu} = \bar{\mu}/\bar{\rho}$, the kinematic viscosity of the fluid. Equation (2.41) becomes linear if a is small and

$$\bar{\rho}\frac{\partial U_i}{\partial x_i} \ll \frac{\bar{\mu}}{a^2}. \tag{2.42}$$

It remains first-order if

$$U_{pi}\frac{\partial U_i}{\partial x_i} \gg \bar{\nu}\frac{\partial^2 U_i}{\partial x_i\,\partial x_j},$$

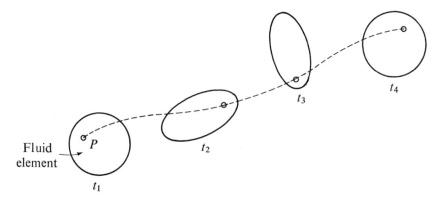

Figure 2.6 Tchen's assumption of transport of a particle in a fluid element.

which gives, when combined with the conditions in Eq. (2.42),

$$\frac{U_{pi}}{a^2(\partial^2 U_i/\partial x_j\,\partial x_j)} \gg 1. \tag{2.43}$$

As a first approximation, Tchen neglects the term $\bar{\rho}(U_k - U_{pk})\,\partial U_i/\partial x_k$ and assumes Eq. (2.43) to be the case; then assumes:

4. During the motion of the solid particle, the same fluid element remains in its neighborhood. This assumption is rather restrictive and makes small particle size necessary in that one has to visualize that the fluid element continues to contain the particle P as both proceed along, although as time progresses the fluid element may distort as shown in Fig. 2.6. This specifies the condition of no overshooting and that the path of the solid particle and the streamline nearly coincide, or

$$\frac{d}{dt} \cong \frac{d}{dt_p}.$$

This assumption inherently specifies that in a turbulent stream, the long-time diffusivity of the particle is equal to that of the turbulent diffusivity of the fluid, since their streamlines coincide. This was shown by Tchen in his computations. Note that this is really the most limiting of all the assumptions. However, no rigorous solution is available when this assumption is removed [L59]. We now get the original form of Tchen's equation of motion (taking one component of velocity and dropping the subscript i):

$$\frac{\mathrm{d}U_p}{\mathrm{d}t} - \alpha\beta U_p = -\alpha\beta U + \beta\frac{\mathrm{d}U}{\mathrm{d}t} + \beta\left(\frac{3\alpha}{\pi}\right)^{\frac{1}{2}}\int_{t_o}^t \mathrm{d}\tau\, \frac{(\mathrm{d}/\mathrm{d}\tau)(U - U_p)}{\sqrt{t - \tau}}, \quad (2.44)$$

where

$$\alpha = \frac{3\bar{\nu}}{a^2}$$

$$\beta = \frac{3\bar{\rho}}{2\bar{\rho}_p + \bar{\rho}},$$

β is the ratio of the effective mass of a sphere of the fluid to that of the solid particle.

For the solution of Eq. (2.44), Tchen further assumes:

5. The turbulence of the fluid is homogeneous and steady.

6. The domain of turbulence is infinite in extent.

Assumption (5) makes possible the use of a simple velocity spectrum; assumption (6) removes the need for considering the interaction with a solid boundary (wall). The latter is taken up in Sec. 2.5.

Tchen took a Lagrangian spectrum of turbulence and treated the stationary case; thus the starting time t_o is set at minus infinity. In the Lagrangian frame of reference we follow the particle along its path and note the statistical average behavior of the stream and the solid particle. Tchen's original procedure was modified by Hinze in the determination of intensities and diffusivities. Chao [C16] further generalized these analyses and those of Liu [L51], Soo [S48], Friedlander [F25], and Csanady [C46] by treating the above Lagrangian equation of motion as a stochastic equation to which a Fourier transform is applied at the outset. Chao's procedures are given here.

Chao [C16] applied the Fourier transform of the velocity component $u(t)$ as defined by (dropping the subscript i for simplicity)

$$\tilde{u}(\omega) = \int_{-\infty}^{\infty} u(t)\exp\left(-i\omega t\right)\mathrm{d}t, \quad (2.45)$$

and a similar expression for the particle, $\tilde{u}_p$. All transformed quantities will hereafter be designated with a tilde. Unlike $\tilde{u}$, $\tilde{u}_p$ is not only a function of ω, but also dependent on the parameters α and β. The "sample" function $u(t)$

is nonperiodic and undamped, thus introducing the assumption of non-decaying turbulence. However, Wiener [W10] showed that the integral was not only permissible but also meaningful in the spirit of generalized harmonic analysis.

The Fourier transform solution of Eq. (2.44) with $t_o = -\infty$ gives

$$\tilde{u}_p = \frac{\left[\alpha + \left(\dfrac{3\alpha\omega}{2}\right)^{1/2}\right] + i\left[\omega + \left(\dfrac{3\alpha\omega}{2}\right)^{1/2}\right]}{\left[\alpha + \left(\dfrac{3\alpha\omega}{2}\right)^{1/2}\right] + i\left[\dfrac{\omega}{\beta} + \left(\dfrac{3\alpha\omega}{2}\right)^{1/2}\right]}\tilde{u}, \qquad (2.46)$$

with

$$\int_{-\infty}^{\infty} \exp\left(-i\omega t\right) dt \int_{-\infty}^{t} \frac{\dot{u}(\tau)\, d\tau}{(t-\tau)^{1/2}} = \left(\frac{\pi}{2}\right)^{1/2}(1+i)\omega^{1/2}\tilde{u}. \qquad (2.47)$$

$\tilde{u}_p$ and $\tilde{u}$ have the following relation with their complex conjugates $\tilde{u}_p^*$ and $\tilde{u}^*$

$$\frac{\tilde{u}_p^*\tilde{u}_p}{\tilde{u}^*\tilde{u}} = \frac{\Omega^{(1)}\left(\dfrac{\omega}{\alpha}\right)}{\Omega^{(2)}\left(\dfrac{\omega}{\alpha}, \beta\right)}, \qquad (2.48)$$

where

$$\Omega^{(1)}\left(\frac{\omega}{\alpha}\right) = \left(\frac{\omega}{\alpha}\right)^2 + \sqrt{6}\left(\frac{\omega}{\alpha}\right)^{3/2} + 3\left(\frac{\omega}{\alpha}\right) + \sqrt{6}\left(\frac{\omega}{\alpha}\right)^{1/2} + 1,$$

and

$$\Omega^{(2)}\left(\frac{\omega}{\alpha}, \beta\right) = \frac{1}{\beta^2}\left(\frac{\omega}{\alpha}\right)^2 + \frac{\sqrt{6}}{\beta}\left(\frac{\omega}{\alpha}\right)^{3/2} + 3\left(\frac{\omega}{\alpha}\right) + \sqrt{6}\left(\frac{\omega}{\alpha}\right)^{1/2} + 1. \qquad (2.49)$$

It is seen that as $\omega/\alpha \to 0$, $\Omega^{(1)}/\Omega^{(2)} \to 1$; and as $\omega/\alpha \to \infty$, $\Omega^{(1)}/\Omega^{(2)} \to \beta^2$. Also, as $\beta \to 0$, i.e., $\bar{\rho} \ll \bar{\rho}_p$, $\Omega^{(1)}/\Omega^{(2)} \to 0$ for all finite values of ω/α; and if $\beta = 1$, i.e., $\bar{\rho} = \bar{\rho}_p$, then $\Omega^{(1)}/\Omega^{(2)} = 1$ for all values of ω/α. The values of β range from 0 to 3.

The stationary double velocity Lagrangian autocorrelation coefficient for the fluid motion is given by

$$\mathscr{R}(\tau) = \frac{\langle u(t)u(t+\tau)\rangle}{\langle u^2\rangle}, \qquad (2.50)$$

where

$$\langle u(t)u(t+\tau)\rangle = \lim_{T\to\infty} \frac{1}{2T}\int_{-T}^{T} u(t)u(t+\tau)\, dt. \qquad (2.51)$$

The energy-spectrum density function $f(\omega)$ is introduced such that

$$\langle u^2\rangle f(\omega) = \lim_{T\to\infty} \frac{\tilde{u}_T^*\tilde{u}_T}{2\pi T}, \qquad (2.52)$$

wherein $\tilde{u}_T$ is the truncated Fourier transform,

$$\tilde{u}_T(\omega) = \int_{-T}^{T} u(t) \exp(-i\omega t)\, dt, \qquad (2.53)$$

and $\tilde{u}_T^*$ is the conjugate. The Wiener-Khintchine theorem gives

$$\mathscr{R}(\tau) = \int_0^\infty f(\omega) \cos \omega\tau\, d\omega, \qquad (2.54)$$

and

$$f(\omega) = \frac{2}{\pi} \int_0^\infty \mathscr{R}(\tau) \cos \omega\tau\, d\tau, \qquad (2.55)$$

that is, $\mathscr{R}(\tau)$ and $f(\omega)$ are mutually the Fourier cosine transforms of one another. An analogous set of expressions may be written for the particle, or

$$\mathscr{R}_p(\tau) = \frac{\langle u_p(t) u_p(t+\tau)\rangle}{\langle u_p^2 \rangle}$$

$$\langle u_p^2 \rangle f_p(\omega) = \lim_{T\to\infty} \frac{\tilde{u}_{p,T}^* \tilde{u}_{p,T}}{2\pi T}, \text{ etc.}$$

The dependence of $\mathscr{R}_p$ and f_p on the parameters α and β is seen.

The above correlation coefficient relates the velocity of the fluid in the neighborhood of the particle at different times. A precise specification of the correlation coefficient $\mathscr{R}(\tau)$ in Eq. (2.54) requires taking into consideration the nonlinear effects. This is accounted for by an alternate approximation in Sec. 2.6.

For the particle, we obtain by integration with respect to ω,

$$\langle u_p^2 \rangle = \int_0^\infty \lim_{T\to\infty} \frac{\tilde{u}_{p,T}^* \tilde{u}_{p,T}}{2\pi T}\, d\omega = \langle u^2 \rangle \int_0^\infty \frac{\Omega^{(1)}}{\Omega^{(2)}} f(\omega)\, d\omega, \qquad (2.56)$$

since $\int_0^\infty f_p(\omega)\, d\omega = 1$. The ratio of the energy-spectrum density functions from Eqs. (2.48) and (2.56) is

$$\frac{f_p}{f} = \frac{\langle u^2 \rangle}{\langle u_p^2 \rangle} \frac{\Omega^{(1)}}{\Omega^{(2)}} = \frac{\Omega^{(1)}}{\Omega^{(2)}} \left[\int_0^\infty \frac{\Omega^{(1)}}{\Omega^{(2)}} f(\omega)\, d\omega \right]^{-1}. \qquad (2.57)$$

The double velocity autocorrelation coefficient for the particle is,

$$\mathscr{R}_p(\tau) = \int_0^\infty f_p(\omega) \cos \omega\tau\, d\omega = \frac{\langle u^2 \rangle}{\langle u_p^2 \rangle} \int_0^\infty \frac{\Omega^{(1)}}{\Omega^{(2)}} f(\omega) \cos \omega\tau\, d\omega \qquad (2.58)$$

Following Kampé de Fériét [K2], a simple relationship exists between the mean square displacement and the Lagrangian velocity autocorrelation coefficient for a homogeneous turbulent field, or

$$\langle x_p^2(t) \rangle = 2 \langle u_p^2 \rangle \int_0^t (t - \tau) \mathscr{R}_p(\tau) \, d\tau \qquad (2.59)$$

and its corresponding eddy diffusivity is

$$D_p(t) = \frac{d}{dt} \frac{\langle x_p^2 \rangle}{2} = \langle u_p^2 \rangle \int_0^t \mathscr{R}_p(\tau) \, d\tau$$

$$= \langle u_p^2 \rangle \int_0^\infty \frac{\sin \omega t}{\omega} f_p(\omega) \, d\omega \qquad (2.60)$$

which becomes, for short and long diffusion times, respectively,

$$\lim_{t \to 0} D_p = \langle u^2 \rangle t \qquad \lim_{\to \infty} D_p = \frac{\pi}{2} \langle u_p^2 \rangle f_p(0). \qquad (2.61)$$

The ratio D_p/D is given by

$$\frac{D_p}{D} = \frac{\langle u_p^2 \rangle \int_0^t \mathscr{R}_p(\tau) \, d\tau}{\langle u^2 \rangle \int_0^t \mathscr{R}(\tau) \, d\tau} = \frac{\langle u_p^2 \rangle \int_0^\infty \frac{\sin \omega t}{\omega} f_p(\omega) \, d\omega}{\langle u^2 \rangle \int_0^\infty \frac{\sin \omega t}{\omega} f(\omega) \, d\omega}, \qquad (2.62)$$

which leads to

$$\lim_{t \to 0} \frac{D_p}{D} = \frac{\langle u_p^2 \rangle}{\langle u^2 \rangle}, \qquad \lim_{t \to \infty} \frac{D_p}{D} = 1,$$

and $\lim_{\omega \to 0} \Omega^{(1)}/\Omega^{(2)} = 1$ as noted earlier. These results of diffusivity ratio were first given by Tchen [T15] who assumed that $\mathscr{R}(\tau)$ is Lagrangian.

$\langle u_p^2 \rangle f_p(\omega) \, d\omega$ and $\langle u^2 \rangle f(\omega) \, d\omega$ represent the average turbulent kinetic energy per unit mass of the particle and the fluid respectively for angular frequencies between ω and $\omega + d\omega$. Equation (2.57) shows that $\Omega^{(1)}/\Omega^{(2)}$ is simply the ratio of the two "spectral" energies.

Heat and mass transfer and the phenomenon of coagulation in dilute suspensions of small particles in turbulent flow are influenced by the mean square relative velocity [F25]. The Reynolds number of particle motion is based on such a relative velocity:

$$u_R = u_p - u. \qquad (2.63)$$

This value, when substituted into Eq. (2.44), again with $t_o = -\infty$, followed by the Fourier transformation and solving for u_R, gives

$$\tilde{u}_R = -\frac{i(1 - \beta)\omega}{\left[\alpha + \beta\left(\dfrac{3\alpha\omega}{2}\right)^{1/2}\right] + i\left[\omega + \beta\left(\dfrac{3\alpha\omega}{2}\right)^{1/2}\right]}\ \tilde{u}(\omega). \tag{2.64}$$

Here again $\tilde{u}_R$ implies $\tilde{u}_R(\omega,\alpha,\beta)$ and

$$\frac{\tilde{u}_R^* \tilde{u}_R}{\tilde{u}^* \tilde{u}} = \frac{\Omega_R^{(1)}\left(\dfrac{\omega}{\alpha}, \beta\right)}{\Omega^{(2)}\left(\dfrac{\omega}{\alpha}, \beta\right)}, \tag{2.65}$$

where

$$\Omega_R^{(1)}\left(\frac{\omega}{\alpha}, \beta\right) = \left(\frac{1 - \beta}{\beta} \cdot \frac{\omega}{\alpha}\right)^2 \quad \text{and} \quad \Omega^{(2)}\left(\frac{\omega}{\alpha}, \beta\right)$$

are given by Eq. (2.49). As $\omega/\alpha \to 0$, $\Omega_R^{(1)}/\Omega^{(2)} \to 0$; and as $\omega/\alpha \to \infty$, $\Omega_R^{(1)}/\Omega^{(2)} \to (1 - \beta)^2$. As $\beta \to 0$, $\Omega_R^{(1)}/\Omega^{(2)} \to 1$ and if $\beta = 1$, $\Omega_R^{(1)}/\Omega^{(2)} = 0$ for all values of ω/α. The mean square relative velocity is now given by

$$\langle u_R^2\rangle = \int_0^\infty \lim_{T\to\infty} \frac{\tilde{u}_{R,T}^* \tilde{u}_{R,T}}{2\pi T}\ d\omega = \langle u^2\rangle \int_0^\infty \frac{\Omega_R^{(1)}}{\Omega^{(2)}} f(\omega)\ d\omega. \tag{2.66}$$

The intensity of the relative turbulent motion is thus calculable from that of the fluid, its energy spectrum and knowledge of the quantity $\Omega_R^{(1)}/\Omega^{(2)}$. The latter is completely determined by the stochastic equation of the relative motion.

Take the case of carbon particles of 5 μ and 50 μ diameter in turbulent air at room conditions. Pertinent physical properties are: $\bar{\nu} = 0.157$ cm²/sec, $\bar{\rho} = 1.18 \times 10^{-3}$ g/cc, and $\bar{\rho}_p = 2.25$ g/cc, giving $\alpha = 7.52 \times 10^6$ and 7.52×10^4 sec⁻¹ respectively for the small and the large particle; and $\beta = 0.00079$. Laufer [L24] showed that, for fully developed turbulent flow of air in a 10-in. pipe at a Reynolds number of 500,000, the turbulence is very nearly isotropic at the pipe axis and has an intensity equal to 85.5 cm/sec, which corresponds to approximately 2.8 per cent of the center-line velocity or 80 per cent of the friction velocity. His data of the turbulent-energy spectrum are shown in relative magnitudes vs. the angular frequency in Fig. 2.7a. Application to the present Lagrangian system follows the results of Mickelson [M28, B9]. Included are the two curves depicting the variation of $\Omega_R^{(1)}/\Omega^{(2)}$ with ω for the two particle sizes selected. Aside from a constant scaling factor, the integral is given by the area under a new curve whose ordinate is the product of the relative "spectral" energy and the ratio $\Omega_R^{(1)}/\Omega^{(2)}$, shown dotted in Fig. 2.7b.

The scaling factor is given by the normalizing condition that $\displaystyle\int_0^\infty f(\omega)\ d\omega = 1$.

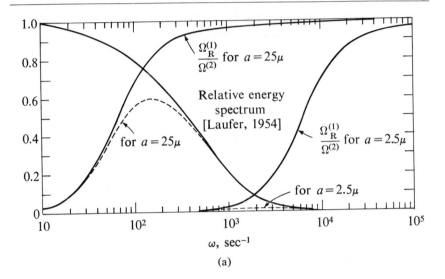

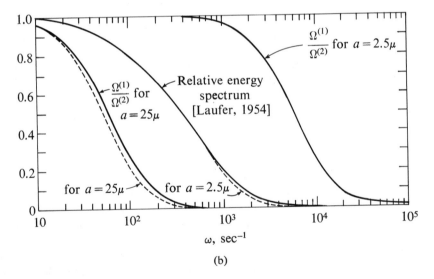

Figure 2.7 Behavior of carbon particles in turbulent air [C16].
(a) Evaluation of root-mean-square relative velocity.
(b) Determination of "slip" measure.

The particle Reynolds number based on the root-mean-square relative velocity, $\dfrac{2a\langle u_R^2\rangle^{\frac{1}{2}}}{\bar{\nu}}$, has been found to be 0.095 and 2.52 respectively for the small and the large particle. The corresponding Reynolds numbers of the particles falling under gravity at their terminal velocities in quiescent air are 0.00053 and 0.53 respectively.

For the particle of $a = 2.5\ \mu$, it is seen that the spectral intensity of the particle motion closely approximates that of the fluid up to $\omega = 10^3\ \text{sec}^{-1}$. At this point, however, the relative "spectral" energy of the fluid has already dropped to about 20 per cent of its maximum. At $\omega = 10^4\ \text{sec}^{-1}$, $\Omega^{(1)}/\Omega^{(2)} = 0.28$ but the relative "spectral" energy has decreased to 0.005. If the ordinate of the relative energy spectrum for the fluid turbulence is multiplied by the corresponding ordinate of $\Omega^{(1)}/\Omega^{(2)}$, we obtain the two dotted curves shown in Fig. 2.7b. If we now designate the area under the new curve by A_1 and that under the original relative energy spectrum by A_2, then A_1/A_2 is a measure of the degree of departure of the particle motion from the fluid motion (in the statistical sense). The particle would closely follow the fluid motion when $A_1/A_2 \to 1$. Figure 2.7b indicates that the 50 μ diameter particle could not follow the fluid motion. It is expected that for small air bubbles in water, $\bar{\rho}_p \ll \bar{\rho}$; the ratio A_1/A_2 would be larger than unity.

Chao also considered the case of sand particles of 100 μ and 200 μ diameter in turbulent water at room temperature, with $\rho = 1.00$ g/cc, $\bar{\rho}_p = 2.60$ g/cc, and $\bar{\nu} = 0.0114$ cm²/sec. The corresponding values of α are 1368 and 342 sec^{-1}, and $\beta = 0.484$. Using the intensity and energy spectrum data reported by Ippen and Raichlen [I5] for open-channel flow at Reynolds number of 54,300, the particle Reynolds numbers based on the root-mean-square relative velocities were found to be 1.51 and 10.3 respectively. Ippen and Raichlen's measurements were made at approximately half-depth and the intensity there was 18.2 cm/sec, or 8 per cent of the temporal mean velocity in the flow direction. Figure 2.8 illustrates the behavior of motion of such sand particles.

The significance of various terms is seen by comparing Chao's results with those of Soo [S48] in which both the second term and the third term on the right-hand side of Eq. (2.44) were neglected but the effect of gravity was considered, and Friedlander [F25] (who neglected only the third term). The comparison is shown in Fig. 2.9. It is seen that for $\beta = 0.01$ the density of the solid particle is much larger than that of the fluid; good agreement was obtained since the contributions of apparent mass, pressure gradient, and Basset force are all small. However, when $\beta = 0.5$, neither Soo's nor Friedlander's analysis can be expected to be accurate. This condition is noted in later derivations. We shall account for the deviation in streamlines of particle paths (Chap. 6).

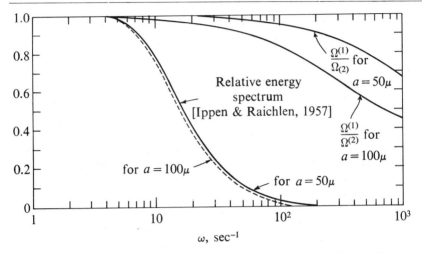

Figure 2.8 Behavior of sand particles in turbulent water—determination of slip measure [C16].

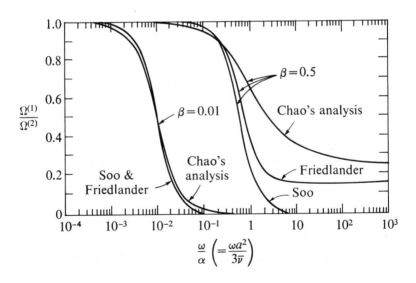

Figure 2.9 Comparison of Chao's analysis with that of Soo and Friedlander [C16]

Some further aspects of theory of dispersion by continuous movement was discussed by Lin [L44].

2.5 Effect of a Wall

As a preliminary to treating the interaction of a multiphase fluid with a body, motion of a single spherical solid particle near the wall of a turbulent fluid was treated by Soo and Tien [S69]. The analysis consisted of the basic equation of motion of wall interferences on a two-phase turbulent field, and solution of the equations including only significant contributions for the stationary case. The simplified system adopted for this study consisted of a

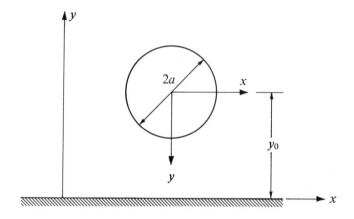

Figure 2.10 Coordinate system of a sphere moving near a wall.

spherical solid particle in a semi-infinite body of turbulent fluid bounded by an infinite wall (Fig. 2.10). The solid particle was taken to be much smaller than the size of eddy or microscale of stream turbulence, so that the contributions of various fluctuation velocities are linear. Description of the character of stream motion was based on Laufer [L22], Chapman and Kester [C17] and Klebanoff [K18] for the distribution of intensities and scales of turbulence. The stream, especially near the wall, was anisotropic and nonhomogeneous, but the concept of local isotropy [L22] was accepted as a basic constraint. The turbulence was fully developed so that intermittency [K18] could be neglected.

The motion of a particle in a fluid bounded by an infinite fixed wall can be treated by extending the method due to Stokes [L5]. Assuming potential motion for particle-wall interaction, the motion of a sphere moving perpendicularly to a wall is identical to the case where two identical spheres are moving along the line connecting the centers. The kinetic energy of the fluid is

$$2K_y = \tfrac{2}{3}\pi\bar{\rho}a^3\left(1 + \frac{3}{8}\frac{a^3}{y^3}\right)\dot{y}^2, \tag{2.67}$$

where $\bar{\rho}$ is the density of the fluid. For a sphere moving parallel to the wall, the kinetic energy of the fluid is

$$2K_x = \tfrac{2}{3}\pi\bar{\rho}a^3\left(1 + \frac{3}{16}\frac{a^3}{y^3}\right)\dot{x}^2. \tag{2.68}$$

In general, for a spherical particle moving in a fluid as shown in Fig. 2.10, the total kinetic energy of the system can be represented by

$$K = \tfrac{1}{2}(A\dot{x}^2 + B\dot{y}^2), \tag{2.69}$$

where

$$A = \tfrac{4}{3}\pi\bar{\rho}_p a^3 + \tfrac{2}{3}\pi\bar{\rho}a^3\left(1 + \frac{3}{16}\frac{a^3}{y^3}\right),$$

$$B = \tfrac{4}{3}\pi\bar{\rho}_p a^3 + \tfrac{2}{3}\pi\bar{\rho}a^3\left(1 + \frac{3}{8}\frac{a^3}{y^3}\right).$$

and $\bar{\rho}_p$ is the density of the particle material. Assuming holonomic motion, the Lagrange equation for the system based on generalized space coordinate x_i and velocity $\dot{x}_i$ gives for generalized external force $\mathscr{F}_i$:

$$\mathscr{F}_i = \frac{\mathrm{d}}{\mathrm{d}t}\left(\frac{\partial K}{\partial \dot{x}_i}\right) - \left(\frac{\partial K}{\partial x_i}\right). \tag{2.70}$$

Hence

$$\mathscr{F}_x = \frac{\mathrm{d}}{\mathrm{d}t}A\dot{x} = \tfrac{4}{3}\pi a^3(\bar{\rho}_p + \tfrac{1}{2}\bar{\rho})\ddot{x} + \tfrac{1}{8}\pi\bar{\rho}\frac{a^6}{y^4}(\dot{y}\dot{x} - 3\dot{x}\dot{y}), \tag{2.71}$$

and

$$\mathscr{F}_y = \frac{\mathrm{d}}{\mathrm{d}t}(B\dot{y}) - \tfrac{1}{2}\dot{x}^2\frac{\partial A}{\partial y} - \tfrac{1}{2}\dot{y}^2\frac{\partial B}{\partial y}$$

$$= \tfrac{4}{3}\pi a^3(\bar{\rho}_p + \tfrac{1}{2}\bar{\rho})\ddot{y} + \tfrac{1}{4}\pi\bar{\rho}\frac{a^6}{y^4}(y\dot{y} - \tfrac{3}{2}\dot{y}^2 + \tfrac{3}{4}\dot{x}^2). \tag{2.72}$$

These are components of the generalized Bernoulli force.

The other forces acting on the spherical particle in a turbulent fluid in a gravitational field of acceleration g are as given in Sec. 2.4, or

$$\mathscr{F}_i = \tfrac{4}{3}\pi a^3 g(\bar{\rho}_p - \bar{\rho}) + 6\pi a\bar{\mu}(\dot{x}_i - u_i)$$

$$+ 6\pi a\bar{\mu}\left[\frac{a}{\sqrt{(\pi\bar{\nu})}}\int_{-\infty}^t \frac{(\ddot{x}_i - \dot{u}_i)}{\sqrt{t - \tau}}\,d\tau\right]. \quad (2.73)$$

($i = x,y$), and components u, v of the fluid velocity which, when combined with Eqs. (2.71) and (2.72) and following a similar treatment as in Sec. 2.4 gives

$$\tfrac{4}{3}\pi a^3 \bar{\rho}_p \ddot{x} = -6\pi a\bar{\mu}(\dot{x} - u) - 6\pi a\bar{\mu}\left[\frac{a}{\sqrt{\pi\bar{\nu}}}\int_{-\infty}^t \frac{\ddot{x} - \dot{u}}{\sqrt{t - \tau}}\,d\tau\right]$$

$$- \tfrac{2}{3}\pi\bar{\rho}a^3(\ddot{x} - \dot{u}) - \tfrac{1}{8}\pi\bar{\rho}\frac{a^6}{y^4}[y(\ddot{x} - \dot{u}) - 3(\dot{x} - u)(\dot{y} - v)]$$

$$+ \tfrac{4}{3}\pi a^3 \bar{\rho}\dot{u}. \quad (2.74)$$

$$\tfrac{4}{3}\pi a^3 \bar{\rho}_p \ddot{y} = -\tfrac{4}{3}\pi a^3 g(\bar{\rho}_p - \bar{\rho}) - 6\pi a\bar{\mu}(\dot{y} - v) - 6\pi a\bar{\mu}\left[\frac{a}{\sqrt{\pi\bar{\nu}}}\int_{-\infty}^t \frac{(\ddot{y} - \dot{v})}{\sqrt{t - \tau}}\,d\tau\right]$$

$$- \tfrac{2}{3}\pi\bar{\rho}a^3(\ddot{y} - \dot{v}) - \tfrac{1}{4}\pi\bar{\rho}\frac{a^6}{y^4}[y(\ddot{y} - \dot{v}) - \tfrac{3}{2}(\dot{y} - v)^2 + \tfrac{3}{4}(\dot{x} - u)^2]$$

$$+ \tfrac{4}{3}\pi a^3 \bar{\rho}\dot{v}. \quad (2.75)$$

Equations (2.74) and (2.75) are the basic equations of motion of the system.

The solution of Eqs. (2.74) and (2.75), the basic equations of motion of the system, together with the statistical prescriptions of the turbulent field, is obviously a formidable task. To develop some understanding of the property of the system, a stationary solution (i.e., without considering the probability for a particle to be at a certain state at any time, but considering what would happen if it were there) was given together with simplifications from order of magnitude considerations.

Neglecting the Basset term since its ratio to the Stokes' term amounts to $a\sqrt{\omega/\bar{\nu}}$, and the buoyancy force, the basic equations become

$$\ddot{x} + \alpha\beta(\dot{x} - u) + \left(\frac{a^3\beta}{8}\right)\frac{1}{y^3}(\ddot{x} - \dot{u}) = \beta\dot{u}, \quad (2.76)$$

$$\ddot{y} + \alpha\beta(\dot{y} - v) + \left(\frac{a^3\beta}{8}\right)\frac{1}{y^3}(\ddot{y} - \dot{v}) = \beta\dot{v}. \quad (2.77)$$

Further, for a gas-solid system, the term $\beta\dot{u}$ and $\beta\dot{v}$ can be neglected, and that $a^3\beta/8 = \epsilon$ is a small quantity and was treated as the perturbation parameter, or

$$y = {}_0y + \epsilon({}_1y) + \epsilon^2({}_2y) + \cdots. \quad (2.78)$$

Rapid convergence is expected because y must be greater than the thickness of the laminar sublayer for the turbulence to be felt.

Substitution of Eq. (2.78) into Eq. (2.77) gives for various orders of ϵ

$$({}_0\ddot{y}) + \alpha\beta({}_0\dot{y}) = \alpha\beta v \tag{2.79}$$

$$({}_1\ddot{y}) + \alpha\beta({}_1\dot{y}) = \frac{\dot{v} - ({}_0\ddot{y})}{({}_0y)^3}, \tag{2.80}$$

with v represented by a spectrum

$$v = \sum_n A_n \sin 2\pi n t. \tag{2.81}$$

as before, and the Lagrangian power spectrum $f(n)$ of the fluid phase, where

$$\tfrac{1}{2}A_n^2 = \langle v^2 \rangle f(n)\, dn, \tag{2.82}$$

in which $\langle v^2 \rangle$ is the mean squared velocity of the stream, the intensities and correlations of the spherical particle can be evaluated. When there is no wall interference,

$$\langle {}_0v_p^2 \rangle = \langle {}_0\dot{y}^2 \rangle = \langle v^2 \rangle \int_0^\infty \frac{f(n)\, dn}{1 + \left(\dfrac{2\pi n}{\alpha\beta}\right)^2}. \tag{2.83}$$

With an approximation of $f(n)$ as [S48],

$$f(n) = \frac{2\sqrt{\pi}\lambda}{\sqrt{\langle v^2 \rangle}} e^{-\lambda^2 \pi^2 n^2/\langle v^2 \rangle}, \tag{2.84}$$

where λ is the Lagrangian microscale:

$$\frac{\langle {}_0v_p^2 \rangle}{\langle v^2 \rangle} = \sqrt{\pi} e^{1/K^2} \operatorname{erfc} \frac{1/K}{K}, \tag{2.85}$$

and where

$$K = \frac{2\langle v^2 \rangle^{1/2}}{\lambda\alpha\beta} = \tfrac{2}{9}\langle N_{\mathrm{Re}} \rangle \left(\frac{a}{\lambda}\right)\frac{(\bar{\rho}_p + \bar{\rho}/2)}{\bar{\rho}}, \tag{2.86}$$

in which $\langle N_{\mathrm{Re}} \rangle = 2a\langle v^2 \rangle^{1/2}/\bar{v}$. Considering wall interference, for

$$\dot{y} \cong {}_0\dot{y} + \epsilon\, {}_1\dot{y}, \tag{2.87}$$

$$\dot{y}^2 \cong {}_0\dot{y}^2 + 2\epsilon\, {}_0\dot{y}\, {}_1\dot{y}, \tag{2.88}$$

and

$$\langle v_p^2 \rangle = \langle \dot{y}^2 \rangle = \langle {}_0\dot{y}^2 \rangle + 2\epsilon\langle {}_0\dot{y}\, {}_1\dot{y} \rangle, \tag{2.89}$$

we have

$$\frac{\langle v_p^2 \rangle}{\langle v^2 \rangle} = \frac{\sqrt{\pi}}{K}\left[1 - \frac{2\epsilon}{y_o^3}\left(\frac{1}{2} + \frac{1}{K^2}\right)\right] e^{1/K^2} \operatorname{erfc}\left(\frac{1}{K}\right) + \frac{2\epsilon}{y_o^3 K^2}. \tag{2.90}$$

This relation and Eq. (2.85) were plotted as shown in Fig. 2.11, in terms of $(\langle v^2 \rangle - \langle v_p^2 \rangle)/\langle v^2 \rangle$.

Similarly, Eq. (2.76) can be solved with the approximation

$$x = (_0x) + \epsilon(_1x),$$ (2.91)

leading to

$$(_0\ddot{x}) + \alpha\beta(_0\dot{x}) = \alpha\beta\,u$$ (2.92)

$$(_1\ddot{x}) + \alpha\beta(_1\dot{x}) = \frac{\dot{u} - (_0\ddot{x})}{(_0y)^3}.$$ (2.93)

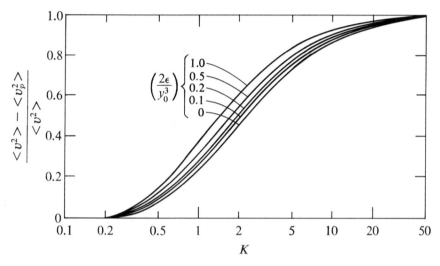

Figure 2.11 Deviation of local intensity of motion of a particle from that of the stream at various distances from the wall [S69].

Using a similar spectrum approximation, for $_0y = $ constant $= y_o$, we get a similar solution as Eq. (2.90):

$$\frac{\langle u_p^2 \rangle}{\langle u^2 \rangle} = \frac{\sqrt{\pi}}{K}\left[1 - \frac{2\epsilon}{y_o^3}\left(\frac{1}{2} + \frac{1}{K^2}\right)\right]e^{1/K^2}\,\text{erfc}\left(\frac{1}{K}\right) - \frac{2\epsilon}{y_o^3 K^2}.$$ (2.94)

(Note the difference in sign of the last term, and that the K's in Eqs. (2.90) and (2.94) are in general different.)

The Lagrangian correlation coefficients of the particle motion can be evaluated as before, the trend is as indicated in Figs. 2.12 for various values of K.

It can be further shown that the diffusivity of the particle is identical to the eddy diffusivity of the stream as obtained before. It was shown that, based

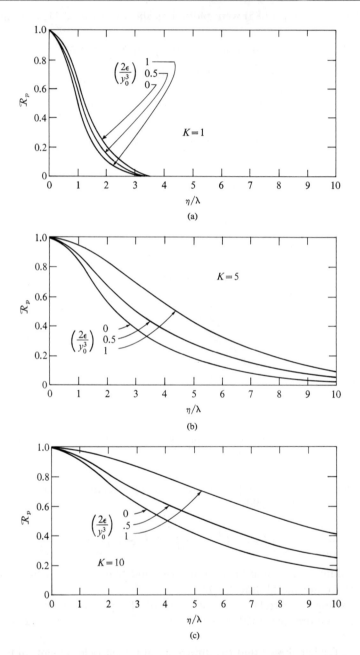

Figure 2.12 Effect of the wall on the correlation of particle motion [S69].
(a) $K = 1$ (b) $K = 5$ (c) $K = 10$

on local stream intensity, contribution of wall interference actually reduces the intensity of motion of solid particles such that the local quantity of $[(\langle v^2 \rangle - \langle v_p^2 \rangle)/\langle v^2 \rangle]$ is less than 1 but greater than zero (Fig. 2.11). The local value of $\langle v^2 \rangle$ or $\langle u^2 \rangle$ varies with the distance from the wall as shown in Fig. 2.13 according to Laufer [L22]. In Fig. 2.13, y_o is the distance from the wall while R_o is the duct radius. When corrected to the mean stream

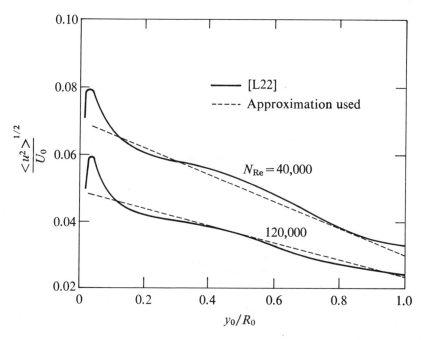

Figure 2.13 Variation of intensity of motion of the stream from the wall [L22].

condition (subscript m), assuming constant eddy diffusivity [S31] in the stream, the relation in Fig. 2.11 can be expressed as in Figs. 2.14a and b, showing the intensity that a particle at various values of y_o/R_o tends to attain. These figures show that at low-stream Reynolds numbers, a particle moving across the turbulence field is constantly accelerated and decelerated by the changing turbulence and wall interaction as well as by the constant turbulence intensity in the middle portion of the stream, resulting in high particle intensity in that portion. This effect is more pronounced for low Reynolds numbers based on the dimension of the duct than high Reynolds numbers.

The above analysis is seen to be valid when the particle diffusivity is of similar order of the eddy diffusivity of the stream, i.e., for very small particles. The eddy diffusivity has been reported to be sensibly constant over the duct

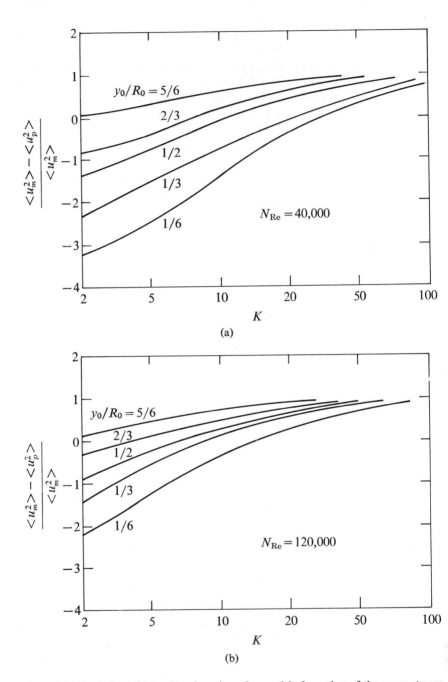

Figure 2.14 Deviation of intensity of motion of a particle from that of the mean stream at various distances from the wall [S69].
(a) Duct Reynolds number 40,000
(b) Duct Reynolds number 120,000

50

height. The present analysis indicates that the effect of the wall on the particle diffusivity is secondary. It is seen that the presence of the wall affects the intensity of motion of the particles in the mean stream of a two-phase duct flow significantly; the intensity of particle motion increases toward the wall; the scale of turbulence of particle motion decreases toward the wall; and the effect of the wall on the mean stream is more predominating when the Reynolds number based on dimensions of the duct is low than when it is high, both for high duct Reynolds numbers. Further details are given in Chap. 4.

2.6 Diffusivity of a Particle in a Turbulent Fluid

Assumption (4) of Tchen in the previous section resulted in intensity of particle motion (average kinetic energy) which agreed reasonably well with experiments, but this assumption also led to the conclusion that the particle diffusivity was identical to the Lagrangian eddy diffusivity of turbulence, which is experimentally incorrect for finite-size particles (Sec. 2.8).

Studies by Lumley [L59], Soo and Peskin [S67], Peskin [P14, P15], and Friedlander [F25] have the general conclusion that the particles do not follow fluid points and that the correlation of velocities encountered by the solid particle is not the Lagrangian correlation of turbulence. This effect has been called "probability of encounter" [S67, P15] and in a detailed experimental investigation [S66] it was concluded that this effect was significant in lowering particle diffusivity. The same investigation also showed that increased flow Reynolds number also reduces particle diffusivity (Sec. 2.8). Peskin [P15] introduced additional statistical inference to previous studies [S67, P14] and presented a calculation showing how "probability of encounter" affects particle diffusivity. It was shown that the ratio of particle diffusivity to eddy diffusivity is a function of particle response time and both the Lagrangian and Eulerian microscale. The relation between these microscales was explored by Lumley [L60] and Kraichman [K33] and experimentally, by Mickelson [M28].

In order to simplify computations, it will be assumed that the Reynolds number based on relative velocity between the particle and its surrounding fluid is small enough so that particle drag is given by Stokes' law. The equation of motion for the particle is then given by [L59]:

$$\frac{d^2 \hat{y}_i(\alpha_k, t)}{dt^2} + F \frac{d}{dt} \hat{y}(\alpha_k, t) = F U_i(\hat{y}_j(\alpha_k, t); t), \tag{2.95}$$

where $\hat{y}_i(\alpha_k, t)$ is the ith component of particle displacement $\hat{\mathbf{y}}$, α_k the initial position, $F = 6\pi a \bar{\mu}/m_p$, m_p being the mass of the particle, and $U_i(\hat{y}_j; t)$ is the

ith component of the Eulerian fluid velocity field **U**. Since the fluid velocity field is turbulent, $U_i(x_j;t)$ will be considered a random function in space, **x**, and time, t, with zero mean relative to some uniform mean flow velocity. Equation (2.95) is a stochastic nonlinear equation, and a solution would consist of finding the complete probability density of $\hat{y}_i(\alpha_k,t)$ given the statistical description of $U_i(x_j;t)$ for all space **x**, and time t. This problem was considered by Lumley [L59]; however, difficulties of integration have so far prevented finding much statistical information about the particle displacement. Rather than attempt to solve Eq. (2.95) directly, we will consider a different equation of motion which will be a statistical approximation of Eq. (2.95) as introduced by Peskin [P15] in the following.

The velocity, $U_i(\hat{y}_i;t)$, is the velocity of the fluid "encountered" by the solid particle at its displacement, $\hat{\mathbf{y}}$, at some time t, and this fluid element is not necessarily the same fluid element that the solid had encountered initially at t_0. One would like to relate the velocity encountered by the solid at any time, t, to the Lagrangian velocity of the fluid element encountered by the solid initially at time t_0. This relation can be obtained statistically by computing the most probable velocity encountered by the solid particle at position $\hat{\mathbf{y}}$ given the Lagrangian velocity of the fluid element located at position **x** as represented by Fig. 2.15a.

At time $t = 0$ the solid particle and fluid element are coincident; at $t = t_1$ the solid is at $\hat{\mathbf{y}}_1$ and encounters there a fluid element with Lagrangian velocity $\mathbf{V}(a;t_1)$ and the original fluid element is at $\mathbf{x}_1$ with Lagrangian velocity $\mathbf{V}(0;t_1)$. Figure 2.15b is a second realization of the same system. The fluid path is the same and the solid particle path is the same for $t \leq t_1$, but the surrounding fluid-velocity field is different from case (a). At position $\hat{\mathbf{y}} = \hat{\mathbf{y}}_1$ the solid particle now encounters a fluid element velocity $\mathbf{V}(b;t_1)$ which in general is not equal to $\mathbf{V}(a;t_1)$. That is, in configuration (b) the solid encountered a fluid element that had a different initial position than in case (a). If we average over all realization of the type **a**, **b**, **c**, ... (i.e., over the initial positions of fluid elements that are at $\hat{\mathbf{y}}_1$ at time t_1) we get the average velocity encountered by the solid particle given a certain fixed Lagrangian fluid process, $\mathbf{V}(0;t)$. Mathematically, this encountered velocity is expressed as the conditional expectation [F23] of $\mathbf{U}(\hat{\mathbf{y}};t)$ given $\mathbf{V}(0;t)$ at **x**.

$$E_{[V_i(0;t)]_\mathbf{x}}\{U_j(\hat{y}_k;t)\} = \int U_j(\hat{y}_k;t)\,dp\{U_j(\hat{y}_k;t) \mid [V_i(0;t)]_\mathbf{x}\} \qquad (2.96)$$

$$[V_j(0;t)]_\mathbf{x} = U_i(x_k(0;t);t),$$

where $p\{\mathbf{U}(\hat{\mathbf{y}};t) \mid [\mathbf{V}(0;t)]_\mathbf{x}\}$ is the conditional probability of $\mathbf{U}(\hat{\mathbf{y}};t)$ for given $\mathbf{V}(t)$ at **x**.

$$p\{\mathbf{U}(\hat{\boldsymbol{y}};t) \mid [\mathbf{V}(0,t)]_\mathbf{x}\} = \frac{p\{[\mathbf{V}(0;t)]_\mathbf{x}\mathbf{U}(\hat{\boldsymbol{y}};t)\}}{p\{[\mathbf{V}(0;t)]_\mathbf{x}\}}. \qquad (2.97)$$

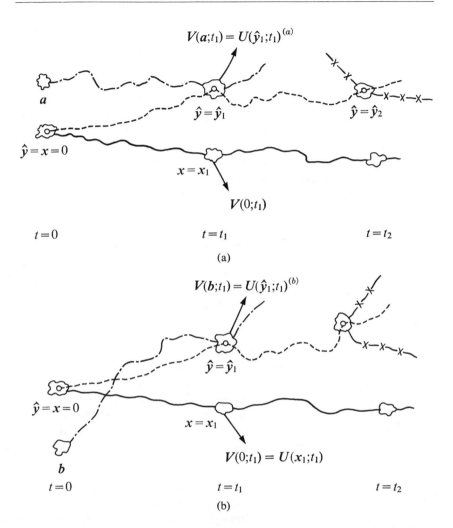

Figure 2.15 Probability of encounter of particle and stream in turbulent motion [P15].

The meaning of Eq. (2.96) becomes clear if we consider a specific case. Take $U(\hat{y};t)$ and $V(0;t)$ at x to be distributed according to a joint Gaussian distribution with correlation $\mathscr{R}_E(\hat{y},x)$. In this case

$$E_{[V_i(0;t)]x}\{U_j(\hat{y}_k;t)\} = V_i(0;t)\mathscr{R}_{Eij}(\hat{y}, x). \tag{2.98}$$

That is, the expected velocity encountered by a solid particle at position $\hat{y}$ given a fluid particle at x is just the Lagrangian fluid velocity $[V(0;t)]_x$ times the Eulerian correlation coefficient $\mathscr{R}_E(\hat{\mathbf{y}},\mathbf{x})$ [F23]. Since Eq. (2.96) was concerned only with second-moment properties of random variables, Gaussian distribution assumptions were sufficient [D32]. The turbulent field will be assumed isotropic so that the correlation will be a function only of the radial distance from the fluid particle at $\mathbf{x}$. In addition, random variables will be assumed stationary.

We consider a solid particle acted upon by the average encountered velocity, Eq. (2.96), or more specifically, Eq. (2.98), and denote the position of this solid particle by $\mathbf{y}$. ($\mathbf{y}$ is related to $\hat{\mathbf{y}}$ by the formula, $\mathbf{y} = E_{\mathbf{V}(0;t)}\{\hat{\mathbf{y}}\}$.) Physically, one might think of this solid particle as the "average" solid particle moving in the vicinity of the fluid element whose Lagrangian velocity is $\mathbf{V}(\alpha,t)$. The equation of motion for this particle can be written in integral form as

$$y_j(t) = \int_0^t g(t - \tau)V_i(\tau)\mathscr{R}_{Eij}(|\mathbf{y} - \mathbf{x}|)\,d\tau \tag{2.99}$$

$$g(t - \tau) = 1 - e^{-F(t-\tau)}. \tag{2.100}$$

(The initial conditions have been suppressed in Eq. (2.99) for convenience only.) Equation (2.99) will allow one to determine the solid-particle statistics from a knowledge of the Lagrangian statistics of a fluid element and the Eulerian correlation of the turbulent field between fluid element and the solid particle position. This equation is a nonlinear stochastic integral equation. It was assumed that stochastic solutions exist and are unique [B19, I10] and solutions can be obtained by successive substitution [T52]. It should be noted that the nonlinearity of Eq. (2.99) is now deterministic (only the $\mathbf{V}(\tau)$ is random), but in Eq. (2.95) the nonlinearity is itself only stochastically defined. As a result of the deterministic nonlinearity, Eq. (2.99) is much easier to deal with than Eq. (2.95).

Computation of Diffusivity—Peskin further applied Eq. (2.99) to the problem of computing the diffusivity of one-dimensional particle motion in isotropic stationary turbulence. Although this is an idealized situation, these conditions have been approximated and the resulting diffusivity measured (Sec. 2.8).

Equation (2.99) for this example becomes:

$$\mathbf{y}(t) = \int_0^t g(t - \tau)\mathbf{V}(\tau)\mathscr{R}_E(\mathbf{y}(\tau) - \mathbf{x}(\tau))\,d\tau, \tag{2.101}$$

where $\mathbf{V}(t)$ is the Lagrangian velocity of a fluid element and $\mathbf{x}(t)$ its Lagrangian position. $\mathscr{R}_E(\mathbf{y}(\tau) - \mathbf{x}(t))$ is the Eulerian correlation coefficient between fluid element position and solid particle position. We assume that the Eulerian correlation can be expanded in the form

$$\mathscr{R}_E(\mathbf{y}(t) - \mathbf{x}(t)) = 1 - \frac{[\mathbf{y}(t) - \mathbf{x}(t)]^2}{\lambda_E^2} + \cdots. \tag{2.102}$$

Here λ_E is the Eulerian microscale. If terms of $0(1/\lambda_E^4)$ and higher are neglected, substitution of Eq. (2.102) into (2.101) gives

$$\mathbf{y}(t) = \int_0^t g(t - \tau)\mathbf{V}(\tau)\, d\tau - \frac{1}{\lambda_E^2} \int_0^t g(t - \tau)\mathbf{V}(\tau)(\mathbf{y} - \mathbf{x})^2\, d\tau + 0\left(\frac{1}{\lambda_E^4}\right). \tag{2.103}$$

Using Eqs. (2.100) in (2.103) and squaring, we obtain an expression for the correlation parameter,

$$[\mathbf{y}(t) - \mathbf{x}(t)]^2 = \int_0^t \int_0^t e^{-F(t-\tau)-F(t-s)}\mathbf{V}(\tau) \cdot \mathbf{V}(s)\, ds\, d\tau$$

$$+ \frac{2}{\lambda_E^2} \int_0^t \int_0^t e^{-F(t-\tau)} g(t - s)\mathbf{V}(\tau) \cdot \mathbf{V}(s)[\mathbf{y}(s) - \mathbf{x}(s)]^2$$

$$\times\, ds\, d\tau + 0\left(\frac{1}{\lambda_E^4}\right). \tag{2.104}$$

When (2.104) is substituted into (2.103) and the resulting equation squared, the following expression is obtained for the square of the particle displacement:

$$y^2(t) = \int_0^t \int_0^t g(t - \tau)g(t - s)V(t)V(s)\, ds\, d\tau - \frac{2}{\lambda_E^2} \int_0^t \int_0^t g(t - \tau)$$

$$\times\, g(t - s)V(\tau)V(s)\left\{\int_0^s \int_0^s e^{-F(s-m)-F(s-n)}\right.$$

$$\times\, V(m)V(n)\, dn\, dm\bigg\}ds\, d\tau + 0\left(\frac{1}{\lambda_E^4}\right). \tag{2.105}$$

It can be seen that the expression for particle displacement (or its powers) can be obtained to any order in $1/\lambda_E^2$ by expressions of this type. Furthermore, for any order expansion, the functions of the particle position, y, can be expressed in terms of the random Lagrangian fluid velocities, $V(\tau)$, $V(s)$, ... at times τ, s, ...

Ensemble or probability averages for functions of y are obtained by integration over the joint probability density of the Lagrangian fluid velocities $V(\tau)$, $V(s)$, etc. That is, the expectation of $y^2(t)$ is given by

$$Ey^2(t) = \int \int \int \int L[V(\tau),V(s),V(m),V(n)]p\{V(\tau),V(s),V(m),V(n)\}$$

$$\times\, dV(\tau)\, dV(s)\, dV(m)\, dV(n), \tag{2.106}$$

where $L[\ ]$ is the multiple integral operation of (2.105). It will be convenient to assume that the Lagrangian fluid velocities appearing in (2.105) have a joint Gaussian distribution

$$p\{V(\tau), V(s), V(m), V(n)\} = \frac{\exp\left\{-\dfrac{1}{2\,|\lambda|\,\langle V^2\rangle}\displaystyle\sum_{r=1}^{N}\sum_{q=1}^{N}V(r)V(q)|\lambda|_{rq}\right\}}{(2\pi)^{N/2}\,|\lambda|^{\frac{1}{2}}\langle V^2\rangle^{N/2}}$$

$$|\lambda| = \mathrm{Det}\,[\mathscr{R}_{E_{rq}}];\quad |\lambda|_{rq} = \text{Cofactor of } \mathscr{R}_{E_r} \text{ in } [\mathscr{R}_{E_{rq}}];\quad N = 4.\quad (2.107)$$

It can then be shown that

$$E\{V(\tau), V(s), V(m), V(n)\} = E\{V(\tau), V(s)\}E\{V(m), V(n)\}$$

$$+ E\{V(\tau), V(m)\}E\{V(s), V(n)\} + E\{V(\tau), V(n)\}E\{V(s), V(m)\}. \quad (2.108)$$

Using the assumption of stationary statistics for the Lagrangian velocities, one can express the correlation in the form

$$E\{V(\tau), V(s)\} = \langle V^2\rangle\mathscr{R}(|\tau - s|);\quad E\{V^2\} = \langle V^2\rangle, \quad (2.109)$$

where $\langle V^2\rangle^{\frac{1}{2}}$ is the intensity of turbulence, and $\mathscr{R}$ is the Lagrangian correlation coefficient. Using Eqs. (2.105), (2.108), and (2.109) in (2.106), the mean square particle displacement becomes

$$E\{y^2(t)\} = \langle V^2\rangle\int_0^t\int_0^t g(t - \tau)g(t - s)\mathscr{R}(|\tau - s|)\,ds\,d\tau$$

$$- \frac{2}{\lambda_E^2}\langle V^2\rangle^2\int_0^t d\tau\int_0^t ds\int_0^s dm\int_0^s dn\,g(t - \tau)g(t - s)e^{-F(s-m)-F(s-n)}$$

$$\times \{\mathscr{R}(|\tau - s|)\mathscr{R}(|m - n|) + \mathscr{R}(|\tau - m|)\mathscr{R}(|s - n|)$$

$$+ \mathscr{R}(|\tau - n|)\mathscr{R}(|s - m|)\} + 0\!\left(\frac{1}{\lambda_E^4}\right). \quad (2.110)$$

In order to proceed, one must know the form of the Lagrangian correlation coefficient, $\mathscr{R}(|\tau - s|)$, which, for $\lambda^* = \lambda/\langle V^2\rangle^{\frac{1}{2}}$, is given by

$$\mathscr{R}(|\tau - s|) = e^{-\frac{|\tau - s|}{\lambda^*}} \quad (2.111)$$

as an approximation to the data for Lagrangian correlation coefficients [F23], and will be used in this diffusivity computation. Equation (2.111) is inserted into Eq. (2.110) and integration regions are changed. That is, the formula

$$\int_0^t\int_0^t f(\tau, s)\,ds\,d\tau = \int_0^t d\tau\int_0^\tau ds\,f(\tau, s) + \int_0^t ds\int_0^s d\tau\,f(\tau, s) \quad (2.112)$$

is used. These operations result in the following equation for the mean square particle displacement:

$$E\{y^2(t)\} = \langle V^2 \rangle^2 \int_0^t \int_0^\tau g(t - \tau)g(t - s)e^{-\frac{\tau-s}{\lambda^*}} \, ds \, d\tau$$

$$- \frac{4\langle V^2 \rangle^2}{\lambda_E^2} \int_0^t d\tau \int_0^\tau ds \int_0^s dm \int_0^m dn \, g(t - \tau) \, g(t - s)$$

$$\times \{ e^{-F(\tau-m)-F(\tau-n)} + e^{-F(\tau-s)-F(\tau-n)} + e^{-F(\tau-s)-F(\tau-m)} \}$$

$$\times \{ e^{-\frac{\tau-s}{\lambda^*}\frac{m-n}{\lambda^*}} + e^{-\frac{s-m}{\lambda^*}\frac{\tau-n}{\lambda^*}} + e^{-\frac{s-n}{\lambda^*}\frac{\tau-m}{\lambda^*}} \} - \frac{4\langle V^2 \rangle^2}{\lambda_E^2}$$

$$\times \int_0^t d\tau \int_0^\tau ds \int_0^s dm \int_0^m dn \, g(t - \tau) \, g(t - s)\{ e^{-F(s-m)-F(s-n)} \}$$

$$\times \{ e^{-\frac{\tau-s}{\lambda^*}\frac{m-n}{\lambda^*}} + e^{-\frac{\tau-m}{\lambda^*}\frac{s-n}{\lambda^*}} + e^{-\frac{\tau-n}{\lambda^*}\frac{s-m}{\lambda^*}} \} + 0\left(\frac{1}{\lambda_E^4}\right). \quad (2.113)$$

The evaluation of Eq. (2.113) is algebraically involved but elementary, thus the details will not be presented.

The diffusivity in classical macroscopic diffusion theory (Fick's law) is generally defined for this case. However, it is important to note that Eq. (2.110) gives a "diffusivity" for all times t, and there are many practical applications where "transient diffusivity" must be considered. In the limit of large t,

$$\lim_{t \to \infty} E\{y^2(t)\} = 2t\lambda^* \langle V^2 \rangle - \frac{2\langle V^2 \rangle^2}{\lambda_E^2} t \frac{\lambda^{*2}}{F}\left(\frac{6}{F\lambda^* + 1}\right) + 0\left(\frac{1}{\lambda_E^4}\right). \quad (2.114)$$

The restrictions on the parameters of Eq. (2.114) such that $E\{y^2(t)\}$ remains positive are consistent with the restriction on these same parameters which would be obtained from the requirement $(y - x)^2/\lambda_E^2 \ll 1$, necessary in order that terms $0(1/\lambda_E^4)$ be neglected, as estimated by Eq. (2.104).

We define the particle diffusivity, D_p, by the equation [C13]:

$$D_p = \lim_{t \to \infty} \frac{1}{2t} E\{y^2(t)\}. \quad (2.115)$$

Thus

$$D_p = \langle V^2 \rangle \lambda^*\left\{ 1 - \frac{\lambda^{*2}\langle V^2 \rangle}{\lambda_E^2} \frac{1}{F\lambda^*}\left(\frac{6}{F\lambda^* + 1}\right) \right\}. \quad (2.116)$$

The first term on the right-hand side of Eq. (2.110) becomes the mean square fluid particle displacement in the limit of large t. The fluid diffusivity (eddy diffusivity) obtained from the Taylor formula, using the correlation of Eq. (2.111), is

$$D = \lambda^* \langle V^2 \rangle = \lambda \langle V^2 \rangle^{1/2}. \quad (2.117)$$

The ratio of particle diffusivity to eddy diffusivity is

$$\frac{D_p}{D} = 1 - \frac{\lambda^{*2}\langle V^2 \rangle}{\lambda_E^2} \frac{1}{F\lambda^*}\left(\frac{6}{F\lambda^* + 1}\right) + 0\left(\frac{1}{\lambda_E^4}\right). \qquad (2.118)$$

It is convenient to introduce the parameters K and λ_L

$$K = \frac{2}{F\lambda^*}, \qquad \lambda = \lambda^*\langle V^2 \rangle^{1/2}. \qquad (2.119)$$

λ is the Lagrangian microscale of turbulence and K is the ratio of particle impulse response time to the time a fluid particle remains in a velocity correlated region. (For spherical particles $K = (\sqrt{\pi}/18)\langle N_{\text{Re}} \rangle(\bar{\rho}_p/\bar{\rho})(2a/\lambda)$ where $\langle N_{\text{Re}} \rangle = (2a/\bar{\nu})\langle V^2 \rangle^{1/2}$ is the particle Reynolds number; $2a$ particle diameter, $\bar{\nu}$ kinematic viscosity of the fluid.) Equation (2.119) is now written

$$\frac{D_p}{D} = 1 - \frac{\lambda^2}{\lambda_E^2}\left(\frac{3K^2}{K + 2}\right) + 0\left(\frac{1}{\lambda_E^4}\right). \qquad (2.120)$$

Equation (2.120) is plotted in Fig. 2.16 as D_p/D vs. K parametric in λ/λ_E. Only those values of D_p/D which are consistent with neglect of higher-order terms are shown. Higher-order computation should show that these curves turn and become asymptotic to the axis $D_p/D = 0$ at a value of D_p/D below that shown in Fig. 2.16.

Equation (2.120) shows clearly that the solid-particle diffusivity is a function not only of the impulse response parameter K as earlier theory had suggested [S48], but it is also a function of the Lagrangian and Eulerian scales of turbulence. Physical interpretation of Eq. (2.120) is not difficult when one remembers that the particle diffusivity is proportional to the integral scale of the correlation of encountered velocities [P14, P15]. For a fixed finite λ/λ_E a particle with $K = 0$ "follows" the fluid particles perfectly and its diffusivity is equal to the fluid diffusivity. Again, for fixed λ/λ_E a particle with large K does not respond to the fluid motion; it would tend to remain stationary and not diffuse.

Now consider the case when K is fixed and $K > 0$. In this case the solid particle will not follow the first fluid element it encounters. If λ/λ_E is small, this implies that fluid elements in the neighborhood of any given fluid element tend to have the same velocity as the given fluid element. Thus, even though the solid particle does not follow the fluid element it first encountered, the large λ_E implies that it will encounter fluid elements with similar velocities. As a result, the correlation of encountered velocities will be similar to the Lagrangian fluid correlation, and the diffusivity ratio will be near unity. Conversely, large λ/λ_E implies that the velocities in the neighborhood of a given fluid particle velocity are uncorrelated with the given fluid element velocity. A solid particle not following this given fluid element encounters a series of uncorrelated fluid velocities and as a result has a small diffusivity.

There are some practical implications of Eq. (2.120) which should be noted. The effect of encountered fluid velocities on solid-phase diffusivity shows that there are three parameters, λ, λ_E, and K, that may be adjusted in a two-phase flow system to alter solid diffusivity. For instance, in two-phase flow in ducts (shear flow), λ increases with mean flow velocity, U, and λ_E is of the order of

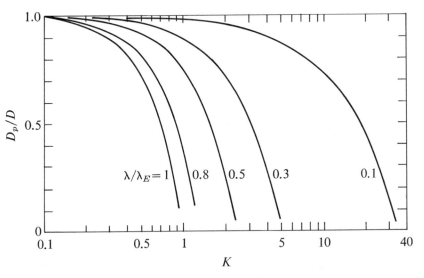

Figure 2.16 Ratio of diffusivities of particle and turbulent fluid [P15].

one-half the duct diameter, R [H41]. Thus in this type of flow one would expect, for a fixed solid-particle size and fluid composition, the solid diffusivity to decrease with flow velocity and increase with duct diameter. That is,

$$\frac{D_p}{D} \sim 1 - \text{const.} \frac{U^2}{R^2} a^2 . \tag{2.121}$$

Low diffusivity caused by large solid particles could be compensated for by use of lower mean flow velocity (as long as the flow can support the solids loading) or larger duct diameter.

Since the previous computations only represent an approximation because of the neglect of higher-order terms, it is difficult to make an accurate comparison with available data. Much of the data lies outside the range of parameters for which neglect of terms $0(1/\lambda_E^4)$ is valid. Comparison can be made with experimental results in Sec. 2.8 which is near the range of validity for Eq. (2.120). Using the values of λ reported and a value of λ_E based on half the duct diameter, we find Eq. (2.120) predicts $0.019 < D_p/D < 0.035$ for $2.5 < K < 5$.

2.7 Heat Transfer in a Turbulent Fluid

Other types of fluctuations in turbulent flow are temperature, density, and composition. Since these quantities are scalar in nature, their treatment is expected to be somewhat simpler. Tien [T31] extended the statistical aspects of turbulence to the fluctuation in temperature and the statistical aspects of heat transport in two-phase turbulent flow. Due to the striking similarity between momentum and heat transport, Tien was able to establish the relations between the respective statistical properties in dynamical and thermal turbulent fields.

As in the momentum-transport case, the Lagrangian reference frame was used here. Additional assumptions needed on the physical system under consideration are:

1. The thermal stream turbulence is homogeneous, isotropic, and non-decaying.

2. The temperatures in the system are within such a range that the fluid phase can be considered to be transparent to thermal radiation. This is in general true for most monatomic and some diatomic gases such as nitrogen, oxygen, and helium at not very high temperatures, say less than 5000°F [M19].

3. The solid particle is assumed to be a blackbody and its size is within the range of the effective wavelength of the radiation spectrum at the corresponding temperature. For particles smaller than the high-energy wavelength of the incident radiation, the particles become effectively partially transparent (Chap. 5).

4. The solid particle is of small enough dimension and has large enough thermal conductivity to have a uniform temperature field throughout the particle all the time.

Let Q_1 be the rate of heat radiation to the solid particle from the external source; then the general equation for the solid-to-solid radiation with non-absorbing medium between them is given [M19] as

$$Q_1 = \sigma_r A_p (T_w^4 - T_p^4) f_g f_e , \qquad (2.122)$$

where σ_r is the Stefan-Boltzmann constant $(0.1714 \times 10^{-8}$ Btu hr ft^2 R$^4)$, A_p the surface area of the particle, T_w the temperature of the solid boundary at infinity (for the requirement of an isotropic turbulent field), T_p the temperature of the particle, f_g the geometrical factor and f_e the emissivity factor.

In our case, the particle can be considered as a completely enclosed body, small compared with the enclosing body; then we have $f_g = 1$ and $f_e = \epsilon_p$, where ϵ_p is the emissivity of the particle. Hence Eq. (2.122) becomes

$$Q_1 = \sigma_r A_p \epsilon_p (T_w^4 - T_p^4). \tag{2.123}$$

From Newton's law of cooling, the rate of heat convection from the particle to fluid Q_2 is given as

$$Q_2 = A_p h_p (T_p - T), \tag{2.124}$$

where h_p is the heat-transfer coefficient of the fluid for this system (Sec. 2.2) and T the temperature of the fluid surrounding the particle. The Nusselt number is given by Eq. (2.14). The main question of applying this empirical expression in our case is that in a turbulent field the Reynolds number $(N_{Re})_o$ is fluctuating. However, for the case of the instantaneous Reynolds number being always of the order of 1 or less, it will be a good approximation to say that the average effective Reynolds number is around 1.

From Eqs. (2.124) and (2.14), we get

$$Q_2 = \frac{(N_{Nu})_o \kappa}{2a} A_p (T_p - T). \tag{2.125}$$

Based on assumption (4), the differential equation for the energy of the particle is given as

$$\bar{\rho}_p v_p c_p \frac{dT_p}{dt} = \sigma_r A_p \epsilon_p (T_w^4 - T_p^4) - \frac{(N_{Nu})_o \kappa}{2a} A_p (T_p - T_f), \tag{2.126}$$

where $\bar{\rho}_p$, v_p, and c_p are the density, the volume and the specific heat of the particle, respectively.

The relative significance of the convection and radiation terms can be seen by writing Eq. (2.126) in a dimensionless form with $T^+ = T/T_w$, and $T_p^+ = T_p/T_w$, and $t^+ = t(\bar{\kappa}/\bar{\rho}_p A_p c_p)$, or

$$\frac{dT_p^+}{dt^+} = m_1(1 - T_p^{+4}) - (N_{Nu})_o m_2 (T_p^+ - T^+), \tag{2.127}$$

where m_1 is a dimensionless group showing the relative effects of the radiation and the convection, $m_1 = \sigma_r A_p^2 \epsilon_p T_w^4 / \bar{\kappa} v_p$; and m_2 is merely a geometrical factor depending on the shape of the solid particle, $m_2 = A_p^2 / 2a v_p$; $m_2 = 6\pi$ for spheres.

Substitution of numerical values into m_r, for instance, glass beads of diameter 200 μ in air, gives $m_1 = [10^{-9}] T_w^3$ for $T_w \sim 100°R$, $m_1 \sim 1$; and for

$T_w \sim 3000°\text{R}$, $m_1 \sim 27$. If T_w in the system is not very large, say $T_w < 1000°\text{F}$, m_1 is small as compared with $(N_{\text{Nu}})_o$, then the first term on the right-hand side can be neglected; i.e., the radiation effect is negligible as compared to the convection effect. In general,

$$\frac{dT_p}{dt} = G_r(T_w^4 - T_p^4) + G(T - T_p), \tag{2.128}$$

with the time constants for convection G, and for radiation G_r

$$G = \frac{(N_{\text{Nu}})_o \bar{\kappa} A_p}{2\bar{\rho}_p v_p c_p a} \quad \text{and} \quad G_r = \frac{\sigma_r A_p \epsilon_p}{\bar{\rho}_p v_p c_p}.$$

To take into account the fluctuating quantities, let

$$T_p = \langle T_p \rangle + T_{pf} \quad \text{and} \quad T = \langle T \rangle + T_f,$$

where $\langle T_p \rangle$ and T_{pf} are the mean and fluctuating temperatures of the particle respectively, and $\langle T \rangle$ and T_f are the mean and fluctuating temperatures of the fluid, respectively. It should be noted that $\langle T_p \rangle$ and $\langle T \rangle$ are in general not equal. Substitution of the mean and fluctuating quantities into Eq. (2.128) gives

$$\frac{d\langle T_p \rangle}{dt} + \frac{dT_{pf}}{dt} = G_r(T_w^4 - \langle T_p \rangle^4 - 4\langle T_p \rangle^3 T_{pf}) - G(\langle T_p \rangle + T_{pf} - \langle T \rangle - T_f)$$

$$\tag{2.129}$$

where approximation has been made such that

$$T_p^4 = (\langle T_p \rangle + T_{pf})^4 = (\langle T_p \rangle^4 + 4\langle T_p \rangle^3 T_{pf}),$$

since T_{pf} is in general small compared to $\langle T_p \rangle$. Taking the average of each term in Eq. (2.129), we get

$$\frac{d\langle T_p \rangle}{dt} = G_r(T_w^4 - \langle T_p \rangle^4) - G(\langle T_p \rangle - \langle T \rangle). \tag{2.130}$$

By subtracting Eq. (2.130) from Eq. (2.129), the following governing equation for the fluctuating temperature is obtained

$$\frac{dT_{pf}}{dt} + (G + 4G_r\langle T_p \rangle^3)T_{pf} = GT_f, \tag{2.131}$$

where $G_r = 0$ for the case with no radiation effect.

When the average radiation heat input to the particle is close to the amount of average convection loss from the particle, or after long-time mixing and heating in the system, $\langle T_p \rangle$ can be considered as a constant. Hence we can write

$$\frac{dT_{pf}}{dt} + G'T_{pf} = GT_f , \qquad (2.132)$$

where $G' = G + 4G_r \langle T_p \rangle^3$. It is easily seen that in the case with no radiation effect, $G = G'$.

On account of the striking similarity of the approximate equation on the fluctuating temperatures (2.132) to that on the fluctuating velocities, the well-known hypothesis that the transport mechanisms in momentum and heat are similar in nature has been shown to be applicable for the fluctuating quantities in two-phase flow.

Decaying Processes of Particle Temperature Fluctuation—The decaying mechanism in the heat-transport case is expected to be similar to that in the momentum-transport case because of the similarity of the governing equations in both cases. By use of the same argument as in dealing with momentum transfer, a similar result will be obtained. The intensity-correlation equation is given as

$$\frac{d}{dt}\left[\langle T_{pf}^2 \rangle(t)\mathscr{R}(t,\tau)\right] + 2G'\left[\langle T_{pf}^2 \rangle(t)\mathscr{R}(t,\tau)\right]$$

$$= G\sqrt{\langle T_{pf}^2 \rangle(t)}\sqrt{\langle T_f^2 \rangle}[\mathscr{R}_{c1}(t,\tau) + \mathscr{R}_{c2}(t,\tau)], \quad (2.133)$$

where

$$\mathscr{R}(t,\tau) = \frac{\langle T_{pf}(t)T_{pf}(t+\tau)\rangle}{\langle T_{pf}^2 \rangle(t)},$$

$$\mathscr{R}_{c1}(t,\tau) = \frac{\langle T_{pf}(t+\tau)T_f(t)\rangle}{\sqrt{\langle T_{pf}^2 \rangle(t)}\sqrt{\langle T_f^2 \rangle}},$$

$$\mathscr{R}_{c2}(t,\tau) = \frac{\langle T_{pf}(t)T_f(t+\tau)\rangle}{\sqrt{\langle T_{pf}^2 \rangle(t)}\sqrt{\langle T_f^2 \rangle}},$$

and from Schwarz inequality, $0 < \mathscr{R}$ (or $\mathscr{R}_{c1}$ or $\mathscr{R}_{c2}$) ≤ 1. Terms on the right-hand side of Eq. (2.133) can be neglected if either of the two quantities, (G/G') or $\langle T_f^2 \rangle$, is sufficiently small. The former quantity can be expressed explicitly as

$$\frac{G}{G'} = \left[1 + \frac{8\sigma_r\epsilon_p \langle T_p \rangle^3 a}{(N_{Nu})\bar{\kappa}}\right]^{-1}.$$

Equation (2.133) after neglecting terms on the right-hand side has a solution as

$$\langle T_{pf}^2 \rangle(t)\mathscr{R}(t,\tau) = \langle T_{pf}^2 \rangle(0)\mathscr{R}(0,\tau)e^{-2G't}, \qquad (2.134)$$

and when $\tau \rightarrow 0$,

$$\langle T_{pf}^2 \rangle = \langle T_{pf}^2 \rangle(0)e^{-2G't}. \tag{2.135}$$

This states that the fluctuation temperature in the solid phase is exponentially decaying and the rate of decay is governed by the parameter G'. For small G' the fluctuation temperature in the solid phase is very slowly decaying and the nondecaying case in the solid phase is the asymptotic state of G' approaching zero, i.e., $G' \rightarrow 0$

$$\langle T_{pf}^2 \rangle = \langle T_{pf}^2 \rangle(0) = \text{constant}. \tag{2.136}$$

From Eqs. (2.134) and (2.135), we get

$$\mathscr{R}(t,\tau) = \mathscr{R}(0,\tau)$$

or

$$\mathscr{R} = \mathscr{R}(\tau). \tag{2.137}$$

The intensity of the relative temperature between the two phases, which is useful in predicting the average heat transport between the two phases, can be obtained in a similar way as in the momentum-transport case:

$$\langle (T_f - T_{pf})^2 \rangle = \left(1 - \frac{2G'}{G}\right)\langle T_{pf}^2 \rangle + \langle T_f^2 \rangle. \tag{2.138}$$

In the case with no radiation effect, i.e., $G' = G$, Eq. (2.138) becomes

$$\langle (T_f - T_{pf})^2 \rangle = \langle T_f^2 \rangle - \langle T_{pf}^2 \rangle, \tag{2.139}$$

analogous to the case of momentum transport.

Statistical Relations—By concept of the turbulent spectrum, let

$$T_f = \sum_n B_n \sin 2\pi nt, \tag{2.140}$$

and the solution to the approximate Eq. (2.141) gives

$$T_{pf} = \sum_n \frac{G}{G'} \frac{B_n}{\sqrt{1 + (2\pi n/G')^2}} \sin(2\pi nt - \theta_n),$$

where θ_n is the phase lag and $\theta_n = \tan^{-1}(2\pi n/G')$. By use of the Parseval theorem, we get

$$\langle T_{pf}^2 \rangle = \left(\frac{G}{G'}\right)^2 \frac{1}{2} \sum_n \frac{B_n^2}{1 + (2\pi n/G')^2}.$$

With the definition of Lagrangian temperature frequency function $f_T(n)$

$$\langle T_f^2 \rangle = \frac{1}{2} \sum_n B_n^2 = \int_0^\infty \langle T_f^2 \rangle f_T(n)\, dn,$$

where $\int_0^\infty f_T(n)\,dn = 1$, we can obtain

$$\langle T_{pf}^2 \rangle = \langle T_f^2 \rangle \left(\frac{G}{G'}\right)^2 \int_0^\infty \frac{f_T(n)\,dn}{1 + (2\pi n/G')^2}. \tag{2.141}$$

The Lagrangian correlation of the fluctuation temperature or the solid phase can be shown to be

$$\mathscr{R}_p = \frac{\langle T_{pf}(t)T_{pf}(t+\tau)\rangle}{\langle T_{pf}^2 \rangle} = \frac{\displaystyle\int_0^\infty \frac{f_T(n)\cos 2\pi n\tau}{1 + (2\pi n/G')^2}\,dn}{\displaystyle\int_0^\infty \frac{f_T(n)}{1 + (2\pi n/G')^2}\,dn}. \tag{2.142}$$

Similar to the Lagrangian dynamical scale l_p, the thermal scale of the particle is given as

$$\mathscr{L}_p = \sqrt{\langle u_p^2 \rangle} \int_0^\infty \mathscr{R}_p\,d\tau. \tag{2.143}$$

In the above we have seen that all the statistical properties of the temperature fluctuation are in terms of the Lagrangian temperature frequency function $f_T(n)$. From the theory of the turbulent spectrum [T7],

$$f_N(n) = 4 \int_0^\infty \mathscr{R}(\tau)\cos 2\pi n\tau\,d\tau,$$

and

$$\mathscr{R}(\tau) = \int_0^\infty f_T(n)\cos 2\pi n\tau\,dn. \tag{2.144}$$

We understand that all these properties can be determined if the correlation function of the temperature fluctuation in the fluid phase $\mathscr{R}(\tau)$ is known. While a large number of experiments have been done in order to determine the Eulerian temperature correlation since 1950, no experimental data is available for the Lagrangian temperature correlation.

Since in the case of turbulent transport the effects due to molecular viscosity and conductivity are usually negligibly small as compared with the effects due to eddy mixing (except at very large velocity and temperature gradients), the temperature fluctuation is largely due to the eddy mixing of fluid elements, which preserves their original temperatures. To have different temperatures in the fluid elements is to require a mean-temperature gradient in the mean flow. Therefore it is expected that the statistical properties of the temperature fluctuation are governed by two factors: (1) the mean-temperature gradient of the flow field, and (2) the nature of the velocity field. In the following we will show through a simple, ideal case the role of the mean-temperature gradient in the temperature fluctuation case and the relations between the corresponding statistical properties in cases of momentum and heat transport. This case was first suggested by Corrsin [C42] for the study of heat transfer in isotropic turbulence. Consider an isotropic and homogeneous turbulent field with a constant mean-temperature gradient in the direction y, normal to the axis of main flow x, and which does not vary along x. The assumptions needed for the turbulent field in this case are:

1. No interaction exists between the velocity and temperature fields. This is equivalent to postulating an ideal fluid with constant density.

2. Effects due to molecular viscosity and conductivity are negligibly small. This is approximately the case in a turbulent field when the velocity and temperature gradients are not very large. Hence we have

$$T_f(t) = -Y(t) \frac{d\langle T \rangle}{dy} , \qquad (2.145)$$

where $Y(t) = \int_0^t v(\tau)\, d\tau$, and consequently

$$\langle T_f^2 \rangle = \frac{d\langle T \rangle^2}{dy} \langle Y^2 \rangle. \qquad (2.146)$$

From Taylor's theory of diffusion by continuous movements the following well-known relation is given as

$$\frac{d}{dt} \langle Y^2 \rangle = 2\langle v^2 \rangle \int_0^t \mathcal{R}\, d\tau. \qquad (2.147)$$

In order to have a homogeneous temperature fluctuation field, i.e., $\langle T_f^2 \rangle$ is a constant, we must have $\langle Y^2 \rangle$ a constant, or in other words, the left-hand side of (2.147) must vanish. For the reason that both the intensity and the correlation function are nonzero functions, we must have the Lagrangian scale of turbulence:

$$l = \int_0^{t_1} \mathcal{R}\, d\tau = \int_0^{\langle v^2 \rangle^{1/2} t_1} \mathcal{R}\, d\eta, \qquad (2.148)$$

where $\lim_{t \to t_1} \mathcal{R} = 0$ and $d\eta = \sqrt{\langle v^2 \rangle}\, d\tau$. By the definition of the microscale [T6]:

$$\frac{1}{\lambda^2} = \lim_{\eta \to 0} \frac{1 - \mathcal{R}}{\eta^2} , \qquad (2.149)$$

and the correlation function being an even function [T5], we must have in the present case a correlation function of the following form

$$\mathcal{R} = e^{-\alpha_o^2 \frac{\eta^2}{\lambda^2}} \left(1 - 2\alpha_o^2 \frac{\eta^2}{\lambda^2} \right), \qquad (2.150)$$

where $\alpha_o^2 = \frac{1}{3}$ (Fig. 2.17). The Fourier transform of the correlation function is the frequency function

$$f(n) = \frac{\sqrt{\pi}\lambda^3(2\pi n)^2}{\alpha_o^3\langle u^2\rangle^{3/2}}\, e^{-\frac{(2\pi n)^2\lambda^2}{4\langle u^2\rangle\alpha_o^2}}. \tag{2.151}$$

By use of the turbulent spectrum of velocity v, Eq. (2.145) becomes

$$T_f = -\sum_n \frac{A_n}{2\pi n}\cos 2\pi nt\, \frac{d\langle T\rangle}{dy},$$

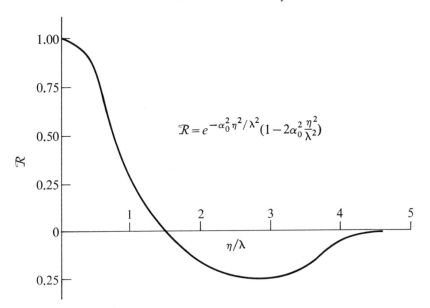

$$\mathcal{R} = e^{-\alpha_0^2\eta^2/\lambda^2}\left(1 - 2\alpha_0^2\frac{\eta^2}{\lambda^2}\right)$$

Figure 2.17 Lagrangian temperature correlation curve [T31].

and consequently

$$\langle T_f^2\rangle = -\frac{1}{2}\left(\frac{d\langle T\rangle}{dy}\right)^2\sum_n \frac{A_n}{(2\pi n)^2} = -\left(\frac{d\langle T\rangle}{dy}\right)^2\int_0^\infty \frac{\langle u^2\rangle f(n)}{(2\pi n)^2}\, dn. \tag{2.152}$$

From the definition of Lagrangian temperature-frequency function $f_T(n)$, we have

$$\langle T_f^2\rangle f_T(n) = -\left(\frac{d\langle T\rangle}{dy}\right)^2\frac{f(n)\langle u^2\rangle}{(2\pi n)^2},$$

and from the result of integration in Eq. (2.161)

$$\langle T_f^2\rangle = -\frac{1}{2}\frac{\lambda^2}{\alpha_o^2}\left(\frac{d\langle T\rangle}{dy}\right)^2, \tag{2.153}$$

we get

$$f_T(n) = \frac{2\sqrt{\pi}\lambda}{\alpha_o \sqrt{\langle u^2 \rangle}} e^{-\frac{(2\pi n)^2 \lambda^2}{4\langle u^2 \rangle \alpha_o^2}}. \tag{2.154}$$

While the Lagrangian temperature-frequency function, Eq. (2.154), is only a function of parameters in the fluctuating velocity field, the intensity of the fluctuation temperature in fluid phase, Eq. (2.153), clearly indicates its dependence on both the characteristics of the velocity fluctuation field and the mean-temperature gradient.

From Eq. (2.151) the intensity of the temperature fluctuation in the solid phase can be expressed as

$$\langle T_{pf}^2 \rangle = \langle T_f^2 \rangle (G/G')^2 \frac{\sqrt{\pi}}{K_T} e^{-(1/K_T)^2} \operatorname{erfc}\left(\frac{1}{K_T}\right), \tag{2.155}$$

where $K_T^2 = 4\langle u^2 \rangle \alpha_o^2 / \lambda^2 G'^2$. It is clearly seen that the graphical presentation will be the same as in momentum fluctuation [S69] except that different meanings will be given to the parameters.

The Lagrangian correlations of the temperature fluctuation in the fluid and solid phases can be obtained respectively from Eqs. (2.144) and (2.142) and are given as

$$\mathcal{R}_p\left(\frac{\eta}{\lambda}, K_T\right) = \frac{1}{2\operatorname{erfc}(1/K_T)}\left[e^{-\frac{2\alpha_o}{K_T}\frac{\eta}{\lambda}}\left\{2 - \operatorname{erfc}\left(\frac{\alpha_o \eta}{\lambda} - \frac{1}{K_T}\right)\right\}\right.$$
$$\left. + e^{\frac{2}{K_T}\frac{\alpha_o \eta}{\lambda}} \operatorname{erfc}\left(\frac{\alpha_o \eta}{\lambda} + \frac{1}{K_T}\right)\right]. \tag{2.156}$$

When K_T is zero, i.e., the size and the density of the solid particle are infinitesimally small, $\mathcal{R}_p$ expectedly becomes $\mathcal{R}$. The variations of $\mathcal{R}_p$ with respect to (η/λ) and K_T can be easily seen with the aid of corresponding curves for momentum transfer.

The thermal scale of the solid particle from Eq. (2.143) is given as:

$$\mathcal{L}_p = \frac{\sqrt{\pi}}{2}\frac{\lambda}{\alpha_o}\frac{\sqrt{\langle u^2 \rangle}}{\sqrt{\langle u_p^2 \rangle}} = \frac{\sqrt{\pi}}{2}\frac{\lambda}{\alpha_o}\left[\frac{\sqrt{\pi}}{K} e^{1/K^2} \operatorname{erfc}\frac{1}{K}\right]^{1/2}. \tag{2.157}$$

In this special case we see that $\mathcal{L}_p$ depends only on the nature of the velocity fluctuation field; however, in general, after integration of (2.156), K_T does not disappear and $\mathcal{L}_p$ is a function dependent on the characteristics of both the velocity and the temperature fields.

It is significant to note that, although the whole analysis is based on a system with a proposed mean-temperature gradient in the main flow field, the results, except for the intensity in the fluid phase, are independent of this mean-temperature gradient. Of course we cannot draw any general conclusion from a special case; however, it would be appropriate to say that the nature of the velocity-fluctuation field plays a major role in the turbulent heat-transport mechanism.

2.8 Experimental Determination of Statistical Properties of Momentum Transfer

Experimental determination of the turbulence characteristics of both the solid and fluid phases of a gas-solid suspension was made by Soo, Ihrig, and El Kouh [S66]. The stream is a fully developed turbulent air stream flowing

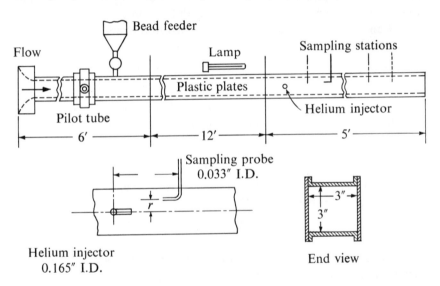

Figure 2.18 3-in. × 3-in. duct used for measurement [S66].

horizontally and transporting spherical glass beads (50, 105, and 210 μ) of close size range.

A flow duct of 3 in. × 3 in. square cross section with air velocities of 20 to 100 fps was used (Fig. 2.18). Measurements were made at locations where fully developed turbulent flow [T48] was maintained. The length of the duct also provided for the acceleration of the solid particles from the point of introduction into the duct (by a screw feeder) to a steady state of random motion. In order that single-particle effects be assured, low mass ratios (Chap. 4) were maintained by a particle feed rate below 0.5 lb/min.

Fluid Turbulence—Although hot-wire techniques for the study of turbulence in gas streams are widely used, their application here is difficult because of the presence of solid particles. Hence a tracer diffusion technique similar to that used by Towle and Sherwood [T47] and by Hanratty, Latinen, and Wilhelm [H9] was used for the measurement of stream turbulence. This technique, based on the Lagrangian system of coordinates, also renders comparison with the above analyses simple. For the measurement of eddy diffusivity of turbulence, a tracer gas is introduced into the center of the stream, and the tracer-air mixture concentration C is sampled at various normal stations r downstream (x-direction) through the cross sections of the duct. Effect of molecular diffusivity (nearly $\frac{1}{10}$ of thermal diffusivity of air) due to local concentration gradient [T49] was offset by measuring the concentration gradient at $r = 0$ such that $r/2x$ remains small or approaches zero.

The mean squared displacement $\langle x^2 \rangle$ is related to the radial concentration gradient $\partial C/\partial r$ at time t (given by axial location) by

$$\langle x^2(t) \rangle = -r(C/C_o) \Big/ \frac{\partial(C/C_o)}{\partial r} = -\frac{1}{2}\left[\frac{\partial \ln (C/C_o)}{\partial(r^2)}\right]^{-1}, \qquad (2.158)$$

where C_o is the ratio of the volume rate of the flow of helium to that of air plus helium. For nondecaying turbulence [T7],

$$\frac{1}{2}\frac{d}{dt}\langle x^2 \rangle = \langle u^2 \rangle \int_0^T \mathscr{R}\, dt, \qquad (2.159)$$

over long-time T; and $\mathscr{R}$ is the Lagrangian correlation and $\langle u^2 \rangle$ is the mean squared velocity. Further,

$$\langle u^2 \rangle = \frac{1}{2}\frac{d^2}{dt^2}\langle x^2 \rangle \Big|_{t=0} \qquad (2.160)$$

gives the intensity of the fluid-phase turbulence, and the scale of turbulence (Lagrangian integral scale) is

$$l_1 = \langle u^2 \rangle^{1/2} \int_0^T \mathscr{R}\, dt. \qquad (2.161)$$

Under the condition of nearly isotropic turbulence in the middle third of portion of the duct height, we have a sufficient description. The eddy diffusivity is given by

$$D = l_1 \langle u^2 \rangle^{1/2} = \frac{1}{2}\frac{d\langle dx^2 \rangle}{dt}\Big|_{t=T}. \qquad (2.162)$$

To measure the helium concentration, a thermal-conductivity cell bridge was used [R52]. Accuracy of better than ± 0.1 per cent helium in air by volume was attained. The location of the tracer tube and the sampling tubes is shown in Fig. 2.18.

Photographic Method—Since at any given time there are many beads moving at rather high speeds in the air stream, the measurement of their turbulence characteristics presented a unique problem. A technique of photographic recording by successive exposures was developed.

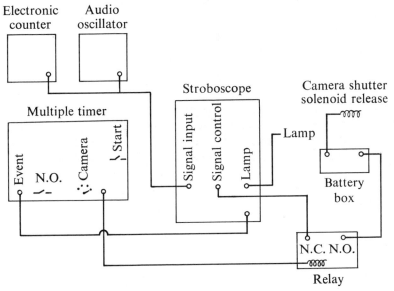

Figure 2.19 Apparatus for photographing particles in the stream [S66].

In order to do this a slit of light $\frac{1}{16}$ in. thick is projected through the top of the duct vertically downward along the axis. The lamp used is a standard line-source flashlamp driven by an Edgerton high-speed stroboscope (5000–8000 flashes/sec). The light is collimated by a cylindrical Plexiglas condenser lens of approximately $1\frac{1}{2}$ in. focal length. After collimation, the light is passed through a $\frac{1}{16}$-in. aperture, 4 in. long, to form the desired slit of light. A 4 × 5-in. view camera with a f4.5, $6\frac{3}{8}$-in. focal-length lens is set up perpendicular to the slit of light and focused on its plane (at approximately one-to-one magnification). When the shutter is opened and the lamp flashed at a high repetitive rate, the resulting photograph will be a multiple-exposure record of bead positions as they flow down the duct. The lamp is triggered by an audio oscillator whose frequency is monitored by a high-speed electronic counter and the shutter-lamp sequence is controlled by a multiple timer. Figure 2.19 is a block diagram of the camera, lamp, oscillator, timer, and counter system.

The photographic record gives the Δx and Δy displacements in the axial and the vertical directions from an initial point in the region of steady turbulent motion, from which

$$\langle x^2 \rangle = \sum (\Delta x)^2 \qquad (2.163)$$

$$\langle y^2 \rangle = \sum (\Delta y)^2 \qquad (2.164)$$

Thus the particle phase motion can be determined. (For measurements of particle velocities in supersonic gas stream, see Sec. 7.4).

The data obtained from tracer diffusion measurements were evaluated according to Eqs. (2.158) to (2.162). A convenient scale of helium concentration was introduced by introducing an effluent concentration

$$C_o = \frac{\dot{\mathscr{V}}_o}{\dot{\mathscr{V}}_a}, \qquad (2.165)$$

where $\dot{\mathscr{V}}_o$ is the volume rate of flow of helium and $\dot{\mathscr{V}}_a$ is the volume rate of flow of air plus helium, both corrected for temperature, pressure and humidity. $\langle x^2 \rangle$ at different times (or axial locations) is determined from the slope at $r = 0$ of the curve of $\ln C/C_o$ plotted vs. r^2, where the influence of finite boundary is least felt. Thus, from the concentration distribution the mean squared displacement and the scale of turbulence were obtained from the correlation [R52] for the approximation $\mathscr{R}_\eta = e^{-\eta^2/\lambda^2}$

$$l_1 = \frac{\sqrt{\pi}}{2} \lambda, \qquad (2.166)$$

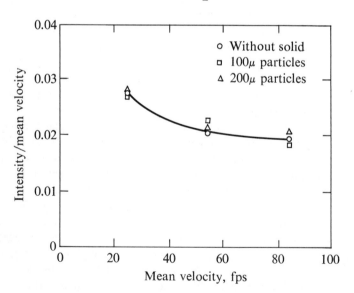

Figure 2.20 Stream intensities with or without solid particles [S66].

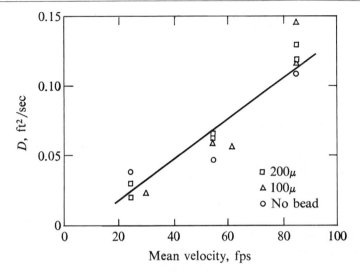

Figure 2.21 Eddy diffusivities of stream [S66].

(λ being the Lagrangian microscale) which were found to be less consistent than the one obtained from calculation of eddy diffusivity by Eq. (2.162). This is because of the slow convergence of the correlation with time.

The intensities of stream turbulence with various types (size and flow rate) of solid-particle loadings (0.2 to 0.4 lb/min for all cases) is shown in Fig. 2.20. Figure 2.20 shows that within the range of particle loading (up to 0.06 lb solid per pound of air) in this experiment, the presence of particles does not substantially affect the turbulence of the air stream. This is further seen from the scale of turbulence and eddy diffusivity presented in Figs. 2.21 and 2.22.

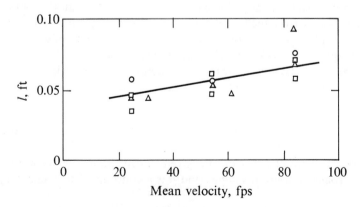

Figure 2.22 Scales of turbulence of stream [S66].

The eddy diffusivities measured were somewhat higher than those for a round duct. Diffusivities of the fluid in turbulent pipe flow were measured by Kada and Hanratty [K1] for water, and Baldwin and Walsh [B11], Towle and Sherwood [T47] for air. Based on the correlation of $(D/2RU)$, suggested by Kada and Hanratty, U being the velocity of the fluid core, these results give:

	$(D/2RU) \times 10^4$	$(2RU\bar{\rho}/\bar{\mu}) \times 10^{-4}$
Kada and Hanratty (water)	11.1	2.03
	11.0	2.03
	8.2	5.05
Baldwin and Walsh (air)	11.1	28.7
	10.2	41.9
	9.77	53.4
	11.25	63.2
Towle and Sherwood (air)		
$2R = 15.24$ cm	13.4	11.9
	15.4	5.6
	18.5	2.5
	27.2	1.22
$2R = 30.5$ cm	18.2	9.1
	19.7	4.4
Soo, Ihrig, and El Kouh (air)	40	3.8
Square duct	43.6	8.35
$2R \sim 3$ in.	56.5	12.9

Comparison of these data shows that greater extent of mixing exists in the square duct than in circular pipes.

The evaluation of the motion of the particle phase was made at first by measuring Δx and Δy for each successive image of each trace from an arbitrary initial point, since steady fluctuating condition exists at the optical section. The distance from the launching point is immaterial here. The root-mean-square displacements were plotted against time, and differentiated graphically to obtain the velocities u_p and v_p of the particles in the x (axial) and y (normal) direction. To determine mean squared value of particle velocities u_p^2 or v_p^2 according to statistical treatment includes assuming Gaussian distribution:

$$\frac{n}{N} = \frac{u_p^2}{\beta^2} e^{-u_p^2/\beta^2}, \tag{2.167}$$

where n is the number of particles in a given velocity range, N is the total number of particles in a given sample, and β is a constant. From matching of β scale,

$$\langle u_p^2 \rangle \text{ (or } \langle v_p^2 \rangle) = \tfrac{3}{2}\beta^2. \tag{2.168}$$

These results of intensity measurements are presented in Fig. 2.23. Results here indicate that the particle motion is nonisotropic.

The particle diffusivity (from which scale of turbulence of particles can be determined) was determined following an analogous statistical scheme. By plotting displacement (y-direction) of particles spreading from a similar initial time on a histogram, the particle diffusivity can be determined from

$$\frac{n}{N} = \frac{e^{-r^2/4\mathrm{D}t}}{4\pi Dt} .$$ (2.169)

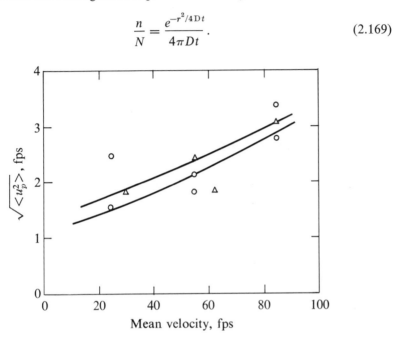

Figure 2.23 Intensities of particle motion [S66].

Consistency of this approximation was tested over two downstream stations in each case. The particle diffusivity and scale of turbulence for various stream and loading conditions are shown in Figs. 2.24 and 2.25. The scale of turbulence of solid particles should be recognized as due to particle-fluid interaction rather than interactions among particles.

Optical Autocorrelation [S70]—Subsequently, applications of optical auto-correlation techniques were made in studying turbulences in high speed flow where density fluctuation is significant [K31, K32].

Since the photo-optical technique of recording depends on the scattering of light, small particles down to 4-μ size could be recorded, which enabled their use as turbulence tracer in the study of one-phase turbulence.

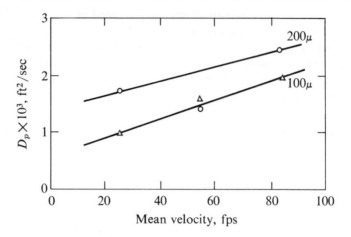

Figure 2.24 Average particle diffusivities [S66].

Direct application of optical autocorrelation [K32] to a photographic record of a two-phase stream obtained by high-frequency successive exposure was difficult because of the minuteness of beads in the record and the non-uniformity of size due to changes in light scattering (the solid particles are within close size ranges). Also, the dot size was too small with respect to fluctuation in velocity and made determination of intensity of motion complicated. A hole of $\frac{3}{32}$ in. diameter was punched at each image of a particle on cards from an enlargement of a record (Fig. 2.26). Two cards punched at the same time were used with the optical bench setup as shown in Fig. 2.27.

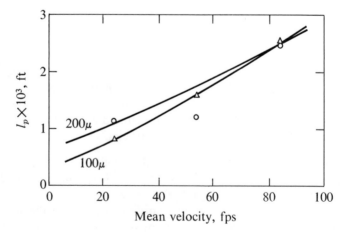

Figure 2.25 Average scales of turbulence of particle motion [S66].

This hole size was small enough so that they would not overlap on the card. It was big enough so that their autocorrelation images merge to give an integrated optical density representing the integral of velocity distribution. Considering each two neighboring dots in the cardboards with the same corresponding time interval τ between them, the distance between each two dots

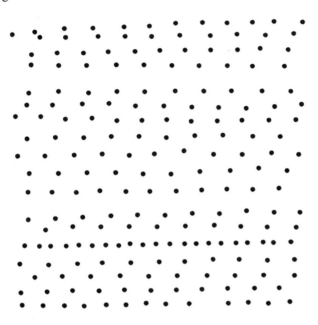

Figure 2.26 Card for optical autocorrelation [S70].

is not the same and the variation from the mean is the fluctuation displacement or the product of time τ and the vector fluctuation velocity $\mathbf{u}(t + \tau)$, where $\mathbf{u}(t)$ is the vector fluctuation velocity at t. Then, the summation of the parallel light beam passing one dot (representing $\mathbf{u}(t)$) in the first carboard and the corresponding neighboring dot (representing $\mathbf{u}(t + \tau)$) in the second one is proportional to the autocorrelation coefficient at τ of the fluctuation velocity [K32, R13]. Direct exposure on a sheet film was made at the screen in Fig. 2.27. The distance between each two dots of the plate is the product of the corresponding time interval (τ) between the two and the mean velocity of motion while the integral of horizontal distribution of light intensity is proportional to the correlation of the longitudinal velocities:

$$\langle u(t)u(t + \tau)\rangle = \lim_{T\to\infty} \frac{1}{T}\int_0^T u(t)u(t + \tau)\, \mathrm{d}t, \qquad (2.170)$$

where $u(t)$ is the longitudinal component of the fluctuation velocity at t along the main flow direction. The center dot corresponding to $\tau = 0$ gives the light distribution (including scattering) whose integral is proportional to $\langle u^2 \rangle$, the intensity of motion.

The longitudinal light distribution through the centers of the dots in Fig. 2.27 was measured by a photodensitometer giving the distribution curves as shown in Fig. 2.28a. The area under each curve (after subtracting the background-light intensity), after normalizing with respect to the area of curve

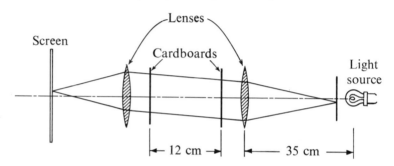

Figure 2.27 Setup of optical bench for autocorrelation [S70].

corresponding to the center dot ($\tau = 0$), gives the longitudinal Lagrangian correlation curve as shown in Fig. 2.29.

The scattering involved in the optical autocorrelation is obvious as seen from the center dot, which ought to have constant light intensity over the hole size rather than the distribution as shown. The light scattering is a complicated phenomenon. As an approximation, we take a constant scattering factor β for each dot such that the area of true velocity distribution can be obtained (Fig. 2.30):

$$2 \times \left(\begin{array}{c} \text{area of true} \\ \text{velocity distribution} \end{array} \right) = \left(\begin{array}{c} \text{area under the curve} \\ \text{of light intensity distribution} \end{array} \right) - \beta I_o d \tag{2.171}$$

where d is the hole diameter and I_o is the reference intensity of light as shown in Fig. 2.30. Assuming a Gaussian distribution for the light intensity, i.e., $I = I_o \exp(-\alpha x^2)$, area of true velocity distribution:

$$A = \tfrac{1}{2} I_o \sqrt{\frac{\pi}{\alpha}}. \tag{2.172}$$

By definition,

$$\langle x^2 \rangle = \int_0^\infty x^2 I_o e^{-\alpha x^2} \frac{dx}{A} = \frac{1}{2\alpha}. \tag{2.173}$$

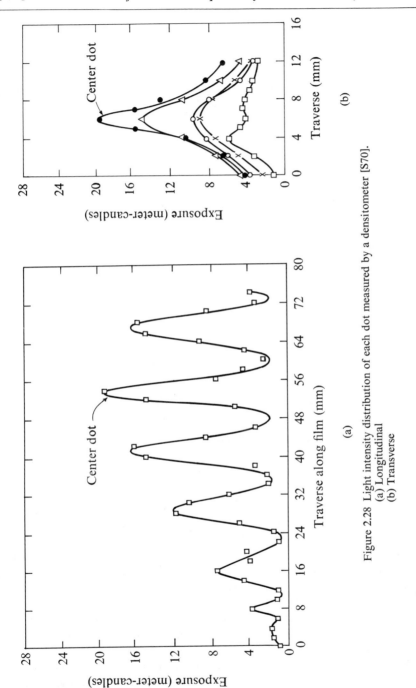

Figure 2.28 Light intensity distribution of each dot measured by a densitometer [S70].
(a) Longitudinal
(b) Transverse

Hence, the intensity of particle motion

$$\sqrt{\langle u^2 \rangle} = \frac{C_1}{C_2} \sqrt{\langle x^2 \rangle} = \frac{C_1}{C_2} \frac{1}{\sqrt{2\alpha}},$$ (2.174)

where C_1 is the scale factor in feet per inch, C_2 the time interval during which x is measured, and α is determined from Eq. (2.172). Consistency was checked over three dots from each record.

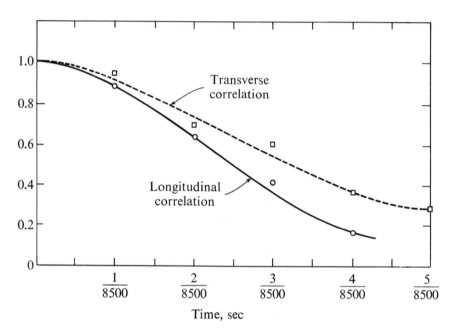

Figure 2.29 Lagrangian correlation curves (obtained from normalized area of each dot with respect to the center one) [S70].

The ratio of actual distance traveled by a particle along the flow direction in the time for one exposure to the corresponding distance in Fig. 2.28a between two successive dots determines the scale factor C_1. The scale factor allows for the differences arising from choosing the scale for abscissa in Figs. 2.28a and 2.28b arbitrarily as has been done here.

C_2 is merely the reciprocal of the frequency of exposure, in this case, a frequency of 8500 flashes per second, and hence C_2 is $1/8500$ sec. The unit of time interval used in plotting the Lagrangian correlation curve (Fig. 2.29) is also $1/8500$ sec.

Since the punched card can only cover a small portion of the field of motion, a large number of autocorrelations has to be made to obtain the turbulent properties of the field. However, even a single picture gives a reasonably consistent set of results as compared to that of direct count and measurement (see Table 2.1). The scale of turbulence was obtained by integrating the correlation curves.

The transverse measurements tend to give irregular patterns of correlation and intensities of motion, but this depends, to a large extent, on the choice

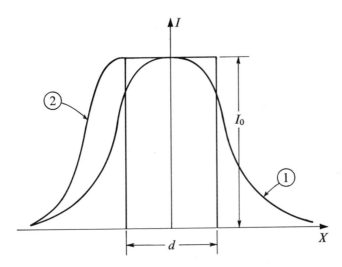

Figure 2.30 Correlation for light scattering [S70].
(1) Light-intensity distribution
(2) True-velocity distribution

of sample. The longitudinal measurements, however, are in general consistent. The difference between the longitudinal and transverse correlations suggests further analytical study on the Lagrangian correlations. At this time there is no simple method to relate these two components of the Lagrangian diffusion-method correlation to those of Eulerian [M28]. Moreover, the usual gaseous diffusion method [M28] does not permit determination of transverse Lagrangian correlations. Either for measuring turbulent motion of solid particles as in the above, or when using very small particles as tracers [S48], this method is also valid for studying anisotropic motion in the Lagrangian system.

Because the sampling is relatively small, this method sometimes gives non-representative results such as the fact that l_y of case 4 cannot be obtained. Statistically representative number of analysis is necessary.

The above results enable us to determine the relation between the turbulence characteristics of the two phases.

Since we are dealing with the middle third of the fluid stream only,

$$\langle u^2 \rangle \cong \langle v^2 \rangle, \tag{2.175}$$

when compared with the preliminary analytical results [S48], $\langle u_p^2 \rangle$ and $\langle v_p^2 \rangle$ are quite different as shown in Table 2.1. As basic parameter relating particle and stream motion, parameter K is now defined as:

$$K = \frac{\sqrt{\pi}}{18} \langle N_{\text{Re}} \rangle \left(\frac{2a}{l_1} \right) \left(\frac{\bar{\rho}_p}{\bar{\rho}} \right), \tag{2.176}$$

TABLE 2.1

EXPERIMENTAL RESULTS OF TWO-PHASE TURBULENT FLOW
IN A 3″ × 3″ DUCT [S70]

Case	1	2	3	4
Mean Air Stream Velocity, fps	85	85	55	55
Particle (Glass Beads) size, μ	210–250	105–125	210–250	105–125
Intensity of motion of Particles, fps				
Longitudinal,* $\sqrt{\langle u_p^2 \rangle}$	2.92	3.05	2.10	2.40
Transverse,* $\sqrt{\langle v_p^2 \rangle}$	0.98	0.82	1.23	1.00
Optical Autocorrelation [S70]				
Longitudinal, $\sqrt{\langle u_p^2 \rangle}$	2.47	3.04	2.20	2.60
Transverse, $\sqrt{\langle v_p^2 \rangle}$	1.1	0.85	1.20	—
Scale of Turbulence of Particles, ft				
Based on Transverse Intensity,				
$D_p / \sqrt{\langle v_p^2 \rangle}$	2.45×10^{-3}	2.53×10^{-3}	1.16×10^{-3}	1.55×10^{-3}
Optical Autocorrelation [S70]				
Longitudinal, l_x	1.16×10^{-3}	1.32×10^{-3}	1.39×10^{-3}	1.15×10^{-3}
Transverse, l_y	0.306×10^{-3}	0.433×10^{-3}	0.854×10^{-3}	1.55×10^{-3}
Particle Diffusivity, D_p, Ft^2/sec	2.40×10^{-3}	2.16×10^{-3}	1.39×10^{-3}	1.55×10^{-3}
Optical Autocorrelation [S70]				
$\frac{_x \sqrt{\langle u_p^2 \rangle}}{l_y \sqrt{\langle v_p^2 \rangle}}$	2.87×10^{-3}	2.82×10^{-3}	3.06×10^{-3}	3.00×10^{-3}
	0.336×10^{-3}	0.368×10^{-3}	1.02×10^{-3}	

* Direct measurement [S66].

the particle Reynolds number $\langle N_{\text{Re}} \rangle = 2a\sqrt{\langle u^2 \rangle} \bar{\rho}/\bar{\mu}$; $\bar{\rho}_p/\bar{\rho}$ is the ratio of density of particle and stream, and $\bar{\mu}$ is the viscosity of the stream. K is therefore based on the limiting case of a particle moving at constant velocity (equal to mean stream velocity) in a fluctuating fluid field and is therefore a reference measure of momentum exchange. It was shown that the solution of Soo [S48] as an upper limit of $(\langle u^2 \rangle - \langle u_p^2 \rangle / \langle u^2 \rangle)$ is nearly true not only for small $\langle N_{\text{Re}} \rangle$ and K, but in addition, large Froude number $\langle N_{\text{Fr}} \rangle = g/F\langle u^2 \rangle^{1/2}$, g is the gravitational acceleration, and stream Reynolds number $N_{\text{Re}} = 2RU/\bar{\nu}$, even though the value of K may be quite large. The trend of the experimental results, however, is believed to be strongly influenced by the electrostatic charges on the solid particles (Sec. 10.8).

Correlation based on the dimensionless group K is shown in Figs. 2.31 for the ratio D_p/D. Included in Fig. 2.31 are also experimental results showing deviation from the above limiting value. For the density ratio of particle to stream (1780 in this case) in the experiment, the value of D_p/D is much smaller than 1—to the order of 10^{-2} to 10^{-1}. The trend is that as K increases, for a given mean stream Reynolds number N_{Re}, D_p/D first decreases below 1

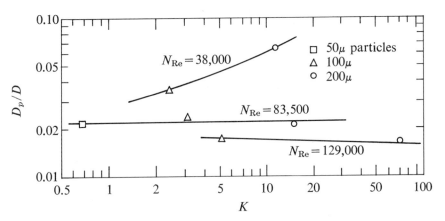

Figure 2.31 Ratio of particle diffusivity to eddy diffusivity.

and then starts to increase again. The ratio of D_p/D is also smaller for greater mean stream Reynolds numbers. These facts, besides suggesting that the parameter K is not a sufficient generalization due to wall, electrostatic, and gravity effects, indicate that the probability of encounter between a solid particle and the field of fluid turbulence has a more significant contribution here than in the case of intensity of motion.

Using photomultiplier tubes and light fields, Kennedy [K14] made measurements of diffusion coefficients, particle velocity autocorrelation, and scales of turbulence of various particles. They included soap bubbles (1.25 mm diameter), and polystyrene spheres (0.7 and 0.9 mm). His results showed similar trends as given in the above. His method is not applicable to particles below 0.5 mm in diameter.

2.9 Brownian Motion of a Particle in Fluid

We have so far dealt with cases of interaction of a particle with its surrounding fluid when the thermal random motion due to statistical partition of energy is negligible. It is readily shown that the average kinetic energy of a particle of mass m along each coordinate axis ($mv_x^2/2$ in the x-direction) is given by:

$$\tfrac{1}{2}m\langle v_x^2 \rangle = \tfrac{1}{2}kT, \tag{2.177}$$

where k is the Boltzmann constant and T is the absolute temperature. When a particle is small enough, appreciable motion, that is, Brownian motion [K13], may become observable. The root-mean-square velocity is given by

$$\sqrt{\langle v_x^2 \rangle} = \sqrt{\frac{kT}{m}}$$

$$= \sqrt{\frac{kT}{(4\pi/3)a^3 \bar{\rho}_p}}. \tag{2.178}$$

For $\bar{\rho}_p = 1000$ kg/m³, $T = 300°$K, $\sqrt{\langle v^2 \rangle} \sim 10^{-3}$ m/sec for $a = 1$ $\bar{\mu}$; and 3×10^{-2} m/sec for 0.1 μ.

The motion of a single particle (or particles in a dilute suspension in a fluid; that is, when there is no force of interaction) was given by Einstein [K13] in terms of root-mean-square displacement $\langle (\Delta x)^2 \rangle$ over a long time τ as

$$\frac{\langle (\Delta x)^2 \rangle}{\tau} = \frac{2kT}{6\pi\bar{\mu}a} = D, \tag{2.179}$$

where D is the diffusivity of the particle in the fluid of viscosity $\bar{\mu}$. Equation (2.179) is based on random motion with drag force applicable to the regime where Stokes' law is valid. Modifications based on rarefaction can be made as given previously. Within the Stokes'-law range it is seen that for particles in air at room condition this diffusivity has the magnitude $(3 \times 10^{-10}/a)$ m²/sec for a in microns.

It is seen that even without interaction among the particles, the above diffusivity plays an important role in the concentration distribution of a cloud of particles (Chap. 6).

Quantitative theory of translational and rotational Brownian motion of rigid spheres was given by Einstein [E7]. That of ellipsoidal particles was treated by Perrin [P12] and Gans [G3]. Brenner [B59] treated cross-coupling effects between translational and rotational Brownian motion for bodies of more general shape. Brenner took cognizance of the additional terms in the diffusion flux vector in physical orientation space, beyond those normally identified with the conventional translational and rotational fluxes. This gives rise to a third diffusion coefficient independent of the classical translational and rotational diffusivities. Extensive treatment of Brownian motion is given in the treatises by Fuchs [F36] and Levich [L35].

SUMMARY OF BASIC CONCEPTS

Spherical Particle in Uniform Motion

Drag due to inertia effect—Newton (1710) [L5]
Drag due to viscous effect—Stokes (1845), Lorentz (1896) [L5, H11]
Inertia correlation to Stokes' law—Oseen (1911) [L5]
Wake formation in laminar motion—Homann (1936) [S13]
Slip motion in rarefied gas—Basset (1888) [B21]

Spherical Particle in Periodic Motion and Acceleration

Apparent mass in oscillatory motion—Stokes (1898) [L5]
Force due to change in flow field—Basset (1888) [B21]
Effect of acceleration and deceleration—Lapple and Shepherd (1940) [L19]

Nonspherical Particle in Free Motion

Inertia effect in potential motion of rods—Kirchhoff (1869), Kelvin (1880),
   Tait, and Greenhill (1897) [L5]
Secondary oscillatory motion—Rayleigh (1920) [S94]
Stokesian resistance of arbitrary particle—Brenner (1964) [B57]

Spherical Particle in Nonuniform Fluid

Velocity gradient—Einstein (1906) [E6], Jeffery (1922) [J6]
Temperature gradient—Cawood (1936) [C11]
Radiation—Rubinowitz (1920) [R45]
Concentration gradient—Stefan flow [F35]

Free Motion in Turbulent Fluid

Relative acceleration—Lin (1943) [T15]
General motion—Tchen (1947) [T15]
Probability of encounter—(1958) [S67]

Transport Processes of a Deformable Particle

As preparatory to treating multiphase systems and as a continuation of the previous chapter, behaviors of single deformable particles are treated in the present chapter. Phenomena include momentum, heat and mass transfers, and chemical reactions. Although for much of the details the reader is again referred to texts on simple systems, here the general background and bibliography are included for study and research in multiphase systems. Other details are given where phenomena are related to dynamics of particles. It is believed that the present survey on the nature of deformable particles may assist the application of methods in Chaps. 4–10, with pertinent qualifications, to bubbles and droplets.

3.1 Drag of Fluid Spheres

In determining the drag force acting by a fluid medium on a fluid sphere in relative motion, it has long been recognized that velocity distributions in both phases have to be accounted for. A large number of studies of gas-bubble motion in liquids have been reported. A complete literature survey up to 1956 was made by Haberman and Morton [H1, H2]. The basic concepts also apply to liquid spheres in an immiscible liquid, and liquid spheres in a gas.

Early theoretical studies were confined to creeping motion of fluid spheres in a infinite medium, introducing modifications to the Stokes' law of drag on rigid spheres (Eq. 2.2 p. 17). Hadamard [H3] and Rybczynski [R53] solved the equation of motion assuming zero inertia in the flow field and gave

$$\mathscr{F} = 6\pi a \bar{\mu} v_o \frac{2\bar{\mu} + 3\bar{\mu}_p}{3(\bar{\mu} + \bar{\mu}_p)}, \tag{3.1}$$

where $\bar{\mu}$ and $\bar{\mu}_p$ are the viscosities of fluid outside and inside the sphere, v_o is the velocity of the center of the sphere relative to the fluid medium. Boussinesq [B50] included changes in interfacial stresses resulting from motion. These changes were attributed to combined effect of the surface tension and a "dynamic" increment, with the latter varying over the surface. The drag force is now

$$\mathscr{F} = 6\pi a \bar{\mu} v_o \frac{\mu_s + a(2\bar{\mu} + 3\bar{\mu}_p)}{\mu_s + 3a(\bar{\mu} + \bar{u}_p)}, \tag{3.2}$$

where μ_s is the coefficient of surface viscosity. For small a or large μ_s, Boussinesq's expression approaches Stokes' law; the other limit is Eq. (3.1).

For large Reynolds numbers ($N_{\text{Re}} = 2a v_o \bar{\rho}/\bar{\mu} \gg 1$), Levich [L35], postulating that the tangential stress vanishes at the bubble-liquid interface, gives the drag coefficient, C_D as

$$C_D = \frac{48}{N_{\text{Re}}}. \tag{3.3}$$

Moore [M43] examined the motion of spherical air bubbles at high, but subcritical, Reynolds numbers and introduced a fictitious tangential stress distribution at the bubble surface and gave

$$C_D = \frac{31}{N_{\text{Re}}}. \tag{3.4}$$

Hill [M36] analyzed the circulating motion of an inviscid fluid inside a sphere due to external irrotational flow. The tangential velocity distribution both inside and outside the sphere for $\theta = \pi/2$ is shown in Fig. 3.1. Hartunian and Sears [H23] observed that the irrotational solution is, at high Reynolds numbers, a good approximation to the actual external viscous flow. Chao [C15] recognized that the disturbance due to velocity gradient in a very thin layer (Fig. 3.1) and applied the boundary-layer approximation to compute the drag coefficient C_D:

$$C_D = \frac{32}{N_{\text{Re}}} \left[1 + 2\frac{\bar{\mu}_p}{\bar{\mu}} - 0.314 \frac{1 + 4(\bar{\mu}_p/\bar{\mu})}{N_{\text{Re}}^{1/2}} \right]. \tag{3.5}$$

Experimental studies showed that a bubble is nearly spherical even when the Reynolds number becomes large, provided that the Weber number ($N_{\text{We}} = 2a\bar{\rho}v_o^2/\sigma$; σ is the surface tension at the interface) remains small [M43]. Rosenberg [R34] performed extensive experiments on the terminal velocity and shape of air bubbles in water. He found that the bubbles were

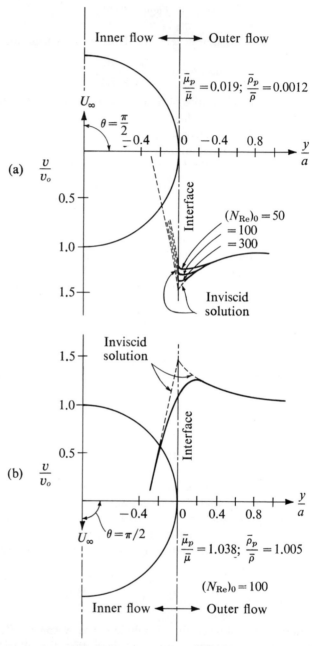

Figure 3.1 Tangential velocity distribution in equatorial plane [C15].
  (a) Air bubbles rising steadily in water at room temperature, observer stationed with bubble.
  (b) Droplet (40 per cent butyl alcohol, 27 per cent chloroform, 33 per cent benxene) falling steadily in water at room temperature, observer stationed with droplet.

spherical with Reynolds number up to 400. Haberman and Morton [H1] gave the approximate ranges as 275 for cold water and 80 for Varsol. At higher Reynolds numbers, the bubbles become flattened, passing from oblate spheroids to spherical cap bubbles. Garner and Hammerton [G5] reported the existence of regular circulating currents in gas bubbles rising through liquids using freshly formed ammonium chloride fog. For gas bubbles of diameter greater than 0.03 cm in water, toroidal circulation sets in which

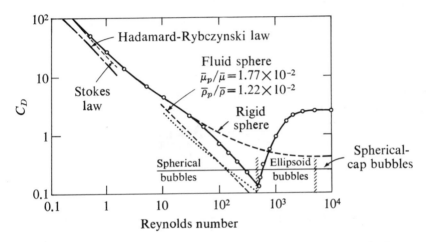

Figure 3.2 Drag coefficients of air bubbles rising at their terminal velocity in filtered or distilled water [C15].

········ Lower envelope of experimental fluid sphere (gas bubble) data proposed by Haberman & Morton

○ Data taken from Haberman & Morton's exptl. curve for air bubbles in filtered water at 19° C

increases in vigor with increasing bubble diameter. Good agreement with Hadamard-Rybczynski analysis and the measured rising velocity of gas bubbles in five liquids was observed. At higher Reynolds numbers, however, the inertia effect becomes more significant.

Garner and Skelland [G6] studied the mechanics causing internal circulation within a droplet. For droplets containing 40 per cent by volume of *n*-butyl alcohol, 27 per cent chloroform, and 33 per cent benzene falling in quiescent water, internal circulation was observed when Reynolds number was over 71.5. The data are included in Fig. 3.1.

Haberman and Morton [H1] proposed a drag curve for fluid spheres, or more correctly, gas bubbles which behave like fluid spheres, by drawing the lower envelope of all experimental curves available. Figure 3.2 shows this drag curve in comparison with theoretical relations; ellipsoidal and spherical cap bubbles are also included. Good agreement was obtained also with the results of Johnson and Braida [J14].

Taylor and Acrivos [T14] computed the motion of a drop in a quiescent unbounded fluid at low Reynolds number by singular-perturbation solution of equation of motion. It was shown at low Weber number N_{We}, the drop first deforms into an oblate spheroid and as N_{We} increases, into a geometry approaching a spherical cap. For surface of a drop given by $r/a = 1 + \zeta(\cos \theta)$, a is the radius of a corresponding spherical drop, $\mu^* = \bar{\mu}_p/\bar{\mu}$

$$\zeta \sim -\Lambda\left(\frac{\bar{\rho}\bar{v}^2}{a\sigma}\right)N_{Re}^2 P_2\,(\cos\,\theta), \tag{3.6}$$

where $\Lambda = \Lambda(\mu^*)$, P_2 is the Legendre polynomial of the second degree. The drag coefficient is given by

$$(C_D - C_{Da}) \sim 2\pi\Lambda\,\frac{3\mu^{*2} - \mu^* + 8}{5(\mu^* + 1)^2}\left(\frac{\bar{\rho}\bar{v}^2}{a\sigma}\right)N_{Re}\cdots. \tag{3.7}$$

3.2 Mass Transfer from a Fluid Sphere

The heat and mass transfer of a fluid sphere moving uniformly in a continuous fluid medium are affected by the motion inside the sphere. Observations of Hammerton and Garner [H7] showed that the transfer rate from circulating bubbles of slightly soluble pure gases was about five times as large as from noncirculating bubbles. This increase cannot be attributed to improved mixing inside the sphere (since the entire resistance to transfer is in the continuum phase) and the effect of internal circulation on the external flow pattern must be accounted for. Griffith [G42] described a partially hindered surface flow in his study of mass transfer from drops and bubbles.

Bowman, Ward, Johnson, and Trass [B52] computed the effect of internal circulation predicted by Hadamard [H3] on the transfer rate from spherical fluid particles at $N_{Re} < 1$. The continuous phase mass-transfer coefficient was calculated for a typical liquid-liquid and gas-liquid system and compared with that obtained for the analogous case of solid sphere (Fig. 3.3). Their results of computation were expressed as Sherwood number ($N_{Sh} = 2ak_c/D$, where k_c is the mass-transfer coefficient, D is the diffusivity) vs. Peclet number ($N_{Pe} = 2av_o/D$) and are shown in Fig. 3.4. It was shown that for thin boundary layer or large N_{Pe},

$$N_{Sh} = 0.978\,N_{Pe}^{1/3}, \tag{3.8}$$

the coefficient is 0.89 for solid sphere following a similar procedure (compare to Eq. 2.19). For thick boundary layer or small N_{Pe},

$$N_{\mathrm{Sh}} = 2 + \tfrac{9}{16}N_{\mathrm{Pe}} + \tfrac{9}{64}N_{\mathrm{Pe}}^2 + \cdots \qquad (3.9)$$

in comparison to

$$N_{\mathrm{Sh}} = 2 + \tfrac{1}{2}N_{\mathrm{Pe}} + \tfrac{1}{6}N_{\mathrm{Pe}}^2 + \cdots \qquad (3.10)$$

for a solid sphere, with an analogous series expansion.

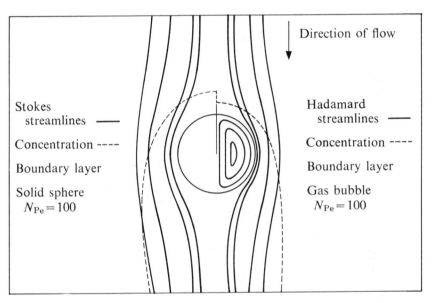

Figure 3.3 Comparison of solid and gas sphere in forced convection ($N_{\mathrm{Re}} < 1$) [B52]

The results show that at a Peclet number of 10^4, circulation movements within a gas bubble increase the mass-transfer rate about threefold over a noncirculating bubble or a solid sphere. The enhancement of a typical circulating liquid drop at the same Peclet number is about $2\frac{1}{2}$ times that of a solid particle. The increase due to circulation decreases with decreasing Peclet number and almost vanishes for $N_{\mathrm{Pe}} < 10^{-2}$. The correlation by Froessling reported in Fig. 2.4 (p. 25) was based on liquid droplets.

Contaminants of the interface have an important effect on the transfer rate. Hammerton and Garner [H7] reported a fivefold reduction in mass transfer when ethylene bubbles rising in water had previously contacted petroleum jelly which presumably prevented circulation.

The rate of gas bubble dissolution was studied by Ledig and Weaver [L26] and Shabalin [L35] to give

$$N_{\mathrm{Sh}} = \sqrt{\frac{2}{\pi}} \, N_{\mathrm{Pe}}^{\frac{1}{2}}. \tag{3.11}$$

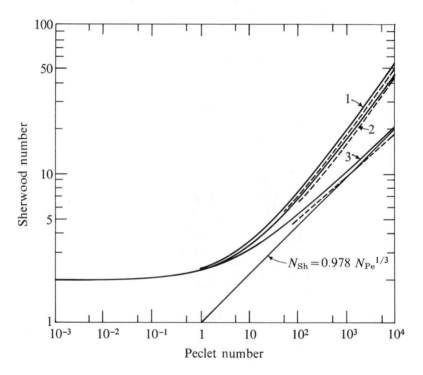

Figure 3.4 Transfer from fluid and solid spheres [B52].

The effect of turbulence was to give, for a gas bubble rising or gravitational field of acceleration g such that lifting and resisting forces are equal [L35],

$$v_o = \frac{1}{9} \frac{g a^2 \bar{\rho}}{\bar{\mu}}, \tag{3.12}$$

the mass transfer is given by

$$N_{\mathrm{Sh}} = \sqrt{\frac{2}{\pi} \left(\frac{\bar{\rho} g a^3}{9 \bar{\mu} D} \right)^{\frac{1}{2}}}. \tag{3.13}$$

Effects of turbulence on evaporation rate were studied by Sherwood and Maisel [S30]. The effect of high relative velocity between a droplet and gas was studied by Ranz and Marshall [R4]. A general discussion of transient evaporation rate of droplets was given by Fuchs [F34]; cases involving absorption were studied by Arnold [A14]. Many studies were made on transient evaporation of droplets in high-temperature surroundings because of interests in combustion. Penner [P7], Hartwig [H24], and Gilbert, Howard, and Hicks [G15] applied the Knudsen equation of effusion for estimating the maximum evaporation rate. The evaporation rate as controlled by convection and diffusion was treated by El Wahil, Uyehara, and Myers [E12] and by Ranz [R2]. The effectiveness of each range was discussed by Soo and Ihrig [S65]. Experimental data of diffusivity including the effect of molecular convection was presented by Houghton [H55] and Topley and Whythan-Gray [T43]. Frossling [F33] determined, both from theoretical analysis and from experimental results, that the generalized evaporation law can be written as

$$\frac{da^2}{dt} = \left(\frac{da^2}{dt}\right)_o [1 + 0.276(N_{Sc})^{1/3}(N_{Re})^{1/2}], \tag{3.14}$$

where $\left(\dfrac{da^2}{dt}\right)_o$ represents the evaporation rate in still air.

3.3 Reaction Rate of a Single Droplet

Studies were made on the chemical reaction rate of a single particle in an effort to generalize the combustion process of solid or liquid fuels. El Wahil, Uyehara, and Myers [E12] determined theoretically that the heating-up period of a droplet is significant. Nishiwaki [N8] concluded from experimental data that the heating-up period increased linearly with the diameter of the droplet. The evaporation period prior to ignition, however, decreased linearly with drop diameter and also decreased with oxygen content. The latter was also noted by Mueller [M48] in the combustion of nitromethane. Mullins [M51] noted that the ignition delay when fuel is injected into hot air streams is mainly chemical in nature.

The linear variation of the square of droplet diameter with time (Sec. 3.2) was established experimentally for combustion process. Spalding [S73] noted in addition the dependence on the square root of the Reynolds number for the combustion of liquids from the surface of a porous sphere. Wise, Lorell, and Wood [W29] noted that addition of oxygen in either fuel or atmosphere increases the burning rate. The distance between the droplet surface and the flame front appeared to be independent of the droplet diameter. A similar relation as noted by Spalding was obtained by Godsave [G26], and Goldsmith and Perkins [G32] for droplets suspended from a wire filament. Bolt, Boyle, and Mirsky [B46], and Topps [T44] however, found that for a single droplet supported by updraft from a tube, the diameter varies linearly with time. Godsave [G26] derived the rate of change in mass of droplet as

$$\frac{dm}{dt} = \frac{4\pi\bar{\kappa}\ln\left[1 - (c\,\Delta T/\Delta H)\right]}{c[(1/a) - (1/a_f)]}, \qquad (3.15)$$

where $\bar{\kappa}$ and c are the thermal conductivity and the specific heat of the vapor, ΔT the difference between the flame temperature and the liquid, ΔH the latent heat of vaporization, a_f the radius of the flame surface, a is the droplet radius. This was confirmed experimentally by Goldsmith and Penner [G31].

The effect of drop size on flame propagation was studied experimentally by Browning and Krall [B65] and by Burgoyne and Cohen [B71]. Both groups of authors reported that for drop size below 10 μ, the suspension behaves like a vapor; individual burning definitely occurs for drop size above 40 μ. The fact that a_f/a increased as a decreased [W29] was confirmed. Bolt and Boyle [B46] observed the lowering of burning rates for smaller drop sizes. The effect of ambient pressure oscillation on burning rate was studied by Kumagai and Isode [K45]. Miesse [M33] considered the stability of flame front of a bipropellant system. An attempt toward generalizing combustion rate in terms of basic properties was made by Peskin, Wise, and Rosser [P19]. Crowe, Nichols, and Morrison [C45] correlated the effect of burning on the drag coefficient of droplets and particles.

Combustion of Metals—Combustion of metallic powders for the production of high temperature [G45] and for the application in rockets is characterized by the very large latent heat and the presence of solid product of combustion. The presence of condensed-phase reactants and products makes heterogeneous reaction processes significant. Ignition of metals is usually preceded by reaction on the surface or through an oxide layer. A simple criterion for predicting whether surface or vapor-phase burning will take place was proposed by Glassman [S98].

Low temperature and low rate of oxidation were dealt with in comprehensive texts [E26, K43]. Cases of interest in multiphase systems usually involve high reaction rates and the problem of ignition. Grosse and Conway [G45] reported ignition temperatures of various metals. Reynolds [R12] performed an analysis that links the ignition temperature to the low-temperature oxidation properties of the metal. Recent experimental studies [D7] indicate that ignition temperatures are well defined only for those metals that do not form a protective oxide layer, such as magnesium. Littman [L49] showed that oxide layers (such as titanium, zirconium) make ignition temperatures difficult to reproduce.

Ignition and combustion of powder in cloud form was studied by many

[A11, C9, F29, F30, H22]. This subdivision, which can be expressed as specific surface area in cm^2/g, lowers the ignition temperature in general. The influence of particle concentrations in dust clouds on ignition temperature was studied by Cassal and Liebman [C9]. Friedman and Maček [F29] dealt with the ignition and burning of single aluminum particles injected into a hot gas stream, with photographic recording of ignition and combustion.

After ignition, the burning process may either continue to take place on the surface of a molten oxide layer covering the metal, or the reaction may occur in the surrounding vapor phase. Heterogeneous reactions on the surface of growing oxide-smoke particles play an important role. Surface burning has been observed to take place if the oxide is more volatile than the metal. Vapor-phase burning may occur only if the metal is more volatile than the oxide, but may be suppressed by formation of a protective oxide layer, or by reduction of flame temperature to below the metal boiling point, owing to heat losses. Experiments were carried out by Grosse and Conway [G45, G44] with molten pools of aluminum. Burning of magnesium ribbon was studied by Coffin [C35]; titanium, zirconium, aluminum, and magnesium wires by Harrison and Yolte [H19, H20]; boron rods by Talley [S98]. The majority of metal combustion experiments was performed with metal powders [C36, C47, D26, D34, S10, W30].

Pyrolysis and combustion of solid hydrocarbons is another broad field. A recent study was presented by Essenhigh and Howard [E24]. Studies have been made on the combustion and ignition process of solid rocket fuels. Recent results were presented by Hermance et al. [H32].

One-dimensional noncatalytic-gas solid reaction was analyzed by Lacey, Bowen, and Basden [L1] based on first-order reaction using finite difference method. Shen and Smith [S27] studied diffusional effects in the reaction of a solid spherical pellet, taking into account the interaction of physical transfer processes and chemical reaction.

3.4 Bubble Formation

The mechanism of bubble formation is seen from studies on single bubbles. Very small bubbles were obtained with capillary tubes and filters with fine pores [D9], and submerged orifice [S97]. Although not useful due to their low capacities, results of studies give basic factors affecting bubble formation and coalescence.

From study of aeration of liquids, Pattle [P3] presented a theory of detachment of a bubble as follows: For a capillary of radius R with a meniscus dividing a liquid and a gas, the ends are connected to a liquid reservoir of pressure P and a gas reservoir of pressure P_2. If $P_2 - P < 2\sigma/R$; the meniscus will retreat to the inner end of the capillary; if $P_2 - P > 2\sigma/R$, the meniscus will pass up the capillary.

When it has just begun to protrude into the liquid, the pressure in the incipient bubble will be given by

$$P_1 - P = \frac{2\sigma}{R}, \tag{3.16}$$

where P_1 is the pressure in the bubble, P_2 is still the pressure in the bulk of the gas supply, and P is the pressure in the liquid. When the bubble begins to expand at the end of the capillary, its radius will become greater than R, and the pressure inside the bubble will fall still further by

$$P_1 - P = \frac{2\sigma}{a}. \tag{3.17}$$

A bubble blown slowly from a horizontal circular orifice has a radius given by

$$a^3 = 3R\sigma f\left(\frac{R}{a}\right)2\bar{\rho}g, \tag{3.18}$$

where a is the radius of a bubble, R the radius of the orifice, σ the surface tension of the liquid-gas interface; $\bar{\rho}$ the density of the liquid, and $f(R/a) \simeq 1$.

It is found that the size of the bubbles produced by porous bodies is very much dependent on the liquid in which they are produced. A porcelain candle in pure water produced bubbles of diameter about 2 mm. On adding 0.1 per cent of acetic acid to the water, the bubble diameter fell to about 0.1 mm. The difference between 1 per cent acetic acid and pure water lies in the ability of the former to maintain a temporary liquid film between two bubbles, thus reducing or preventing the recombination of small bubbles.

There are two classes of liquids from the point of view of bubble formation:

Class A liquids include aqueous solutions of alcohols, organic acid, ether, or benzene, concentrated HNO_3 and strong solutions of salts; a bubble formed will not recombine with another adjacent bubble.

Class B liquids include all viscous liquids; e.g., olive oil, tap or distilled water, dilute salt solutions, H_2SO_4 in all concentrations, methylene iodide, and nitrobenzene; bubbles have strong tendency to combine.

The highest dilutions (weight of water per unit weight of solute) in which various solutes would change water from class B to class A are given below:

Methyl alcohol	600	Acetic acid	2,000
Ethyl alcohol	2,000	Sodium oleate	2,500
Isobutyl alcohol	16,000	Sodium chloride	100
Capryl alcohol	80,000		

A special device for studying breaking off of bubbles is the P-Jet. The observations on the breaking up of columns of bubbles led to the idea of obstructing the orifice of a capillary with something which would push the bubbles aside and break them off prematurely. A capillary a few cm long and 0.100 mm in diameter is therefore bent into the form of a P, so that its orifice is obstructed by its stem. On blowing down into a class A liquid a jet of small bubbles shoots out sideways from the orifice. Bubbles of 0.01 mm^3 to 1 mm^3 can be formed, at a rate of 100 to 2000 per second.

It was suggested that the production of small bubbles by a porous body is due to the closing in of the liquid behind the bubble by way of side pores or irregularities in the orifice when the pressure in the bubble has fallen sufficiently.

In pure water, the bubble which is forming touches the one which has just broken off and recombines with it. This recombination causes an immediate drop in pressure and the bubble breaks off at the orifice where another bubble starts to form. This may again combine with the same one and be broken off in the same way. In class A liquids, such as 1 per cent acetic acid, a bubble jostling against one in front would merely push it away or itself be pushed to one side.

If the orifice of the capillary is placed just below the surface of the liquid, a column of spray is blown upward and small bubbles move downward into the liquid. They are produced very near the orifice, and must be torn from the surface just outside the orifice. They are not formed solely by the impaction of the spray into the walls of the larger bubbles. The necessary length or thickness for the production of very small bubbles appears to decrease with decreasing bore or pore size.

Bubble formation was observed on filters [V9]. At a very low rate few pores come into operation; their number increases with the gas flow rate. At highest flow rate, small bubbles show a tendency to coalesce into large ones. On increasing the gas rate, there is a possibility that besides new pores coming into action, the first ones are yielding larger bubbles. The bubble is many times larger (10 to 100) than the pore from which it escapes.

Adding ethanol to water results in a swarm of minute gas bubbles, due not so much to the lowering of surface tension as to the following phenomena: If two bubbles moving in a liquid approach each other, there will be a resistance when the liquid layer between the two becomes very thin. The liquid film between the two bubbles may prevent them from coalescing. In the case of pure liquids, no such resistance exists, whereas it may be present when the liquid contains some dissolved matter. The source of this resistance seems to be in the difference between the concentration of the solute in the interface bubble, surrounding liquid, and that in the bulk of the liquid.

Orifices and slots have been basic configurations of gas outlets in down-comer tubes. The behavior of bubbles formed from circular orifices was reported by Coppock and Micklejohn [C40]. The size of a bubble formed at a circular orifice has been related to the diameter of the orifice $(2R)$, the surface tension of the liquid, and its density.

$$v_p = \frac{2\pi R\sigma}{g\Delta\bar{\rho}} \qquad (3.19)$$

where v_p is the volume of a bubble in cubic centimeters, $\Delta\bar{\rho}$ is the difference between $\bar{\rho}$, the density of the liquid in grams per cubic centimeter, and $\bar{\rho}_p$ of the bubble; assuming that the angle of wetting was zero and that the bubble was quite spherical. It is usually written as

$$v_p = c\,\frac{2R\sigma}{\Delta\bar{\rho}}, \qquad (3.20)$$

where c is an empirical constant depending on the conditions of the experiment.

The effects of configurations and state parameters are:

(a) *Influence of temperature:* the volume of bubbles does not change with temperature. The value of constant c (nearly 0.003) shows a tendency to increase with rising temperature.

(b) *Influence of pressure:* the size of bubble remains unchanged within the range of pressure investigated (30 cm to 180 cm hydrostatic bead). For a given size of orifice, the mass of gas within a bubble is proportional to the total pressure at the orifice.

(c) *Orifice diameters:* the bubble size varies considerably as the flow rate to the orifice is varied and at high rates the results tend to be erratic. The trend is shown in Fig. 3.5. At this high flow rate, the bubbles are not of uniform size, and coalescence may take place in the rising stream of bubbles.

(d) *Liquid density:* the value of c remains constant and the bubble size is nearly inversely proportional to the liquid density.

(e) *Surface tension:* the bubble volume is approximately proportional to the surface tension.

With very dilute solutions (33–72 dyne/cm) the bubbles are much larger than expected on the basis of Eq. (3.19), and the volume of a bubble should increase with surface tension of the liquid.

(f) *Influence of viscosity on bubble size:* viscosity plays a very little part in determining bubble size. For orifices of diameter 0.036 to 0.63 cm, a hundred-fold increase in viscosity causes a diminution in volume of about 10 per cent at low gas velocities [D9]; if a bubble is assumed to be spherical, the inter-acting forces are: Buoyancy force $= \frac{4}{3}\pi a^3\Delta\bar{\rho}g$, and Surface tension force $=$

$2\pi R\sigma(\cos\theta)f(R/a')$; where a' is the radius of a bubble at the moment of release, θ is the angle of contact at the triple interface, ($\theta = 0$ for perfect wetting); $f(R/a')$ is the shape factor ($= 1$ for sphere) and $a' = 2\sigma/\bar{\rho}g$. Since the two forces equalize for a given bubble size,

$$\tfrac{4}{3}\pi a^3 \Delta\bar{\rho}g = 2\pi R\sigma$$

or

$$a = \left(\frac{3}{2}\frac{R\sigma}{\Delta\bar{\rho}g}\right)^{\!\!1/3}. \tag{3.21}$$

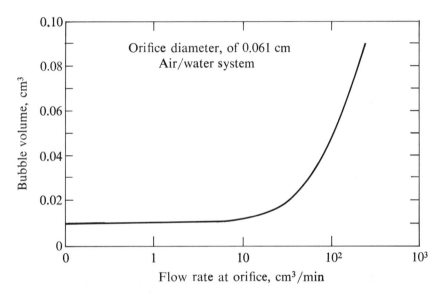

Figure 3.5 Variation of bubble size with flow rate [C40].

For a system involving air water at 20°C, $R = 9.05a^3$ and $v_p/2R = 0.231$ were given empirically. It is assumed that no forces other than buoyancy contribute to the release of the bubble and that the surface tension is approximately that of the corresponding static or equilibrium value. At low gas velocities, it was found that the radius of the gas bubble is independent of the flow rate and increases with the cube root of the orifice diameter.

The shape of gas bubbles formed at an orifice and rising in a column of liquid was observed to have the following ranges:

1. For a circular orifice up to 0.04 cm in diameter, the bubbles are substantially spherical and after an initial acceleration on release, travel upward at a uniform velocity, following a vertical path.

2. For orifices between 0.04 and 0.4 cm in diameter, the bubbles are spherical at the orifice, but on release rapidly assume an ellipsoidal shape with the longer axis horizontal. In this form they travel upward, following a zigzag path.

3. With orifice diameter exceeding 0.4 cm, the bubbles become unstable. They may assume a symmetrical saucer shape, or, more frequently, an unsymmetrical shape.

4. When (diameter of bubble)/(diameter of liquid column) > 0.75, the bubbles assume a cylindrical shape with an ogival head and a flat tail.

For very viscous liquids, the bubbles tend to preserve symmetrical shapes up to much larger sizes than in the case with water and their paths tend to remain vertical.

As the bubbles rise through the liquid, they expand with diminution of the hydrostatic pressure and in consequence a bubble having a stable spherical or ellipsoidal form near the orifice may expand into the region of instability.

Single slots for bubble formation were reported by Spells and Bokowski [S75]. An investigation of the mechanism of bubble formation at single slots submerged in water was made with the aid of high-speed cinematography (measurement of size, frequency, and rate of growth of bubbles). The variation of the shape of the slot and the physical properties of a gas and liquid had relatively little effect on the order of size of the bubble under different conditions.

The mechanism of energy transfer from liquid to a gas bubble at a submerged orifice was treated by L'Ecuyur and Murthy [L25].

Formation of Multiple Bubbles [V6]—Two types of formation and rising of gas bubbles in liquids can be distinguished: (1) bubbles formed separately, (2) bubbles formed in series (chain bubbling).

In the first case the diameter of the bubbles is independent of the flow rate and proportional to the cube root of the orifice diameter. Chain bubbling takes place above a certain critical flow rate. Here bubble diameters are independent of the orifice diameter and increase with increasing flow rate.

The above principle for separate gas bubbles is valid up to a certain critical value of the flow rate. Above this limit the bubble diameter increases with the flow rate.

At high flow rates the formation of bubbles is hindered by the presence of preceding bubbles. When, for a given orifice, the flow rate is gradually increased, the bubble diameter will remain constant at first. To a constant bubble diameter belongs a constant ascending velocity. This means that the distance between two successive bubbles is inversely proportional to the frequency of bubble formation. Because this distance can never be smaller than the bubble diameter, it is not possible above a certain value of the flow rate to transport the actual quantity of gas by means of bubbles of the theoretical diameter. The only possibility is that the bubbles become greater. In this way the phenomenon of increasing bubble diameter above a certain critical flow rate can be explained qualitatively. A quantitative relation is given as

$$\dot{\mathscr{V}}_G = \frac{\pi}{6} (2a)^3 \frac{v_p}{(2a)} = \frac{2\pi}{3} a^2 v_p \tag{3.22}$$

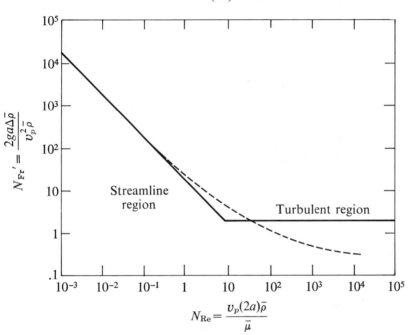

Figure 3.6 Flow relations for bubbles in chainlike formation [V6].

where $\dot{\mathscr{V}}_G$ is the gas-flow rate, and v_p is the ascending velocity. Generalization is achieved by introducing a modified Froude number N'_{Fr}

$$N'_{\mathrm{Fr}} = \frac{2ga\,\Delta\bar{\rho}}{v_p^2\bar{\rho}}, \tag{3.23}$$

and

$$N_{\mathrm{Re}} = \frac{2v_p a\bar{\rho}}{\bar{\mu}}, \tag{3.24}$$

$\bar{\mu}$ is the viscosity of the liquid, $\bar{\rho}$ its density, $\Delta\bar{\rho}$ is the difference between $\bar{\rho}$ and $\bar{\rho}_p$, the density of the material of the bubble. The relation of N'_{Fr} and N_{Re} in chainlike formation of bubbles can be represented by the broken line shown in Fig. 3.6. For the streamline part, $N'_{\mathrm{Fr}} = 18/N_{\mathrm{Re}}$; for the turbulent part, $N'_{\mathrm{Fr}} = 2$, independent of N_{Re}.

Prediction of the critical flow rate (below which the bubble formation will lead to theoretical diameter):

(a) In the turbulent region, $N'_{Fr} = 2$, Eq. (3.22) gives

$$2a = \left(\frac{72\dot{\mathscr{V}}_G^2\bar{\rho}}{\pi^2 g\,\Delta\bar{\rho}}\right)^{\frac{1}{5}},$$ (3.25)

and from Eq. (3.21)

$$2a = \left(\frac{12\sigma R}{g\,\Delta\bar{\rho}}\right)^{\frac{1}{3}}.$$ (3.26)

Equating Eq. (3.25) and (3.26) for critical flow rate, the critical value of $\dot{\mathscr{V}}_G$ is given by

$$\frac{\dot{\mathscr{V}}_G^3\bar{\rho}^3 g^2(\Delta\bar{\rho})^2}{\sigma^5(2R)^5} = 20,$$ (3.27)

(b) In the streamline region,

$$\frac{2ag\,\Delta\bar{\rho}}{v_p^2\bar{\rho}} = 18\,\frac{\bar{\mu}}{v_p\bar{\rho}2a},$$

with $N_{Fr} = 18/N_{Re}$, so that

$$2a = \left(\frac{(18)(6)\dot{\mathscr{V}}_G\bar{\mu}}{\pi g\,\Delta\bar{\rho}}\right)^{\frac{1}{4}}.$$ (3.28)

At critical flow rate, Eqs. (3.28) and (3.26) are identical; thus

$$\frac{\dot{\mathscr{V}}_G^3 g\bar{\mu}^3\,\Delta\bar{\rho}}{\sigma^4(2R)^4} = 0.03.$$ (3.29)

Various ranges are shown in Fig. 3.7, correlated with experimental data.

Practical applications are as follows:

(a) Bubble diameter as a function of the flow rate is shown in Fig. 3.8. For chainlike bubble formation,

$$2a = \left(\frac{72\bar{\rho}}{\pi^2 g\,\Delta\bar{\rho}}\right)^{\frac{1}{5}}\dot{\mathscr{V}}_G^{0.4},$$ (3.30)

giving one single line in Fig. 3.8, independent of orifice diameter.

For separate bubbles,

$$2a = \left(\frac{12\sigma R}{g\,\Delta\bar{\rho}}\right)^{\frac{1}{3}},$$ (3.31)

independent of flow rate, represented by horizontal lines in Fig. 3.8 with orifice diameter as parameter.

(b) Ascending velocity: from Fig. 3.9 for bubbles in series,

$$v_p = \sqrt{ga}, \qquad (3.32)$$

giving a single line in Fig. 3.9 independent of orifice diameter.

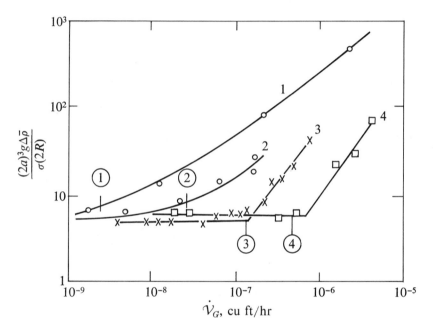

Figure 3.7 Critical flow rate [V6]. Vertical marks = critical values predicted.
1. Guyer, ricinus oil, $2a = 0.22$ mm
2. Guyer, olive oil (0.22 mm)
3. Breitner, water (0.5 mm)
4. Maier, water (0.12 mm)

For separate bubbles, to each orifice diameter belongs a certain value of bubble diameter.

The ascending velocity at the critical point is always smaller than that for separate bubbles of the same diameter. Thus, there must be a sudden change in ascending velocity in the neighborhood of critical flow rate. This sudden change is denoted by dashed lines in Fig. 3.9. Moore [M42] made measurements on the velocity of rise of distorted gas bubbles in a liquid of small viscosity.

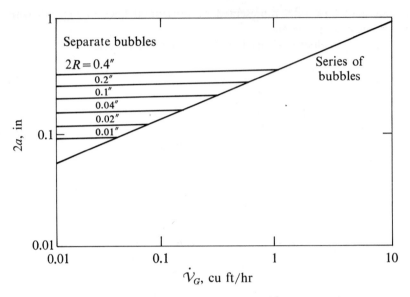

Figure 3.8 Diameter as a function of $\dot{\mathscr{V}}_G$ (water) [V6].

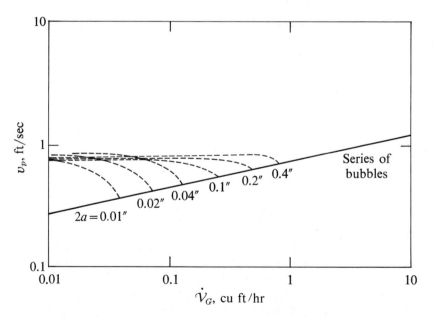

Figure 3.9 v_p as a function of $\dot{\mathscr{V}}_G$ (water) [V6].

(c) Area of gas-liquid interphase (Fig. 3.10): A_h is the bubble area per unit column height; for a chainlike formation, $A_h = 2\pi a$; for separate bubbles, $A_h = 3\dot{\mathscr{V}}_G/v_p a$.

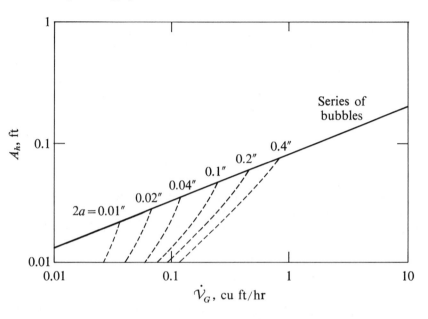

Figure 3.10 A_h as a function of $\dot{\mathscr{V}}_G$ (water) [V6].

3.5 Mass and Heat Transfer from Gas to Liquid

A bubble and its liquid environment may be considered as a two-phase system in which it is possible for mass transfer to take place at the liquid-vapor interface. Due to the variation of the film thickness and the fact that bubbles are not always spherical in shape, only the average mass transfer rate will be considered.

A single bubble grows as it moves freely upwards in still liquid due to the decrease in hydrostatic head. The velocity of its ascent will then vary in proportion to its size. If at the same time, heat (cooling by liquid) and mass (absorption and condensation) transfer take place from the bubble to the liquid, the bubble will decrease in size, and the velocity and film thickness will vary accordingly. The effect of heat and mass transfer from the bubble to the liquid opposes that of decreasing hydrostatic head.

Let us first consider the mass transfer from a stationary bubble. Assuming that mass transfer takes place only from the bubble to the liquid and that a sphere would approximate the shape of a bubble, Liebermann [L42] obtains, for the solubility of the stationary bubble in terms of rate of change of bubble radius a:

$$\frac{da}{dt} = \left(\frac{D}{\bar{\rho}}\right)(C_S - C)\left(\frac{1}{a} - \frac{1}{\sqrt{\pi D t}}\right),\qquad(3.33)$$

where a is the radius of the bubble, D the coefficient of diffusion, $\bar{\rho}$ is the density of the liquid, C_S the gas concentration at saturation, C the actual gas concentration, and t the time. Since the process of diffusion in this particular case is very slow, the last term of Eq. (3.33) containing the time element may be neglected; the solution after integration is then

$$a^2 = a_0^2 - \frac{2D}{\bar{\rho}}(C_S - C)t,\qquad(3.34)$$

i.e., the square of bubble radius diminishes linearly with time as shown in Fig. 3.11 for two individual free bubbles.

Due to the unavoidable contamination at the surface of the bubble, Eq. (3.34) has to be modified such that it takes into account the thickness of the thin film of contamination, Δa, and its respective diffusivity D_1. The modification is given by Libermann [L42] as:

$$a^2 = a_0^2 - \frac{2D}{\bar{\rho}}(C_S - C)t + \frac{2D_1\,\Delta a}{D}(a_0 - a),\qquad(3.35)$$

which is shown in Fig. 3.12 as a solid line.

The coefficient of diffusion may be obtained from the Einstein relation for diffusion of small spheres in a viscous fluid. For the coefficient of diffusion of air into water, we have

$$D = \frac{kT}{6\pi r_o \bar{\mu}}\qquad(3.36)$$

where k is the Boltzmann constant, T the temperature, r_o the molecular diameter of air, and $\bar{\mu}$ the viscosity of water.

In considering the mass transfer from a rising bubble to its liquid surrounding, a few assumptions and simplifications are made. It is assumed that in a relatively shallow liquid, since the effects of heat and mass transfer from the bubble and of hydrostatic head oppose each other and also since both effects will be very small, the bubble volume may be regarded as constant; hence, the velocity of ascent and the effective film thickness may also be treated as constant. It is further assumed that the bubble rises under its own buoyancy, and that at the immediate vicinity of the bubble the composition of the liquid is homogeneous at all points. With these assumptions, Coppock

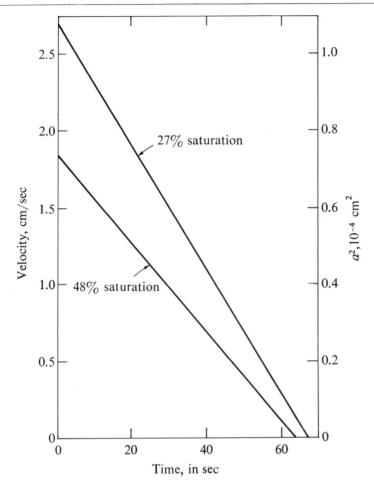

Figure 3.11 Velocity of rise and solubility of two individual free bubbles [L42].

and Meicklejohn [C40] derive the equation for the mass transfer from bubble to liquid,

$$\mathscr{V}_L \, dC = k_L a \dot{N} \frac{z}{v_p} (C_S - C) \, dt, \qquad (3.37)$$

where $\mathscr{V}_L$ is the volume of liquid being aerated, k_L is the overall mass transfer coefficient, $\dot{N}$ is the number of bubbles released per unit time, z is the depth of orifice below surface of liquid in centimeters, v_p is the velocity of ascent of the bubble in centimeters per second, t is the time in seconds, C is the concentration of gas in solution in grams per cubic centimeter, C_S is the equilibrium concentration of gas in solution, also in grams per cubic centimeter.

Integration of Eq. (3.37) gives

$$\ln \frac{C_S - C_1}{C_S - C_2} = k_L a \dot{N} \frac{z}{v_p} (t_2 - t_1), \tag{3.38}$$

and k_L can thus be calculated. An example for oxygen-water systems is given by Coppock and Meiklejohn [C40] as shown in Table 3.1.

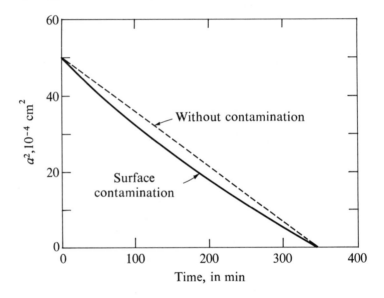

Figure 3.12 A stationary (trapped) air bubble dissolving in water at 14.5°C, 60 per cent solution [L42].

A similar treatment of mass transfer of rising bubbles was also considered experimentally by Pattle [P3] and mathematically by Forster and Zuber [F19].

Mass transfer from gas bubbles in an agitated vessel (gas-liquid contactor) with and without simultaneous chemical reaction was treated by Gal-Or and Resnick [G2].

Heat Transfer—The heat transfer of a vapor bubble embedded in an infinite fluid has been treated mathematically and experimentally by Forster [F16], Grossmann [G46], Plesset and Zwick [P23], Levenspiel [L34], Jakob [J2], and others. Due to the complexity of the problem, assumptions and approximations have to be made in connection with the physical factors that govern the problem and the boundary conditions at the vapor-liquid interface.

The phenomenon of local boiling is a heat-transfer problem which has long been studied. Local boiling has found important applications in liquid boiling industries because the formation and the destruction of vapor bubbles on or close to the heating surface disturb the boundary layer, causing turbulent flow and therefore increasing the heat-transfer coefficient at the interface.

TABLE 3.1   [C40]

MASS-TRANSFER COEFFICIENT: OXYGEN/WATER

Bubble Radius, cm	Upward Velocity, cm/sec	Temperature, °C	k_L $\dfrac{\text{gm of } O_2}{\text{cm}^2/\text{sec} \dfrac{\text{gm of } O_2}{\text{cm}^3}}$
0.150	28.5	19.5	0.0550
0.185	26.0	19.1	0.0420
0.188	25.8	18.3	0.0378
0.202	25.0	8.5	0.0303
0.206	24.9	20.1	0.0433
0.237	23.6	22.0	0.0364
0.240	23.4	20.8	0.0353
0.242	23.3	20.8	0.0372
0.278	22.6	20.0	0.0272
0.292	22.3	21.5	0.0297
0.150	28.5	20.0	0.0453
0.203	25.0	20.0	0.0430
0.237	23.6	20.0	0.0336
0.275	22.8	20.0	0.0375
0.330	22.1	20.0	0.0344
0.200	21.4	20.0	0.0245
0.201	21.9	20.0	0.0250
0.203	22.8	20.0	0.0306
0.204	22.8	20.0	0.0331

Investigation of local boiling was made by McAdams, Kennel, Minder, Carl, Picornell, and Dew [M19], who studied the process by experiments with water in forced flow through vertical annuli of 0.77, 0.73, and 0.43 in. outer diameter and 0.25 in. inner diameter, which were electrically heated from the inside. Some results are shown in Fig. 3.13, in which the heat flux is plotted against the temperature difference, ΔT with the bulk velocity v_b of the water as the parameter and where T_S is the surface temperature, T_b is the bulk temperature of water, T_{sat} is the saturation temperature. The burnout point is that temperature at which the tube is destroyed.

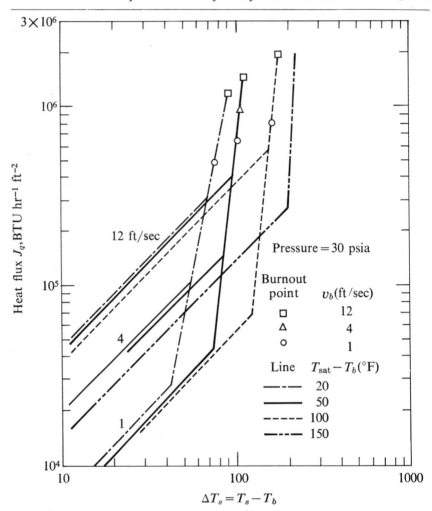

Figure 3.13 Effect of velocity and subcooling in local boiling of degassed distilled water, according to McAdams and associates [M19].

Figure 3.13 shows that for constant v_b and T_{sat}, the heat flux density J_q first decreases linearly with ΔT_S. Local boiling starts if the surface has reached the saturation temperature T_{sat}. A steep increase in J_q follows until the burnout point is reached. v_b has a greater influence on J_q in the non-boiling range then in the boiling range. For the same v_b, the lines are slightly displaced due to the dependency of the physical properties on temperature.

In the range of experiments ($v_b = 1$ to 36 ft/sec, $\Delta T_{sat} = 20$ to 150°F, $P = 30$ to 90 psia, and equivalent diameter of the annulus cross section $2R = 0.17$

to 0.48 in.) the authors established the following empirical equation:

$$J_q = C(\Delta T_{sat})^{3.86}, \tag{3.39}$$

where $\Delta T_{sat} = T_S - T_{sat}$; $C = 0.074$ for 0.06 ml air at STP per liter of water, and 0.190 for 0.30 ml air per liter of water.

The growth and the collapse of vapor bubbles are two different processes governed by evaporation and condensation, respectively. The former can occur in such a way that vapor is produced at the liquid-vapor interface. This happens when the heat of evaporation is transported into the fluid right at its surface, and as a result, vapor is produced in the form of bubbles which grow and rise through the liquid. This mode of evaporation is called boiling. Condensation is just the reverse process of evaporation. Here the saturation temperature is higher than the fluid temperature and therefore the bubbles start collapsing. The two processes, especially the heat-transfer processes in connection with them, will be discussed in greater detail in the following paragraphs.

Evaporation—The degree of superheating of a boiling liquid depends largely on the statistical mean of the radius of curvature of bubbles adhering to the wall on which the liquid can evaporate. Accordingly, a rapidly boiling liquid could not be greatly superheated, since the bubble arising on such surface curvatures would disturb the state of high surface tension which is essential for high superheating.

A quantitative study of heat transfer from the liquid to a growing bubble was made by Bosnjakovic [B47]. He considered the fact that, in a given time element, the product of the mass increment dm of a growing bubble and of the latent heat of vaporization ΔH, must be equal to the heat energy dQ conveyed to the bubble. Mathematically, this relation can be written as

$$dQ = \Delta H\, dm = hA_p\, \Delta T\, dt, \tag{3.40}$$

because the same heat energy will pass through the surface area A_p of the bubble with the temperature difference ΔT between the liquid outside and the vapor inside the bubble. h is the heat-transfer coefficient.

By introducing the time rate of heat flow J_q and a length element dr such that $dv_p = A_p\, dr$ where v_p is the bubble volume of radius a, we obtain, after some manipulations,

$$h = \frac{\bar{\rho}_g\, \Delta H}{\Delta T} \frac{da}{dt}, \tag{3.41}$$

where $\bar{\rho}_g$ is the density of the saturated vapor, with the assumption of spherical bubbles.

Consider a spherical bubble stationary with respect to the extent of the liquid. We see readily that the heat-transfer coefficient can be calculated from Eq. (3.41) for a given temperature and a particular rate of change of bubble diameter at any time t. Since the growth of a bubble at rest (da/dt) could be observed with sufficient exactness on rather large bubbles, it is seen that for a certain fixed growth of the bubble, the heat-transfer coefficient is inversely proportional to the temperature difference for a given fluid and vapor for which ρ_g and ΔH are known. It is further observed that for a constant temperature difference, the heat-transfer coefficient is directly proportional to the bubble growth.

For illustration, let us consider an example using water and air as the media. For water at 14.7 psia and 240°F, $\Delta H = 17,000$ Btu/lb-mole = 944 Btu/lb; and air at 220°F, $\bar{\rho}_g \cong 0.06$ lb/ft³. Equation (3.41) thus becomes

$$h = 335 \frac{2}{\Delta T} \frac{da}{dt}, \tag{3.42}$$

where the unit of h is (Btu/hr ft² °F), ΔT is in °F and da/dt in millimeters per second.

Generally, a vapor bubble is surrounded by a very thin boundary layer of liquid across which the temperature decreases from the higher value of the superheated liquid to the saturation value. Then the heat-transfer coefficient may be approximately expressed as

$$h = \frac{\bar{\kappa}}{\delta}, \tag{3.43}$$

where $\bar{\kappa}$ is the thermal conductivity of the liquid, δ is the boundary layer thickness.

Condensation—The process of condensation of a bubble results in the collapse of vapor bubbles as heat is transported in the reverse direction as in the case of evaporation. The heat-transfer coefficient can be calculated from the rate of collapse of vapor bubbles. Levenspiel [L34] studied the collapse of steam bubbles in water experimentally by photographic means. Some of the results are shown in Fig. 3.14 which gives the plot of bubble diameter vs. the time for one of the runs. The collapsing region is rectified in the semilog plot, in which values of $m = (d \ln a)/dt$ are given for different bubbles. Figure 3.15 shows the linear relation between $(d \ln a)/dt$ and ΔT.

For a collapsing vapor bubble of diameter $2a$ with an instability temperature difference ΔT, the heat-transfer coefficient h is given by Levenspiel as

$$h = 3.54 \frac{2a \, \Delta H}{\bar{\rho}_g^{-1} - \bar{\rho}_f^{-1}}, \tag{3.44}$$

where $\bar{\rho}_g$ is the density of vapor, $\bar{\rho}_f$ is the density of liquid, ΔH is the heat of condensation.

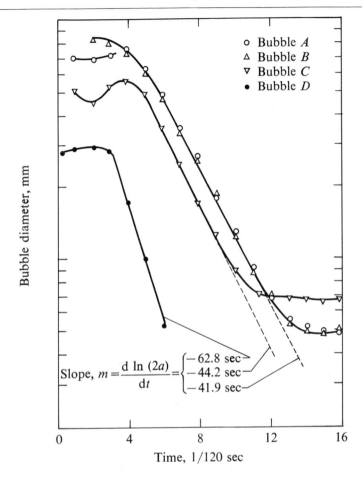

Figure 3.14 A semilog plot of bubble diameter vs. time shows rectification in collapsing region [L34].

If, however, $\bar{\rho}_g \ll \bar{\rho}_f$, which is true in most cases, we then have

$$h = 7.08a\,\Delta H\bar{\rho}_g . \tag{3.45}$$

The relation of mean or average heat-transfer coefficient is obtained by integrating Eq. (3.45) with respect to dQ and divided by the integral of dQ and assuming that $1/\bar{\rho}_f$ is negligible with respect to $1/\bar{\rho}_g$ and that the final diameter is much smaller than the initial diameter; thus,

$$h_m = \tfrac{3}{4}h_o , \tag{3.46}$$

where $h_o = 7.08\,\Delta H\bar{\rho}_g a_o$; and a_o is the initial diameter.

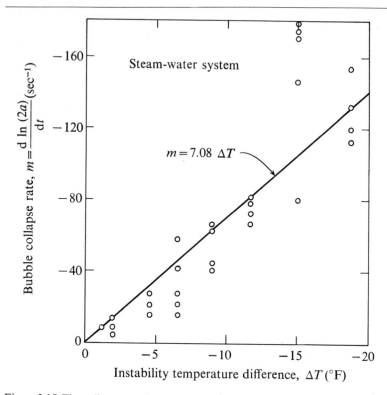

Figure 3.15 The collapse rate is proportional to the instability temperature difference ΔT. For bubbles of the same size, the rate of collapse increases with increasing ΔT [L34].

Many recent studies on flow boiling and condensation processes were reported in Proceedings of Third International Heat Transfer Conference, 1966.

3.6 Dynamics of a Vapor Bubble

Various effects enter into the dynamics of a vapor bubble in a liquid, depending on the particular stage of its growth or collapse, and the particular circumstance in which the bubble grows or collapses. They include the effects of viscosity, surface tension, the compressibility of the liquid, liquid inertia, and the rate of heat transfer from the bubble to the liquid due to condensation or evaporation. A complete survey was given by Florschuetz [F11].

Besant [B34] in 1859 formulated the collapse of a spherical cavity. Rayleigh [S95] gave results based on inertia effect of bubble collapse. Dergarabedian [D24] further included the effect of surface tension. Plesset [P21] investigated the influence of liquid inertia on cavitation bubbles, solved the momentum equations for the motion of the bubble wall, including the effect of surface tension for the case of constant internal pressure and time-varying external pressure. Bosnjakovic [B47] considered the growth of vapor bubbles in a boiling liquid as affected by heat transfer only.

Forster and Zuber [F19], and Plesset and Zwick [P24] showed that for bubble growth from equilibrium the temperature at the bubble wall quickly approached the saturation temperature corresponding to the external pressure and liquid inertia became negligible. Both gave approximate solutions for the temperature at the bubble wall [F16, P23]. The question of how to take proper account of the convective heat transfer due to spherically symmetrical motion of the liquid has not been settled [F17, Z9].

Birkhoff, Margulies, and Horning [B39] gave a similarity solution for the above asymptotic bubble growth problem based on heat-transfer effects only. Their solution contains the asymptotic solution of Plesset and Zwick as a limiting case.

A general set of governing equations and results for radially symmetric phase growth controlled by diffusion was reported by Scriven [S19]. His approach is similar to that used by Birkhoff et al. His calculations cover the case of growth controlled by both mass and heat transfer in a binary solution. Additional studies which assumed a heat-transfer controlled-growth process are those by Griffith [G39], Forster [F18], and Savic and Gosnell [S7]. They considered vapor bubbles growing in a liquid with both superheat and sub-cooling, and gave results for spherical bubbles as well as for the case of a hemispherical bubble growing on a plane heating surface.

Dergarabedian [D25] reported experimental radius-time data for bubbles growing in several liquids under superheats up to about 6°C in volume-heated systems. The data given in his earlier paper compared favorably with the theoretical solutions mentioned for the asymptotic phase of bubble growth [F19, P24].

Levenspiel [L34] gave radius-time data for steam bubbles collapsing in a bulk boiling system, where the collapse was initiated by an increase in the pressure of the system. The pressure differences correspond to subcoolings up to about 10°C, although radius-time data are given for only one degree of subcooling, about 5°C. The complete lack of agreement between his experimental results and the Rayleigh theory is believed to be due to the conditions of his experiments which were quite different from those treated by Plesset and Zwick [P25].

Most other experimental studies on the behavior of vapor bubbles have been performed in systems where subcooled nucleate boiling occurs at a heated surface or incipient cavitation occurs at the surface of a submerged body. Bubble histories are recorded photographically and include both the growth and collapse history of any particular bubble. The experimental results of this type were given by Knapp and Hollander [K22] on cavitation bubbles formed in water at room temperature flowing at 30–70 fps past a 1.5-caliber ogive body. The pressure distribution in the water flowing past the body was such that a reduced pressure existed at a point on the nose of the body causing the bubble to form. The bubble was then carried along the body into a region of higher pressure which caused the collapse. They compared their results for the collapse phase to Rayleigh's solution and obtained fairly good agreement.

Bubble histories in subcooled nucleate boiling were measured by Gunther and Kreith [G53], Gunther [G52], and Ellion [E9]. It was pointed out by Bankoff and Mikesell [B15] that for higher degrees of subcooling the growth and collapse curves obtained in these experiments are very nearly mirror images of each other and show strong similarities to bubble histories obtained in cavitating flow. On this basis, they considered the bubble to be controlled solely by liquid inertia and demonstrated that, when the Rayleigh curve was made to match the experimental point for the maximum bubble radius, a good fit was obtained for some growth-and-collapse data from Gunther [G52] and Ellion [E9]. Three different degrees of subcooling ranging from 20°C to 83°C were selected for the comparison.

In contrast, Zuber [Z8], also using the data of Ellion [E9] claimed reasonable agreement using a heat-transfer model for the growth phase and a purely inertia controlled process for the collapse phase.

Bankoff and Mikesell also noted that, for the case of a slightly subcooled liquid, experimental results [E9, G52, G53] showed that the time of collapse from the maximum radius was frequently two or more times greater than the growth time.

For bubbles collapsing in highly subcooled boiling, it was asserted that liquid inertia appears to be the dominant mechanism [B15, Z8]. However, for slightly subcooled boiling it was noted that experimental results have shown collapse times frequently two or three times greater than the growth times [B15]. The effect of heat transfer on the collapse rate was considered theoretically for one condition and found to retard the collapse only by an insignificant amount [P25, Z9].

Several investigators noted that the bubbles in their studies did not completely disappear and attributed this to the presence of permanent gases. Rayleigh [S95] gave a theoretical result for the collapse of a cavity containing *only* a permanent gas obeying Boyle's law. Nishiwaki and Klein [N10] reported the possibility that the presence of air in a steam-air bubble may reduce the condensation rate, and the results of a theoretical calculation were given for the following initial conditions: subcooling of 180°F, 0.25 in. initial bubble radius, initial air-mass fractions of 0.1, 0.5, and 0.8. They neglected the influence of liquid inertia on the collapse rate. Subsequently Nishiwaki [N9] suggested that the collapse of a vapor-air bubble is sensitively affected by the presence of air and the diffusion process of vapor in air might cause a marked effect on the mechanism of bubble collapse. A different model was suggested based on diffusion of vapor in the bubble and the liquid inertia.

When a vapor bubble collapses, most of the latent heat released by the condensing vapor is transferred into the liquid phase. The increase in temperature of the liquid at the bubble wall, however, raises the pressure of the vapor, thus tending to retard the collapse rate. These effects were taken into consideration by Plesset and Zwick [P25] in a numerical solution. Experimental work of Levenspiel [L34] on steam bubbles in water and a study by Zuber [Z8] based on nonuniform temperature field suggested possible ranges of significance of heat-transfer and inertia effects.

A study by Florschuetz and Chao [F11] further delineated these effects with experimental verification utilizing a zero-gravity system. By photographic measurement of bubble size made on a dropping frame, the sphericity of the bubble was assured.

Solution of basic conservation equations gives, for the inertia controlled collapse

$$\tau_I = \frac{t}{a_o}\sqrt{\frac{2}{3}\frac{\Delta P}{\bar{\rho}}} = \int_\gamma^1 \frac{x^{3/2}}{(1 - x^3)^{1/2}}\,dx, \tag{3.47}$$

where γ is a/a_o, t is the time, a is the bubble radius, and a_o is the initial radius; $\bar{\rho}$ is the density of the liquid, ΔP is the difference between the final system pressure P_∞ and the initial system pressure P_v. This relation is shown in Fig. 3.16.

In the case where heat-transfer controls, the Plesset-Zwick "zero-order" temperature solution gives

$$\tau_H = 4(N_{\mathrm{Ja}})^2\,\frac{\bar{\kappa}t}{a_o^2} = \frac{1}{3}\left(\frac{2}{\gamma} + \gamma^2 - 3\right), \tag{3.48}$$

where (N_{Ja}) is the Jakob number ($= \bar{\rho}c\,\Delta T/\bar{\rho}_v L$; $\bar{\rho}$, c are the density and specific heat of the liquid respectively, T_{sat}, ΔT is the difference between the final saturation temperature and the system temperature T_∞; $\bar{\rho}_v$ is the reference vapor density, L is the latent heat), $\bar{\kappa}$ is the thermal conductivity of the liquid. Figure 3.17 shows the relation.

With the relation

$$B = \frac{(N_{\mathrm{Ja}})^2}{\sqrt{c}}, \tag{3.49}$$

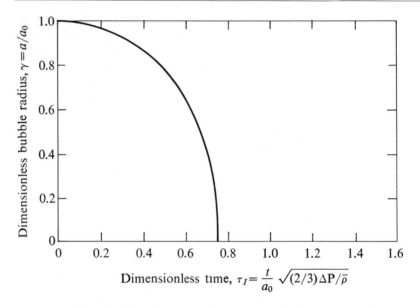

Figure 3.16 Inertia-controlled collapse—Rayleigh solution [F11].

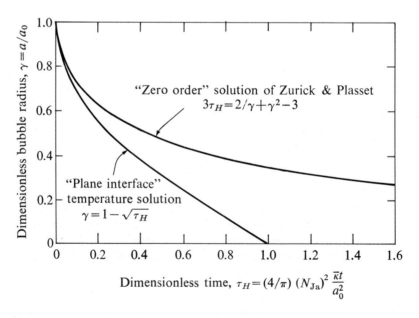

Figure 3.17 Heat-transfer controlled collapse [F11].

where $c = a_o^2 \Delta P / \bar{\rho} \bar{\kappa}^2$, the experimental results are shown in Fig. 3.18, including results of Levenspiel. To account for the effective temperature difference at an arbitrary instant, a factor ψ is introduced,

$$\psi = \frac{2}{(\Delta T)(\Delta P)} \int_T^{T\text{sat}} [P_\infty - P_v] \, dt, \tag{3.50}$$

modifying B by

$$B_{\text{eff}} = \psi B. \tag{3.51}$$

It was shown that for $B_{\text{eff}} < 0.05$, heat-transfer controls the collapse rate; inertia controls when $B_{\text{eff}} > 0.05$.

Growth of vapor bubbles in a rapidly heated liquid was studied by Zuberwick [Z10] with determination of the asymptotic growth rates.

Vibrations of a globule were first treated by Rayleigh [L5], who gave

$$\omega_n^2 = n(n - 1)(n + 2) \frac{\sigma}{[(n + 1)\bar{\rho}_p + n\bar{\rho}]a^3}, \tag{3.52}$$

where ω_n is the natural circular frequency, σ is the surface tension; $\bar{\rho}_p$, $\bar{\rho}$ are the densities of fluid inside and outside the globule, n is the mode of vibration. Detailed analysis of dynamics of a gas bubble in an oscillating pressure field by Plesset and Hsieh [P22] showed that even at the high-frequency limit, the bubble demonstrates an isothermal behavior. Vibrations due to forced deformations of viscous liquid globules were studied by Hinze [H39] with external pressure distribution on the globule surface expressed in terms of zonal harmonics.

3.7 Bubble Velocity [C40]

It was found that the way in which most bubbles were formed gives rise to a high initial velocity, and also that in the range 0.1–0.4-cm radius the bubble followed a helical path during its ascent. Very large and very small bubbles followed a straight path; in the case of large bubbles the shape was that of a mushroom. With a bubble generator the following items were studied;

(a) Effect of tube diameter—with bubbles of about 0.1-cm radius, the wall effect of the column of liquid is noticeable up to about 10–15 cm diameter. The effect is small but increases greatly as the tube diameter is decreased.

(b) Effect of liquid viscosity—data given in Fig. 3.19.

(c) Effect of bubble size—the most convenient way of producing very small or very large bubbles of known size is to produce them singly rather than as a stream from a jet.

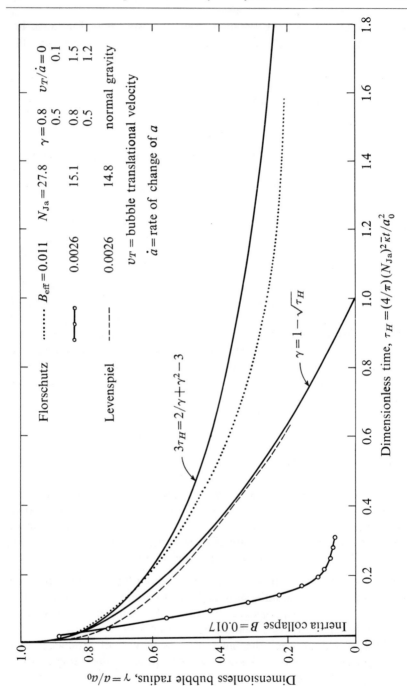

Figure 3.18 Comparison of experiments to theory [F11].

With bubbles of less than 0.10-cm radius, the wall effect is small, and towards 0.01-cm radius, it becomes almost negligible for liquid columns of 5–15-cm diameter. Velocity of successive bubbles is higher than that for single bubbles of the same size, particularly in the region of 0.1-cm radius, due to reduced effect of the wakes (Sec. 6.3).

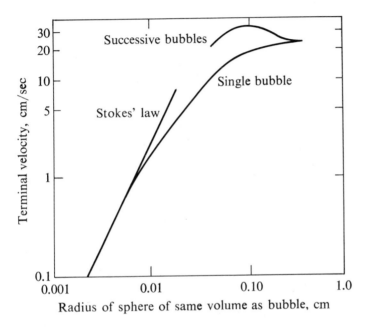

Figure 3.19 Variation in terminal velocity with bubble size [C40].

Comparison of the relations between volume of bubble and diameter of the nozzle was made by Datta [D9]. Figure 3.20 gives the terminal velocity of bubbles in various ranges for air-water systems. Figure 3.21 plots the variation bubble volume and bubble velocity as a function of the height from the nozzle.

Motion of Large Bubbles [O1]—The linear relationship between velocity and radius of a bubble has been found to extend to a radius of about 1.2 mm (Miyagi). For air bubbles in water, this size may be taken as the dividing line between large and small bubbles.

The velocity of small bubbles appears to be controlled by viscosity and surface tension, whereas both the relationship between velocity and radius and the appearance of the motion point to turbulence as the controlling factor in the motion of large bubbles (Fig. 3.22).

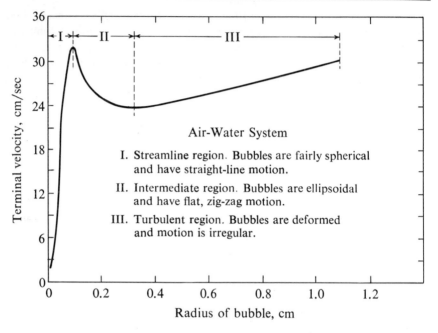

Figure 3.20 Flow regimes of bubble motion [D9].

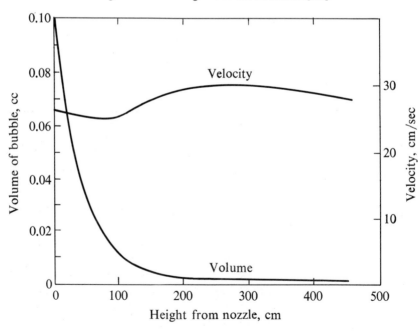

Figure 3.21 Velocity and size of bubble at different heights from nozzle [D9].

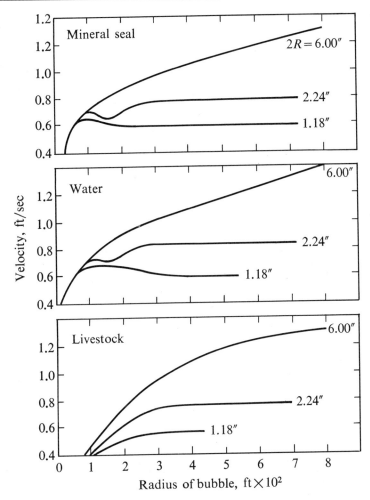

Figure 3.22 Air bubble in liquids [O1].

A study of the motion of a swarm of gas bubbles rising through a vertical liquid column was performed by Verschoor [V9]:

Let l_o be the length of liquid column, A the cross-sectional area, $\dot{V}_G$ the gas rate of the stream (volume/unit time), l the length of the column after the gas stream is introduced into the liquid column, a the average radius of a bubble, n_p the number of bubbles per unit volume, and v_p the average bubble velocity. The following relations are of interest.

(a) The amount of gas passing any cross section is constant, hence

$$\dot{V}_G = A v_p n_p \tfrac{4}{3}\pi a^3.$$

(b) The gas volume in the extended liquid column is

$$A(l - l_o) = Aln_p \tfrac{4}{3}\pi a^3,$$

giving:

$$v_p = \frac{\dot{\mathscr{V}}_G}{A} \frac{l}{l - l_o}. \qquad (3.53)$$

Kaiszling correlated the data obtained by Schmidt and his co-workers by using combinations of the three groups:

$$\frac{\text{Capillarity group}}{N_{\text{Re}}} = \frac{v_p \bar{\mu}}{\sigma}$$

$$\frac{\text{Capillarity group}}{N_{\text{Fr}}} = \frac{\bar{\rho}g(2a)^2}{\sigma}$$

$$\frac{(\text{Capillarity group})^3}{(N_{\text{Re}})^4 N_{\text{Fr}}} = \frac{\bar{\mu}^4 g}{\sigma^3 \bar{\rho}}.$$

Kaiszling thus arrived at

$$\frac{v_p n_p}{\sigma} = f\left(\frac{l - l_o}{l} \cdot \frac{g\bar{\mu}^4}{\bar{\rho}\sigma^3} \cdot \frac{(2R)^2 g\bar{\rho}}{\sigma}\right), \qquad (3.54)$$

where the Reynolds number is given by

$$\frac{v_p^2}{2a} \bigg/ \frac{\bar{\nu}v_p}{4a^2} = \frac{2av_p}{\bar{\nu}} = N_{\text{Re}},$$

the Froude number by

$$\frac{v_p^2}{2a} \bigg/ g = \frac{v_p^2}{2ag} = N_{\text{Fr}}$$

and the Weber number by

$$\frac{v_p^2}{2a} \bigg/ \frac{2a\sigma}{\bar{\rho}(2a)^3} = \frac{v_p^2 \bar{\rho}(2a)}{\sigma} = N_{\text{We}}.$$

His conclusions are that the speed of the rising vapor bubbles is mostly influenced by the vapor content of the vapor-liquid column and by the second group, which could be varied by changing the pressure of the system. The influence of the group containing the tube diameter $2R$ increases as its numerical value decreases; i.e., as R decreases.

The nature of passage of bubbles through the liquid column is demonstrated by two aspects, the gas content of the liquid-gas mixture and the bubble velocity.

The gas content increases with the gas rate, but here we see that a maximum is reached after which the gas content drops to a minimum, gradually increasing again as the gas rate is further increased. The first critical point coincides with the appearance of large bubbles besides the small ones. A further increase of the gas rate after the second critical point yields more large bubbles (Fig. 3.23).

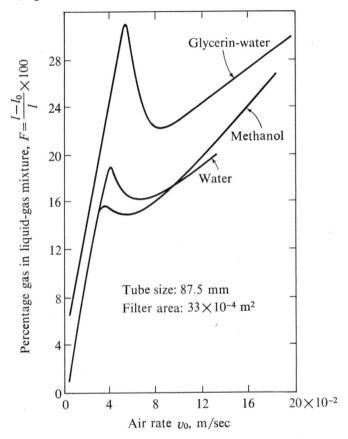

Figure 3.23 Influence of overall gas rate on gas content of a liquid-gas mixture [V9].

3.8 Atomization of Liquids

Atomization of a liquid may be carried out in a gas or in another immiscible liquid. Although the former is by far the more popular, formation of liquid drops in another immiscible liquid is significant to the extraction process [A6].

Elzinga and Banchero [E13], Hu and Kintner [H61] studied the breakup of several organic liquids in water. Agreement of basic relations was obtained with the case of atomization of a liquid in a gas.

A survey by Browning [B64] showed that it is comparatively simple to produce drops larger than a few hundred microns. The general method of atomizing to small sizes rests with the principle of instability of thin filaments or sheets of a liquid, and breakup gives rise to small droplets. Details on atomization were given by Marshall [M13].

Droplets of 1-μ radius may be produced by breaking up of air bubbles at the surface of a mass of water [B40].

Spinning-Disk Atomization—Hottel, Williams, and Simpson [H54] and Hall and Diederichsen [H5] produced streams of droplets by using a spinning disk. Tanasawa [T2] experimented with disks of various shapes. Walton and Prewett [W5] gave the relation

$$2a = \frac{3.8(\sigma/D\bar{\rho}_p)^{\frac{1}{2}}}{\omega} \tag{3.55}$$

where $2a$ is the diameter of the drop, D is the disk diameter, ω is the angular velocity of the disk, σ is the surface tension of the liquid, $\bar{\rho}_p$ is its density.

Pressure Atomization—Pressure atomization consists of forcing a liquid through an orifice. Giffen and Muraszew [G14] published a very complete text on the atomization of liquid fuels. De Juhasz [D20] has determined the effect of many different variables on the process of spraying: pressure drop across the orifice, viscosity of the liquid, and the density of air. Tyler [T56] verified the work of Rayleigh [S94], which is applicable for those liquid jets experiencing little friction drag from the surrounding medium [H15]. A liquid jet under the condition of high surface friction does not immediately break up according to Rayleigh's theory. As shown by Castleman [C10], the jet first breaks into fine ligaments which later undergo Rayleigh breakup. Secondary atomization through breakup of drops first formed was studied by Littaye [L48] and Ohnesorge [O2].

Panasenkov [M30] studied the influence of turbulence on the atomization of a liquid jet. Turbulence contributes to shorten the jet prior to breakup. Miesse [M30, M31, M32] investigated the effect of time lag of jet breakup on combustion stability, and performed basic experiments. A theory of breakup of thin liquid sheets produced by tangential nozzles was studied by York, Stubbs, and Tek [Y4]. Their basic consideration included a force balance between interfacial tension and aerodynamic forces, leading to a stability criterion. Marshall [M13] summarizes aspects of jet breakup, performance characteristics of atomizers, and drop-size distribution.

Gas Atomization—The usefulness of air atomization was shown specifically by Joyce [J23]. Lewis, Edwards, Goglia, Rice, and Smith [L37] found excellent correlation between the measured sizes of drops atomized by high velocity gas streams with the empirical relations of Nukiyama and Tanasawa [N11]. Duffie and Marshall [D40] gave theoretical analysis of the breakup characteristics of a viscous-jet atomizer and verified their result by high-speed photography. The use of high-velocity vaporizers with high-velocity, high-temperature, air stream at the throat of a venturi was studied by Comings, Adams, and Shippee [C38]. Shattering of a liquid jet and drops by a stream of air was studied by Lane [L11] and Clark [C31].

It is well known that when a liquid droplet or jet is subjected to a gas velocity in excess of some critical value, it will disintegrate or shatter. Such a behavior has been the source of nonlinear oscillatory combustion in rocket engines. Measurement of critical breakup conditions was made by Lane [L11] and Volynskii [V14] and the measurements on water jet by transverse shock waves were made by Morrell [M46]. Two general types of breakup were observed. One is by distortion of the droplets forming irregular ligaments; another is blown out of liquid in the form of a bubble. The drop may assume a lenticular shape and liquid streams from its rim. Morrell [M46] further proposed a generalized model for each type of breakup.

For a nonviscous liquid suddenly exposed to a gas stream at constant velocity u, Hinze [H39] gave the critical condition as

$$\frac{\delta/a}{N_{\mathrm{We}}} = \frac{\delta/a}{\bar{\rho}u^2 a/\sigma} = -0.17, \tag{3.56}$$

where δ is the displacement in the radial direction, $\bar{\rho}$ is the density of the gas. The case $\delta = a$ agrees with the critical value of $N_{\mathrm{We}} \sim 6$ given by Lane [L11] and Volynskii [V14]. Morrell [M46] gave -0.2 for the above ratio when applied to a jet. Morrell showed that for an action time t_a, the natural period τ of a jet is

$$\tau = 2\pi\sqrt{\frac{\bar{\rho}_p a^3}{6\sigma}}, \tag{3.57}$$

where $\bar{\rho}_p$ is the density of the liquid, and the decay of dynamic pressure is given by

$$\bar{\rho}u^2 = \bar{\rho}_0 u_0^2 \exp\left(-\frac{t}{t_a}\right), \tag{3.58}$$

$\bar{\rho}$ is the density of the gas and subscript 0 refers to initial conditions. Figure 3.24 gives $\tau/2\pi t_a$ vs. $(\delta/a)/(N_{\mathrm{We}})$. For a sphere the quantity 6 in Eq. (3.57) is replaced by 8.

The breakup by slipping action was studied by Taylor [T10], who computed the liquid boundary-layer thickness and the slipping rate from this boundary layer, leading to the first approximation

$$\frac{\bar{\rho}_0 u_0^2}{(\zeta T \alpha / \beta)} = \text{const.,} \tag{3.59}$$

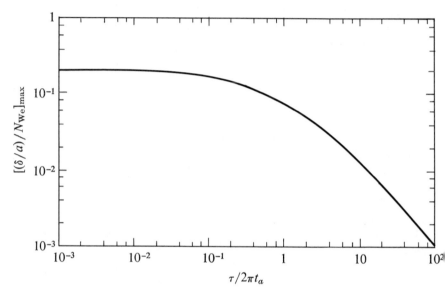

Figure 3.24 Maximum nondimensional displacement of N_{We} as a function of $\tau/2\pi t_a$ [M 45]

where ζ is the ratio of actual tensile strength to the ideal value, T is the absolute temperature, α is the coefficient of thermal expression, β is the coefficient of compressibility. Morrell [M45] suggested the model as

$$\left. \begin{array}{ll} f\left(\dfrac{\tau}{2\pi t_a}\right)\dfrac{\bar{\rho}_0 u_0^2 a}{\sigma} = K; & \text{for } t_a \geq \tau, \quad a \leq a_1 \\[3mm] \dfrac{\rho_0 u_0^2}{\zeta T \alpha / \beta} \sim H; & \text{for } t_a \leq \tau, \quad a \geq a_1 \end{array} \right\}, \tag{3.60}$$

where K and H are constants, and a_1 is the value of radius a at $t_a = \tau$. These conditions were confirmed by most experimental data.

Ultrasonic Atomization—Formation of liquid drops by ultrasonic excitation of a bulk-liquid surface was studied by Crawford [C44], McCubbin [M21], and Lang [L12]. Lang obtained a drop-size frequency relation with experimental verification. Peskin [P18] examined the behavior of a liquid film under an oscillating inertial force, with particular emphasis on the conditions resulting in capillary wave instability. Peskin correlated film thickness δ, amplitude α, and frequency ω of the excitation; the droplet radius is given by

$$2a = \left[\frac{4\pi^3\sigma}{\bar{\rho}_p\omega^2}\right]^{\frac{1}{3}} \qquad (3.61)$$

for large δ. Experimental verification was given by Doyle, Mokler, Perron, and Little [D35].

Electrostatic Atomization—In electrostatic atomization, the initial instabilities grow rapidly as they do in spinning-disk and ultrasonic atomization. The resultant projections resemble small jets. In the spinning-disk and ultrasonic cases these jets are unstable and break up rapidly. In electrostatic atomization, Vonnegut and Neubauer [V16], Nayyar and Murty [N2] showed that the electric field tends to stabilize any jet formed. As a result the large amplitude stage can persist and the projections can be drawn out into thin jets which then break up. Experimental photographs of Luther and Paterson [L63] show these jets.

Peskin and Lawler [P17] summarized and generalized the mechanisms of atomization of a liquid. They showed, for electrostatic atomization,

$$2a \sim \frac{\sigma}{\epsilon_r E^2}, \qquad (3.62)$$

where ϵ_r is the dielectric constant and E is the applied electric field.

Study of the resonance breakup mechanism [P17] showed that for natural frequency given by Eq. (3.52), the Strouhal number N_{S1} is given by

$$N_{S1} = \frac{2a\omega_n}{v} = \left(\frac{8\sigma}{\bar{\mu}v}\right)\left(\frac{\bar{\rho}}{\bar{\rho}_p}\right)(n^3 + n^2 - 2n)^{\frac{1}{2}}(N_{Re})^{-\frac{1}{2}}, \qquad (3.63)$$

for $N_{Re} = 2a\bar{\rho}v/\bar{\mu}$, v is the relative velocity and $\sigma/\bar{\mu}v = N_{Re}/N_{We}$. Elzinga's data for vortex-discharge frequency gives

$$\frac{2a\omega_n}{v} = 7.76 \times 10^{-6}N_{Re}^{1.63}, \qquad (3.64)$$

for $N_{Re} < 2000$, and

$$\frac{2a\omega_n}{v} = 1.9 \qquad (3.65)$$

for $N_{Re} > 2000$ (Fig. 3.25).

The maximum stable drop diameter was shown to be

$$2a \sim \frac{k\sigma}{\bar{\rho}v^2}, \qquad (3.66)$$

with k ranging from 6 to 9.7 as given by Hinze [H40] and Hu and Kintner [H61].

Drop-size distribution for fine atomization can be treated according to probability laws as given in Sec. 1.3. Figure 3.26 illustrates typical results of measurements assembled by Ranz [R3] in his comprehensive study. Particle size distribution in sprays was further studied by Williams [W23].

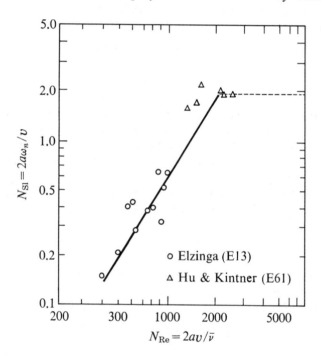

Figure 3.25 Vortex shedding frequency vs. droplet diameter for liquid-liquid systems [P17].

Measurement of drop size distribution based on electrical conductivity of the liquid was given by Wicks and Dukler [D39].

Aerosol Generation—The preparation, deposition, and nucleation of aerosols were presented by La Mer and Hochberg [L6, L7]. In an aerosol generator, nuclei for condensation are supplied by heating salt to just below red heat and are carried through the generator, where they are thoroughly mixed with heated vapor and air. Droplets form around the nuclei as the mixture is cooled. Detailed design of the aerosol generator was presented by Sinclair [S36]. The size (up to 40 μ) of the droplets produced is governed by the mass of the condensable vapor and the number of nuclei and the temperature which also influences the uniformity. The growth of salt particles from the sea by condensation of moisture in the atmosphere was formulated analytically by Keith and Arons [K11]. The particle-size spectrum of a condensing vapor was further studied by Friedlander [F27].

A dense fog of liquid droplets was produced in a venturi atomizer by Johnstone, Field, and Tassler [J18]. Durbin [D42] treated the formation of particles by condensation in a supersaturated hypersonic air flow.

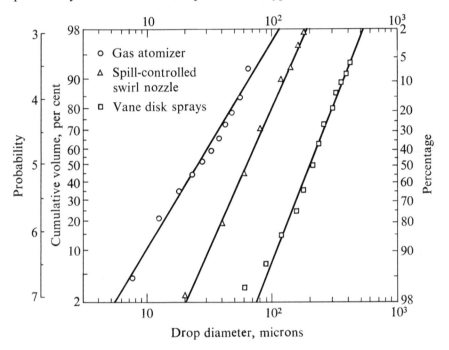

Figure 3.26 Typical drop-size distributions of sprays from nozzles of various types [R3].

SUMMARY OF BASIC CONCEPTS

Fluid Particle in Uniform Motion
   Drag of fluid spheres—Hadamard [H3], Rybczynski (1911) [R53]
   Boundary-layer effect—Chao (1962) [C15]

Bubbles
   Bubble collapse—Besant (1859) [B34]
   Interaction of momentum and heat transfer—Bosnjakovic (1930) [B47]
   Bubble-wall temperature—Forster and Zuber [F19], Plesset and Zwick (1954) [P24]

Droplets
 Atomization due to instability of jet—Rayleigh (1886) [S94]
 Critical breakup condition—Volynskii (1948) [V14], Lane (1951) [L11]
 Ultrasonic atomization—McCubbin (1953) [M21]
 Electrostatic atomization—Vonnegut and Neubauer (1952) [V16]

Condensation
 Nucleation of condensation—La Mer and Hochberg (1949) [L7]

4 | Pipe Flow of a Suspension

Measurements of momentum transfer in fully developed pipe flow are useful because the results are directly applicable to the estimation of power requirement for transferring a fluid over a distance. More importantly, fully developed pipe flow has been a favorite configuration in the studies of fluid mechanics because of its ability to develop fundamental understanding. This is seen from considering the axial component of the Navier-Stokes equation when applied to steady laminar flow in cylindrical coordinates with axial symmetry in the absence of body forces, or [S13]

$$\rho v \frac{\partial u}{\partial r} + \rho u \frac{\partial u}{\partial z} = - \frac{\partial P}{\partial z} + \mu \left[\frac{\partial^2 u}{\partial r^2} + \frac{1}{r} \frac{\partial u}{\partial r} + \frac{\partial^2 u}{\partial z^2} \right], \qquad (4.1)$$

where ρ is the density of the fluid, μ its viscosity, u, v are velocities in the axial (z) and radial (r) directions, P is the pressure. When applied to fully developed pipe flow, $v = 0$, $\partial u / \partial z = 0$, and Eq. (4.1) reduces with approximation to

$$0 = - \frac{\partial P}{\partial z} + \mu \left[\frac{\partial^2 u}{\partial r^2} + \frac{1}{r} \frac{\partial u}{\partial r} \right], \qquad (4.2)$$

which is one of a few cases in fluid mechanics where exact solution is possible to give velocity distribution of Poiseuille motion [S13].

Fully developed pipe flow is also a useful configuration for heat-transfer studies because of applications in tubular heat exchangers and rigorous simplification of heat-transfer equations (the Graetz [E1] method as applied to Poiseuille motion).

For these reasons, earlier measurements of flow of suspensions were made on pipe flow (transfer lines), leading to recognition of basic phenomena and relations.

133

Although transport of solid particles by a fluid ranges from the condition of flow through a packed bed of solid particles, fluidization and transport [W20], we shall take up fully developed motion of transport first because of its simplicity and special significance, while leaving the other range for a later treatment (Chap. 9).

4.1 Friction Factor

Studies of flow of gas-solid suspensions began with pneumatic conveyance of grains. The earliest publication on pipe flow of a gas-solid suspension was one by Gasterstaedt in 1924 [G7]. This study and others in the years following [B18, B30, B45, C32, F3, G12, P20, R31] concern measurement of friction, pressure drop and mass flow in flow through pipes and bends. All consistently reported that loading of solid particles always results in an increase in pressure drop and friction factor.

Under the premise that addition of solid particles would always lead to higher pressure drop per unit length of pipe, attempts toward generalization include that of Belden and Kassel [B30], Clark, Charles, and Richardson [C32], Hariu and Molstad [H13], Rose and Barnacle [R31] on correlation of excess pressure drop due to solid particles with a modified pipe-flow Reynolds number; Gauvin and Torobin [T45] on generalization from single-particle behavior; Kada and Hanratty [K1] on the effect of presence of solid particles on the local turbulence in the fluid. Ratio of particle size to pipe diameter was found to have no effect by Albright, Holden, Simons, and Schmidt [A5], Farber [F3], Korn [K27], in addition to the above authors. Dense phase was investigated by Korn [K27], and Wen and Simons [W12]. Halstrom [H6] reported cases in which addition of solid particles (glass beads of 200-μ size) decreased the pressure drop in pipe flow below that for clean air flow; Richardson and McLeman [R16] also reported the "unpredictable" pressure gradient over a certain range. Conclusive measurements were then reported by Thomas in a series of publications [T21 to T29], and he attributed the decrease in pressure drop over a certain range, due to the presence of solid particles, to the non-Newtonian nature of the suspension. A comprehensive review of articles published in this area was given by Doig and Roper [D31]. A review of correlations for pressure loss and holdup in two-phase flow was given by Dukler, Wicks, and Cleveland [D39], followed by a similarity analysis.

As in the case of flow of a single-phase fluid, generalization of pressure drops in pipe flow has been made in terms of friction factors. Recognizing that the pressure drop (ΔP) over a length (L) of pipe of diameter ($2R$) is related to the total shear stress at the wall (τ_t) by

$$\tau_t = \frac{\Delta P}{4L/2R},$$ (4.3)

the friction factor C_f can be expressed as

$$C_f = \frac{\tau_t}{\frac{1}{8}\bar{\rho}U^2},$$ (4.4)

where $\bar{\rho}$ is the density of the fluid material and U the mean velocity of the fluid phase. For pipe-flow Reynolds number defined as

$$N_{\rm Re} = \frac{2RU\bar{\rho}}{\bar{\mu}},$$ (4.5)

where $\bar{\mu}$ is the viscosity of the fluid, the friction factors of a single-phase Newtonian fluid in smooth pipes are given by [S13]

$$C_f = \frac{64}{N_{\rm Re}},$$ (4.6)

over the laminar flow range, and, in the turbulent flow range

$$C_f = \frac{0.3164}{(N_{\rm Re})^{0.25}},$$ (4.7)

for $N_{\rm Re} < 10^5$ as given by Blasius, and

$$\frac{1}{\sqrt{C_f}} = 2.0 \log{(N_{\rm Re}\sqrt{C_f})} - 0.8,$$ (4.8)

for $N_{\rm Re} < 3.4 \times 10^6$ according to Nikuradse. It is natural that in earlier studies, attempts were made toward modifying Eqs. (4.6) to (4.8) for correlating flow of suspensions.

Of the earlier studies, the method of approach of Rose and Barnacle [R31] may be considered typical. They subdivided the overall pressure drop ΔP as consisting of ΔP_f due to fluid alone as given by the above friction factors and ΔP_p due to solid particles, as shown in Fig. 4.1. Figure 4.1 gives the pressure drop ΔP over a 6-ft length due to flow of mustard seeds (2000 μ, suspended in air at room condition) in horizontal pipe of $1\frac{3}{4}$-in. diameter, with flow rate $\dot{M}_p$ from zero to 300 lb/hr. This scheme gives useful and logical results as long as $\Delta P > 0$. Difficulty arises when $\Delta P_p < 0$, which was observed by Richardson and McLeman [R16] and Halstrom [H6].

Thomas [T21, T22] studied aqueous thorium oxide suspensions as non-Newtonian fluids. The particle sizes were 0.7 μ or larger (determined by electron micrographs), with approximately logarithmic normal distribution. Experiments were made with volume fraction of solids up to 0.10 (1000 g of solid per kg of water), velocities up to 43 fps in tubes with 0.318 and 1.030 in. diameters.

The non-Newtonian character of the suspension was seen from measurements made with a capillary-tube viscometer of $\frac{1}{8}$-in. tube diameter and $L/2R$ of 1000. The relation between the rate of shearing strain, du/dr, and the shear

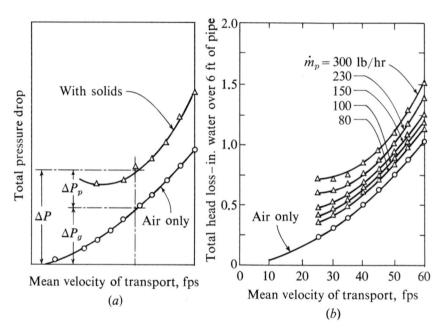

Figure 4.1 Typical results of measurement by Rose and Barnacle [R31].
(a) Composition of the total pressure drop ΔP.
(b) Typical experimental curves of mustard seed at 0° incline for $1\frac{3}{4}$-in. pipe diameter.

stress is shown by the typical shear diagram in Fig. 4.2. At high rates of shear, the slurry curve (AB) is almost parallel to that of the suspending medium (water). At low rates of shear (BCD), marked deviation was observed. At very low rates of shear, data spreads over the region DEF. These characteristics were accounted for by recognizing the following.

(a) The apparent viscosity μ_a is given by

$$\mu_a = \frac{\tau}{du/dr}, \qquad (4.9)$$

which decreases from a large value at low shear rates to a limiting value at high shear rates; therefore data of shear stress as a function of shear rate is required.

(b) The "effective" viscosity μ_e is given by

$$\mu_e = \frac{\tau_w}{8U/2R} = \frac{2R\,\Delta P/4L}{8U/2R}, \tag{4.10}$$

where τ_w is shear stress at the wall. This relation is shown by the pseudo-shear diagram in Fig. 4.3. The difficulty of correlation by μ_e is the pronounced

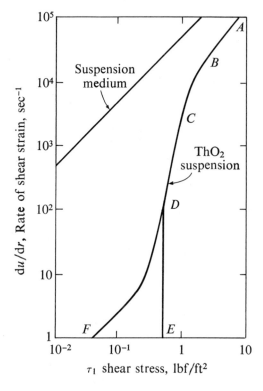

Figure 4.2 Typical laminar-flow shear diagram for ThO_2 suspension [T21].

wall effect with small-diameter capillary tubes, which is believed to be due to a layer of pure suspending medium adjacent to the wall [M4, M41].

(c) The yield stress, τ_y, as suggested by Bingham [B36] is such that

$$\frac{du}{dr} = \frac{\tau - \tau_y}{\eta}, \tag{4.11}$$

for $\tau > \tau_y$; and

$$\frac{du}{dr} = 0, \tag{4.12}$$

for $\tau \leq \tau_y$; η is called the coefficient of rigidity. When applied to a circular pipe, Eqs. (4.11) and (4.12) give

$$\frac{8U}{2R} = \frac{1}{\eta}\left[\tau_w - \frac{4}{3}\tau_y + \frac{1}{3}\frac{\tau_y^4}{\tau_w^3}\right]. \tag{4.13}$$

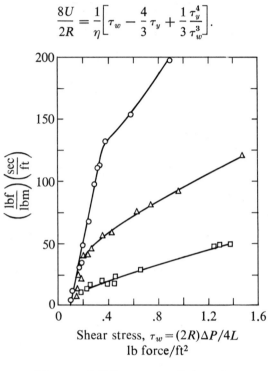

Shear stress, $\tau_w = (2R)\Delta P/4L$
lb force/ft²

	2R	L/2R	Suspension
o	.124	1000	Density: 104 lb/cu ft
△	.318	535	$\tau_y = 0.075$ lbf/ft²
□	1.030	196	$\mu = .0019$ lb/ft sec
			$= 2.9$ C.P.

Figure 4.3 Pseudo-shear diagram for ThO₂ slurry showing agreement of data taken in laminar range with tubes of different diameters [T22].

For $\tau_w \gg \tau_y$, Eq. (4.13) reduces to give

$$\mu_e = \eta\left[1 + \frac{\tau_y 2R}{6\eta U}\right]. \tag{4.14}$$

η is thus the limiting viscosity at high shear rates. The yield stress τ_y was shown to be related to the volume fraction solid, ϕ, according to

$$\tau_y = k_1\phi^3, \tag{4.15}$$

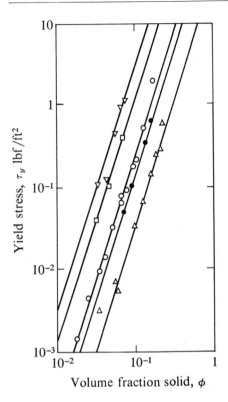

Material	Particle characteristics	
	$2a$, micron	σ
$\triangledown$ ThO$_2$	0.40	1.6
$\square$ Graphite	2.35	1.6
$\circ$ ThO	0.74	2.2
$\bullet$ ThO	1.35	1.4
$\triangle$ Kaolin	2.85	4.0

$\sigma = \log.$ std. deviation

Figure 4.4 Effect of volume fraction solids on suspension yield stress [T23].

where k_1 is a constant coefficient having the dimension of shear stress. τ_y for suspensions of thorium oxide and other materials is given in Fig. 4.4.

Redefining the friction factor [Eq. (4.4)] as

$$C'_f = \frac{\tau}{\frac{1}{2}\rho_m U^2}, \tag{4.16}$$

where ρ_m is the density of the suspension, Thomas introduced, in place of the Blasius relation in Eq. (4.7),

$$C'_f = B_1(N_{\text{Re}})_m^{-b}, \tag{4.17}$$

for turbulent flow where

$$B_1 = 0.079\left(\frac{\bar{\mu}}{\eta}\right)^{0.48}, \tag{4.18}$$

$$b = 0.25\left(\frac{\bar{\mu}}{\eta}\right)^{0.15}, \tag{4.19}$$

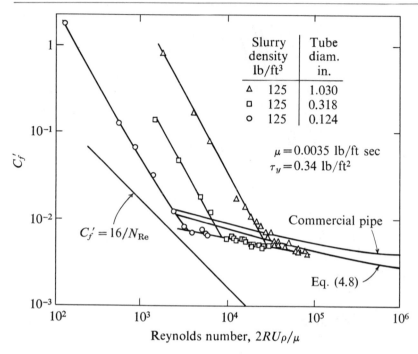

Figure 4.5 Friction factor-Reynolds number relation for aqueous ThO$_2$ slurries [T21].

and

$$(N_{\text{Re}})_m = \frac{2RU\rho_m}{\eta},$$ (4.20)

where $\bar{\mu}$ is the viscosity of the fluid at bulk mean temperature. A typical relation is shown in Fig. 4.5. Thomas further introduced, for core velocity U,

$$\frac{u}{U} = \left(\frac{y}{R}\right)^{1/m}$$ (4.21)

with

$$m = \frac{2-b}{b}.$$ (4.22)

The relation between m and τ_y is as follows.

m	τ_y (lb/sq ft)
7	0.003
8	0.015
9	0.055
10	0.200
11	0.55

Thomas has thus shown conclusively cases in which the solid particles contributed to lower friction factor in the turbulent flow range. If N_{Re} is used in Fig. 4.5 instead of $(N_{Re})_m$, the lowering of friction factor from that of single-phase fluid will be more emphatic. In the meantime Tien and Quan [T35] explored heat transfer of a suspension in pipe and also found lowering of the heat-transfer coefficient over a range and attributed this to a possible change in velocity profile of the fluid.

In an effort to understand why, over a certain range of flow conditions, the presence of solids contributes to lowering of friction factor in fully developed turbulent pipe flow, Soo and Trezek [S58] explored the flow of a magnesia-air suspension. Measurements by Soo, Trezek, Dimick, and Hohnstreiter [S72] showed that, within the range of loading where such a phenomenon occurred, the velocity profile of the gaseous phase was unaltered by the presence of the solid particles.

It is recognized that, within the range where decrease in pipe-flow shear stress occurs with increase in solid loading, the mean concentration of solid particles is such that particles are ten or more diameters apart, so that particle-particle interaction can be neglected. The net shear stress τ at the wall then includes shear stress τ_{gp} in the gas with the presence of solid particles and that due to collision of solid particles τ_p with the wall, or

$$\tau = \tau_{gp} + \tau_p . \tag{4.23}$$

To determine the shear stress τ_{gp} from measured τ, we need to determine τ_p. The shear stress due to collision was derived earlier [S52]:

$$\tau_p = \frac{1}{2\sqrt{\pi}} \rho_{pw} U_{pw} \sqrt{\langle u_{pw}^2 \rangle}, \tag{4.24}$$

where U_{pw} is the mean-particle phase velocity at the wall and $\sqrt{\langle u_{pw}^2 \rangle}$ is the intensity of turbulent motion of particles at the wall. Due to the variation of stream turbulence velocities near the wall as measured by Laufer [L24], the actual value of $\sqrt{\langle u_{pw}^2 \rangle}$ cannot be accurately predicted. However, the mass rate of collision per unit area is

$$\dot{m}_p = m\tfrac{1}{4} \sqrt{\langle u_{pw}^2 \rangle} n_{pw}$$

$$= \tfrac{1}{4} \rho_{pw} \sqrt{\langle u_{pw}^2 \rangle}, \tag{4.25}$$

where m is the mass of a particle and n_{pw} is the number density of particles at the wall. Hence

$$\tau_p = \frac{2}{\sqrt{\pi}} \dot{m}_{pw} U_{pw} , \tag{4.26}$$

and since U_{pw} can be measured accurately [S72], we can determine τ_p by measuring $\dot{m}_{pw}$, the mass rate of collision at the wall.

$\dot{m}_{pw}$ is measured by using a plug mounted with a piece of double-sided Scotch tape, which is then inserted flush with the pipe wall where fully developed turbulent pipe flow exists. By exposing the tape to the suspension for various durations, as long as consistent procedures and speed are used for all insertions and removals, the slope of the curve of accumulated weight

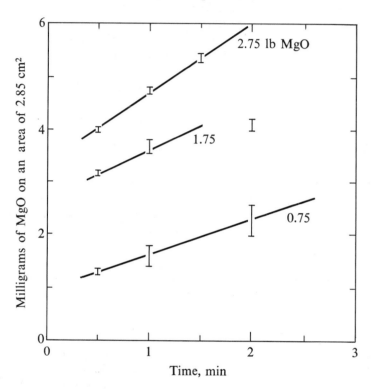

Figure 4.6 Mass of solid particles at different times on scotch tape (35-μ MgO in air 5-in. I.D. brass pipe, $U = 140$ fps [S72]. Size distribution in Fig. 4.18).

on the tape vs. time gives the mass collision rate as shown in Fig. 4.6 for 35-μ magnesia particles in air at 140 fps mean velocity. Figure 4.7 gives the mass rate of collision for various mass ratios m_p^*. It is seen that at 2.75 lb loading (in 1.67 lb of air), the collision rate with the wall amounts only to 5×10^{-3} kg/m^2 min, or nearly 5×10^7/m^2 min. This gives a shear stress due to collision of no more than 8.2×10^{-4} n/m^2 which is extremely small compared to shear stress due to gas, which for the case given in Fig. 4.8 amounts to a measured value of 2.96 n/m^2. Hence the shear stress due to collision of solid particles can be neglected within the range of interest [S71].

At the risk of expressing one unknown in terms of another, one might consider the effect of solid particles on turbulent mixing. Due to the inertia, solid particles conceivably may reduce the scale of turbulence of the gas within a certain range of loading, which will induce greater turbulence with

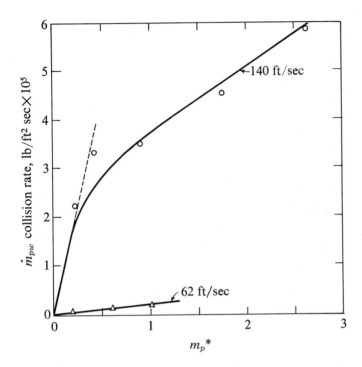

Figure 4.7 Rate of collision of particles at the wall vs. mass flow (MgO in air) [S71].

a further increased loading; the limit being turbulence induced by solid particles in what would have been laminar gas flow as in a fluidized bed.

Figure 4.8 gives the pressure drop ΔP in fully developed turbulent pipe flow of length to diameter $(L/2R)$ ratio of 47.6 in a clean pipe.

$$\tau = \frac{\Delta P}{4(L/2R)}.$$ (4.27)

Without solid particles, the turbulent shear stress was expressed by Prandtl [S13] in terms of mixing length l as

$$\tau_g = l^2 \rho \left(\frac{du}{dy}\right)^2.$$ (4.28)

Since measurements showed that within the range of interest the mean velocity distribution of the gas was unaffected by the presence of solid particles [S72], the shear stress in the gas due to presence of solid particles can be given by

$$\tau_{gp} = l_p^2 \rho \left(\frac{du}{dy}\right)^2,$$

(4.29)

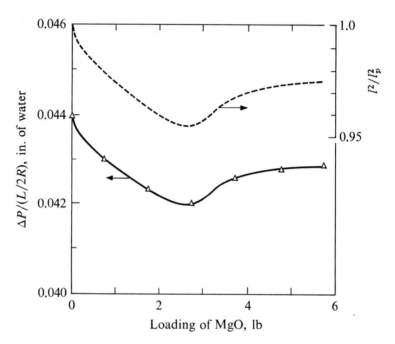

Figure 4.8 Effect of solid particles on pressure drop, ΔP and mixing length in pipe flow ($L/2R = 47.6$, 35 micron MgO in air, clean 5-in. I.D. brass pipe, $U = 140$ fps, Reynolds number based on air 2.9×10^5) [S58].

where l_p is the mixing length due to presence of solid particles. Hence,

$$\frac{\tau_g}{\tau_{gp}} = \frac{l^2}{l_p^2}.$$

(4.30)

Therefore the decrease in friction factor due to presence of solid particles may be attributed to reduced mixing length due to dissipation by the solid particles showing up as a lower pressure drop over a given length of the pipe. The value l^2/l_p^2 for the case of our measurement is shown in Fig. 4.8.

The eddy viscosity is given by [H41]

$$\epsilon_m = l^2 \frac{du}{dx}.$$

(4.31)

The friction factor can be expressed as

$$C_f = 2\epsilon_m \frac{1}{U^2}\frac{du}{dx} = \frac{2l^2(du/dx)^2}{U^2}.$$ (4.32)

The j-factor for convection heat transfer is

$$j \sim \frac{1}{2N_{Pr}}\,C_f \sim \frac{C_f}{2}$$ (4.33)

for air, where N_{Pr} is the Prandtl number. Figure 4.9 shows a case of heat transfer measurement by Tien [T35], showing a greater variation in l^2/l_p^2 at

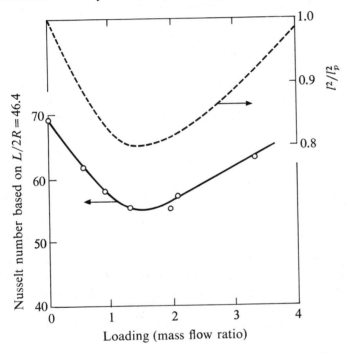

Figure 4.9 Heat-transfer correlation of 30-μ glass particles in air at pipe-flow Reynolds number of 3×10^4—from data of Tien and Quan [T35].

lower pipe flow Reynolds number (3×10^4) as compared to the above experiment ($N_{Re} \sim 3 \times 10^5$).

A recent report by Peskin and Dwyer [P16] suggested subdivision of the flow regimes with respect to various types of effects of solid particles on the laminar sublayer. Their experimental results obtained from a square duct confirm that the gas-velocity profile is unaffected by the presence of solid particles over the above range of experiments. A theoretical study of the effect of solid particles on stability of laminar flow was reported recently by Michael [M27], extending an earlier method due to Saffman [S1].

Gas-Liquid Flow—A broad area of multiphase systems in pipe flow is that of the gas-liquid system. In his recent survey, Griffith [G40] outlined the flow regimes as:

Bubbly or froth (steady flow with bubbles of sizes smaller than the pipe diameter)

Slug (liquid continuum, bubbles have sizes comparable to pipe diameter, flow is unsteady)

Annular flow (gas and liquid both continuous and the flow is steady)

Dispersed flow (liquid droplets in continuous gaseous phase)

Determinations of pressure drops were made by Grovier, Radford, and Dunn [G47], visual studies were made by Kosterin [K29], photographic and motion picture studies were made by Hosler [H53] and Tippets [T37], reporting heat fluxes and flow patterns; X-ray photographs were reported by Derbyshire, Hewitt, and Nicholls [D23]. Using an isokinetic probe, Alexander and Coldren [A8] detected the entrainment of liquid droplets and deposition on the wall. An earlier study of flow of a flashing mixture of water and steam through pipes was made by Benjamin and Miller [B31].

Pressure drop in isothermal gas-liquid flow was correlated by Lockhart and Martinelli [L53]. Film depth, wave height, and pressure drop in two-phase annular flow were studied by Wrobel and McManus [W31] and Slattery [S39]. Recent studies on this system were reported by Laird, Sun, and Wing [L4], and McMillan, Fontaine, and Chaddock [M25] and Kao [K3]. This particular area of gas-liquid flow concerns heat transfer and pressure drop in boiling and is covered in detail in a number of treatises on heat transfer [M19, R27]. The details will not be treated here. Study of nucleate boiling with aqueous thorium oxide slurries was made by Thomas [T24]. Some quantities of suspended solids have been reported by Westwater [W14] as either increasing or decreasing the nucleate-boiling heat-transfer coefficient, depending on the nature of deposition of the solids. Some of the basic aspects of gas-solid flow are applicable to gas-liquid droplet flow.

4.2 Minimum Transport Velocity

Various flow regimes of a suspension include the transition from packed bed to transport condition as delineated by Wilhelm and Kwauk [W20] in a vertical (direction of gravity) flow system, and the flow characteristics as discussed by Wen and Simons [W12] in horizontal pipe flow. A generalization in terms of the concept of minimum transport velocity was given by Thomas [T27].

The minimum transport velocity is defined as the mean stream velocity required to prevent the accumulation of a layer of stationary or sliding particles on the bottom of a horizontal pipe.

Earlier work on sedimentation by Blatch [B41] and Chien [C20] showed that the major factor affecting the vertical (in the direction of gravity) flow of suspended solids in a flowing stream is the ratio of the terminal settling velocity (u_t) to the friction velocity (u^*) where

$$u_w^* = \sqrt{\frac{\tau_w}{\rho_m}} = \sqrt{\frac{(2R)\,\Delta P}{4\rho_m L}},$$

where τ_w is the shear stress at the wall, ρ_m the density of the mixture, $2R$ the pipe diameter, and L the length of the pipe. u_w^* is given by Taylor [T9] as

$$\frac{U}{u_w^*} = 5 \log N_{\text{Re}} - 3.90.$$

where U is the mean stream velocity in a circular pipe. On the basis of these findings, Thomas [T27] represented the nature of flow around a particle as it settles toward the bottom of a conduit in a diagram of u_t/u_o^* vs. $2au_o^*\bar{\rho}/\bar{\mu}$, where u_t is the terminal settling velocity, u_o^* is the friction velocity at minimum transport condition (no particles sliding along the bottom of the pipe) of infinite dilation, by lines of constant-particle Reynolds number $(N_{\text{Re}})_a$, or

$$\left(\frac{2au_o^*\bar{\rho}}{\bar{\mu}}\right)\frac{u_t}{u_o^*} = (N_{\text{Re}})_a = \text{const.} \tag{4.34}$$

for different ranges. Figure 4.10 shows the different settling rates for: (A) $(N_{\text{Re}})_a < 1$ (Stokes' law); (B) $1 < (N_{\text{Re}})_a < 500$ (transition region); and, (C) $(N_{\text{Re}})_a > 500$ (Newton's law). The line of $u_t/u_w^* = 0.2$ is a limit near to one suggested by Durand [D41] such that $u_t/u_w^* < 0.2$ for suspension flow without obvious sedimentation. For the representation of location of particles in relation to the boundary layer and the turbulent core, Thomas applied the thicknesses defined by von Kármán [V15] as

$$y^+ = \frac{yu_w^*\bar{\rho}}{\bar{\mu}}, \tag{4.35}$$

where y is the distance measured from the wall and the range of laminar sublayer for $y^+ < 5$, buffer layer for $5 < y^+ < 30$, and turbulent core for $y^+ > 30$. These subdivisions give three major regions indicated in Fig. 4.10:

Region I: Particles are smaller than the thickness of the laminar sublayer; particles remain predominantly in suspension.

Region II: Transport occurs mainly with higher concentration of particles with settling according to the range (A), (B), (C), given by particle Reynolds numbers.

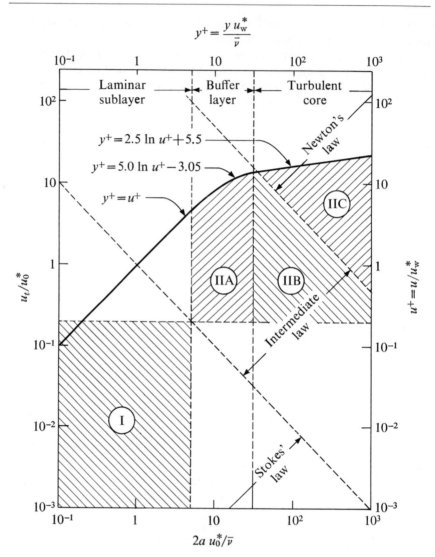

Figure 4.10 Flow-regime classification for minimum-transport correlation [T27]

Not included in Fig. 4.10 is the influence of density ratio of particle and fluid materials $\bar{\rho}_p/\bar{\rho}$ on the minimum-transport condition which was recognized by Bagnold [B1]. With large density ratio such a gas-solid system, a traveling particle hitting a deposit can produce a splash, thus enhancing the ability of gas to transport solids. Liquid-solid systems do not manifest this behavior.

Experiments were carried out by Thomas along a 40-ft section of a 1.045-in. diameter pipe with visual determination in a 10-ft section of glass pipe, with glass beads of 78 μ mean diameter at 10^{-4} to 6 $\times$ 10^{-2} volume fraction solids, transported by air and water. The mean stream velocity for minimum-transport condition was determined with ± 5 per cent reproducibility. Mean settling rates were determined from hindered-settling measurements extrapolated to zero concentration using the relation developed by Steinour [S86], which checks within experimental error to computed value based on the mean diameter. Experiments were carried out with air and water as the suspending fluid. Results are shown in Fig. 4.11, together with results of Durand [D41],

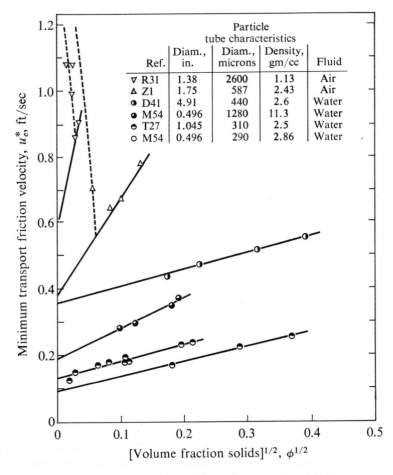

Figure 4.11 Effect of concentration on friction velocity at the minimum-transport condition [T27].

Murphy, Young, and Burian [M54], Zenz [Z1], and Rose and Barnacle [R31]. u_c^*, the friction velocity at the minimum transport condition, was found to be proportional to the square root of the volume fraction solids for all concentrated gas and liquid suspensions. Comparison of the upward forces acting on a particle resting on the bottom of a horizontal pipe showed that the primary contribution was due to Bernoulli forces arising from instantaneous velocity differences accompanying turbulent fluctuations. Irmay [I6] showed that these forces were localized in the buffer layer, although individual particles may have different trajectories in the different flow regimes. From dimensional analysis, Thomas divided the correlations into the limiting case of the minimum-transport conditions at infinite dilutions and the concentration dependence. The functional dependence of u_t/u_o^* to the system dimensions and operating variables is given by

$$\frac{u_t}{u_o^*} = 0.204 \left(\frac{2au_o^*}{\bar{\nu}}\right)\left(\frac{\bar{\nu}}{2Ru_o^*}\right)^{0.60}\left[\frac{\bar{\rho}_p - \bar{\rho}}{\bar{\rho}}\right]^{0.23},\tag{4.36}$$

with $\bar{\nu} = \bar{\mu}/\bar{\rho}$, and

$$\frac{u_c^*}{u_o^*} = 1 + 2.8\left(\frac{u_t}{u_o^*}\right)^{1/3}\phi^{1/2}.\tag{4.37}$$

Good agreement was obtained between the data of gas-solid suspensions and liquid-solid suspensions.

Zenz [Z4] treated the conveyability of materials of mixed particle size and pointed out that the minimum superficial velocity (saltation velocity) may increase with decrease in particle size when the latter falls below a certain limit. It is believed that this character is because of the increased influence of surface effects [C41] and the electrostatic charge effects (Secs. 4.5, 10.8) with small particles.

Due to its economy, the pumping of solid-liquid mixtures has received increasing attention. Recent design aspects were given by Ewing [E27] and Stepanoff [S87].

4.3 Heat Transfer in Pipe Flow

Heat transfer by gas-solid suspensions in pipe flow has been the subject of many studies because of the anticipated large heat-transfer coefficient due to the high volumetric specific heat of the solid particles or liquid droplets compared to a gas and the demand for high heat-transfer coefficient in gas-cooled reactors. Based on the experimental observations on gas-solid suspensions by Farbar and Morley [F5] and Schluderberg [S14], by Johnson [J16] on gas suspensions of liquid droplets, and by Salomone and Newmann [S3] on liquid-solid suspensions, Tien [T31, T32] analyzed the heat transfer by a gas-solid suspension in turbulent pipe flow based on a simplified model specified as follows:

(a) The density of the fluid $\bar{\rho}$ remains constant; thus the velocity distribution is independent of the temperature distribution.

(b) The fluid properties such as the specific heat at constant pressure c, viscosity $\bar{\mu}$, and thermal conductivity $\bar{\kappa}$ are constants.

(c) Each solid particle is small and maintains uniform temperature due to its high thermal conductivity, $\bar{\kappa}_p$.

(d) The fluid and the solid particle cloud have similar velocity profiles. The presence of solid particles does not affect the fluid velocity profile.

(e) The solid particles are uniformly distributed throughout the pipe.

(f) The effect of collision with the wall is neglected.

(g) The suspension is extremely dilute such that each particle is assumed to see the wall without interference of other particles.

Items (d) and (e) are the weakest of the assumptions as will be shown in Section 4.5; item (f) is weak but could be valid (Sec. 4.5 and Chap. 5); item (g) is still a useful approximation (Chap. 5) and is the asymptotic condition. However, the method of Tien has sufficient merit to warrant a discussion as a possible basis for further studies on this topic.

To obtain the heat-transfer performance and the temperatures of the solid particles and of the fluid it is necessary to set down two energy equations, one for the solid particles and one for the fluid-solids mixture. The coordinate system of the flow field is shown in Fig. 4.12.

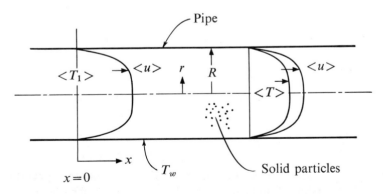

Figure 4.12 Two-phase flow in a circular pipe [T32].

First, consider the equation of heat balance for the solid particle. Including radiation effect, the heat-balance equation is given as (Eq. 2.128)

$$\frac{dT_p}{dt} + G(T_p - T) = G_r(T_w^4 - T_p^4),$$ (4.38)

where

$$G = \frac{h_p A_p}{\bar{\rho}_p v_p c_p} \quad \text{and} \quad G_r = \frac{\sigma_r A_p \epsilon_p}{\bar{\rho}_p v_p c_p},$$

and T_p is the temperature of the solid particle, T is that of the fluid, T_w that of the wall; h_p is the heat-transfer coefficient for flow over the particle, or $(N_{Nu})_p \bar{\kappa}/2a$; A_p is the surface area, v_p is the volume of the solid particle, c_p is the specific heat of the solid particle, σ_r is the Stefan-Boltzmann constant of radiation, ϵ_p is the emissivity of the surface of the solid. The heat-transfer coefficient h_p in general must be determined experimentally. It becomes more complicated when the particle is suspended in a turbulent stream (Sec. 2.7).

Since T_p in polar-cylindrical coordinates (pertinent to flow in a circular pipe) is in general a function of time t, the main flow direction x, the direction radial to the main flow r, and the polar angle φ, the foregoing equation in terms of partial differential quantities is given as

$$\frac{\partial T_p}{\partial t} + u\frac{\partial T_p}{\partial x} + v\frac{\partial T_p}{\partial r} + \frac{w}{r}\frac{\partial T_p}{\partial \varphi} + G(T_p - T) = G_r(T_w^4 - T_p^4),$$ (4.39)

where u, v, and w are the velocity components in the directions x, r, and φ, respectively. By introducing the mean (denoted by $^-$) and fluctuating quantities (denoted by $'$) of the velocities and temperatures, and considering only the steady case, after taking the mean of each term, we get

$$\bar{u}_p\frac{\partial \bar{T}_p}{\partial x} + \bar{v}_p\frac{\partial \bar{T}_p}{\partial r} + \frac{\bar{w}_p}{r}\frac{\partial \bar{T}_p}{\partial \varphi} + G(\bar{T}_p - \bar{T})$$

$$+ \left[\frac{\partial}{\partial x}\langle u_p' T_p'\rangle + \frac{1}{r}\frac{\partial}{\partial r}r\langle v_p' T_p'\rangle + \frac{1}{r}\frac{\partial}{\partial \varphi}\langle w_p' T_p'\rangle\right]$$

$$= G_r(\bar{T}_w^4 - \bar{T}_p^4).$$

Since $\bar{v}_p = \bar{w}_p = 0$, $\langle u_p' T_p'\rangle$ is independent of x and $\langle w_p' T_p'\rangle$ is zero, the equation becomes

$$\bar{u}\frac{\partial \bar{T}_p}{\partial x} + G(\bar{T}_p - \bar{T}) - G_r(\bar{T}_w^4 - \bar{T}_p^4) + \frac{1}{r}\frac{\partial}{\partial r}r\langle v_p' T_p'\rangle = 0.$$ (4.40)

The last term on the left-hand side of Eq. (4.39) is the heat transport due to the turbulent mixing of solid particles. For very small particles as in the present case, it would be expected that $\langle v_p' T_p'\rangle \cong \langle v' T_p'\rangle$.

The energy equation for the two-phase flow field can be derived in a similar manner as that in the single-phase turbulent flow case. Consider the heat transfer to the steady, two-phase flow through a circular pipe, of which the wall, at $x > 0$, is kept at a constant temperature. An energy balance of a small volume element gives the energy equation for the flow field. While the mean velocities $\bar{v} = \bar{w} = 0$ and, of the eddy heat-transfer terms, $\langle u'T' \rangle$ is independent of x and $\langle w'T' \rangle$ is zero, the energy equation in polar-cylindrical coordinates is given as

$$\rho c \bar{u} \frac{\partial \bar{T}}{\partial x} + \rho_p c_p \bar{u} \frac{\partial \bar{T}_p}{\partial x} = \frac{1}{r} \frac{\partial}{\partial r} \left(r \bar{\kappa} \frac{\partial \bar{T}}{\partial r} - \rho c r \langle v'T' \rangle \right), \qquad (4.41)$$

where ρ is the density of the gas phase ($\rho \sim \bar{\rho}$), ρ_p is the density of the cloud of solid particles. The energy equation can be further written as

$$u \frac{\partial \bar{T}}{\partial x} + \frac{\rho_p}{\rho} \bar{u} \frac{\partial \bar{T}p}{\partial x} = \frac{1}{r} \frac{\partial}{\partial r} \left[r \left(\frac{v}{N_{\mathrm{Pr}}} + \epsilon_H \right) \frac{\partial \bar{T}}{\partial r} \right] + \beta_2 (\bar{T}_p - \bar{T}), \qquad (4.42)$$

where

$$\beta_2 = \frac{n_p h_p A_p}{\rho c} = \frac{c_p \rho_p G}{c \rho},$$

and v is the kinematic viscosity, ϵ_H is the eddy diffusivity of heat.

Now consider the relative order of magnitude of different terms in Eqs. (4.40) and (4.42). The first and second terms in Eq. (4.40) are of the same order of magnitude as $\bar{u}(\partial \bar{T}/\partial x)$, and consequently as $(1/r)(\partial/\partial r)(r\langle v'T' \rangle)$. Thus the last term in Eq. (4.40) can be neglected if

$$0\langle v'T' \rangle > 0\langle v'T'_p \rangle \cong \langle v'_p T'_p \rangle.$$

From a statistical point of view, since T' is directly related to the motion of fluid particle while T'_p is not, the correlation between v' and T' is much larger than that between v' and T'_p or v'_p and T'_p. This can be visualized also from the argument that for small heat-transfer coefficient (noting that the relative mean velocity between fluid and solid particles has been neglected) the dynamic response of T'_p due to v' is smaller than T'. In the limiting case of zero heat transfer for the solid particle, $\langle v'T'_p \rangle = \langle v'_p T'_p \rangle = 0$. Therefore the last term in Eq. (4.40) is small as compared to the first and second terms. Although eddy-mixing of particles will be neglected, it is understood that there does exist an eddy-mixing term in the solid phase similar to that in the fluid phase. Neglecting the last term in Eq. (4.40) gives

$$\bar{u} \frac{\partial \bar{T}_p}{\partial x} + G(\bar{T}_p - \bar{T}) - G_r(\bar{T}_w^4 - \bar{T}_p^4) = 0. \qquad (4.43)$$

In the case of a two-phase flow through a circular pipe, Eqs. (4.42) and (4.43) are the governing equations of the system with $\bar{T}$ and $\bar{T}_p$ to be determined. The solution to Eqs. (4.42) and (4.43) must also satisfy the following boundary conditions:

$$r = 0, \quad \frac{\partial \bar{T}}{\partial r} = 0, \quad \frac{\partial \bar{T}_p}{\partial r} = 0; \quad x = 0, \quad \bar{T} = \bar{T}_0, \quad \bar{T}_p = \bar{T}_0;$$

$$r = R, \quad \bar{T} = T_w, \quad \bar{T}_p = T_w; \quad x \to \infty, \quad \bar{T} = T_w, \quad \bar{T}_p = T_w.$$

Neglecting radiation and introducing the following dimensionless quantities

$$\theta = \frac{\bar{T} - T_w}{\bar{T}_0 - T_w} \qquad \theta_p = \frac{\bar{T}_p - T_w}{\bar{T}_0 - T_w}$$

$$\eta = \frac{r}{R} \qquad \xi = \frac{x}{N_{\text{Re}} N_{\text{Pr}} R} \qquad f(\eta) = \frac{\bar{u}}{u_{\text{avg}}}$$

$$g(\eta) = 1 + \frac{\epsilon_H N_{\text{Pr}}}{\bar{\nu}}.$$

the governing Eqs. (4.42) and (4.43) become, respectively,

$$f \frac{\partial \theta_p}{\partial \xi} + \beta_3 (\theta_p - \theta) = 0, \tag{4.44}$$

and

$$f \frac{\partial \theta}{\partial \xi} = \frac{2}{\eta} \frac{\partial}{\partial \eta} \left[\eta g \frac{\partial \theta}{\partial \eta} \right] + \beta_4 (\theta_p - \theta), \tag{4.45}$$

where

$$\beta_3 = \left(\frac{\rho c}{\rho_p c_p} \right) \left(\frac{4 R^2 h_p A_p}{2 \bar{\kappa} v_p} \right),$$

and

$$\beta_4 = \left(\frac{n_p h_p A_p 4 R^2}{2 \bar{\kappa}} \right).$$

The boundary conditions become

$$\left. \begin{array}{lll} \eta = 0, & \dfrac{\partial \theta}{\partial \eta} = 0, & \dfrac{\partial \theta_p}{\partial \eta} = 0 \\[2mm] \eta = 1, & \theta = 0, & \theta_p = 0 \\[2mm] \xi = 0, & \theta = 1, & \theta_p = 1 \\[2mm] \xi \to \infty, & \theta = 0, & \theta_p = 0. \end{array} \right\} \tag{4.46}$$

The last boundary condition in Eq. (4.46) suggests the solutions to Eqs. (4.44) and (4.45) by method of separation of variables, or

$$\theta = \sum_{n=0}^{\infty} C_n R_n \exp(-\lambda_n^2 \xi), \tag{4.47}$$

and

$$\theta_p = \sum_{n=0}^{\infty} C_n R_{pn} \exp(-\lambda_n^2 \xi), \tag{4.48}$$

where $R_n(\eta)$ and $R_{pn}(\eta)$ satisfy

$$R_n - R_{pn}\left(1 - \frac{\lambda_n^2}{\beta_3} f\right) = 0, \tag{4.49}$$

and

$$[\eta g R_n']' + \tfrac{1}{2}\beta_4 \eta (R_{pn} - R_n) + \frac{\lambda_n^2}{2} \eta f R_n = 0, \tag{4.50}$$

with the boundary conditions

$$R_n'(0) = 0 \qquad R_{pn}'(0) = 0 \tag{4.51}$$

$$R_n(1) = 0 \qquad R_{pn}(1) = 0. \tag{4.52}$$

The relation between R_n and R_{pn} is indicated by Eq. (4.49) and satisfies the boundary condition, Eq. (4.51). Substitution of this relation into Eq. (4.50) gives

$$[\eta g R_n']' + \left[\left(1 - \frac{\lambda_n^2}{\beta_3}\right)^{-1} - 1 + \frac{\lambda_n^2 f}{\beta_4}\right]\frac{\beta_4}{2} \eta R_n = 0, \tag{4.53}$$

with the boundary conditions $R_n'(0) = 0$ and $R_n(1) = 0$.

The Sturm-Liouville theory for boundary value problems can be applied to the present case if

$$\frac{\lambda_n^2 f}{\beta_3} \ll 1. \tag{4.54}$$

Since f and β_3 are quantities fixed by the characteristics of the physical system, the validity of this statement is largely dependent on the values of λ_n^2. It is possible that Eq. (4.54) holds true for the first few eigenvalues.

By use of Eq. (4.54) and by letting

$$\bar{\lambda}_n^2 = (1 + \beta_5)\lambda_n^2, \tag{4.55}$$

where

$$\beta_5 = \frac{\beta_4}{\beta_3}.$$

Equation (4.53) becomes

$$[\eta g R_n']' + \tfrac{1}{2}\bar{\lambda}_n^2 f \eta R_n = 0, \tag{4.56}$$

which with the two linear homogeneous boundary conditions

$$R'_n(0) = 0 \qquad R_n(1) = 0$$

is a Sturm-Liouville system.

It is interesting to note that Eq. (4.56) is exactly the same as the governing equations in single-phase turbulent heat transfer in a pipe given by Sleicher and Tribus [S40]. In fact, from Eq. (4.55) it is understood that the single-phase system can be regarded as a special case of the two-phase system; that is, when the number of solid particles per unit volume n_p is zero (and so $\beta_4 = 0$). Hence the results obtained from Eq. (4.56) and its boundary conditions are applicable to both two-phase and single-phase heat-transfer systems.

The heat flux to the two-phase flow at the wall is given by

$$J_q = \bar{\kappa} \left(\frac{\partial \bar{T}}{\partial r} \right)_{r=R} = \frac{-2\bar{\kappa}(\bar{T}_1 - T_w)}{R} \sum_n A_n \exp\left(-\lambda_n^2 \xi\right), \tag{4.57}$$

where

$$A_n = -\frac{C_n R'_n(1)}{2}. \tag{4.58}$$

From the orthogonality property of the solutions, the coefficients C_n are given by

$$C_n = \frac{\displaystyle\int_0^1 f\eta R_n \, d\eta}{\displaystyle\int_0^1 f\eta R_n^2 \, d\eta}. \tag{4.59}$$

The first few successive values of λ_n^2 and R_n can be found from the computed results of the single-phase case [S40] in which the forms of the velocity function $f(\eta)$ and the eddy diffusivity function $g(\eta)$ have been discussed.

By inserting the numerical values into β_3, it is generally found that β_3 is of the order of 10^5 or more. With the known values of λ_n^2, Eq. (4.54) can be readily shown to be valid in most physical systems, say $N_{Pr} < 2$ and $N_{Re} < 500,000$.

The true temperature distribution in this fluid-solids mixture requires a calculation of C_n and R_n. Through the values of A_n at different loading ratios, it can be found qualitatively that the effect of particle concentration is to flatten the temperature profile and, consequently, to increase the heat transfer.

The Nusselt number of the system by definition is given as, for mean temperature T_{mm} of the mixture:

$$N_{Nu} = \frac{h(2R)}{\bar{\kappa}} = \frac{J_q(2R)}{\bar{\kappa}(T_w - T_{mm})},$$

and by appropriate manipulation the Nusselt number for the case of uniform wall temperature is

$$N_{Nu}(\xi) = \frac{\sum\limits_n A_n \exp(-\lambda_n^2 \xi)}{\sum\limits_n \dfrac{A_n \exp(-\lambda_n^2 \xi)}{\lambda_n^2(1 + \beta_5)}}. \tag{4.60}$$

Far downstream from the thermal entrance, all terms but the first become small so that the Nusselt number is

$$(N_{Nu})_a = (\tfrac{1}{2})(1 + \beta_5)\lambda_0^2 = (\tfrac{1}{2})\bar{\lambda}_0^2. \tag{4.61}$$

This suggests that the asymptotic Nusselt numbers for the case of uniform wall temperature are the same for both two-phase and single-phase systems, and is a limit due to the nature of the model.

Tien's analysis shows that the effect due to the presence of solid particles on the heat transfer to a two-phase system is governed by the factor

$$\beta_5 = \frac{\beta_4}{\beta_3} = \frac{\bar{\rho}_p c_p}{\rho c} n_p v_p = \frac{c_p \dot{M}_p}{c \dot{M}}, \tag{4.62}$$

where $\dot{M}_p$ and $\dot{M}$ are the flow rate of the solid phase and fluid phase, respectively. Tien [T31] also furnished a linear approximation including the effect of radiation. The method is applicable to systems with arbitrary wall-temperature variations and wall heat fluxes, as in the case dealt with by Sellars, Tribus, and Klein [S21].

Based on the computed results [S40], the variations of local Nusselt number versus the axial distance at different loading ratios are shown in Fig. 4.13. The Reynolds numbers $N_{Re} = 27,000$ and $13,500$ were chosen in order to compare the analytical results with the experimental data [F5]. The ratio of specific heats $c_p/c = 1.2$ was chosen for the case of a combined flow of alumina-silica solid particles and air at the standard condition, 1 atm and 60°F. The prediction [F5] of a linear relationship between the average Nusselt number and the loading ratio at low mass flow ratios ($\dot{m}_p^* = \dot{M}_p/\dot{M} \leq 1$) is adequately supported by the present analysis as shown in Fig. 4.14. For higher loading ratios the present approximation is no longer valid.

Without specific reference to a gas-solid system, combined effect of radiation and convection heat transfer from a fluid to the inside surface of a tube was studied by Perlmutter and Siegel [P10, P11], Erkku [E21], and Dalton, Schweppe, and Billig [D5]. Irvine [I7] further studied these effects in non-circular ducts. A fundamental treatment will be made in Chap. 5.

Refined measurements in subsequent studies have further shown additional details, especially cases of reduced heat-transfer coefficients due to addition of solid particles. Tien and Quan [T35], as cited in Sec. 4.1, reported the nature of variation of Nusselt number of gas-solid mixtures as in Fig. 4.15, with comparison to results of Farbar and Depew [F4], and variation of local Nusselt number vs. axial distance as in Fig. 4.16 for glass and lead spheres in air, for two pipe-flow Reynolds numbers. Jepson, Poll, and Smith [J10] showed similar trends. All these results indicate the usefulness of further

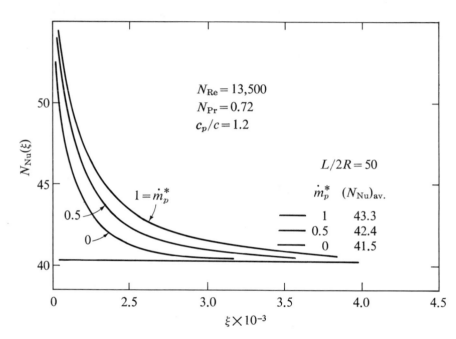

Figure 4.13 Local Nusselt number vs. axial distance of different mass flow ratio [T32].

work by relaxing some of the simplifying specifications of Tien. Studies by Abel, Bluman, and O'Leary [A1] and Garbis and Bakhtionzin [G4] emphasized the application of helium-graphite suspension as a reactor coolant.

From measurements with thorium oxide slurries, Thomas [T21] obtained corresponding relations of friction factor and *j*-factor for heat transfer as shown in Fig. 4.17, with asymptotic relation to turbulent liquid flow:

$$j = \frac{h}{c\bar{\rho}U} (N_{Pr})^{2/3} \left(\frac{\bar{\mu}}{\bar{\mu}_w}\right)^{0.14} = 0.027 \left(\frac{2RU\bar{\rho}}{\bar{\mu}}\right)^{-0.2}, \qquad (4.63)$$

where $\bar{\mu}_w$ is the viscosity of the liquid at the wall, c is its specific heat, and U is the mean velocity of pipe flow.

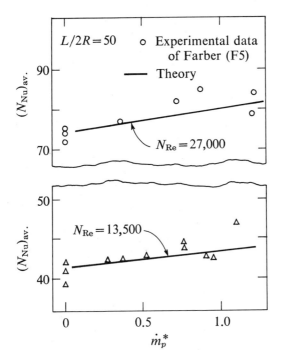

Figure 4.14 Comparison with experimental results of Farbar and Morley [F5, T32].

4.4 Mass Transfer in Pipe Flow

Following the single particle behavior given in Sec. 3.2, the fact that stirring influences the rate of evaporation and reaction in certain heterogeneous systems is well known. When applied to a gas-solid or liquid-solid system, Huber and Reid [H62] suggested that the rate velocity becomes linear with speed of agitation if the rate is controlled by the fluid phase diffusion rate.

Jones and Smith [J20] studied mass transfer from solids (spheres of naphthalene, $\frac{3}{4}$-in. diameter) freely suspended in an air stream and obtained correlation with pipe flow Reynolds number $(N_{Re})_t$ on the mass-transfer rate.

$$(N_{Re})_t = \bar{\rho}\,\frac{(2R)\,U}{\bar{\mu}}. \tag{4.64}$$

The correlation in Sec. 3.2 is extended to

$$N_{Sh} - 2 = 0.25[(N_{Re})_p(N_{Re})_t^{\frac{1}{2}}N_{Sc}]^{\frac{1}{3}}, \tag{4.65}$$

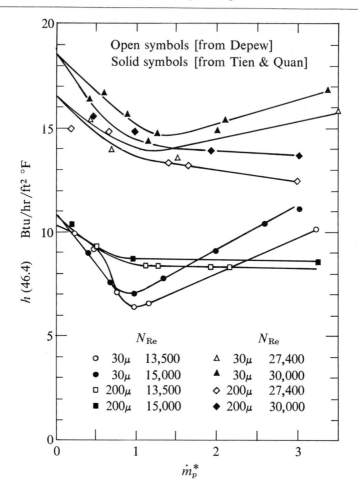

Figure 4.15 Comparison of experimental results of Depew [F4] and of Tien and Quan [T35].

for the laminar flow range, and

$$N_{\text{Sh}} - 2 = 0.055[(N_{\text{Re}})_p (N_{\text{Re}})_t^{\frac{1}{2}} N_{\text{Sc}}]^{\frac{1}{2}}, \tag{4.66}$$

for the turbulent range.

Most of the previous studies on fluid-solid mass transfer were made on stirred reactors. The results are therefore not applicable to pipe flow condition. However, the effect of turbulence in pipe flow can be seen from these measurements. Hixson and Baum [H46] applied the double film concept to

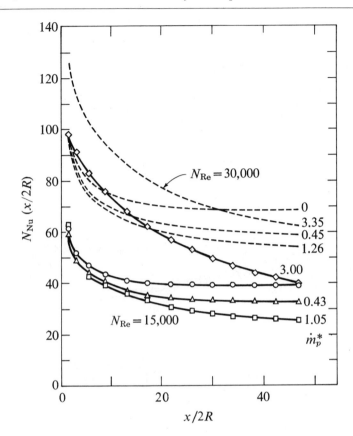

Figure 4.16 Local Nusselt number vs. axial distance from mixture of air and 30-μ glass particles [T35].

the solution of benzoic acid in dilute sodium hydroxide. This system was also studied by Mack and Marriner [M2], using pellets and crushed particles down to 35-mesh sizes. A study by Barker and Treybal [B17] with particles of 1–15-mm diameter yields

$$\frac{k_1 D_v}{B} = 0.06(N_{\mathrm{Re}})^{0.83}(N_{\mathrm{Sc}})^{0.5}, \tag{4.67}$$

where k_1 is the liquid film mass-transfer coefficient, D_v is the vessel diameter, B is the liquid diffusivity, and $N_{\mathrm{Re}} = D_v^2 N \bar{\rho}/\bar{\mu}$, where N is the impeller speed in rpm. A similar relation was obtained by Bieber and Gaden [B35] using ion-exchange beads. The effect of agitation on the microbiological productivity was studied by Hixon and Gaden [H47].

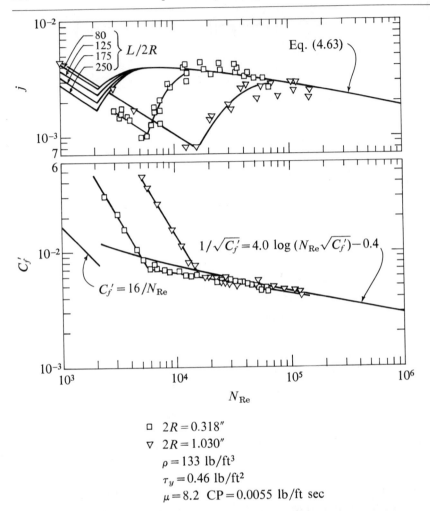

$$\square \quad 2R = 0.318''$$
$$\triangledown \quad 2R = 1.030''$$
$$\rho = 133 \text{ lb/ft}^3$$
$$\tau_y = 0.46 \text{ lb/ft}^2$$
$$\mu = 8.2 \text{ CP} = 0.0055 \text{ lb/ft sec}$$

Figure 4.17 Heat-transfer and flow friction of ThO$_2$ slurry [T21].

4.5 Concentration and Mass Flow Distribution [S72]

It is seen that prediction and correlation of momentum, heat, and mass transfer in a gas-solid suspension call for a knowledge of the concentration distribution of solid particles and the velocities of the phases. In the above sections data correlation was made with overall average concentration. Measurements of mass flow of particulate phase were made with an impact counter system by Soo and Regalbuto [S68] and subsequent evaluation shows different velocities of the phases [S53]. Measurements by point-study probe were made by Trotter [T53], and measurements by capacitance were made by Van Zoonen [V7].

Methods of measurement of concentration of the particulate phase in a suspension consist of electric measurement as applied to aerosols by Hinkle, Orr, and Dallavalle [H37]; optical method by light scattering was used by Rosensweig, Hottel, and Williams [R36] to apply to either the overall measurement of large samples or relatively small number of particles per unit volume (light loading). The impact-counter system [S68] or the point study pickup [T53] applies to relatively large particles as well as light loading; both give local mass flow rather than concentration.

Measurement of particle concentration was made utilizing the attenuation of light through the application of the principle of fiber optics from studies made by Kapany [K4, S93]. For the measurement of particle-phase velocity, an electrostatic mass flow probe was developed to determine the mass flow of the particle phase. These measurements were made by Soo, Trezek, Dimick, and Hohnstreiter [S72] on a 5-in.-diameter, closed loop, two-phase flow system with particles of glass and magnesia around 50 (Fig. 4.18) to 35 μ in diameter, maximum velocity of 130 fps, and holdup mass of air of 1.67 lb.

Concentration Distribution—Improvements led to the probe as shown in Fig. 4.19. In this probe the gap is produced between a miniature light bulb and the glass rod coming out on the left-hand side. The cylinder around the gap channels the flow and eliminates the reflection from the walls of the duct. Measurements with the probe were made in the linear range of the photocell as specified by manufacturers.

Evaluation of concentration distribution was made from the total output of the phototube in each case using a bucking circuit. The major voltage output was cancelled so that fine deviation could be detected across a tube diameter; in effect, the sensitivity was such that a three per cent light intensity would correspond to a full-scale deflection (100 divisions) of the recorder.

The intensity variation or voltage variation due to the particle concentration was counted from the zero-particle reading. Evaluation of the particle concentration involves a normalizing procedure with respect to total mass M_p of solid particles in the pipe, namely

$$\frac{M_p}{\text{Length}} = \int_0^R \rho_p 2\pi r \, dr, \qquad (4.68)$$

where ρ_p is the concentration of solid particles (mass per unit volume), r the radius measured from the axis of the pipe, and R the radius of the pipe. Since any local change in light across the tube diameter would be caused by

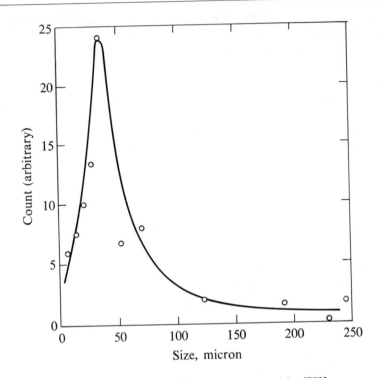

Figure 4.18 Size distribution of glass particles [S72].

a local change in particle concentration, the particle concentration must be proportional to the change in intensity or voltage, or

$$\rho_p = K(\Delta I), \tag{4.69}$$

and

$$\int_0^R \rho_p 2\pi r \, dr = K \int_0^R (\Delta I) 2\pi r \, dr = \frac{M_p}{\text{length}}, \tag{4.70}$$

where K is the optical scale factor and $M_p/$length is the mass of particles per unit length of the pipe. This is in effect normalizing local change across the tube diameter to the total mass of particles of the system. The volume of the system can be related to the mass of air entrained in the system since it is closed. For given m_p^*, mass ratio of solid to gas and $\bar{\rho}$, the density of air at the flow condition, we have

$$K = \frac{m_p^* \pi R^2 \bar{\rho}}{\int_0^R (\Delta I) 2\pi r \, dr} \cong \frac{m_p^* \pi R^2 \bar{\rho}}{2\pi \sum (\Delta I) r (\Delta r)}. \tag{4.71}$$

Integration was carried out numerically on curves of intensity obtained from the recorder. K for each loading was determined and then the local value of the density corresponding to a local change in light intensity was computed. K has the dimension of density and is a function of the total particle mass. The concentration distribution measurement obtained for glass beads is

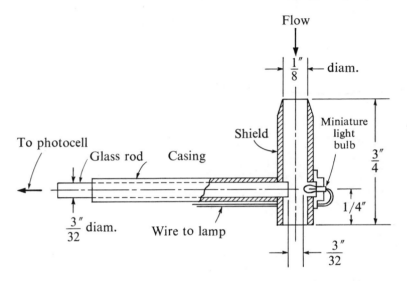

Figure 4.19 Probe with built-in light source [S72].

shown by Fig. 4.20. It is seen that the density in each case increases at the wall as theoretically predicted [S53, S57] and measured by Van Zoonen [V7]. Peskin and Dwyer [P16] obtained higher concentration at the center of a square duct, which is believed to be due to inlet effect.

Mass-Flow Distribution—With the recognition [S57] that the solid particles become charged when flowing through a pipe due to impact with a wall, the possibility of measuring local mass flow was investigated. Since the solid particles become charged due to impact with the wall, particles of the same size will be charged to nearly the same magnitude and with the same sign of charge according to the principle of triboelectricity [M40]. Thus, a probe of a given cross section inserted into the flow stream will pick up charge at a rate proportional to the mass flow. For this purpose a ball probe (Fig. 4.21) was built with measuring circuit as given in Fig. 4.21. In the design of the ball probe, effort was made to maintain a high resistance to ground by the use of glass sleeving to insulate the lead to the ball from the hypodermic tubing serving as the probe shaft. To be acceptable, the probe had to have at least a 10^{11}-ohm resistance so as not to shunt the signal to ground. The background current due to dust particles in the air was checked. Such a background current, if it existed, was not measurable.

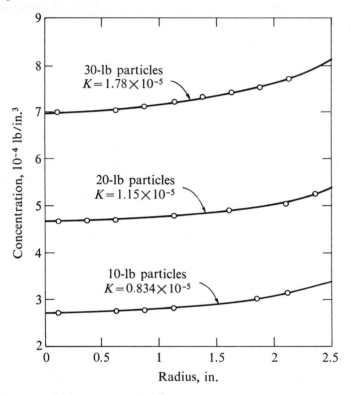

Figure 4.20 Concentration distribution of glass particles 50-μ nominal in air (5-in.-diam pipe, 132 fps maximum velocity) [S72].

The ball probe gave the current distribution as

$$i = \frac{\pi}{4} d_e^2 n_p q u_p,$$ (4.72)

where d_e is the diameter of the probe, n_p the number of particles per unit volume, and q the average charge per particle. Rewriting as

$$i = \frac{\pi}{4} d_e^2 \rho_p u_p \left(\frac{q}{m}\right),$$ (4.73)

where q/m is the average charge-to-mass ratio induced on the solid particles by impact with the wall and resultant charge distribution. Therefore, for narrow size range of particles, q/m is very nearly constant, and the mass flow of solid particles is given by

$$\rho_p u_p = K_m i,$$ (4.74)

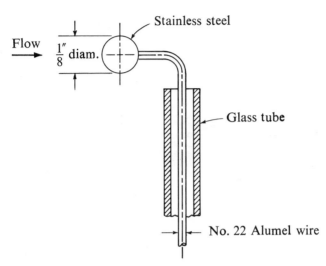

Figure 4.21 Electrostatic ball probe [S72].

where K_m is the constant of proportionality. K_m can be determined from the condition at the center of the pipe where semitheoretical study [S53] and measurements by Soo, Ihrig, and El Kouh [S66] gave

$$u_o \cong u_{po},$$ (4.75)

u_o is the fluid velocity determined by pitot static tube. The basis of measurements made on a dusty gas is given in Chap. 6. The above shows that K_m is a constant for a given distribution. Figure 4.22 gives the mass-flow distribution of glass particles.

From the relation of Eq. (4.74) we can determine three important quantities. One is

$$u_p = \frac{K_m i}{\rho_p},$$ (4.76)

the mean velocity of the particle phase (Fig. 4.23); another is the total flow rate in a recirculating system:

$$\dot{M}_p = 2\pi K_m \int_0^R i r \, dr,$$ (4.77)

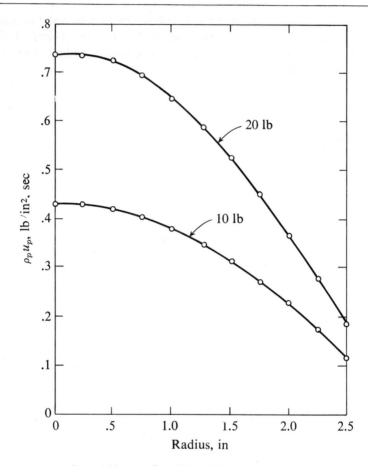

Figure 4.22 Mass-flow distribution of glass particles [S72].

which can be compared to metering by the feeder [S66]. The value of $\dot{M}_p$ gives a check of earlier assumptions in concentration distribution.

Still another quantity which can be determined here is the average value of charge-to-mass ratio. The above implies

$$\left(\frac{q}{m}\right) = \left(K_m \frac{\pi}{4} d^2\right)^{-1}. \tag{4.78}$$

The shear stress due to collision of solid particles of the wall τ_p is given by the mass collision rate of solid particles $\dot{m}_{pw}$ per unit area [S58, S71] as obtained with the sticky tape described in Sec. 4.1, or

$$\tau_{pw} \sim \left(\frac{2}{\sqrt{\pi}}\right) \dot{m}_{pw} u_{pw}, \tag{4.79}$$

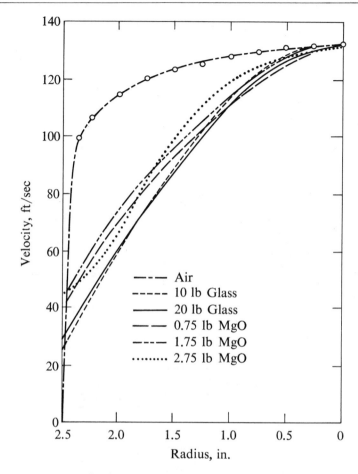

Figure 4.23 Velocity distribution of particles [S72].

and the friction factor is given by

$$C_{pf} = \frac{\tau_{pw}}{\rho_{po} u_{po}^2 / 2}.$$

(4.80)

Following the consideration of collision among particles [S52], the friction factor C_{pf} is correlated according to $C_{pf}(u_{po}/\langle u_p^2 \rangle^{1/2})$.

Particle Diffusivity—The above knowledge and concentrations of solids and charge-to-mass ratio also permits determination of diffusivity D_{pw} of particles at the wall, by using the procedure discussed in Chap. 10 [S71]:

$$D_{pw} = \frac{q}{m}\left(\frac{\rho_{po}}{2\epsilon_o}\right)^{1/2} R^2[(\alpha + 2)^{-1} + B(\alpha + 1)^{-1} - 2B^2(3\alpha + 2)^{-1} + \cdots], \quad (4.81)$$

TABLE 4.1

CONCENTRATION AND MASS FLOW DISTRIBUTIONS OF SOLID PARTICLES [S72]

	Glass Particles		Magnesia Particles			Glass [S53]	Van Zoonen [V7] Catalyst		
1. M_p, lb	10	20	0.75	1.75	2.75		(140)	(330)	(630)
2. $\dot{M}_p$, lb/sec	8.79	5.39	0.2695	0.598	0.946		0.198	0.467	0.892
3. $M_p / \pi R^2 = \bar{G}_p$, lb/in.² sec	0.2742	0.447	0.0137	0.0304	0.0481	0.0273			
4. u_o f.p.s.	133.2	128.4	138.4	137.6	136.9	100	27.8	29.7	31.1
5. $\rho_{po} u_{po} / \bar{G}_p$	1.560	1.643	1.472	1.452	1.480	1.65	1.52	1.362	1.13
6. $\rho_{pw} u_{pw} / \bar{G}_p$	0.397	0.40	0.423	0.486	0.491	0.45	0.536	0.1054	0.118
7. $\dot{M}_p / \pi R^2 u_o$, 10^{-4} lb/in.³	1.735	2.822	0.0863	0.1918	0.304		5.6	13.2	25.3
8. $\rho_{po} / (\bar{G}_p / u_o)$	1.562	1.647	1.485	1.462	1.480	1.67	1.612	1.362	1.00
9. $\rho_{pw} / (\bar{G}_p / u_o)$	1.902	1.876	1.60	1.52	1.526	1.67	3.23	3.27	3.21
10. u_{pw} / u_o	0.2105	0.2055	0.2635	0.32	0.323	0.19	0.18	0.32	0.35
11. m_p^*	6	12	0.448	1.048	1.65	0.18			
12. $\dot{m}_p^*$	4.97	8.13	0.249	0.551	0.876	0.0763	23.7	55.7	106.5
13. K_1	0.1465	0.1465	0.125	0.125	0.125	0.085			
14. K_2	0.017	0.011	0.281	0.127	0.078	1.25			
15. m in Eq. (4.86)	1.14	1	1.504	1.355	0.81	2.30			
16. α in Eq. (4.87)	2.14	2.14	3.29	2.62	2.13				
17. Pipe material	Brass		Brass			Glass 3″ dia	Unrecorded 5 cm dia		
18. Particle size (nominal)	50 μ		35 μ			100 μ to 250 μ	20 μ to 150 μ		

with

$$B = \frac{2(\rho_{pw} - \rho_{po})}{\rho_{po}(\alpha + 2)^2}.$$

The electrostatic effect is generalized according to [S72] the turbulent electroviscous number for space charge:

$$N_{\text{ev}} = \sqrt{\frac{\rho_{pw}}{4\pi\epsilon_o}} \left(\frac{q}{m_p}\right) \frac{R^2}{D_{pw}}. \tag{4.82}$$

Further, we have

$$\dot{m}_{pw} = D_{pw}\left(\frac{d\rho_p}{dr}\right)_w, \tag{4.83}$$

giving diffusivity by measuring density and collision rate.

Table 4.1 presents the concentration and mass-flow data of various sources, covering a wide range of flow rate ratio of solid to air (Item 12). It is seen that due to the difference between the velocity profiles of solid and gas, the mass ratio $(M_p/M_a = m_p^*)$ and the flow-rate ratio $(\dot{M}_p/\dot{M}_a = \dot{m}_p^*)$ are different with the former always at a higher value. The velocity of the solid particles at the center of the pipe does not differ from that of the gas in fully developed turbulent pipe flow in the range of loading of the present experiments, but lags considerably in the case of very high loading of van Zoonen's experiments. It is interesting to note that in spite of the range of average mass flow of particles (Item 3), the mass-flow distribution (Items 5 and 6) and the concentration distribution (Items 8 and 9) follow the same trend, and also the slip velocity of solid particles at the wall (Item 10). Their similarity, however, is due to the narrow range of turbulent suspension parameter [S66] (Item 13),

$$K_1 = \frac{\sqrt{\pi}}{18} \frac{\sqrt{\langle u^2 \rangle}\bar{\rho}2a}{\bar{\mu}}\left(\frac{2a}{l_1}\right)\left(\frac{\bar{\rho}_p}{\bar{\rho}}\right), \tag{4.84}$$

where $\sqrt{\langle u^2 \rangle}$ is the intensity of turbulence of the gas, $\bar{\rho}$ is the density of the gas and $\bar{\mu}$ its viscosity; l_1 is the Lagrangian scale of turbulence of the gas, $\bar{\rho}_p$ is the density of the solid material; and the pipe-flow parameter of turbulent suspension [S53] (Item 14)

$$K_2 = 1.56 \times 10^{-6}\left(\frac{\bar{\rho}_p}{\bar{\rho}}\right)\left(\frac{2a}{R}\right)\left(\frac{u_o R\bar{\rho}}{\bar{\mu}}\right)^{3/2}\left(\frac{\pi R^2 \bar{\rho} u_o}{\dot{M}_p}\right), \tag{4.85}$$

where R is the pipe radius and u_o is the maximum gas velocity. From the distribution, one further sees that the approximations [S53] in

$$u_p = u_{pw} + (u_{po} - u_{pw})\left(1 - \frac{r}{R}\right)^{1/m}, \tag{4.86}$$

and

$$\rho_p = \rho_{po} + (\rho_{pw} - \rho_{po})\left(\frac{r}{R}\right)^{\alpha} \tag{4.87}$$

TABLE 4.2

DIFFUSIVITY AND ELECTROSTATIC CHARGE OF SOLID PARTICLES [S72]

	Glass Particles		Magnesia Particles			Glass [S53]	Van Zoonen [V7] Catalyst		
1. M_p, lb	10	20	0.75	1.75	2.75				
2. $\dot{M}_p$, lb/sec									
3. $M_p/\pi R^2$, lb/m^2 sec						0.0273	0.198	0.467	0.892
4. K_m, 10^8 lb/in.^{2} sec amp	3.381	3.944	0.982	1.062	1.348				
5. (q/m) 10^{-6} coul/kg	0.530	0.445	0.813	0.750	0.591	2.7	1.33	1.27	1.26
6. $\partial\rho_p/\partial r|_w$ 10^{-4} lb/in.^{4}	0.388	0.450	0.01805	0.020	0.0183				
7. D_{pw}, 10^{-4} m^2/sec	8	10	1.2	1.64	1.96	2.7	8	9.45	13.0
8. Pipe temp., °F	106	108	96	98	101	85			
9. Ambient temp., °F	74	77	77	77	77	85			
10. Rel. humidity %	21	5	30	30	30				

can be checked by determining constants m and α from these results as presented such as in Figs. 4.20, 4.22, and 4.23 (Items 15 and 16). It is seen that these values vary over a small range in spite of the large variation in size of particles and speeds.

To compare to the results of Soo on boundary-layer motion [S52] governing slip condition, the value of particle-slip parameter

$$K_3 = 72\sqrt{2}\left(\frac{\dot{m}_{pw}}{\bar{\rho}_p u_{po}}\right)\frac{R}{a} \qquad (4.88)$$

was computed.

It was recognized earlier that in the pipe flow of a gas-solid suspension, there must be a drift component of the solid particles besides diffusion to give the measured solid distribution. Diffusion alone, regardless of diffusivity, would end up with uniform concentration distribution of solid particles at fully developed pipe flow even if the diffusivity varies with the radius. The present result was attributed to the electrostatic charge induced on the solid particles due to impact with the wall and the drift is due to electrostatic repulsion by self-fields [S57].

Table 4.2 presents the relation of diffusivity and electrostatic charges in solid particles. In the case of the first five columns, the charge to mass (q/m) ratio (Item 5) was measured first and the diffusivity D_{pw} was calculated (Item 9); the value of D_{pw} of the glass particles checks with earlier measurements (Sec. 2.8) within the order of magnitude. The values of (q/m) for the last four columns were calculated from their values of D_{pw}. It is seen that for both glass particles and MgO particles the charge-to-mass ratios induced by copper pipe are similar in magnitude and all positive in sign as measured. The glass particles in glass pipe [S53] carried a much larger charge as expected, although the sign of charge is unknown. The (q/m) from Van Zoonen's experiments is deemed as reasonable although the material of the pipe is not reported, nor the type of catalyst.

The average field E at the surface of the particles is given by

$$E \sim \left(\frac{q}{m}\right)\frac{a\bar{\rho}_p}{3\epsilon_o}, \qquad (4.89)$$

where ϵ_o is the permittivity. The value of E varies from 800 v/m for magnesia particles to 900 v/m for glass particles. No electric breakdown occurred under the prevailing humidity. It should be noted that the average charge-to-mass ratios obtained in Table 4.2 are particular to the test system.

Extensive measurements on magnesia-air suspension, over the range of pipe flow Reynolds number of 1.3×10^5 to 2.95×10^5, made possible some generalization of the behavior of such a mixture. Over the range of the experiments by Trezek, the velocity profile of the gas phase is closely represented by the $\frac{1}{7}$th velocity law, but the velocity of the solid phase is represented by Eq. (4.86), with $m \geqslant 1$. This, together with the density distribution of solid particles, led to a difference between mass ratio and mass-flow ratio of solid to gas [S72]. The results of overall measurements and computations from integrating measured density and mass-flow profiles [S72] are shown in Fig. 4.24. It is seen that for pipe flow, these two would be identical if a suspension

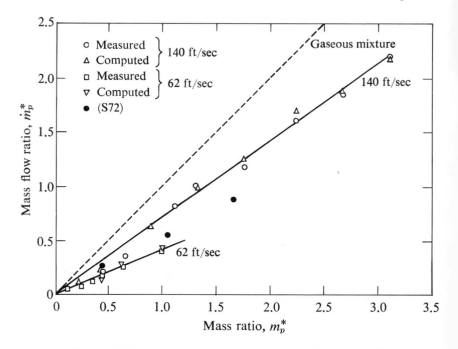

Figure 4.24 Relation between mass ratio and mass-flow ratio [S71].

behaved as a gaseous mixture. The results show that the mass flow ratio is consistently lower than the mass ratio. The comparison of the curve of 140 ft/sec to 62 ft/sec shows that with similar charge-to-mass ratio the electrostatic effect is felt more strongly at low flow velocity. This confirms the concept of minimum transport velocity of Thomas [T27].

The collision rate of solid particles with the wall as measured by the sticky tape is shown in Fig. 4.7. This rate is strongly affected by the turbulent intensity near the wall besides the particle density. It is seen that for 30-μ particle diameter, the time constant for momentum transfer of the particle is $F = 9\bar{\mu}/2a^2\bar{\rho}_p \sim 1340$ sec^{-1}, thus the radial stopping distance is, for an intensity of 4 ft/sec, only 0.036 in., which is smaller than the boundary-layer thickness of the gas. The collision rate with the wall is therefore nearly two

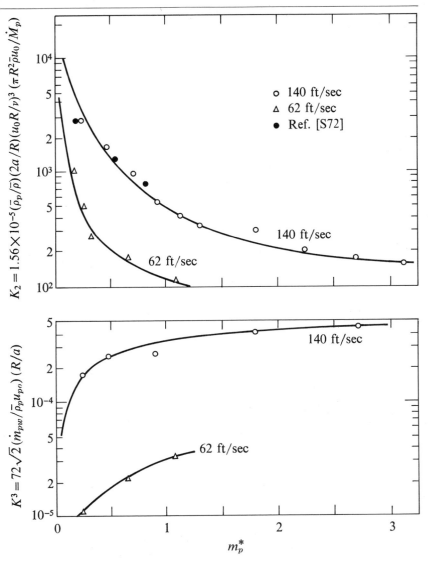

Figure 4.25 Variation of K_2 and K_3 with loading m_p^* [S71].

orders of magnitude smaller than an estimate based on random motion according to the intensity of turbulence because of the shear layer at the wall (Eq. 2.24). This gives small contribution of collision of particles to the shear stress at the wall of the pressure drop in pipe flow (Sec. 4.1). The correlations of the overall flow rate $\dot{M}_p$ or the pipe flow parameter K_2 and the particle-slip parameter K_3 are shown in Fig. 4.25 for various mass ratio m_p^* and flow velocity in the pipe. As the mass ratio m_p^* increases, the carrying capacity of the fluid $\dot{M}_p$ tends to an asymptotic value, the limit being sedimentation and clogging.

Figure 4.26 shows the values of particle diffusivity D_{pw} at the wall for various mass ratios and flow velocities which are comparable to those given

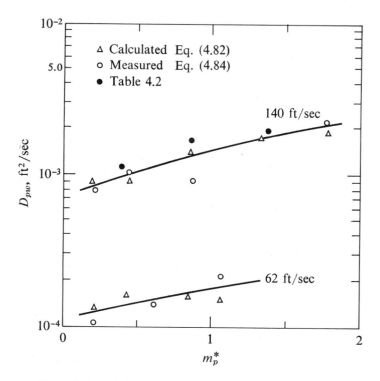

Figure 4.26 Variation of wall diffusivity with particle-loading ratio [S71].

in Sec. 2.8. The calculated result is based on Eq. (4.82) from density profile and electric charge-to-mass ratio. The measured data were obtained from Eq. (4.84). Consistency of D_{pw} from these two different ways shows that similar degree of accuracy was maintained in the measurement of average charge-to-mass ratio and the collision rate at the wall. The previous results in Table 4.2 are included for comparison. The particle diffusivity and the friction-factor parameter obtained from the rate of collision in Eqs. (4.80) and (4.81) are plotted vs. the slip flow parameter K_3 in Fig. 4.27. It is seen that the data shows that the density of solid particles is such that the whole range of experiment is in the "free-particle" range by analogy to free-molecule flow (Sec. 5.5) due to large interparticle spacing and lack of collision among the particles. The velocity profile of the solid particle cloud is therefore analogous to that of free-molecule flow with slip at the wall and nearly linear velocity gradient.

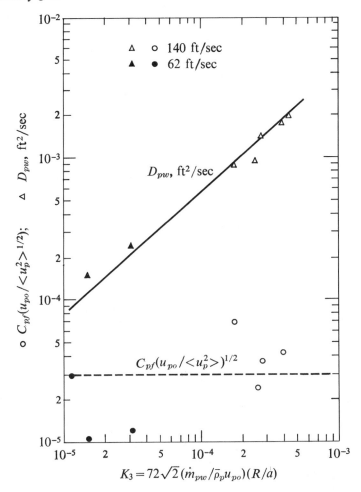

Figure 4.27 Particle friction factor and particle diffusivity [S71].

The fact that the density and velocity distribution of the particle phase is influenced by the charge to mass ratio of particles and the particle diffusivity is demonstrated in Fig. 4.28. With the density and velocity-distribution parameter in Eqs. (4.86) and (4.87) plotted vs. the turbulent electroviscous number N_{ev} the quantity $(u_{po} - u_{pw})/u_{po}$ and m tend to one or the case of

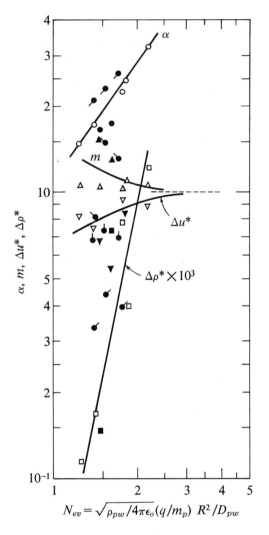

	140 ft/sec	62 ft/sec	Ref. [S72]
α in Eq. (4.87)	○	●	◖
m in Eq. (4.86)	△	▲	◗
$\Delta u^* = \dfrac{u_{po} - u_{pw}}{u_{po}}$	▽	▼	◓
$\Delta \rho^* = \dfrac{\rho_{pw} - \rho_{po}}{\rho_{po}}$	□	■	◔

Figure 4.28 Variation of α, m, Δu^*, $\Delta \rho^*$ with electroviscous number [S71].

"viscous" motion of solid particle phase (Sec. 5.5). However, the density profile is strongly affected by N_{ev}. At large N_{ev} steady flow of the suspension cannot be maintained; deposition of particles will occur as in an electrostatic precipitator [S71].

Figure 4.28 shows that pipe flow of a gas-solid suspension is basically a phenomenon of interaction between electrostatic and hydrodynamic effects; the pertinent parameter being the turbulent electroviscous number N_{ev}, the ratio of electrostatic force to turbulent force. The measured average charge to mass ratios is, in general, in the 10^{-6} coulomb/kg range. Unless the particle charge is truly negligible, steady, fully developed laminar pipe flow of a suspension cannot be maintained. The corresponding N_{ev} for laminar flow is $\sqrt{\rho_p/4\pi}(q/m)R^2/\bar{\nu}$ (Chap. 10).

For a given mass ratio m_p^*, the mean interparticle spacing is

$$n^{-\frac{1}{3}} \sim a\left[\left(\frac{4\pi}{3}\right)\frac{\bar{\rho}_p}{\bar{\rho}} m_p^*\right]^{\frac{1}{3}},\tag{4.90}$$

and $n^{-\frac{1}{3}} \sim 16a$ for $m_p^* = 3$ for magnesia in air, the fraction solid is only 0.001. Hence, as expected, the suspensions tested were entirely in the "free-particle" range. The particle phase is in laminar-slip motion in spite of the fact that the fluid is turbulent (Sec. 5.5).

The above measurements are illustrated as typical methods of approach and the bases for the generalization of observed phenomena to be made later. Other studies include the electrostatic probe developed by Batch, Dalmon, and Hignett [B22], and the capacitance probes developed by Chao, Min, and Wyman [M37], and Daniel and Brackett [D6]. Light-scattering methods have also been used by Van de Hulst [V3] and Foster [F20]. Microphone measurement of particle count as in Soo and Regalbuto [S68] was made by McCracken and Alexander [M20] on interplanetary dust particles near the earth.

Measurements on distributed quantities in a liquid suspension were made by Newitt, Richardson, and Shook [N6]. Other methods applicable to turbulent dispersion in pipe flow are single-particle diffusion techniques given in Sec. 2.8, optical measurements of Becker, Rosensweig, and Gwozdz [B27], and Rosensweig, Hottel, and Williams [R36], direct measurement of particle velocity by photographic method by Hellinckx [H28]. Distribution of particle and slip velocities in hydraulic conveying was measured by Newitt, Richardson, and Shook [N6].

From measurements made on flow in a vertical pipe, Kada and Hanratty [K1] showed that for glass particles and copper particles in air at 0.5 to 2.3 per cent volume fraction ϕ, negligible effect of presence of solid particles on turbulent diffusivity of air was found at pipe-flow Reynolds number $(N_{Re})_R$

of 20,300 and $2a = 0.00394$ in., and ϕ of 1.5 per cent and $(N_{Re})_R$ of 50,550 and $2a = 0.01488$ in. up to ϕ of 1.7 per cent. However, significant effect on turbulent diffusivity of fluid was found with $2a = 0.01488$ in. at $(N_{Re})_R$ of 20,300 at $\phi = 1.5$ per cent. Particle diffusivities were not determined. No definite trend was obtained in their study of concentration distribution of solid particles.

4.6 Laminar Flow of Sols and Coagulation

A number of studies have been made on the viscous flow of suspensoid sols and macromolecular solutions; an important application is in obtaining understanding of flow of blood [M23] and development of a thrombus as in coronary thrombosis.

Richardson and Tyler [R15] showed that the viscosity of disperse systems, such as suspensions of rice starch grains in carbon tetrachloride and paraffin, decreases with increasing shear rate. Higginbotham, Oliver, and Ward [H36], however, found that suspensions of spherical polymer particles in aqueous glycerol solutions behaved as Newtonian fluids. Harland [H14] found that the shear-rate effect on the viscosity of high-polymer solutions is appreciable only where the degree of polymerization exceeds 2000. Immergut and Eirich [I1] suggested that deformation of particles due to shear, porosity of particles, and preferred particle orientation leads to shear-rate effect. Jeffery [J6] and Starkey [S81, S83] suggested a flow mechanism in which particles comprising the disperse phase of the sol will follow flow path during shear such that the resulting change in the configuration of the system conforms to the principle of least action. This implies the existence of forces acting on the particles to displace them from the streamlines to where the velocity gradient is least. The net effect is in the development of a concentration pattern such that maximum concentration occurs where the velocity gradient is least (Sec. 2.3).

Starkey, Hewlett, Roberts, and James (S82) formulated velocity, viscosity, and concentration distribution in the development of viscous flow from the entrance of a pipe. Experimental methods included applications of a low head viscometer and devices for measuring concentration and viscosity ratios. Results show that there is a continuous increase in core concentration down stream from the entrance region. Other studies on flow of suspensions with coagulation are those reported by Segré and Silberberg [S20], Goldsmith and Mason [G30], and Karmis, Goldsmith, and Mason [K5]. Jeffrey and

Pearson [J7] reported similar findings as Segré and Silberberg, whose results could be due to the influence of electrostatic charges on the particles (Sec. 2.3).

4.7 Flow of Suspension of Fibers

Flow of suspensions of fibers was studied by Forgacs, Robertson, and Mason [F14]. Daily and Bugliarello [D1] performed experiments with dilute suspension of different papermaking fibers in the range of concentration between 0.1 and 1.0 per cent by weight. Laminar flow was observed to leave two regions: a central core with all the fibers gathered in an entangled structure (a "plug") and a very thin peripheral annulus of clear water of thickness d across which the velocity drops from the constant value in the core. Friction factors measured show a trend similar to other suspensions (Sec. 4.1). The thickness of clear-water annulus d was found to be related to the wall shear stress

$$\tau_w = \frac{\bar{\mu}U}{d} = \frac{f\rho U^2}{8},$$

d increases with flow rate and decreases with increase in concentration. Depending on pipe size, d is to the order of 10^{-4} ft and for velocities up to 3 fps, in 2 in. and $\frac{3}{4}$-in. diameter pipe, d varies from 10^{-4} to 10^{-2} ft. Daily and Bugliarello [D1] obtained

$$d \sim \frac{200\bar{\nu}}{U},$$

as compared to

$$d \sim \frac{310\bar{\nu}}{U},$$

obtained by Forgacs, Robertson, and Mason [F14].

The peculiar nature of flow of a fiber suspension is seen in the typical friction-loss curves (Fig. 4.29) of sulfite (paper pulp) stock recommended (1930) by the Hydraulic Institute for design purpose [S80]. It is seen that at 4 per cent pulp at bone-dry consistency, the head loss decreases as flow quantity is increased from 800 to 1200 gpm. It is also seen that with 1 per cent pulp the head loss is less than pure water over the whole flow range.

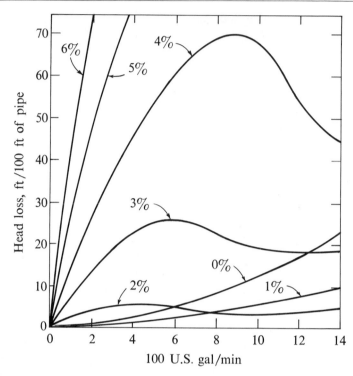

Figure 4.29 Friction loss of sulfite (paper) stock through 6-in. I.D. cast iron pipe, percentage pulp based on bone-dry consistency [S80].

Turbulent flow characteristics of model fibers (staple nylon) suspensions were studied by Bobkowicz and Gauvin [B44]. They found that presence of fibers decreases the pressure drop below that of pure water in pipe flow.

4.8 Chemical Reaction in Conveyed Systems

The concept of subjecting clouds of finely divided droplets or particles to a series of physical and chemical operations in a conveyed system was presented by Gauvin [G8]. In this system, the liquid feed material (solution, slurry, or colloidal suspension) is sprayed into the top of a heated tower and passed through successive zones of evaporation, drying, and chemical reaction in the form of a cloud of particles conveyed by the vapors generated during evaporation. Evaporation and drying will not be involved if the feed enters as solid particles. Reactions include oxidation, reduction and pyrolysis [L30].

A number of chemical reactions was studied in pilot reactors of 4-, 8-, and 12-in. diameter and up to 15 ft in height. The reactions studied include reduction of iron oxide, denitration of uranyl nitrate, roasting of pyrites, decomposition of ferrous and nickel sulphates, conversion of sodium sulphate to the carbonate [L29], and sewage incineration [G9].

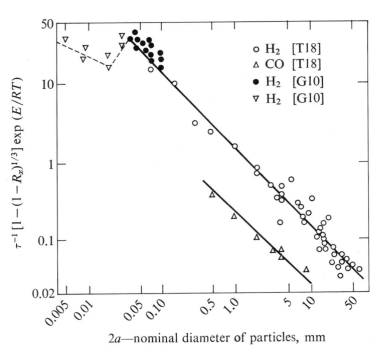

2a—nominal diameter of particles, mm

Figure 4.30 Correlation of reaction constants for the reduction of iron oxide particles, in the presence of hydrogen or carbon monoxide ($E = 4200$ cal/g mole) [T18].

The reduction of iron oxide particles was studied extensively by Gauvin and Gravel [G10], and Themelis and Gauvin [T18]. A generalized rate equation was first developed for the reduction of iron oxide in the presence of hydrogen or carbon monoxide based on extensive analysis by Themelis and Gauvin [T19]. The relation as given in Fig. 4.30 shows that in the absence of diffusional resistance in the particle boundary layer, the overall process is controlled by the rate of reaction at the interface between reduced and unreduced layers of the particle, and that the propagation of this interface toward the center is linear with time. A study of the reduction of small iron oxide spheres, 5 to 100 μ in diameter, was carried out in hydrogen in a 4-in. diameter reactor. Residence time was controlled to 2 to 13 sec at 500 to 1100°C reactor temperature. The temperature of the solid particles was determined by a radiation pyrometer. In Fig. 4.30, τ is the residence time, E is the reaction activation energy, R_x the fractional extent of reaction. The dotted line shows that smaller particles deviate from this linear relation. It is expected that combustion of metal powders (Sec. 3.3) can be correlated in a similar manner.

SUMMARY OF BASIC CONCEPTS

Turbulent Motion

Anomaly of Friction Factor—Halstrom (1953) [H6], Thomas (1960) [T21]
Non-Newtonian Nature of Apparent Viscosity—Thomas (1960) [T21]
Minimum Transport Criterion—Thomas (1962) [T27]
Slip Flow of Particles—(1962) [S50]
Flow Regimes of Turbulent Suspension—(1962) [S52]
Electroviscous Correlation—(1964) [S72]

Laminar Motion

Particles in a Tube—Jeffery (1922) [J6], Segré and Silberberg (1961) [S20]

Transport Properties of a Cloud of Particles

We have already seen that, in a suspension, the particulate phase demonstrates certain general behaviors such as concentration or number density, mean velocity, and diffusivity. In the fundamental sense, other transport phenomena of a cloud of particles can be obtained by proper integration procedure of the basic equation of motion [Eq. (2.37)] in an analogous manner as the determination of transport properties in the kinetic theory of gases. At the same time it must be recognized that the particle motion, in general, arises from fluid motion and any kinetic treatment must account for this basic fact.

5.1 Drag Coefficient, Heat, and Mass Transfer of Dense Cloud

Where the volume fraction of solid (ϕ) is sufficiently high such that the fluid boundary-layer thickness exceeds the interparticle spacing (Sec. 2.1), the drag coefficient of single spheres can no longer apply to a cloud of particles.

Steinour [S86] reported an upper limit of 2 per cent concentration by volume for significant interaction among particles. Dallavalle, McBride, Allred, and Jones [D3] gave the relation for hindered settling in terms of a mean surface diameter D as

$$D^2 = \frac{169 u_o \bar{\mu}}{g(\bar{\rho}_p - \bar{\rho})} \frac{1 - \epsilon}{\epsilon^3}, \tag{5.1}$$

where u_o is the velocity at the interface, $\bar{\mu}$ is the viscosity of the fluid material, g the acceleration due to gravity, $\bar{\rho}_p$, $\bar{\rho}$ the densities of the solid and fluid materials, and ϵ the fraction void which is equal to $1 - \phi$. Kaye and Boardman [K9] further concluded that above 5 per cent volume fraction of solid leads to hindered settling and the terminal velocity is no longer predicted by Stokes' law.

Even for slow motion, extension of the Stokes solution to a random cloud of spheres poses a most challenging task. However, extensive studies have been made on the pressure drop and settling of fluidized beds [O9]. Because of the nature of motion in a fluidized bed (Chap. 9), the pressure-drop data of a fluidized bed can be extended to determine the drag coefficient of a cloud of solid particles.

Ergun [E18], and Orning [E19] recognizing that the pressure loss (ΔP) over height L in a fluidized bed is caused by simultaneous kinetic and viscous energy losses, proposed the following equation:

$$\frac{\Delta P}{L} = 150 \frac{(1 - \epsilon)^2}{\epsilon^3} \frac{\bar{\mu} u_s}{(2a)^2} + 1.75 \frac{(1 - \epsilon)}{\bar{\mu}^3} \frac{G_o u_s}{2a}, \tag{5.2}$$

where u_s is the superficial fluid velocity based on unobstructed flow area for the fluid, ϵ the fraction void ($= 1 - \phi$), and the interstitial velocity is $u_\epsilon = u_s/\epsilon$; G_o is the mass flow of the fluid based on unobstructed flow area.

Equation (2.37), when applied to a steady fluidized bed visualized as a fluid moving past a particle cloud at relative velocity u_ϵ, simplifies to

$$0 \cong F u_\epsilon - g - \frac{1}{\bar{\rho}_p} \frac{\partial P}{\partial z} \tag{5.3}$$

for z in the direction of gravity; g is the acceleration due to gravity, and F is the time constant of momentum transfer between fluid and particle. To obtain F for each individual particle in this cloud, it is seen that, for acceleration $F u_\epsilon$, the overall pressure drop is given by

$$\frac{\Delta P}{L} = \frac{m_p F u_\epsilon N_A N_L}{l_p N_L a_p N_A} = F u_\epsilon (1 - \epsilon) \bar{\rho}_p, \tag{5.4}$$

where m_p is the mass per particle, N_A is the average number of particles per projected area normal to L, N_L is the average number of particles over length L, l_p is the length in space apportioned to each particle, a_p is the area apportioned to each particle, and $a_p l_p$ is just the volume apportioned to each particle and is the volume of a particle divided by $(1 - \epsilon)$. The time constant F is therefore

$$F = \frac{75}{2} \frac{(1 - \epsilon)}{\epsilon^2} \frac{\bar{\mu}}{\bar{\rho}_p a^2} + \frac{1.75}{2\epsilon} \frac{\bar{\rho}}{\bar{\rho}_p} \frac{u_\epsilon}{a}, \tag{5.5}$$

and the drag coefficient is given by

$$C_D = \frac{8}{3}\frac{a}{u_\epsilon}\frac{\bar{\rho}_p}{\bar{\rho}}F = 200\left(\frac{1-\epsilon}{\epsilon^2}\right)\frac{\bar{\mu}}{2au_\epsilon\bar{\rho}} + \frac{7}{3\epsilon}. \tag{5.6}$$

It is seen that the relation for a single sphere is valid as $\epsilon \to 0.92$ or $\phi = 1 - \epsilon = 0.08$ and $u_\epsilon \to u$, the free-stream fluid velocity.

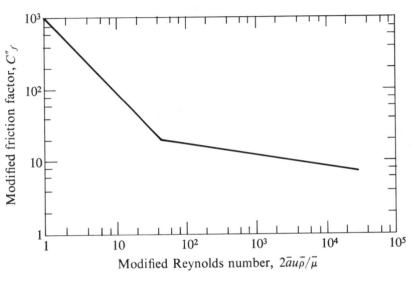

Figure 5.1 Friction factor for solid packing particles [S31].

The upper limit of fraction solid is given by the case of a packed bed, with pressure drop given by Chilton and Colburn [S31] as

$$\frac{\Delta P}{L} = \frac{2C_f''A_wA_pA_LG_o^2}{\bar{\rho}(2\bar{a})}, \tag{5.7}$$

where C_f'' is a modified friction factor given in Fig. 5.1, A_w is a wall-effect correction factor, A_p is a correction factor for hollow packing, A_L is a correction factor for the wetting of the packing by the solvent circulated, and is unity for a gas-solid system; $2\bar{a}$ is the nominal size of packing particle, G_o is the mass flow based on total cross section. Similar conversion to particle drag coefficient as in the above gives

$$C_D = \frac{8}{3}\frac{C_f''A_wA_pA_L\epsilon^2}{(1-\epsilon)}, \tag{5.8}$$

which fits the relation in Eq. (5.5) for $A_w = A_p = A_L = 1$ for $\epsilon \sim 0.42$. The above relations of C_D are compared in Fig. 5.2. Note that for spherical particles, $\epsilon \sim 0.42$ corresponds to an interparticle spacing of 1 diameter, while $\epsilon \sim 0.92$ corresponds to that of 2 diameters. Cluster formation [K9], leading to lower drag coefficient of a group of particles, may be regarded as one source of instability in a fluidized bed. Hindered settling was shown to

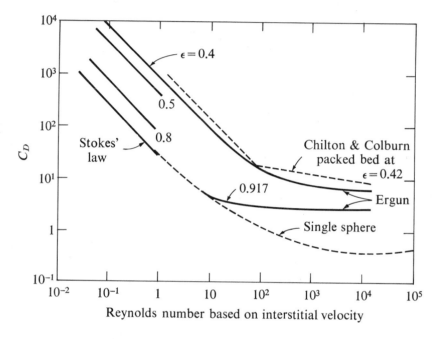

Figure 5.2 Drag coefficient of spheres in a cloud.

be a useful method for particle-size analysis [K10]. Sinclair [S35] further obtained limit deposit-velocity of heterogeneous suspensions such as iron-kerosene, sand-water, and coal-water in pipe flow. A general power relation for terminal velocity in fluidization and settling was given by Pruden and Epstein [P33].

In conjunction with the drag or pressure-drop characteristics of a cloud of particles and the modification of a single sphere relation, corresponding changes in the heat- and mass-transfer relations are expected. The interest in heat transfer involving a dense cloud has largely been in the transfer between the cloud and a wall, rather than heat transfer to a single particle. A comprehensive summary of dimensional correlations is given by Chu [C9]. Chu, Kalil, and Wetteroth [C30] correlated the mass-transfer factor j_d in both

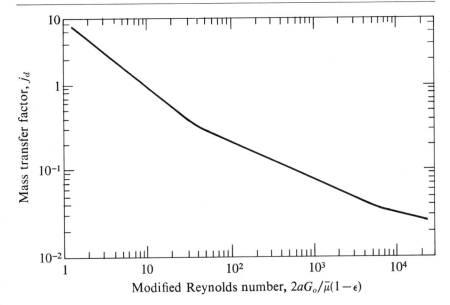

Figure 5.3 Generalized correlation of mass-transfer data in fixed and fluidized bed of granular particles [C30].

fixed and fluidized beds, based on molar concentration

$$j_d = \frac{k_c \mathcal{M}}{G_o} \left(\frac{\bar{\mu}}{\bar{\rho} D} \right)^{3/2},$$

(5.9)

where k_c is the rate constant for mass transfer, G_o is the mass flow based on unobstructed area, $\mathcal{M}$ is the molecular weight of the fluidizing fluid, $(\bar{\mu}/\bar{\rho} D)$ is the Schmidt number. They gave, for

and
$$\left.\begin{array}{ll} \dfrac{2aG_o}{\bar{\mu}(1-\epsilon)} > 30, & j_d = 1.77 \left[\dfrac{2aG_o}{\bar{\mu}(1-\epsilon)} \right]^{-0.44}, \\[4ex] \dfrac{2aG_o}{\bar{\mu}(1-\epsilon)} < 30, & j_d = 5.7 \left[\dfrac{2aG_o}{\bar{\mu}(1-\epsilon)} \right]^{-0.78}. \end{array}\right\}$$

(5.10)

The trend is shown in Fig. 5.3. They further suggested the j factor for heat transfer, by analogy

$$j = \frac{N_{\mathrm{Nu}}}{N_{\mathrm{Pr}} N_{\mathrm{Re}}} = \frac{h}{c G_o} (N_{\mathrm{Pr}})^{2/3} \sim j_d,$$

(5.11)

where h is the heat-transfer coefficient and c is the specific heat of the fluid.

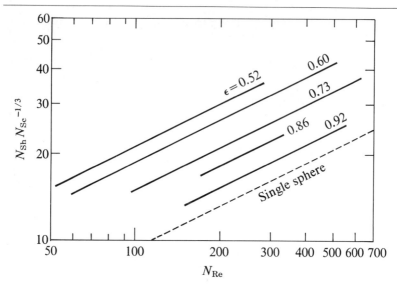

Figure 5.4 Influence of particle concentration on rate of mass transfer [M50].

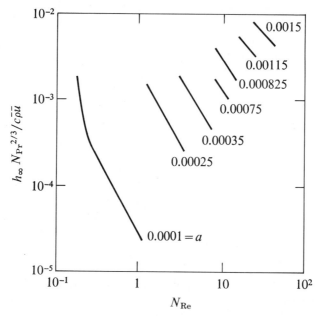

Figure 5.5 Heat-transfer coefficient for complete mixing in dense bed of solid spheres (L/D from 0.6 to 1.25) [F9].

Mullin and Treleaven [M50] made measurements on rate of mass transfer from spheres at fraction voids down to $\epsilon = 0.52$. Their results are shown in Fig. 5.4, applicable to both fluidized and fixed beds. In Fig. 5.4, $N_{Re} = U(2a)/\bar{\nu}$, where U is the average velocity, $N_{Sh} = k_c(2a)/D$, k_c is the mass-transfer coefficient and D is the diffusivity, the Schmidt number $N_{Sc} = \bar{\nu}/D$. General agreement with the correlation suggested by Chu, Kalil, and Wetteroth [C30] is seen.

Ferron and Watson [F9] studied the heat transfer from solid particles in a fluidized bed, but did not correlate with fraction void, although the effect of solid concentration was recognized. Their results ($L/2R = 1$) were correlated with those of Wamsley and Johanson [W7], and Kettenring, Manderfield, and Smith [K16] ($L/2R = 0.6$ to 1.25) as shown in Fig. 5.5, h_∞ is the heat-transfer coefficient for complete mixing. Measurements were made with bed height-to-diameter ratio of 1.

5.2 Impaction of Particles with Surfaces

Applications such as spray painting, sand blasting, and particle collection involve motion of a suspension toward a surface. Langmuir and Blodgett [L16] treated the problem as potential motion of the suspension but with viscous drag on the particles in the cloud. The equation of motion of a particle can be represented by

$$\frac{d\mathbf{u}_p}{dt} = F(\mathbf{u} - \mathbf{u}_p) - \mathbf{g}, \qquad (5.12)$$

where $\mathbf{g}$ is the vector of gravitational acceleration, $\mathbf{u}, \mathbf{u}_p$ are the velocity vectors of the fluid and the particles. For the coordinate system in Fig. 5.6, the boundary condition is given by that of the x-component

$$x = -\infty, \qquad u_x = u_{px} = u_o,$$

$\mathbf{u}(x,y,z)$ is given and it is assumed that it is unaffected by the presence and motion of particles. The motion of the particles is therefore determined by Eq. (5.12).

The nature of the impaction is given by the fraction impacted, η. η is defined as the ratio of the cross-sectional area of the original stream from which particles of a given size are impacted because the trajectories intersect the collector surface, to the projected area of the target in the direction of flow or the cross-sectional area of the original stream. Generalization of the

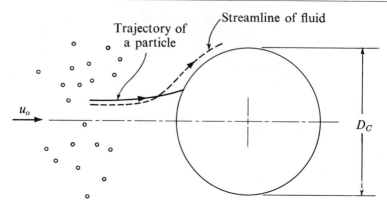

Figure 5.6 Impaction of particles with a body.

results is achieved by introducing the reference Reynolds number $(N_{\text{Re}})_o$:

$$(N_{\text{Re}})_o = \frac{2a\bar{\rho}u_o}{\bar{\mu}}, \tag{5.13}$$

so that the local-particle Reynolds number is given by

$$\frac{N_{\text{Re}}}{(N_{\text{Re}})_o} = \frac{|\mathbf{u} - \mathbf{u}_p|}{u_o}, \tag{5.14}$$

and the relation

$$F = \tfrac{3}{4}C_D\left(\frac{\bar{\rho}}{\bar{\rho}_p}\right)\frac{|\mathbf{u} - \mathbf{u}_p|}{2a} \tag{5.15}$$

is generalized by taking

$$C_D = \frac{24F^*}{(N_{\text{Re}})} \tag{5.16}$$

with

$$F^* = F^*(N_{\text{Re}}) \tag{5.17}$$

to be equal to 1 for the Stokes' law regime. Substitution gives

$$F = \tfrac{9}{2}F^*\frac{\bar{\mu}}{\bar{\rho}_p a^2}. \tag{5.18}$$

Equation (5.12) now becomes (neglecting gravity effect)

$$2\Psi\left(\frac{d\mathbf{u}_p^*}{dt^*}\right) = F^*(\mathbf{u}^* - \mathbf{u}_p^*), \tag{5.19}$$

where $\mathbf{u}^* = \mathbf{u}/u_o$, $\mathbf{u}_p^* = \mathbf{u}_p/u_o$, $t^* = tu_o/D_c$; D_c is the characteristic dimension of the target, and

$$\Psi = \frac{\bar{\rho}_p u_o (2a)^2}{18\bar{\mu} D_c} \tag{5.20}$$

is called an inertia parameter, which is the ratio of inertia force to viscous force. The non-Stokesian behavior is generalized in terms of

$$\Phi = \frac{(N_{Re})_o^2}{2\Psi} = \frac{9\bar{\rho}^2 u_o D_c}{\bar{\rho}_p \bar{\mu}}. \tag{5.21}$$

Calculations of fraction impacted η for potential flow about cylinders, spheres, and ribbons were performed by Langmuir and Blodgett [L16],

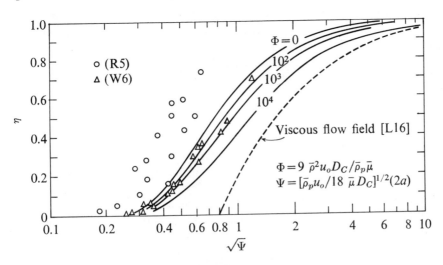

Figure 5.7 Impaction on a sphere [R3].

Mazin [F36], Landahl and Hermann [L9], Davies [D12], Levin [F36], Brun and Mergler [B68], Dorsch, Saper, and Kadow [D33], Fonda and Herne [F13] and Herne [H33]; and for viscous flow about spheres by Langmuir and Blodgett [L16], and Fonda and Herne [F13] with the fluid flow field given by Stokes' law [L5]. The relation for impaction on a sphere [D33] is given in Fig. 5.7, together with experimental results of Ranz and Wong [R5], Walton and Woolcock [W6]. It is seen that $\eta = 0$ at $\sqrt{\Psi} = 0.2$ for potential flow and $\sqrt{\Psi} = 0.8$ for viscous flow.

Ranz and Wong [R5] performed experiments with isodispersed sulfuric acid mists with mean droplet radii of 0.18 to 0.65 μ in a wind tunnel with air speeds of 10 to 100 m/sec. Targets included a wire of 77 μ diameter and a sphere of 0.9 mm. Walton and Woolcock [W6] used a target formed by a water droplet of 0.25–1.0-mm radius suspended by a glass capillary; an iso-disperse aerosol of methylene blue of spherical particles of 1.25 to 2.5 μ radii flowed over the water droplet.

An extensive survey on impaction and jet impingement was given by Ranz [R3]. Further details on inertia deposition of aerosols and fitration were assembled by Fuchs [F36]. Collection of supercooled clouds on airplane wings (which is related to deicer requirements) was studied by Brun, Lewis, Perkins, and Serafini [B67]. Tribus and Guibert [T50] and Serafini [S23] treated the problem of deposition of water drops on a two-dimensional wedge in supersonic flow, including passage of particles through a shock wave. Soo [S47] computed the collection of water droplets on airfoil blades. Ellis and Kelly [E10], using impaction, studied the collection and size measurement of droplet dispersions in the presence of condensable vapors. Collection and impaction including charged particles are treated in Chap. 10.

The magnitude of fraction impacted for bodies in free-molecule flow was determined by Friedlander [F26, F28] to be

$$\eta = S^{-2} \operatorname{erf} S + 2S^{-2} \int_0^S x \operatorname{erf} x \, dx, \qquad (5.22)$$

for a sphere, where $S = u_o / \sqrt{2kT_\infty/m}$; k is the Boltzmann constant, m is the mass of impacting particles, and T is the temperature at a large distance away from the sphere. He also computed η for cylinders and ribbons (Fig. 5.8). The procedure was extended from that of rarefied gas flow [S11].

When all the particles suffering impact with the target (such as a sphere of radius R) are collected, the rate of momentum transferred to the target is given by the force

$$\mathscr{F} = \pi R^2 \eta n_p u_o m u_o = \eta \pi R^2 \rho_p u_o^2, \qquad (5.23)$$

where $\rho_p = n_p m$ is the density of the cloud of particles and n is the number of particles per unit volume, m is the mass of each particle. However, another interesting situation is when the particles undergo elastic collision with the target.

Take the case of collision of particles with a sphere of radius R, with single scattering—that is, a particle after a collision does not return for another collision within a finite amount of time. For simplicity, we take the case where $\eta = 1$. With specular reflection, referring to Fig. 5.9, the rate of change of momentum of a particle approaching at collision angle θ is given by

$$mu_o - [mu_o r^* \cos(180° - 2\theta)] = mu_o[1 + r^* \cos 2\theta],$$

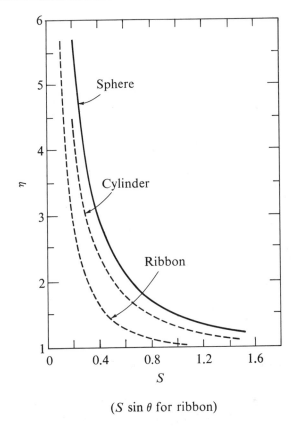

$(S \sin \theta$ for ribbon)

Figure 5.8 Fraction impacted for particles in free-molecule flow [F28].

in the direction of u_o, where r^* is the ratio of rebound speed to incoming speed. The force acting on the target sphere is given by

$$\mathscr{F} = n_p m u_o^2 \int_0^{\pi/2} (1 + r^* \cos 2\theta)(R \, d\theta \cos \theta)(2\pi R \sin \theta)$$

$$= \pi n_p m u_o^2 R^2 = \pi R^2 \rho_p u_o^2. \tag{5.24}$$

That is, the nature of scattering with specular reflection (regardless of r^*) is such that the larger portion of the particles is not reversed in direction.

When applied to the case of $\eta < 1$, the computation of $\mathscr{F}$ is more complicated; it suffices to generalize according to, for specular reflection:

$$\mathscr{F} \leq \eta \pi R^2 \rho_p u_o^2. \tag{5.25}$$

The drag coefficient of a sphere due to particle impaction is given by

$$C_{Dp} = \frac{\mathscr{F}}{\frac{1}{2}\rho_p u_o^2 \pi R^2} \leq 2\eta(\Psi, \Phi). \tag{5.26}$$

Although experimental verification is lacking for the case of a sphere, some comparison was made when the above method was applied to a cylinder,

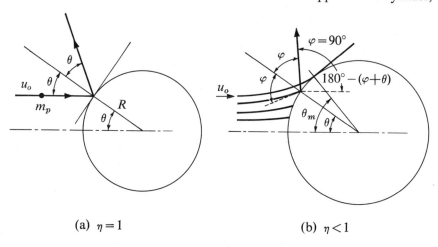

(a) $\eta = 1$ (b) $\eta < 1$

Figure 5.9 Collision and specular reflection of particles from a sphere.

whose particle drag coefficient was measured by Chilton, Sauer, and Lundberg [C21]. The force per unit length acting on an infinitely long cylinder is given by Fig. 5.7*b*:

$$\frac{\mathscr{F}}{L} = 2n_p m u_o \int_0^{\theta_m} u_p [1 + r^* \cos(\theta + \varphi)] R \, d\theta \cos\theta, \tag{5.27}$$

which can be integrated only with $\varphi(\theta)$ and $u_p(\theta)$ given. However, as a limiting case, for $\eta = 1$, $\varphi = 0$, $\theta_m = \pi/2$,

$$\frac{\mathscr{F}}{L} = 2\rho_p u_o^2 R \left(1 + \frac{r^*}{3}\right), \tag{5.28}$$

and at $\eta = 1$,

$$C_{Dp} = \frac{\mathscr{F}}{\frac{1}{2}\rho_p u_o^2 2RL} = 2(1 + \tfrac{1}{3}r^*), \tag{5.29}$$

and, in general,

$$C_{Dp} \leq 2(1 + \tfrac{1}{3}r^*)\eta. \tag{5.30}$$

The degree of approximation is seen by computing C_{Dp} from η given by Brun and Mergler [B68] in Fig. 5.8 for $\Phi = 0$, and corrected with adjusted inertia parameter [L16]

$$2\Psi'' = (2\Psi' - \tfrac{1}{8})\left(\frac{\Lambda}{\Lambda_s}\right),$$ (5.31)

where

$$\frac{\Lambda}{\Lambda_s} = (N_{\text{Re}})_o^{-1}\int_0^{(N_{\text{Re}})_o} \frac{1}{24}\left[C_D(N_{\text{Re}})\right]^{-1} d(N_{\text{Re}}),$$

where $(N_{\text{Re}})_o = 2au_o\bar{\rho}/\bar{\mu}$ is the particle Reynolds number based on u_o. As shown in Fig. 5.10, the range of r^* from 0 (sticking) to 1 (perfect elastic collision) appears to be well substantiated by the experimental data of Chilton, Sauer, and Lundberg [C21]. Their theoretical procedure is not clear, however. Instead of fraction impacted, their impaction data was expressed in terms of maximum impingement angle θ_m (Fig. 5.9b), which compared favorably with Brun and Mergler [B68], which in turn was well substantiated by Ranz and Wong [R5], but their predicted drag coefficients do not compare to the above asymptotic relation in the limit of $\eta = 1$ (their integration was carried out giving the total pressure force over the cylinder instead of the net force in the direction of u_o as given by Eq. (5.24) which constitutes the drag due to collision).

If one treats the particles as a continuum, a momentum-transfer drag would be expected. This is because of momentum exchange between the particles and air, resulting in a change in the gas-phase pressure distribution; that is, an additional drag due to increase in gas pressure by slowing down of particles [C21]. This is to be expected in an extremely dense cloud of particles where multiple scattering (Sec. 5.5) has to be accounted for. For particles greater than 10 diameters apart, dissipation will occur almost entirely in the wakes of particles without localized increase in static pressure of the gas (Sec. 6.3).

5.3 Momentum Transfer among Clouds in Single Scattering

Direct interaction among particles in a fluid suspension was first treated by Peskin [P13], who accounted for the fact that relative motion of two spheres in a fluid gives rise to a force of interaction even in the case of potential motion as recognized by Hicks, Herman, and Basset [L5]. Using kinetic analogy, he postulated a potential of interaction. Due to the complexity, direct application of the result is difficult. Interaction of particles in slow motion was treated extensively by Happel and Brenner [H11]. Marble [M7] treated interparticle forces but neglected the effect of the presence of the fluid during collision. The interaction force thus estimated will be many times larger than could be expected, as can be seen from the magnitudes of fraction impacted as given in the above.

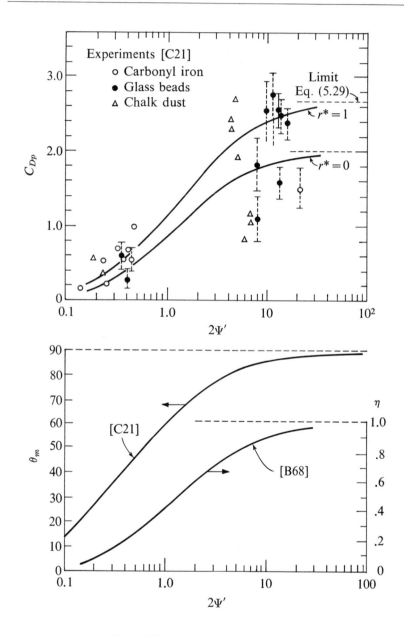

Figure 5.10 Drag coefficient of a dust cloud.

The following extends on the generalization reported by Soo [S60]. Since the relations in Sec. 5.2 account for forces due to fluid between particles, the particle interaction can be treated by extending the idea of impaction. This method is still an approximation, since the fluid velocity, in general, will be different from particle velocities.

The force acting on a particle (s) due to collision by a cloud of particles (r) in addition to fluid drag can be written as

$$\frac{d\mathbf{u}_p^{(s)}}{dt} = F^{(s)}(\mathbf{u} - \mathbf{u}_p^{(s)}) + F_p^{(sr)}(\mathbf{u}_p^{(r)} - \mathbf{u}_p^{(s)}), \tag{5.32}$$

leaving out the effects of gravity, pressure gradient, etc., for the present. By analogy with $F^{(s)}$, that is,

$$F^{(s)} = \frac{6\pi\bar{\mu}aF^*}{m} = \frac{9\bar{\mu}F^*}{2\bar{\rho}_p^{(s)}a_s^2}, \tag{5.33}$$

for cases in the Stokes' law range, the time constant $F_p^{(sr)}$ is given by

$$F_p^{(sr)} = \frac{[\text{Drag force due to collision by } (r) \text{ particles}]}{m_s|\mathbf{u}_p^{(r)} - \mathbf{u}_p^{(s)}|}. \tag{5.34}$$

When there is sufficient frequency of collision among the (r) particles themselves to constitute a viscosity $\mu_p^{(r)}$ (Sec. 5.5), direct analogy of Eq. (5.33) would be feasible. When interaction among the (r) particles can be neglected, the drag force due to collision by (r) particles is given by Eq. (5.25). Following the procedures of classical mechanics [G33], the relative motion between particles (s) and particles (r) can be expressed in the center of mass frame of reference. For relative motion of (r) to (s), with relative speed $\Delta u_p^{(sr)} = |\mathbf{u}_p^{(s)} - \mathbf{u}_p^{(r)}|$, Eq. (5.12) becomes

$$\left[\frac{m_r m_s}{m_r + m_s}\right]\frac{\Delta u_p^{(sr)}}{2(a_s + a_r)}\frac{du^{*(r)}}{dt^*} = \mathscr{F}(r) = F^{(r)}F^*(\mathbf{u}^* - \mathbf{u}^{*r}) \tag{5.35}$$

which gives rise to

$$\Psi^{(sr)} = \left[1 + \frac{m_r}{m_s}\right]^{-1}\frac{\bar{\rho}_p^{(r)}\Delta u_p^{(sr)}}{2(a_s + a_r)18\bar{\mu}}(2a_r)^2$$

$$= \left[\sqrt{\frac{m_r}{m_s}} + \sqrt{\frac{m_s}{m_r}}\right]^{-1}\left[\sqrt{\frac{a_r}{a_s}} + \sqrt{\frac{a_s}{a_r}}\right]^{-1}\left[\frac{2\sqrt{a_s a_r}\bar{\rho}\Delta u_p^{(sr)}}{18\bar{\mu}}\right]\frac{\sqrt{\bar{\rho}_p^{(s)}\bar{\rho}_p^{(r)}}}{\bar{\rho}}\sqrt{\frac{a_s}{a_r}} \tag{5.36}$$

$$\Phi^{(sr)} = \left[1 + \frac{m_r}{m_s}\right]\frac{9\bar{\rho}^2\Delta u_p^{(sr)}[2(a_r + a_s)]}{\bar{\rho}_p^{(r)}\bar{\mu}}$$

$$= \left[\sqrt{\frac{m_r}{m_s}} + \sqrt{\frac{m_s}{m_r}}\right]\left[\sqrt{\frac{a_r}{a_s}} + \sqrt{\frac{a_s}{a_r}}\right]\left[\frac{18\sqrt{a_s a_r}\bar{\rho}\Delta u_p^{(sr)}}{\bar{\mu}}\right]\frac{\bar{\rho}}{\sqrt{\bar{\rho}_p^{(s)}\bar{\rho}_p^{(r)}}}\left(\frac{a_r}{a_s}\right)^{3/2}, \tag{5.37}$$

which gives $\eta^{(sr)}$, the fraction of impaction of (r) particles on (s). Equations (5.36) and (5.37) reduce to Eqs. (5.20) and (5.21) for $m_s > m_r$ and $a_s \gg a_r$. From Eq. (5.25), when there is negligible collision by reflected particles, (secondary scattering) the force acting on an (s) particle due to collision of (r) particles is

$$\mathscr{F}^{(sr)} \simeq \eta^{(sr)} n_p^{(r)} \pi (a_s + a_r)^2 \frac{m_s m_r}{m_s + m_r} \Delta u_p^{(sr)}(\mathbf{u}_p^{(r)} - \mathbf{u}_p^{(s)})$$

$$= \eta^{(sr)} \left[1 + \frac{m_r}{m_s} \right]^{-1} \rho_p^{(r)} \pi (a_s + a_r)^2 \Delta u_p^{(sr)}(\mathbf{u}_p^{(r)} - \mathbf{u}_p^{(s)}), \qquad (5.38)$$

and

$$F^{(sr)} = \frac{3}{4} \frac{\eta^{(sr)} (a_s + a_r)^2 \Delta u_p^{(sr)} \rho_p^{(r)}}{a_s^3 \bar{\rho}_p^{(s)} [1 + (m_r/m_s)]}$$

$$= \tfrac{3}{4}\eta^{(sr)} \frac{(\sqrt{a_s/a_r} + \sqrt{a_r/a_s})^2 \Delta u_p^{(sr)} \rho_p^{(r)}}{\sqrt{a_s a_r}\sqrt{\bar{\rho}_p^{(s)} \bar{\rho}_p^{(r)}}(\sqrt{m_r/m_s} + \sqrt{m_s/m_r})}. \qquad (5.39)$$

The latter expression is convenient for particles of nearly similar sizes and serves to demonstrate the symmetry of functions. For two clouds of particles in a given volume, equality of action and reaction leads to

$$\rho_p^{(s)} F^{(sr)} = \rho_p^{(r)} F^{(rs)}, \qquad (5.40)$$

where for

$$\eta^{(rs)} = \eta^{(rs)}(\Psi^{(rs)}, \Phi^{(rs)}),$$

we get

$$F^{(rs)} = \frac{3}{4} \frac{\eta^{(rs)} (a_s + a_r)^2 \Delta u_p^{(sr)} \rho_p^{(s)}}{a_r^3 \bar{\rho}_p^{(r)} [1 + (m_s/m_r)]}. \qquad (5.41)$$

For small particles $\Phi \sim 0$ (Stokes'-law range), while Ψ might take on various values. For the case of $2a_r$ of $10\,\mu$, $2a_s$ of $20\,\mu$, for $\bar{\rho}_p = 10^3$ kg, $\bar{\mu} = 10^{-5}$ kg/msec, $\Delta u_p^{(sr)}$ of 0.1 m/sec, $\sqrt{\Psi} \sim 1$, and, since Φ is small, $\eta \sim 0.65$ for potential flow and $\eta \sim 0.2$ for viscous flow (Fig. 5.6). However, for $2a_r = 1\,\mu$, $2a_s = 2\,\mu$, $\sqrt{\Psi} \sim 0.3$, and $\eta \sim 0.03$ for potential flow and $\eta \sim 0$ for viscous flow; that is, no collision would occur. Hence, distant interaction due to presence of fluid is more significant for small particles. Where the mean free path of the fluid is near to or greater than the particle dimension, slip flow or free-molecule flow is expected. The values of η given by Friedlander [F28] in Eq. (5.22) should be used for free-molecule flow of particles.

In the case of laminar motion of a dilute suspension, collisions are expected only between clouds of particles of different sizes. When applied to a dense suspension, besides mutual interaction, self-interaction—that is, interaction among all particles due to shear motion, can be significant.

Viscosity of Particle Cloud in Shear Flow—$F^{(sr)}$ accounts for interaction of particles of different sizes without local shear flow. At high enough concentration, shear flow, even in a "laminar" situation would give rise to interaction of particles, giving rise to a viscosity μ_p.

Consider a sphere of radius r in a shear stream of gradient $\partial u/\partial y$ of a particle cloud of number density n and mass m, and denote the velocity u as

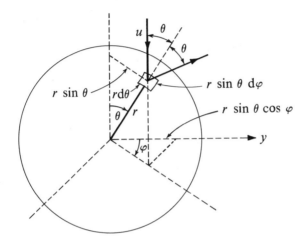

Figure 5.11 Impaction due to shear motion.

zero in the center plane of the sphere; the relative velocity (Fig. 5.11) is given by

$$\Delta u = \frac{\partial u}{\partial y} \Delta y = \frac{\partial u}{\partial y} r \sin \theta \cos \varphi,$$

φ being the azimuthal angle measured from the plane of $\Delta u = 0$; the projected area of impact is $r \sin \theta \, d\varphi \, r \, d\theta \cos \theta$; and the change of momentum is $m \, \Delta u(1 + r^* \cos 2\theta)$. Assuming $\eta = 1$, the force acting on the sphere from $\theta = 0$ to $\theta = \pi/2$ is, assuming each incoming particle is scattered only once,

$$\mathscr{F} \sim 2\eta \int_0^{\pi/2} \int_0^{\pi/2} n(\Delta u)m(\Delta u)(1 + r^* \cos 2\theta)r^2 \sin \theta \cos \theta \, d\theta \, d\varphi$$

$$= \eta \frac{\pi n m}{8} \left(\frac{\partial u}{\partial y}\right)^2 r^4 \left(1 - \frac{r^*}{3}\right). \tag{5.42}$$

Note that $\eta \leq 1$ here is different from the η given in Sec. 5.2 and the previous parts of this section.

It is seen that over a thickness $a_s + a_r$, the total shear stress on the cloud (s) due to velocity gradient tensor $\mathbf{\Delta}^{(r)}$ of cloud (r) is

$$\tau^{(sr)} \simeq -\eta^{(sr)} n^{(s)}(a_s + a_r) \frac{\pi}{8} n^{(r)} \frac{m_r m_s}{m_r + m_s} (a_s + a_r)^4 \left(1 - \frac{r^*}{3}\right) |(\mathbf{\Delta}_p^{(r)} : \mathbf{\Delta}_p^{(r)})^{\frac{1}{2}}| \mathbf{\Delta}_p^{(r)}$$

$$= -\mu_p^{(sr)} \mathbf{\Delta}_p^{(r)}, \tag{5.43}$$

or

$$\mu_p^{(sr)} = \frac{\pi}{8} \eta^{(sr)} \rho_p^{(s)} \rho_p^{(r)} [m_r + m_s]^{-1} (a_s + a_r)^5 \left(1 - \frac{r^*}{3}\right) |(\mathbf{\Delta}_p^{(r)} : \mathbf{\Delta}_p^{(r)})^{\frac{1}{2}}|$$

$$= \eta^{(sr)} \frac{3}{32} \frac{\rho_p^{(s)} \rho_p^{(r)} a_r a_s}{\sqrt{\bar{\rho}_p^{(s)} \bar{\rho}_p^{(r)}}} \left[\sqrt{\frac{m_r}{m_s}} + \sqrt{\frac{m_s}{m_r}}\right]^{-1} \left[\sqrt{\frac{a_r}{a_s}} + \sqrt{\frac{a_s}{a_r}}\right]^5 \left(1 - \frac{r^*}{3}\right)$$

$$\times |(\mathbf{\Delta}_p^{(r)} : \mathbf{\Delta}_p^{(r)})^{\frac{1}{2}}|$$

$$\equiv \mu_{po}^{(sr)} |(\mathbf{\Delta}^{(r)} : \mathbf{\Delta}^{(r)})^{\frac{1}{2}}|, \tag{5.44}$$

where $\mathbf{\Delta}$ has the cartesian components

$$\Delta_{pij}^{(r)} = \frac{\partial u_{pi}^{(r)}}{\partial x_j} + \frac{\partial u_{pj}^{(r)}}{\partial x_i}, \tag{5.45}$$

and

$$\mathbf{\Delta}_p : \mathbf{\Delta}_p = \sum_i \sum_j \Delta_{pij} \Delta_{pij} \tag{5.46}$$

It is seen that the viscosity of the particle cloud due to the simple model of interaction falls into the class of Ostwald-de Waele model [B38]($\tau = \{m |\sqrt{\frac{1}{2}(\mathbf{\Delta} : \mathbf{\Delta})}|^{n-1}\} \mathbf{\Delta}$; m and n are empirical constants) of non-Newtonian fluid (a fact demonstrated by Thomas—Sec. 4.1). The above relation also applies to the shear stress on a particle cloud due to free-molecule flow of a gas.

Viscosity Due to Fluid Shear and Bulk Viscosity—Besides the discussions in Sec. 2.3, the contribution of drag, lift, and torque on a particle in a fluid-shear layer was discussed by Edelman and Kiely [E2]. The shear stress in a particle cloud due to velocity gradient can be approximated by

$$\mu_p^{(s)} \Delta_{ij} = \tau_{ij}^{(s)} \sim n^{(s)} a(3\pi\bar{\mu}a) \Delta_{ij}a,$$

or the apparent viscosity as it appears to the particle cloud is

$$\mu_p^{(s)} \sim n^{(s)} 3\pi\bar{\mu}a^3 = \frac{9}{4} \frac{\rho_p^{(s)}}{\bar{\rho}_p^{(s)}} \bar{\mu} = \tfrac{9}{4}\phi^{(s)}\bar{\mu}. \tag{5.47}$$

Murray [M55] estimated the shear viscosity μ_p and bulk viscosity ζ_p of a suspension due to fluid-particle interaction and gave

$$\mu_p = \bar{\mu}A\phi(\phi_s - \phi)^{-1}, \tag{5.48}$$

where ϕ_s is the volume fraction solid of the same particles in a packed bed, and A is a constant of order 1.

Following a similar procedure of Taylor [T12] (Sec. 5.5) for the determination of the bulk viscosity ζ_p, Murray [M55] considered the separation of two cylinders of radius a lying close together end to end at distance $2h$. The fluid motion due to the opposite velocity W in the axial (x) direction is taken slow enough so that induced viscous streams are important. The radial velocity v in the gap is approximated by

$$v \propto \frac{h^2 - x^2}{h^2}$$

$$= \frac{v_o(h^2 - x^2)}{h^2}.$$

The continuity condition gives

$$\pi a^2 2W = \int_{-h}^{h} 2\pi a v \, dx = -\tfrac{8}{3}\pi a v_o h,$$

or

$$v_o = -\frac{3}{4}\frac{W}{h}$$

at $r = a$. In general,

$$v = -\frac{3}{4}\frac{aW(h^2 - x^2)}{h^3}$$

and conservation is satisfied by

$$v = -\frac{3}{4}\frac{rW(h^2 - x^2)}{h^3},$$

momentum balance gives

$$\frac{\partial P}{\partial r} = \bar{\mu}\frac{\partial^2 v}{\partial x^2},$$

or

$$P(r,x) = P(a,x) - \bar{\mu}\frac{3}{4}\frac{W(a^2 - r^2)}{h^3}.$$

The force F acting on the particle is $\bar{\mu}3\pi a^4 W/8h^3$. In general, for isotropic forces, take $D_s = \phi/(\phi_s - \phi)$, the volume fraction solid ϕ_s of a packed bed, we get

$$\delta_{ij}\bar{\mu}B\left(\frac{a}{h}\right)^3(\text{div } \mathbf{v}_p) \sim \delta_{ij}\bar{\mu}BD_s^3 \text{ div } \mathbf{v}_p,$$

or

$$\zeta_p = \bar{\mu}BD_s^3, \tag{5.49}$$

where B is a constant of order 1.

Bagnold [B2] measured forces exerted by a dense suspension in a rotating viscometer. Millimeter size spheres of 50% mixture of paraffin wax and lead stearate were suspended in water ($\bar{\rho}_p \sim \bar{\rho}$). He gave, from consideration of glancing collisions of particles, $2.25\left(\dfrac{3}{4\pi}\right)^{1/3}\phi^{1/2}[1 + 0(\phi^{1/3})]$, and a repulsive pressure due to shear motion of the magnitude $0.042\left(\dfrac{3}{4\pi}\right)^{1/3}(2a)^2(\partial u/\partial y)^2\phi^{2/3}$ $[1 + 0(\phi^{1/3})]$. Similar velocity of phases was assumed in his correlation.

Moment Acting on a Particle Due to Shear Flow—Obviously the moment acting on a particle due to velocity gradient tends to set the particle in rotation and thereby displacement due to Magnus effect (Sec. 2.3). Extending the above considerations, the moment acting on the sphere by a particle cloud is

$$\mathscr{L} = 2\eta nm\left(\frac{\partial u}{\partial y}\right)^2 r^5 \int_0^{\pi/2}\int_0^{\pi/2}(1 + r^* \cos 2\theta)\cos\theta\sin^4\theta\cos^3\varphi\, d\theta\, d\varphi$$

$$= \tfrac{4}{15}\eta nm\left(\frac{\partial u}{\partial y}\right)^2 r^5(1 - \tfrac{3}{7}r^*).$$

This gives rise to an angular acceleration $\dot{\omega}$, for moment of inertia $I = \tfrac{2}{5}mr^2$, or (sr) interaction

$$\dot{\omega} = \frac{\mathscr{L}}{I_s} \sim \frac{\eta^{(sr)}}{2\pi}\frac{\rho_p^{(r)}}{\sqrt{\bar{\rho}_p^{(r)}\bar{\rho}_p^{(s)}}}\left[\sqrt{\frac{m_s}{m_r}} + \sqrt{\frac{m_r}{m_s}}\right]^{-1}\frac{a_r}{a_s}\left(\sqrt{\frac{a_s}{a_r}} + \sqrt{\frac{a_r}{a_s}}\right)^5(1 - \tfrac{3}{7}r^*)\left(\frac{\partial u}{\partial y}\right)^2.$$

$$(5.50)$$

For the case of shear in a fluid,

$$2\cdot 3\pi\bar{\mu}a_s\cdot\frac{a_s}{2}\left(\frac{\partial u}{\partial y}\right)a_s \sim \mathscr{L} = I\dot{\omega} = \tfrac{2}{5}m_s a_s^2\dot{\omega},$$

and

$$\dot{\omega} \sim \frac{45}{8}\frac{\bar{\mu}}{\bar{\rho}_p^{(s)}a_s^2}\frac{\partial u}{\partial y} \sim F^{(s)}\frac{\partial u}{\partial y}. \qquad (5.51)$$

Turbulent Motion—When applied to turbulent motion, collisions among all elements of a cloud of particles of similar size can be expressed as

$$\frac{du_p^{(s)}}{dt} \cong F^{(s)}(\mathbf{u} - \mathbf{u}_p) + F_p^{(ss)}l^{(s)}\,\text{grad}\,\mathbf{u}_p^{(s)}, \qquad (5.52)$$

where $l^{(s)}$ is to the order of the mixing length of turbulence of (s) particles.

$$F^{(ss)} = \tfrac{3}{4}\eta^{(ss)}\frac{(2a_s)^2 l^{(s)}\,|\text{grad}\,\mathbf{u}_p^{(s)}|\,\rho_p^{(s)}}{2a_s^3\bar{\rho}_p^{(s)}}, \qquad (5.53)$$

and

$$F^{(ss)}l^{(s)}\,\text{grad}\,\mathbf{u}_p^{(s)} = \tfrac{3}{4}\eta^{(ss)}\frac{2}{a_s}\frac{\rho_p^{(s)}}{\bar{\rho}_p^{(s)}}l^{(s)2}\,|\text{grad}\,\mathbf{u}_p^{(s)}|\,(\text{grad}\,\mathbf{u}_p^{(s)}), \qquad (5.54)$$

which is analogous to the Reynolds stress of turbulence expressed in terms of mixing-length theory [S13]. A direct analogy is that the turbulent shear stress τ is now

$$\frac{\tau_{xy}}{\rho_p^{(s)}} = 3\eta^{(ss)}\left(\frac{l^{(s)}}{2a_s}\right)\frac{\rho_p^{(s)}}{\bar{\rho}_p^{(s)}}\,(l^{(s)})\sqrt{\langle u_p^{(s)2}\rangle}\,\frac{\partial u_p^{(s)}}{\partial y}\,,$$

where $\sqrt{\langle u_p^{(s)2}\rangle}$ is the intensity of turbulence of the particle cloud [S52] (for $u_p^{(s)}$ in the x-direction and y normal to it) and the momentum diffusivity $\epsilon^{(s)}$ is

$$\epsilon^{(s)} \sim \sqrt{\langle u_p^{(s)2}\rangle}\,l_t^{(s)} \sim 3\eta^{(ss)}\left(\frac{l^{(s)}}{2a_s}\right)\frac{\rho_p^{(s)}}{\bar{\rho}_p^{(s)}}\,l^{(s)}\sqrt{\langle u_p^{(s)2}\rangle}, \tag{5.55}$$

where $l_t^{(s)}$ is the scale of turbulence of the particle cloud (s). Note that $\epsilon^{(s)}$ is not just the turbulent diffusivity of particles due to fluid turbulence discussed in Chaps. 2 and 4, but arises due to motions involving turbulent eddies of a particle cloud. Experimental information on this subject exists only in the case of fluidized beds (Chap. 9).

5.4 Transfer of Heat by Collisions of Particles

For the collision of an (s) particle by a cloud of (r) particles in a suspension, the temperature of the (s) particle changes according to, for spheres [S60],

$$\frac{dT_p^{(s)}}{dt} = G^{(s)}(T - T_p) + G_p^{(sr)}(T_p^{(r)} - T_p^{(s)}), \tag{5.56}$$

where $G^{(s)}$ is the time constant of the heat transfer between the fluid and the particle,

$$G^{(s)} = \frac{4\pi a_s^2 h^{(s)}}{m_s c_p^{(s)}} = \frac{4\pi a_s^2 \bar{\kappa} N_{\mathrm{Nu}}^{(s)}/2a_s}{m_s c_p^{(s)}} = \frac{3G^{*(s)}\bar{\kappa}}{c_p^{(s)}\bar{\rho}_p^{(s)}a_s^2}\,, \tag{5.57}$$

and $h^{(s)}$ is the heat-transfer coefficient between the fluid and the particle (s), $\bar{\kappa}$ is the thermal conductivity of the fluid material. The temperature of the particles (s) and (r) is assumed to be uniform throughout due to high thermal conductivity $\bar{\kappa}_p^{(s)}$ as compared to $\bar{\kappa}$. $G^{*(s)}$ is a modification analogous to F^* for finite Reynolds number of motion of particle (s) relative to the gas with the functional relation to $N_{\mathrm{Re}}^{(s)}$ according to

$$G^{*(s)} = G^{*(s)}(N_{\mathrm{Re}}^{(s)}) = \tfrac{1}{2}N_{\mathrm{Nu}}^{(s)}(N_{\mathrm{Re}}^{(s)}). \tag{5.58}$$

$G_p^{(sr)}$ is the time constant for heat transfer by collisions of (s) particles by (r) particles. Determination of $G_p^{(sr)}$ calls for fundamental considerations of the mechanism of heat transfer by collision and impaction.

Transfer of heat by impaction of solid particles with a wall and by collision of clouds of solid particles cannot be treated by direct analogy of the above transfer of momentum. When dealing with the energy of a cloud of particles

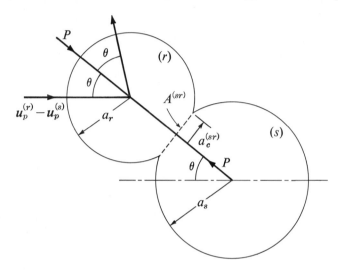

Figure 5.12 Collision and contact of two elastic spheres.

of sizes above $\frac{1}{10}\,\mu$, we have the temperature of the solid particles to be concerned with, rather than just the kinetic energy of random motion of solid particles. This problem was treated by Soo [S52] and is further extended here.

When an (r) particle collides with an (s) particle, at a given moment they have an area of surface of contact $A^{(sr)}$ at T_c as shown in Fig. 5.12. We assume that the particles are small enough and the thermal conductivity of the solid materials high enough such that the temperatures $T_p^{(s)}$ and $T_p^{(r)}$ of the particles remain nearly uniform in the respective particles. In this case, conservation of energy gives

$$\frac{\bar{\kappa}_p^{(s)}}{d_s'}(T_p^{(s)} - T_c) = \frac{\bar{\kappa}_p^{(r)}}{d_r'}(T_c - T_p^{(r)}),$$

where d_s', d_r' are characteristic lengths of heat conduction in each particle and are expected to be of the order of their radii a_s, a_r; $\bar{\kappa}_p^{(s)}$, $\bar{\kappa}_p^{(r)}$ are the thermal conductivities of the materials constituting the particles. The time (t) rate of change of the temperature of each particle is given by

$$
\frac{c_p^{(s)} m_s \, \mathrm{d} T_p^{(s)}}{\mathrm{d}t} = - \frac{\bar{\kappa}_p^{(s)}}{d_s'} A_c^{(sr)} (T_p^{(s)} - T_c)
$$

$$
= - \frac{\bar{\kappa}_p^{(r)}}{d_r'} A_c^{(sr)} (T_c - T_p^{(r)})
$$

$$
= - \frac{c_p^{(r)} m_r \, \mathrm{d} T_p^{(r)}}{\mathrm{d}t}, \tag{5.59}
$$

where $c_p^{(s)}$ and $c_p^{(r)}$ are the specific heats of the solid materials; m_s and m_r are the masses of particles. Elimination of T_c gives

$$
\frac{c_p^{(s)} m_s \, \mathrm{d} T_p^{(s)}}{\mathrm{d}t} = - \frac{c_p^{(r)} m_r \, \mathrm{d} T_p^{(r)}}{\mathrm{d}t}
$$

$$
= - \frac{\dfrac{\bar{\kappa}_p^{(r)}}{d_r'}}{1 + \dfrac{\kappa_p^{(r)} d_s'}{\bar{\kappa}_p^{(s)} d_r'}} (T_p^{(s)} - T_p^{(r)}) \tag{5.60a}
$$

$$
= - \sqrt{\frac{\bar{\kappa}_p^{(s)} \bar{\kappa}_p^{(r)}}{d_s' d_r'}} \left[\sqrt{\frac{\bar{\kappa}_p^{(s)} d_r'}{\bar{\kappa}_p^{(r)} d_s'}} + \sqrt{\frac{\bar{\kappa}_p^{(r)} d_s'}{\bar{\kappa}_p^{(s)} d_r'}} \right]^{-1} (T_p^{(s)} - T_p^{(r)}), \tag{5.60b}
$$

where Eq. (5.60a) is convenient for particles (s) much larger than particles (r), and Eq. (5.60b) is convenient when they are near in size. Since d_s' and d_r' are not known in detail, the variation of $T_p^{(s)}$ and $T_p^{(r)}$ with time is approximately:

$$
T_p^{(s)} \sim T_{pi}^{(s)} + (\bar{T}_p^{(r)} - \bar{T}_p^{(s)}) \left[1 - \exp\left(- \frac{\sqrt{\bar{\kappa}_p^{(s)} \bar{\kappa}_p^{(r)}} A^{(sr)} t}{m_s c_p^{(s)} \sqrt{d_s' d_r'}} \right) \right]. \tag{5.61}
$$

After time Δt, the duration of contact, the heat transferred is

$$
q \sim m_s c_p^{(s)} (\bar{T}_p^{(r)} - \bar{T}_p^{(s)}) \left[1 - \exp\left(- \frac{\sqrt{\bar{\kappa}_p^{(s)} \bar{\kappa}_p^{(r)}} A^{(sr)} t}{m_s c_p^{(s)} \sqrt{d_s' d_r'}} \right) \right]
$$

$$
\sim (\bar{T}_p^{(r)} - \bar{T}_p^{(s)}) \frac{\sqrt{\bar{\kappa}_p^{(s)} \bar{\kappa}_p^{(r)}} A^{(sr)} \Delta t}{\sqrt{d_s' d_r'}}. \tag{5.62}
$$

It is noted that $A^{(sr)}$ and Δt can be evaluated from the elastic properties of materials of (s) and (r) for spherical particles.

The problem of pressure and deformation of elastic bodies such as two spheres in contact or impact has received considerable attention in the theory of elasticity with basic formulation given by Herz and Rayleigh [T36]. Rayleigh recognized that the duration of contact is very long compared to the period of the lowest mode of vibration in the spheres. He gave, for two spheres of radii a_s and a_r, masses m_s and m_r, colliding at velocities $u_p^{(s)}$ and $u_p^{(r)}$ as shown in Fig. 5.12, the duration of impact $\Delta t^{(sr)}$

$$\Delta t^{(sr)} = \frac{2.94\alpha_1}{\Delta u_p^{(sr)} \cos \theta}, \tag{5.63}$$

where $\Delta u_p^{(sr)} = |\mathbf{u}_p^{(s)} - \mathbf{u}_p^{(r)}|$ is the velocity of approach at the beginning of impact. α_1 is the distance of the two spheres approaching each other at the instant of maximum compression P given by

$$\alpha_1 = \left[\frac{9\pi^2}{16} P^2 k_s^2 \left(1 + \frac{k_r}{k_s}\right)^2 \left(\frac{1 + \dfrac{a_r}{a_s}}{a_r}\right) \right]^{1/3}, \tag{5.64}$$

in general, and α_1 is, with reduced mass consideration (Sec. 5.3),

$$\alpha_1 = \left[\frac{5}{4}\left(\frac{1 + r^*}{2}\right)(\Delta u_p^{(sr)})^2 \cos \theta \, \frac{m_r}{1 + \dfrac{m_r}{m_s}} \, \frac{3\pi}{4}\left(\frac{1 + \dfrac{a_r}{a_s}}{a_r}\right)^{1/2} k_s\left(1 + \frac{k_r}{k_s}\right) \right]^{2/5}, \tag{5.65}$$

and

$$P = \frac{2^{1/5}\pi^{1/5}}{3}\left(1 + \frac{m_r}{m_s}\right)^{-3/5}\left(1 + \frac{k_r}{k_s}\right)^{-2/5}\left(1 + \frac{a_r}{a_s}\right)^{-1/5} a_r^2$$

$$\times \left[5(\Delta u_p^{(sr)})^2 \left(\frac{1 + r^*}{2}\right) \cos \theta \bar{\rho}_p^{(r)} \right]^{3/5} k_s^{-2/5}, \tag{5.66}$$

where m_r, m_s are the masses of the particles, k_r and k_s are elastic properties given by

$$k_s = \frac{(1 - \nu_s^2)}{\pi E_s}, \quad k_r = \frac{(1 - \nu_r^2)}{\pi E_r}, \tag{5.67}$$

ν_s, ν_r are the Poisson ratios; E_s, E_r are the moduli of elasticity of materials of (s) and (r) particles. The radius $a_c^{(rs)}$ of the surface of contact at the maximum compressive force P was given by Herz as

$$a_c^{(sr)} = \left[\frac{3\pi}{4} \frac{P(k_s + k_r)a_s a_r}{a_s + a_r} \right]^{1/3}$$

$$= 2^{4/15} \left(1 + \frac{a_r}{a_s} \right)^{-2/5} \left(1 + \frac{k_r}{k_s} \right)^{1/5} \left(1 + \frac{m_r}{m_s} \right)^{-1/5}$$

$$\times \left[5\pi^2 (\Delta u_p^{(sr)})^2 \cos\theta \left(\frac{1 + r^*}{2} \right) k_s \bar{\rho}_p^{(r)} \right]^{1/5} a_r$$

$$= 2^{4/15} \left(\sqrt{\frac{a_r}{a_s}} + \sqrt{\frac{a_s}{a_r}} \right)^{-2/5} \left(\sqrt{\frac{k_r}{k_s}} + \sqrt{\frac{k_s}{k_r}} \right)^{1/5} \left(\sqrt{\frac{m_r}{m_s}} + \sqrt{\frac{m_s}{m_r}} \right)^{-1/5}$$

$$\times [N_{\text{Im}}^{(sr)}]^{1/5} (\cos\theta)^{1/5} \sqrt{a_r a_s} , \tag{5.68}$$

where $N_{\text{Im}}^{(sr)}$ is the dimensionless "impact number" correlating impact and deformation, and:

$$N_{\text{Im}}^{(sr)} = 5\pi^2 (\Delta u_p^{(sr)})^2 \sqrt{\bar{\rho}_p^{(s)} \bar{\rho}_p^{(r)}} \sqrt{k_s k_r} \frac{1 + r^*}{2}$$

$$= 5\pi (\Delta u_p^{(sr)})^2 \sqrt{\bar{\rho}_p^{(s)} \bar{\rho}_p^{(r)}} \left[\frac{(1 - \nu_s^2)(1 - \nu_r^2)}{E_s E_r} \right]^{1/2} \frac{1 + r^*}{2} . \tag{5.69}$$

Since

$$A^{(sr)} = \pi [a_c^{(sr)}]^2, \tag{5.70}$$

the product $A^{(sr)} \Delta t^{(sr)}$ is now

$$A^{(sr)} \Delta t^{(sr)} = \pi 2^{-2/5} (2.94) a_r^3 \left(1 + \frac{m_r}{m_s} \right)^{-4/5} \left(1 + \frac{k_r}{k_s} \right)^{4/5} \left(1 + \frac{a_r}{a_s} \right)^{-3/5}$$

$$\times \left(\frac{k_r}{k_s} \right)^{2/5} \left(\frac{\bar{\rho}_p^{(r)}}{\bar{\rho}_p^{(s)}} \right)^{2/5} [N_{\text{Im}}^{(sr)}]^{1/5} \frac{(\cos\theta)^{-1/5}}{\Delta u_p^{(sr)}}$$

$$= A_o^{(sr)} \Delta t^{(sr)} (\cos\theta)^{-1/5}. \tag{5.71}$$

The resultant time constant for heat transfer based on Eqs. (5.55) and (5.60) is now (Fig. 5.12)

$$G_p^{(sr)} = \frac{h^{(sr)} 4\pi a_s^2}{m_s c_p^{(s)}}$$

$$\cong \frac{\eta^{(sr)} \Delta u_p^{(sr)}}{m_s c_p^{(s)}} \frac{\sqrt{\bar{\kappa}_p^{(s)} \bar{\kappa}_p^{(r)}}}{\sqrt{a_s a_r}}$$

$$\times \int_0^{\pi/2} A_o^{(sr)} \Delta t^{(sr)} (a_s + a_r) \, d\theta \, 2\pi (a_s + a_r) \sin\theta$$

$$\sim \frac{\eta^{(sr)} n_p^{(r)}}{m_s c_p^{(s)}} \frac{\sqrt{\bar{\kappa}_p^{(s)} \bar{\kappa}_p^{(r)}}}{\sqrt{a_s a_r}} 2\pi (a_s + a_r)^2 A_o^{(sr)} \Delta t^{(sr)} \frac{5}{4} , \tag{5.72}$$

or

$$G_p^{(sr)} = C^{(sr)} \frac{\rho_p^{(r)}}{c_p^{(s)}} \frac{\sqrt{\bar{\kappa}_p^{(s)} \bar{\kappa}_p^{(r)}}}{\bar{\rho}_p^{(s)} \bar{\rho}_p^{(r)}} \frac{1}{a_r a_s}, \tag{5.73}$$

with the collision coefficient $C^{(sr)}$ given by

$$C^{(sr)} = 2.94 \frac{45}{2^{2/5} \pi 32} \eta^{(sr)} \left[\sqrt{\frac{m_s}{m_r}} + \sqrt{\frac{m_r}{m_s}} \right]^{-4/5} \left[\sqrt{\frac{a_s}{a_r}} + \sqrt{\frac{a_r}{a_s}} \right]^{1/5}$$

$$\times \left[\sqrt{\frac{k_s}{k_r}} + \sqrt{\frac{k_r}{k_s}} \right]^{4/5} [N_{\mathrm{Im}}^{(sr)}]^{1/5},$$

$$= C^{(rs)} \tag{5.74}$$

and we have the relation between $G_p^{(sr)}$ and $G_p^{(rs)}$

$$c_p^{(s)} \rho_p^{(s)} G_p^{(sr)} = c_p^{(r)} \rho_p^{(r)} G_p^{(rs)}. \tag{5.75}$$

It is further seen that $C^{(sr)}$ concerns impaction and deformation. In addition, rewriting Eq. (5.73) shows that

$$G_p^{(sr)} = C^{(sr)} \frac{\rho_p^{(r)}}{\bar{\rho}_p^{(r)}} \left[\frac{\bar{\kappa}_p^{(s)}}{a_s a_r c_p^{(s)} \bar{\rho}_p^{(s)}} \right] \sqrt{\frac{\bar{\kappa}_p^{(r)}}{\bar{\kappa}_p^{(s)}}} \tag{5.76}$$

correlates the fraction solid of (r) particles $\rho_p^{(r)}/\bar{\rho}_p^{(r)} = \phi_r$, and $\bar{\kappa}_p^{(s)}/c_p^{(s)} \bar{\rho}_p^{(s)}$ is the thermal-diffusion coefficient of the material of the (s) particles. The quantity $[\kappa_p^{(s)}/c_p^{(s)} \rho_r^{(s)} a_s a_r] \sqrt{\kappa_p^{(r)}/\kappa_p^{(s)}}$ correlates thermal diffusion in an (s) particle with the characteristic diffusion length $a_s a_r$.

When $a_s \gg a_r$, and $m_s \gg m_r$, the above relation reduces to

$$A_o^{(sr)} \Delta t^{(sr)} = \frac{\pi 2^{-2/5} (2.94) a_r^3 \left[\sqrt{\frac{k_r}{k_s}} + \sqrt{\frac{k_s}{k_r}} \right]^{1/5} [N_{\mathrm{Im}}^{(sr)}]^{1/5}}{\Delta u_p^{(sr)}} \tag{5.77}$$

$$N_{\mathrm{Im}}^{(sr)} = 5\pi^2 (\Delta u_p^{(sr)})^2 \bar{\rho}_p^{(r)} \sqrt{k_s k_r} \frac{1 + r^*}{2}, \tag{5.78}$$

and

$$C^{(sr)} = (2.94) \frac{45}{2^{2/5} \pi 64} \left[\sqrt{\frac{k_r}{k_s}} + \sqrt{\frac{k_s}{k_r}} \right]^{1/5} [N_{\mathrm{Im}}^{(sr)}]^{4/5} \tag{5.79}$$

and

$$G_p^{(sr)} = C^{(sr)} \frac{\rho_p^{(r)}}{\bar{\rho}_p^{(r)}} \frac{\sqrt{\bar{\kappa}_p^{(s)} \bar{\kappa}_p^{(r)}}}{c_p^{(s)} \bar{\rho}_p^{(s)} a_r^2}. \tag{5.80}$$

Analogous to $F^{(ss)}$, $G^{(ss)}$ is again significant for particles of similar size m in a turbulent field, of mixing length l_s, and the temperature change is given by

$$\frac{G_p^{(ss)} l^{(s)} d T_p^{(s)}}{dy} . \tag{5.81}$$

Similarity in the transport processes is therefore seen.

Collision with a Wall—To learn something about the order of magnitude of heat transfer by impaction, we now determine the heat-transfer coefficient at a flat surface by impaction of solid particles with density ρ_p and intensity of turbulence $\sqrt{\langle u_p^2 \rangle}$. We denote the wall material as (s) with constant wall temperature T_w. The incoming particle temperature is denoted as T_{pi}. The heat-transfer coefficient h_w is given by

$$h_w = \eta^{(rs)} n_p^{(r)} \frac{\bar{\kappa}_p^{(r)}}{a_r} \langle u_p^{(r)2} \rangle^{\frac{1}{2}} \cos \theta A_o \, \Delta t \, (\cos \theta)^{-\frac{1}{5}}$$

$$= (2.94)[\tfrac{3}{4}(2)^{\frac{2}{5}}] \rho_p^{(r)} \frac{\bar{\kappa}_p^{(r)}}{\bar{\rho}_p^{(r)} a_r} \left(\sqrt{\frac{k_r}{k_s}} + \sqrt{\frac{k_s}{k_r}} \right)^{\frac{1}{5}} [N_{Im}]^{\frac{4}{5}}, \tag{5.82}$$

and

$$N_{Im} = 5\pi^2 \langle u_p^{(r)2} \rangle \bar{\rho}_p^{(r)} \sqrt{k_s k_r} \frac{1 + r^*}{2} . \tag{5.83}$$

Take both particle and wall as steel ($\nu = 0.3$, $E = 3 \times 10^7 \text{ lb/in.}^2$, $\bar{\rho}_p = 437$ lb/cu ft, $\bar{\kappa}_p = 16.6$ Btu/ft °F hr, $c_p = 0.12$ Btu/lb °F), $r^* = 1$; that is, perfect elastic collision

$$N_{Im} = \frac{5\pi \langle u_p^2 \rangle \bar{\rho}_p (1 - \nu^2)}{E}$$

$$= \frac{1.442 \times 10^{-4} \langle u_p^2 \rangle}{32.2} , \tag{5.84}$$

for $\langle u_p \rangle$ in ft^2/sec^2, we get for $\phi = \rho_p / \bar{\rho}_p$,

$$h = \frac{3.34 \phi 16.6 (N_{Im})^{\frac{4}{5}}}{a_r} , \tag{5.85}$$

and

$$a_c = 2^{\frac{2}{3}} (N_{Im})^{\frac{1}{5}} a_r . \tag{5.86}$$

We get, for $\sqrt{\langle u_p^2 \rangle}$ of 1 fps and 10 fps,

$$\sqrt{\langle u_p^2 \rangle} = 1 \text{ fps}, \quad a_c = 0.1348 a_r, \quad h = \frac{882 \phi}{a_{r\mu}} \text{ Btu/ft}^2 \text{ hr °F}$$

$$\sqrt{\langle u_p^2 \rangle} = 10 \text{ fps}, \quad a_c = 0.34 a_r, \quad h = \frac{3.58 \times 10^4 \phi}{a_{r\mu}} \text{ Btu/ft}^2 \text{ hr °F},$$

where $a_{r\mu}$ is the particle radius in microns. It is seen that for $\phi = 0.01$, $\sqrt{\langle u_p^2 \rangle} = 1$ fps and $a_{r\mu} = 1$ μ, $h = 8.82$ Btu/ft² hr °F, but at $\sqrt{\langle u_p^2 \rangle} = 10$ fps, $h \sim 358$ Btu/ft² hr °F, which is quite significant.

Comparison of Thermal and Momentum Response—The relative importance of momentum and thermal interaction is given by the ratio $G_p^{(sr)}/F_p^{(sr)}$, or

$$\frac{G_p^{(sr)}}{F_p^{(sr)}} = \frac{(2.94)(15)}{8\pi 2^{\frac{2}{5}}} \left[\sqrt{\frac{m_s}{m_r}} + \sqrt{\frac{m_r}{m_s}} \right]^{\frac{1}{5}} \left[\sqrt{\frac{a_s}{a_r}} + \sqrt{\frac{a_r}{a_s}} \right]^{-\frac{3}{5}} \left[\sqrt{\frac{k_s}{k_r}} + \sqrt{\frac{k_r}{k_s}} \right]^{\frac{1}{5}}$$

$$\times \frac{[N_{\mathrm{Im}}^{(sr)}]^{\frac{4}{5}} \left[\dfrac{\bar{\kappa}_p^{(s)} \bar{\kappa}_p^{(r)}}{\bar{\rho}_p^{(s)} \bar{\rho}_p^{(r)} c_p^{(s)} c_p^{(r)}} \right]^{\frac{1}{2}}}{\Delta u_p^{(sr)} \sqrt{a_r a_s}} . \quad (5.87)$$

When applied to steel balls ($c_p = 0.12$ Btu/lb °F, $\nu = 0.3$, $E = 3 \times 10^7$ lb/in.², $\bar{\rho}_p = 437$ lb/cu ft, $\bar{\kappa}_p = 16.6$ Btu/ft °F hr, and $r^* = 1$) of nearly equal diameters,

$$\frac{G_p^{(sr)}}{F_p^{(sr)}} \sim \frac{(2.94)(15)}{\pi 8} N_{\mathrm{Im}}^{\frac{4}{5}} \left(\frac{\bar{\kappa}_p}{\bar{\rho}_p c_p} \right) \frac{1}{(\Delta u_p)a} . \quad (5.88)$$

For $\Delta u_p = 1$ fps,

$$\frac{G_p^{(sr)}}{F_p^{(sr)}} \sim \frac{0.0395}{a_\mu} .$$

For $\Delta u_p = 10$ fps,

$$\frac{G_p^{(sr)}}{F_p^{(sr)}} \sim \frac{0.1594}{a_\mu} ,$$

where a_μ is for a in microns. Therefore, for steel spheres, $G_p^{(sr)} < F_p^{(sr)}$ for $a_\mu > 1$ μ. Note that for materials of smaller E and/or larger $\bar{\rho}_p$, $N_{\mathrm{Im}}^{(sr)}$ could be significantly larger. Hence $G_p^{(sr)}$ and $F_p^{(sr)}$ are of equal importance and have to be accounted for consistently.

5.5 Viscosity, Thermal Conductivity of Dense Clouds, and Flow Regimes

When applied to the situation where there is no lag of particle motion from fluid motion, Einstein [E6] showed that the viscosity μ_m of an incompressible fluid containing solid spheres is given by

$$\mu_m = \bar{\mu}(1 + 2.5\phi),$$

for small ϕ, where ϕ is the proportion of the total volume occupied by the particles. Taylor [T11] modified this relation to apply to liquid droplets of viscosity $\bar{\mu}_p$ of the liquid material to give

$$\mu_m = \bar{\mu}\left[1 + 2.5\phi\left(\frac{\bar{\mu}_p + \frac{2}{5}\bar{\mu}}{\bar{\mu}_p + \bar{\mu}}\right)\right]. \tag{5.89}$$

It was noted that an incompressible fluid possesses only one coefficient of viscosity because, by definition, no change in volume can occur. When applied to a liquid containing small volumes of air bubbles, Taylor [T12] accounted for the compressibility due to air bubbles by introducing a second coefficient of viscosity ζ. He considered the momentum equation of a spherical bubble in a viscous liquid:

$$\frac{\partial P}{\partial r} = \bar{\mu}\left(\frac{1}{r^2}\frac{\partial}{\partial r}r^2\frac{\partial u}{\partial r}\right) - \rho\frac{\partial u}{\partial t} - \rho u\frac{\partial u}{\partial r}, \tag{5.90}$$

for radial velocity u and radial coordinate r. u is given by the continuity equation

$$u = \frac{u_o a^2}{r^2}, \tag{5.91}$$

and $u_o = da/dt$ is the velocity of expansion. Equation (5.91) gave $r^{-2}(\partial/\partial r)r^2(\partial u/\partial r) = 0$, and $\partial P/\partial r = 0$ from Eq. (5.90) and $P = P_o$, the latter is the pressure outside the surface. Neglecting the density of air, for n bubbles per unit volume

$$\frac{1}{\rho} = \frac{1}{\bar{\rho}} + \tfrac{4}{3}\pi n a^3, \tag{5.92}$$

giving

$$\rho^{-2}\frac{d\rho}{dt} = 4\pi n a^2\frac{da}{dt} = 4\pi n a^2 u_o.$$

The continuity equation further gives

$$\rho^{-1}\frac{d\rho}{dt} = -\frac{\partial u}{\partial r} = -3\frac{\phi u_o}{a}.$$

Taylor treated the change as small changes from equilibrium condition (subscript o below) under the propagation of sound. Thus for surface terms $\mathscr{F}_s$, the pressure in the inside of a bubble P_i or normal force on the inner surface, at equilibrium, we get

$$P_{io} - P_o = \frac{2\mathscr{F}_s}{a}. \tag{5.93}$$

The stress p_{rr} is given by

$$p_{rr} = -P_o + 2\bar{\mu}\frac{\partial u}{\partial r}\bigg]_{r=a} = -\left\{P + 4\bar{\mu}\left(\frac{u_o}{a}\right)\right\}, \tag{5.94}$$

and at the surface

$$P_i - P - 4\bar{\mu}\frac{u_o}{a} = \frac{2\mathscr{F}_s}{a + \delta a} \sim 2\frac{\mathscr{F}_s}{a}\left[1 - \frac{\delta a}{a}\right], \tag{5.95}$$

for small increment δa of radius. For small changes $P' = P - P_o$, $\rho' = \rho - \rho_o$, $P' = P'_o$, $P'_i = P_i - P_{io}$, we get by subtracting Eq. (5.93) from Eq. (5.95)

$$P'_i - P' = 4\bar{\mu}\frac{u_o}{a} - 2\mathscr{F}_s\frac{\delta a}{a^2}. \tag{5.96}$$

For isothermal change in small bubble

$$P'_i = -3P_{io}\frac{\delta a}{a} = -3\left(P_o + \frac{2\mathscr{F}_s}{a}\right)\frac{\delta a}{a}, \tag{5.97}$$

elimination of P'_i from Eqs. (5.96) and (5.97)

$$P' = -\left(P_o + \frac{4}{3}\frac{\mathscr{F}_s}{a}\right)\frac{3\delta a}{a} - 4\bar{\mu}\frac{u_o}{a},$$

and

$$\frac{\rho'}{\rho} = -4\pi n a^2\,\delta a = -3\phi\frac{\delta a}{a}.$$

Equation (5.94) of p_{rr} gives for the x-component

$$p_{xx} = -\left(P_o + \frac{4}{3}\frac{\mathscr{F}_s}{a}\right)\frac{\rho'}{\phi\rho_o} + \frac{4}{3}\bar{\mu}\frac{\nabla u}{\phi} + 2\bar{\mu}\frac{\partial u}{\partial x}$$

$$= -P + \zeta\nabla u + 2\bar{\mu}\frac{\partial u}{\partial x},$$

for small change in ρ', or

$$\zeta = \frac{4}{3}\frac{\bar{\mu}}{\phi}.$$

Allowance for the compressibility of liquid is given by

$$y = \frac{\text{equilibrium effective compressibility}}{\text{compressibility of liquid}},$$

Taylor gave

$$\zeta = \frac{4}{3}\bar{\mu}y\frac{\phi y}{(1 + \phi y)^2}. \tag{5.98}$$

Viscosity and Thermal Conductivity of Particle Clouds—Methods in Sec. 5.4 treat only cases where the incoming (r) particles collide only once with the particles (s) in analogy to the case of free-molecule flow. It is expected that if a_s were large enough and the number density of the (r) particles high enough, collision of a reflected (r) particle (r_1) with an incoming particle (r_2) will send (r_1) back for another collision with (s), and we have the situation such as transition from free-molecule flow to viscous flow of the (r) particles. Rather than treating a finite number of reflections, such as was carried out by Baker and Charwat [B7] for molecular flow, we consider the case where the mean free path $\Lambda_p^{(r)}$ is much smaller than a_s, or

$$\Lambda_p^{(r)} = \frac{1}{\sqrt{2} n_p^{(r)} 4\pi a_r^2 \eta^{(rr)}} < a_s . \tag{5.99}$$

That is, when the fraction solid of (r) particles is such that

$$\phi^{(r)} = \frac{\rho_p^{(r)}}{\bar{\rho}_p^{(r)}} > \frac{\left(\dfrac{a_r}{a_s}\right)}{3\sqrt{2}} \eta^{(rr)}, \tag{5.100}$$

we have an apparent viscosity $\mu^{(r)}$ of the (r) particles which would set in random motion by multiple collisions with intensity of motion $\langle u_p^{(r)2} \rangle^{1/2}$, or [S46]

$$\mu_p^{(r)} \sim \tfrac{1}{3} \rho_p^{(r)} \langle u_p^{(r)2} \rangle^{1/2} \Lambda^{(r)}$$

$$= \frac{1}{9\sqrt{2}} \frac{a_r \bar{\rho}_p^{(r)} \langle u_p^{(r)2} \rangle^{1/2}}{\eta^{(rr)}} . \tag{5.101}$$

The time constant of momentum transfer $F^{(sr)}$ is now

$$F_p^{(sr)} = \frac{9 F^{*(s)} \mu_p^{(r)}}{2 a_s^2 \bar{\rho}_p^{(s)} \left[1 + \dfrac{\bar{\rho}}{2 \bar{\rho}_p^{(s)}} \right]}, \tag{5.102}$$

and phase (r) is treated as a fluid. In another way of speaking, $F^{(sr)}$ given in Eq. (5.92) is the upper limit of $F^{(sr)}$ for Eq. (5.39). $F^{(rs)}$ reverts to contribution of $\mu^{(r)}$ to the overall momentum of the suspension (Chap. 6). $F^{*(s)}$ is a corresponding correction for F as given by Eq. (5.17), with

$$N_{\text{Re}}^{(sr)} = \frac{2 a_s \rho_p^{(r)} \Delta u_p^{(sr)}}{\mu_p^{(r)}} \tag{5.103}$$

The above recognition of apparent viscosity gives rise to an apparent thermal conductivity $\kappa_p^{(r)}$ of the cloud of (r) particles, and

$$\kappa_p^{(r)} \sim \mu_p^{(r)} c_p^{(r)}$$

$$= \frac{c_p^{(r)} a_r \bar{\rho}_p^{(r)} \langle u_p^{(r)2} \rangle^{1/2}}{9\sqrt{2}} \tag{5.104}$$

$$G_p^{(rs)} = 3 G^{*(s)} \frac{\kappa_p^{(r)} \alpha_p^{(sr)}}{c_p^{(s)} \bar{\rho}_p^{(s)} a_s^2}, \tag{5.105}$$

where $G^{*(s)}$ is a similar correction for "convection" heat transfer due to collision of (r) particles; $\alpha_p^{(sr)}$ is the accommodation coefficient for the (sr) collision.

Viscosity of a dusty gas was measured by Sproull [S78] on air laden with dusts of limestone and talc of the order of 1μ in diameter with a rotating viscometer. A reduction in the viscosity was observed: with limestone at $\rho_p = 240 \text{ g/m}^3$, reductions were nearly 40 per cent below that of clean air; with talc the reduction was 10 per cent at $\rho_p = 60 \text{ g/m}^3$ and 35 per cent at 240 g/m^3. These results are believed to be due to the nearness of the mean free path of the gas to the particle size (Sec. 6.1).

Measurement of heat transfer coefficient between a moving surface in a bed of slag particles was made by Dunsky, Zabrodsky, and Tamarin [D44]. For relative velocities from 0.01 to 0.1 m/sec, their system appears to conform to the above multiple scattering model with local fraction solids from 0.4 to 0.1 and an "accommodation" coefficient of 0.8 between the particles and the wall in laminar flow [E1]. Below 0.01 m/sec, the effect of conductivity of the porous bed sliding past the surface appears to be more significant. Conceivably their experimental system may be used to check the single scattering model of particle-wall heat transfer at still higher relative velocities.

Flow Regimes of a Cloud of Particles in a Turbulent Fluid—For very low density of particles such that the number of collisions among the particles is negligible when compared with that with the wall, we have an analogous situation to that of flow of rarefied gases. The shear stress at a solid wall τ_p, following that analogy, can be represented by

$$\tau_{pw} \cong \frac{1}{2\sqrt{\pi}} \rho_{pw} U_{pw} \sqrt{\langle u_{pw}^2 \rangle}$$

$$= \tfrac{1}{2} C_{pf} \rho_{po} U_{po}^2 , \tag{5.106}$$

where $\sqrt{\langle u_{pw}^2 \rangle}$ is the intensity of particle motion [H41, S66] near the wall and U_{pw}, U_{po} are the mean speed of particles at the wall and in the free stream. C_{pf} is the friction factor, and

$$\left(\frac{U_{po}}{\sqrt{\langle u_{pw}^2 \rangle}} \right) C_{pf} \cong \frac{1}{\sqrt{\pi}} \frac{\rho_{pw}}{\rho_{po}} \frac{U_{pw}}{U_{po}} . \tag{5.107}$$

The next situation is such that collision is significant among the particles, but the scale of motion of particles is small such that as far as the particles are concerned, it is analogous to viscous motion with slip. The "viscosity" of the particle phase is simply a microscopic representation of particle interaction. In a region where the particle density is ρ_p, the shear stress due to

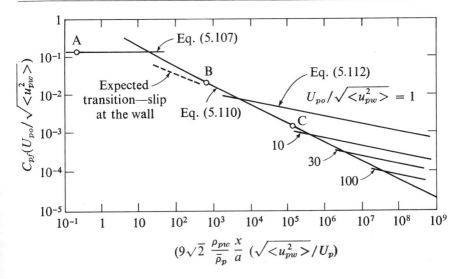

Figure 5.13 Friction factor of flat plate due to solid particles [S52].

particles over a flat plate and friction coefficient in this range, by analogy of laminar boundary layer [S13], is given by

$$\frac{\tau_{pw}}{\frac{1}{2}\rho_{po}U_{po}^2} = C_{pf} = \frac{0.664}{\sqrt{N_{\text{Re},x}}}, \tag{5.108}$$

where

$$N_{\text{Re},x} = \frac{U_{po}x\rho_{pw}}{\mu_{pw}} = 9\sqrt{2}\,\frac{U_{po}}{\sqrt{\langle u_p^2\rangle}}\,\frac{\rho_{pw}}{\bar{\rho}_p}\,\frac{x}{a}, \tag{5.109}$$

and x is measured from the leading edge. Expressed in a similar form as Eq. (5.107),

$$\frac{U_{po}}{\sqrt{\langle u_{pw}^2\rangle}}\,C_{pf} = 0.664\left[9\sqrt{2}\,\frac{\rho_{pw}}{\bar{\rho}_p}\,\frac{x}{a}\right]^{-\frac{1}{2}}\left[\frac{U_{po}}{\sqrt{\langle u_{pw}^2\rangle}}\right]^{\frac{1}{2}}. \tag{5.110}$$

Equations (5.107) and (5.110) are plotted as shown in Fig. 5.13 for $\rho_{po}U_{po}/\rho_{pw}U_{pw} = 3.67$. The transition between the two ranges occurs at

$$\left[9\sqrt{2}\,\frac{\rho_{pw}}{\bar{\rho}_p}\,\frac{x}{a}\right]\left[\frac{U_{po}}{\sqrt{\langle u_{pw}^2\rangle}}\right] \sim 20. \tag{5.111}$$

Below the value 20, we call the range a free-particle range due to lack of particle-particle interaction. For the case of transport of 0.15 mass ratio of solid to air, 200 μ glass beads in air at room condition ($\rho = 0.071$ lb/cu ft), at 100 fps, with $\sqrt{\langle u_{pw}^2\rangle} \sim 6$ fps [S66], the product in Eq. (5.111) is 0.2 at

$x = 1$ ft. The particles in this case have negligible mutual collision (point A in Fig. 5.13). The experiments of Wen and Simons [W12] are still largely in the range given by Eq. (5.107).

The third range is such that large-scale turbulence of particles occurs and the density of particles is high such that we have the condition of turbulence of particles. In this case the particles and stream act as a mixture of heavy and light gases. The shear stress and friction factor due to the solid particles are

$$\frac{\tau_{pw}}{\frac{1}{2}\rho_{po}U_{po}^2} = C_{pf} = 0.0592(N_{\text{Re},x})^{-\frac{1}{5}}, \tag{5.112}$$

which is also plotted in Fig. 5.13. In the above numerical example, if we change the mass ratio to 5 and a to 1 μ, at $x = 1$ ft, the product in Eq. (5.111) is 666 (point B in Fig. 5.13). However, if we raise the pressure to 20 atm and change a to 0.1 μ, the product in Eq. (5.111) is 1.33×10^5 at $x = 1$ ft (point C in Fig. 5.13). Point C in Fig. 5.13 is close to the condition of turbulence. For a ratio of $U_{po}/\sqrt{\langle u_{pw}^2 \rangle} = 16.6$, turbulence occurs at

$$\left[9\sqrt{2}\,\frac{\rho_{pw}}{\bar{\rho}_p}\frac{x}{a}\right]\left[\frac{\sqrt{\langle u_{pw}^2 \rangle}}{U_{po}}\right] > 10^6. \tag{5.113}$$

Still another case is when in the given potential field sedimentation of solid particles occurs and the solid particles move as a slug with little or no relative motion between a large number of solid particles [W6]. We shall neglect this range here.

To get some idea of the order of magnitude of various parameters, we consider the case of interaction between solid particles and the wall for motion of solid particles in a turbulent field when dealing with small solid particles of, say, 1 μ in diameter and up to a gas-solid mass ratio of three to one, and density ratio of, say, 2000 to 1. The friction factor at the wall due to impact of the solid particles is given in the above for friction factor to the order of 0.1; the shear stress is to the order of 10 lb/ft² for gas with friction factor of 0.001 and shear stress of 0.01 lb/ft². From the measurements on pipe flow (Sec. 4.1), however, we may expect the actual impaction rate at the wall to be 1 order of magnitude smaller than those computed here due to the lift force exerted on the particles in the shear layer (Eq. 2.23).

In general, when collision or interaction among particles is absent, the turbulent motion of the particles is correlated only to the fluid turbulence (Sec. 2.8). Therefore, turbulent motion of the cloud of particles is really nonexistent in pipe flow experiments such as reported in Sec. 4.5. The particle cloud can only be visualized to a random motion superposed on its mass motion in the way analogous to free molecule flow. The motion of solid particles is not correlated indirectly through fluid correlation because the position of particles is not correlated without particle collision.

A study by Culick [C48] accounted for the particle collision through a solution of the Boltzmann transport equation. Even though the presence of fluid was neglected (Sec. 5.3), when corrected, the higher-order distribution functions would lead to a more accurate expression for the apparent viscosity and diffusivity.

5.6 Interaction with Radiation

When dealing with transmission of radiant energy through a cloud of particles (smoke, flame, dust cloud, fluidized bed, fog, etc.), absorption, emission, and scattering must be taken into account except when the cloud is extremely dilute. Basic information of diffuse radiation is available from studies in colloid chemistry, astrophysics, and meteorology. A thorough review of studies in this area prior to 1957 was made by van de Hulst [V3].

The diffusion of light was first studied by Milne in connection with the flow of light in a stellar atmosphere and is called the Milne problem [M47, C14]. The intensity of scattered radiation by a single spherical particle from incident radiation consisting of infinite plane waves was computed from the Maxwell's wave equation and is known as the Mie theory [C26]. Scattering includes the combined effects of reflection, refraction, diffraction, and transmission of radiation by the particle.

In a space containing only a few particles, the scattered intensity is nearly equal to the scattered intensity from a single particle multiplied by the number of particles. For large number density of particles, multiple scattering—that is, scattering of the radiation two or more times—becomes important.

Equations of transfer along a pencil of rays expressing multiple scattering in terms of single scattering have been derived by Chandrasekhar [C14] and by Kourganoff [K30]. Viskanta and Grosh [V11] computed radiative transfer of a one-dimensional slab. Computation of radiative transfer of a semi-infinite cylindrical gas body neglecting scattering was given by Tien and Abu-Romia [T33]. Love and Grosh [L58] treated a scattering medium consisting of spherical particles of uniform diameter and complex refractive index. Because of its direct applicability to the problem of a cloud of spherical particles, their method will be presented here. Love and Grosh gave the transfer equation along a ray in the following form:

$$\frac{dI(s,\theta,\varphi)}{ds} = -\rho_p\beta_m I(s,\theta,\varphi) + \rho_p\alpha_m I_{bb}(s)$$

$$+ \frac{\rho_p\sigma_m}{\pi}\int_0^{2\pi}\int_0^{\pi} I(s,\theta',\varphi')S(\theta,\varphi,\theta',\varphi')\sin\theta'\,d\theta'\,d\varphi', \quad (5.114)$$

where I is the monochromatic intensity of radiation, and I_{bb} is that of the blackbody (Planck) in (Btu)(ft)$^{-2}$(stearad)$^{-1}$; s is the distance along a ray (ft), ρ_p is the mass density (lbm)(ft)$^{-3}$, β_m is the monochromatic mass extinction coefficient (ft)^2(lbm)$^{-1}$, α_m is the monochromatic mass-absorption coefficient (ft)^2(lbm)$^{-1}$, σ_m is the monochromatic mass-scattering coefficient (ft)^2(lbm)$^{-1}$, θ is the polar angle in radians, φ is the azimuthal angle in radians, and

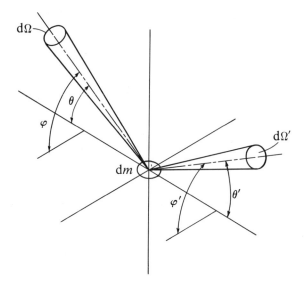

Figure 5.14 Coordinate system for scattering function.

$S(\theta,\varphi,\theta',\varphi')$ is a scattering function. Equation (5.114) expresses the change in monochromatic intensity with respect to distance along the ray at s, θ, φ with respect to the reference direction in terms of the extinction of the ray in accordance with the Bouguer-Beer relation, the increase in intensity due to thermal-energy emission from the particles in the elemental volume, and the energy scattered into θ, φ from rays traversing the elemental volume from all directions. The scattering function S is defined such that

$$\sigma_m I(s,\theta',\varphi') S(\theta,\varphi,\theta',\varphi') \frac{d\Omega'}{4\pi} \, d\nu \, dm \, d\Omega \qquad (5.115)$$

is the rate at which radiant energy is scattered by the differential element of mass dm from the pencil of rays enclosed in the solid angle Ω' having intensity $I(s,\theta',\varphi')$ within the frequency range ν and $\nu + d\nu$ into solid angle $d\omega$ characterized by θ, φ, as shown in Fig. 5.14. Note that the integral of scattering function has the range

$$\Sigma = \frac{1}{4\pi} \int_0^{4\pi} S(\theta,\varphi,\theta',\varphi') \, d\Omega', \tag{5.116}$$

and $0 < \Sigma < 1$, depending on absorption. When it is equal to 1, the scattering is conserved and absorption is neglected. Due to the lack of data on scattering by particles having a complex refractive index corresponding to

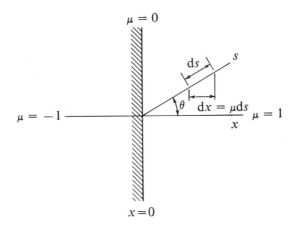

Figure 5.15 Coordinate system for axisymmetric radiation.

absorption, $\Sigma = 1$ is taken by Love [L58]. S then corresponds to the real part of the refractive index, and absorption is accounted for by σ_m taken from computed values of the scattering cross section given by Chromey [C26], and

$$\beta_m = \sigma_m + \alpha_m . \tag{5.117}$$

Equation (5.104) can be reduced by imposing certain geometrical and optical restrictions. A system consisting of uniform plane cloud of particles suspended in a transparent medium and bounded by infinite surfaces which emit and reflect radiation in a diffuse manner is taken. The particles are specified as homogeneous spheres of uniform diameter and known refractive index. As shown in Fig. 5.14, x is the geometrical distance from surface 1 measured along a normal to the surface. Due to symmetry, the intensity will vary only with respect to polar angle θ measured from the normal to plane 1 and is independent of the azimuthal angle, φ. Introducing optical depth τ according to (Fig. 5.15):

$$d\tau = \rho_p \beta_m \, dx, \tag{5.118}$$

with

$$dx = ds \cos \theta \equiv ds \, \mu, \tag{5.119}$$

and

$$\tau = \int_0^x \rho_p \beta_m \, dx. \tag{5.120}$$

Equation (5.114) becomes

$$\mu \frac{dI(\tau,u)}{d\tau} = -I(\tau,\mu) + \frac{\alpha_m}{\beta_m} I_{bb}(\tau) + \frac{\sigma_m}{2\beta_m} \int_{-1}^{1} I(\tau,\mu')S(\mu,\mu') \, d\mu', \tag{5.121}$$

where

$$S(\mu,\mu') = \frac{1}{2\pi} \int_0^{2\pi} S(\theta,\varphi,\theta',\varphi') \, d\varphi'. \tag{5.122}$$

Further simplification is made possible by assuming isotropy and substituting the Gaussian quadrature formula [C14] for the integral in Eq. (5.122), or

$$\int_0^1 S(\mu,\mu')I(\tau,\mu') \, d\mu' \cong \sum_{j=1}^{n} a_j S(\mu_i,\mu_j)I(\tau,\mu_i), \tag{5.123}$$

where n is the order of the quadrature. The discontinuity in the intensity function for $\mu = 0$ is accounted for by Sykes [S103] by dividing the intensity to a forward component $I(\tau, +\mu)$ for $0 < \mu \le 1$ and a backward component $I(\tau, -\mu)$ for $-1 \le \mu < 0$, leading to a double Gaussian quadrature of a polynomial of order $2n - 1$. Equation (5.121) now becomes

$$\mu_i \frac{dI(\tau,\mu_i)}{d\tau} = -I(\tau,\mu_i) + \frac{\alpha_m}{\beta_m} I_{bb}(\tau) + \frac{\sigma_m}{2\beta_m} \left[\sum_{j=1}^{n} a_j S(\mu_i,\mu_j)I(\tau,\mu_j) \right.$$

$$\left. + \sum_{j=1}^{n} a_j S(\mu_i,-\mu_j)I(\tau,-\mu_j) \right], \tag{5.124}$$

and

$$-\mu_i \frac{dI(\tau,-\mu_i)}{d\tau} = -I(\tau,-\mu_i) + \frac{\alpha_m}{\beta_m} I_{bb}(\tau)$$

$$+ \frac{\sigma_m}{2\beta_m} \left[\sum_{j=1}^{n} a_j S(-\mu_i, \mu_j)I(\tau,\mu_j) \right.$$

$$\left. + \sum_{j=1}^{n} a_j S(-\mu_i,-\mu_j)\tau(\tau,-\mu_j) \right]. \tag{5.125}$$

Solution of the problem is relatively simple for the cases of isothermal scattering media [L58] and diffuse nonisothermal media [V11]. These cases will be illustrated here.

Isothermal Scattering Media—With the specification

$$I_{bb}(\tau) = I_{bb}(T_a), \tag{5.126}$$

for the media at temperature T_a, we postulate a solution of the type

$$I(\tau,\mu_i) = x_i e^{\gamma\tau}, \quad I(\tau,-\mu_i) = x_{(i+n)}e^{\gamma\tau}, \tag{5.127}$$

which reduces Eqs. (5.124) and (5.125) to $2n$ linear algebraic equations in x_i and $x_{(i+n)}$ with the parameter γ. The matrix of the coefficients gives $2n$ eigenvalues γ_k and $2n$ sets of eigenvectors $x_{i,k}$ and $x_{(i+n),k}$ for each γ_k. k is the iterative index. The complete solution (including the particular integral I_{bb}) takes the form

$$
\left.
\begin{aligned}
I(\tau,\mu_i) &= \sum_{k=1}^{2n} c_k x_{i,k} \exp(\gamma_k \tau) + I_{bb}(T_a) \\
I(\tau,-\mu_i) &= \sum_{k=1}^{2n} c_k x_{(i+n),k} \exp(\gamma_k \tau) + I_{bb}(T_a)
\end{aligned}
\right\},
\qquad (5.128)
$$

where c_k's are the $2n$ constants of integration, resulting from the determination of the eigenvectors of the homogeneous set only as a linear combination. These constants of integration are determined by the boundary conditions of the problem.

Assuming diffuse walls 1 and 2, the boundary conditions may be expressed in terms of the radiosity R_1 and R_2 of the surfaces, or

$$
I(0,\mu_i) = \frac{R_1}{\pi}, \qquad I(\tau_o,-\mu_i) = \frac{R_2}{\pi}, \qquad (5.129)
$$

and

$$
I(0,\mu_i) = \epsilon_1 I_{bb}(T_1) + 2\rho_1 \sum_{j=1}^{n} a_j \mu_j I(0,-\mu_j)
$$
$$
\qquad (5.130)
$$
$$
I(\tau_o,-\mu_i) = \epsilon_2 I_{bb}(T_2) + 2\rho_2 \sum_{j=1}^{n} a_j \mu_j I(\tau_o,\mu_j).
$$

The quadrature formula has thus been substituted for the integral and ϵ_1, ϵ_2, ρ_1, ρ_2 are the emissivity and reflectivity of surfaces 1 and 2, and a_j's are the quadrature weight factor. Substitution of Eqs. (5.128) into Eqs. (5.130) yields:

$$
\left.
\begin{aligned}
\sum_{k=1}^{2n} c_k \left[x_{i,k} - 2\rho_1 \sum_{j=1}^{n} a_j \mu_j x_{(j+n),k} \right] &= \epsilon_1 [I_{bb}(T_1) - I_{bb}(T_a)] \\
\sum_{k=1}^{2n} c_k \left[x_{(i+n),k} \exp(\gamma_k \tau_o) - 2\rho_2 \sum_{j=1}^{n} a_j \mu_j \exp(\gamma_k \tau_o) \right] & \\
&= \epsilon_2 [I_{bb}(T_2) - I_{bb}(T_a)]
\end{aligned}
\right\}. \quad (5.131)
$$

Equation (5.131) represents a set of linear algebraic equations which can be solved for c_α in terms of $I_{bb}(T_1)$, $I_{bb}(T_2)$, and $I_{bb}(T_a)$, and the resulting intensities at τ_1 can be written as

$$
I(\tau_1,\mu_i) = D_i I_{bb}(T_1) + E_i I_{bb}(T_2) + F_i I_{bb}(T_a) \qquad (5.132)
$$
$$
I(\tau_1,-\mu_i) = G_i I_{bb}(T_1) + H_i I_{bb}(T_2) + K_i I_{bb}(T_a), \qquad (5.133)
$$

where D_i, E_i, F_i, G_i, H_i, and K_i are computed parameters independent of temperature but are functions of single scattering and emissivity of the bounding surfaces, the optical spacing τ_o, and optical depth τ_1.

The net monochromatic flux $J(\tau_1)$ is given by

$$J(\tau_1) = 2\pi \int_{-1}^{1} \mu I(\tau_1,\mu) \, d\mu$$

$$= 2\pi \sum_{j=1}^{n} a_j \mu_j [I(\tau_1,\mu_j) - I(\tau_1,-\mu_j)]$$

$$= MI_{bb}(T_1) - NI_{bb}(T_2) - QI_{bb}(T_a), \qquad (5.134)$$

where M, N, Q are computed dimensionless parameters of similar nature as D_i, etc.

When concerned with only heat transfer, values of M, N, Q at $\tau = 0$ are the major concern. The net heat transfer is obtained by integrating over the wavelengths, or

$$\dot{q}_{net} = \int_0^{\infty} J \, d\nu = \int_0^{\infty} [MI_{bb}(T_1) - NI_{bb}(T_2) - QI_{bb}(T_a)] \, d\nu, \quad (5.135)$$

$I_{bb}(T)$ is given by the Planck function as

$$I_{bb}(T) = \left(\frac{2h\nu^3}{c^2}\right) \exp\left(\frac{-h\nu}{kT}\right) \left[1 - \exp\left(\frac{-h\nu}{kT}\right)\right]^{-1}, \qquad (5.136)$$

when h is the Planck constant, k the Boltzmann constant, and c the speed of light. The flux integral is given by

$$\int_0^{\infty} MI_{bb}(T) \, d\nu = \int_0^{\infty} \left(\frac{2h\nu^3}{c^2}\right) M \exp\left(\frac{-h\nu}{kT}\right) \left[1 - \exp\left(\frac{-h\nu}{kT}\right)\right]^{-1} d\nu,$$

$$(5.137)$$

which can be expressed in terms of the Riez [R21] quadrature according to, by transformation of variables with $x = h\nu/kT$, $\nu = c/\Lambda$, Λ being the wavelength:

$$\int_0^{\infty} MI_{bb}(T) \, d\nu = \int_0^{\infty} \left(\frac{2k^4 T^4}{h^3 c^2}\right) M x^3 e^{-x} [1 - e^{-x}]^{-1} \, dx$$

$$\equiv T^4 \sum_{j=1}^{n} A_j M_j, \qquad (5.138)$$

with

$$A_j = \left(\frac{2k^4}{h^3 c^2}\right) a_j x_j^3 [1 - e^{-x_j}]^{-1}. \qquad (5.139)$$

Noting that a_j, x_j are specified by the quadrature formula, A_j's are universal and have the following values for a fifth-order approximation, in 10^{-11} $(Btu)(hr)^{-1}ft^{-2}(R)^{-4}$:

$$A_1 = 0.347, \qquad A_2 = 12.46, \qquad A_3 = 30.42,$$

$$A_4 = 10.78, \qquad A_5 = 0.396.$$

The radiant heat flux at wall 1 is now

$$\dot{q}_{net} = T_1^4 \sum_{j=1}^{n} A_j M_j - T_2^4 \sum_{j=1}^{n} A_j N_j - T_a^4 \sum_{j=1}^{n} A_j Q_j. \tag{5.140}$$

The frequencies at which M_j, N_j, Q_j must be determined correspond to T_1, T_2, T_a and x_j with Eq. (5.134). The values of particle-size parameter α_j which determines M_j, N_j, and Q_j are given by

$$\alpha_j = \frac{2\pi a}{\Lambda_j} = \frac{\pi x_j 2akT}{ch}, \tag{5.141}$$

since $\Lambda = c/\nu$ and $\nu = x_j kT/h$, where a is the particle radius. Corresponding to the fifth-degree polynomial, let $\alpha_j = \alpha_j^* 2aT \times 10^{-4}$, for a in microns:

$$\alpha_1^* = 0.320, \quad \alpha_2^* = 1.714, \quad \alpha_3^* = 4.362,$$

$$\alpha_4^* = 8.595, \quad \alpha_5^* = 15.334.$$

For complex refractive index $m^* = (n^* - iK^*)$, Chromey [C26] gave values of parameters for determining the extinction cross section K_e and σ_m/β_m, and particle size parameter $\alpha = 2\pi a/\Lambda$, and

$$\beta_m = \frac{3K_e}{4a\bar{\rho}_p}, \tag{5.142}$$

and

$$K_e = 24n^* K^* \alpha[(n^{*2} + K^{*2})^2 + 4(n^{*2} - K^{*2}) + 4]^{-1}. \tag{5.143}$$

Values of β_m, σ_m, K_e computed from tables of Chromey [C26] and approximated by Penndorf [P6] are shown in Figs. 5.16 and 5.17; $m^* = 1.25 - 1.25i$ nearly for iron and $m^* = 2.00 - 0.60i$ for carbon in the visible range of wavelength. Knowing K_e, the optical depth τ_o is given by

$$\tau_o = \int_0^{x_0} \rho_p \beta_m \, dx \cong \frac{3}{4a} \frac{\rho_p}{\bar{\rho}_p} K_e x_o. \tag{5.144}$$

Data of scattering function were tabulated by Chu, Clark, and Churchill [C28], with α from 1 to 30 and n^* from 0.90 to 2.0 and ∞. Love [L58] expressed the scattering function in terms of a Legrendre series as

$$S(\Gamma) = 1 + \sum_{n=1}^{\infty} a_n P_n (\cos \Gamma), \tag{5.145}$$

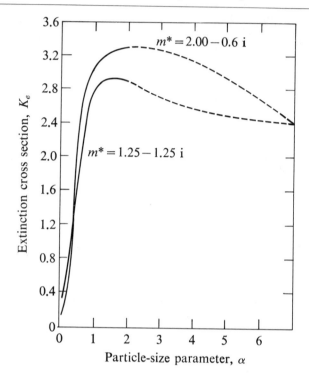

Figure 5.16 Extinction cross section K_e as a function of particle-size parameter for complex refractive indices as indicated [L58].

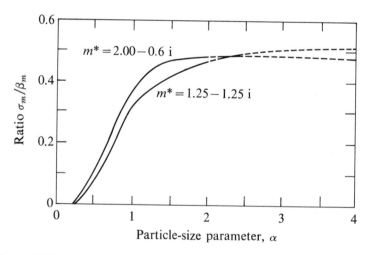

Figure 5.17 The ratio of scattering to extinction σ/β as a function of particle-size parameter α for the complex refractive indices as indicated [L58].

where $a_n = a_n(\alpha, m^*)$ only, $P_n(\cos \Gamma)$ is the nth order Legendre polynomial with $\cos \Gamma$ as argument, and Γ is the angle between the direction of incident ray and the scattered ray. The integration of Γ over the azimuthal angle φ as given in Eq. (5.122) involves only the Legendre polynomials and need be

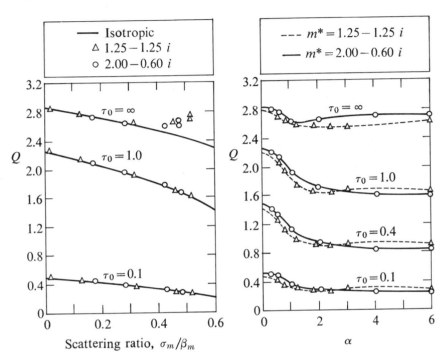

Figure 5.18 Comparisons of computed Q for isotropic scattering and for anisotropic scattering by spheres with m^* as indicated; reflectivity of both walls is 0.1 [L58].

done only once. For $\alpha < 1$, graphical interpolation was made between $\alpha > 1$ and the values for Rayleigh scattering as α approaches zero, namely

$$S(\theta) = \tfrac{3}{4}(1 + \cos^2 \theta). \tag{5.146}$$

The parameters M, N, and Q are given in Figs. 5.18 and 5.19 based on a fourth order approximation ($n = 4$) for given reflectivity of the bounding walls. For small τ_o and α, the effect of anisotropic scattering is closely approximated by the isotropic approximate. Further, even for $\tau_o = \infty$, a cloud of carbon particles is still not a blackbody. Extensive data were given by Love [L57].

The effect of particle cloud is seen from considering an example of wall 1 at $2000°R$, reflectivity $\rho_1 = 0.10$; wall 2 at $500°R$, $\rho_2 = 0.90$ at 0.2 ft apart, with the gap filled by 2-μ-diameter iron particles at $\rho_p = 0.01$ lbm/ft³. It is seen that at steady state with stationary cloud, both the wall heat flux and the average particle temperature are dependent on these giving conditions. The

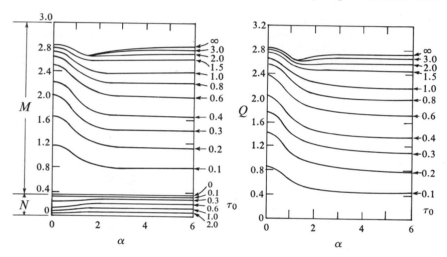

Figure 5.19 Relations of parameters M, N, Q, with $m^* = 1.25$–$1.25i$; reflectivity of wall $1 = 0.1$ and of wall $2 = 0.9$ [L57].

net radiation flux at the walls can be computed by taking j from 1 to 5, compute α_j's, get K_{ij} from Fig. 5.16, compute τ_{oj} from Eq. (5.144), M_j, N_j, and Q_j for trial values of T_a from Fig. 5.19 for the walls and the cloud of particles. The net radiation flux at wall 1 is

$$\dot{q}_{1,\text{net}} = \sum_j A_j M_{j1} T_1^4 - \sum_j A_j N_{j2} T_2^4 - \sum_j A_j Q_{ja} T_a^4, \qquad (5.147)$$

and at wall 2

$$\dot{q}_{2,\text{net}} = \sum_j A_j M_{j2} T_2^4 - \sum_j A_j N_{j1} T_1^4 - \sum_j A_j Q_{ja} T_a^4. \qquad (5.148)$$

At steady state with stationary cloud it is seen that $\dot{q}_{1,\text{net}} = -\dot{q}_{2,\text{net}}$ for

$T_a = 1000°R$	$q_{1,\text{net}} = 21{,}960$ Btu/ft²hr	$q_{2,\text{net}} = -1{,}640$ Btu/ft²hr
$= 1500°R$	$= 16{,}170$ Btu/ft²hr	$= -7{,}432$ Btu/ft²hr
$= 1800°R$	$= 8{,}180$ Btu/ft²hr	$= -15{,}430$ Btu/ft²hr

Interpolation gives: $T_a = 1700°R$ and $\dot{q}_{1,net} = 12,600 = -\dot{q}_{2,net}$. This, when compared to the case where wall 1 and 2 are separated by a vacuum [R27],

$$\dot{q}_{net} = \frac{\sigma_r(T_1^4 - T_2^4)}{\left(\dfrac{1}{1-\rho_1} + \dfrac{1}{1-\rho_2} - 1\right)} = 2710 \text{ Btu/ft}^2\text{hr.}$$

The significance of scattering and emission by the particle cloud is thus seen. It is further seen that for the same example, if we have instead a flowing cloud of particles with mean particle temperature of $1000°R$, the net heat input into the cloud is $\dot{q}_{net} = 21,960 - 1,640 = 20,320 \text{ Btu/ft}^2\text{hr.}$

Diffuse Radiation in Nonisothermal Conducting Media—Obviously, the above cloud temperature will not, in general, remain uniform. However, in order to determine the distribution of temperature in the absorbing, conducting medium, scattering has to be neglected, and this was studied by Viskanta and Grosh [V11]. In this case, the medium may be represented as isotropic and homogeneous, and the infinite plates as in the above is specified to be isothermal and diffuse. The equation of transfer of a monochromatic ray may be expressed as $(\beta_m \sim \alpha_m)$:

$$\mu \frac{dI(x,\mu)}{dx} = -\rho_m\alpha_m(x)\{I(x,\mu) - [n_m(x)]^2 I_{bb}(x)\}, \tag{5.149}$$

where n_m is the index of refraction. The net output of radiation from an element of unit volume per unit time is (for $\alpha'_m = \alpha_m\rho_m$, the absorption coefficient in ft^{-1})

$$\mathscr{E}_n(x) = \alpha'_m(x)\{4[n_m(x)]^2 E_{bb}(x) - \mathscr{E}'(x)\}. \tag{5.150}$$

The first term accounts for emission and the second term for the amount of energy which is incident on the element and the fraction of this energy that is absorbed, noting that

$$\mathscr{E}'(x) = \int_{\Omega=4\pi} I(x,\mu)\, d\Omega, \tag{5.151}$$

where Ω is the solid angle.

The energy equation for simultaneous conduction and radiation in this absorbing medium is

$$\frac{d}{dx}\kappa\frac{dT}{dx} = \int_0^\infty \mathscr{E}_n(x)\, d\nu = \mathscr{E}_{no}. \tag{5.152}$$

Equations (5.149) and (5.152) suffice to determine the temperature distribution and heat transfer in the medium for given boundary conditions. They are, as explained before,

$$\left.\begin{array}{ll} I(x,\mu) = I(0) & \text{at } x = 0 \text{ and } \mu < 0 \\ I(x,\mu) = I(x_o) & \text{at } x = 0 \text{ and } \mu > 0 \end{array}\right\}. \tag{5.153}$$

Using integrating factor $\exp\left(\int d\tau/\mu\right)$, the solution of Eq. (5.149) is

$$I(\tau,\mu) = I(\tau_o) \exp\left[\frac{-(\tau_o - \tau)}{\mu}\right] + \int_\tau^{\tau_o} [n_m(\tau')]^2 I_{bb}(\tau') \exp\left[\frac{-(\tau' - \tau)}{\mu}\right] \frac{d\tau'}{\mu}$$

$$\text{for} \quad 0 \le \mu \le 1 \quad (5.154)$$

$$I(\tau,\mu) = I(0) \exp\left[\frac{\tau}{\mu}\right] - \int_0^\tau [n_m(\tau')]^2 I_{bb}(\tau') \exp\left[\frac{-(\tau' - \tau)}{\mu}\right] \frac{d\tau'}{\mu}$$

$$\text{for} \quad -1 \le \mu \le 0. \quad (5.155)$$

Substitution of Eqs. (5.154) and (5.155) into Eq. (5.150), noting that $d\Omega = -d\mu\, d\varphi$, and integrating over the complete range of μ, φ, and ν gives

$$\mathscr{E}_{no}(\tau) = \int_0^\infty \alpha'_m(\tau)\left\{4[n_m(\tau)]^2 E_{bb}(\tau) - 2\left[R(0)E_2(\tau) + R(\tau_o)E_2(\tau_o - \tau)\right.\right.$$

$$\left.\left. + \int_0^{\tau_o} [n_m(\tau')]^2 E_1(|\tau - \tau'|)E_{bb}(\tau')\, d\tau'\right]\right\} d\nu, \quad (5.156)$$

where E_n is the exponential integral:

$$E_n(\tau) = \int_0^1 \mu^{n-2} \exp\left[\frac{-\tau}{\mu}\right] d\mu = \int_1^\infty e^{-\tau\mu} \mu^{-n}\, d\mu. \quad (5.157)$$

Further simplification is made possible by taking κ and α_m as constants and introducing a dimensionless quantity radiative conductivity number N_{RC} for reference temperature T^*,

$$N_{RC} = \frac{\kappa\alpha'^2_m T^*}{4\alpha'_m \sigma_r T^{*4}} = \frac{\kappa\alpha'_m}{4\sigma_r T^{*3}}, \quad (5.158)$$

and $\Theta = T/T^*$, we get

$$N_{RC} \frac{d^2\Theta}{d\tau^2} = n_m^2(\tau)\Theta^4(\tau) - \frac{1}{2}\left[\frac{R(\tau)}{\sigma_r T^{*4}} E_2(\tau) + \frac{R(\tau_o)}{\sigma_r T^{*4}} E_2(\tau_o - \tau)\right.$$

$$\left. + \int_0^{\tau_o} n_m^2(\tau')E_1(|\tau - \tau'|)\Theta^4(\tau')\, d\tau'\right], \quad (5.159)$$

with boundary conditions

$$\begin{rcases} \Theta(\tau) = \Theta(0) & \tau = 0 \ (x = 0) \\ \Theta(\tau) = \Theta(\tau_o), & \tau = \tau_o \ (x = x_o) \end{rcases}. \quad (5.160)$$

It is seen that large N_{RC} means radiation effect is small. For small N_{RC} the Θ^4 terms on the right-hand side of Eq. (5.159) make the solution difficult.

Methods of solution were discussed by Lichtenstein [L41]. They include:

1. Linearization according to, for an average $\overline{\Theta}$

$$\Theta^4 = \Theta^4\left[1 + \left(\frac{\Theta - \overline{\Theta}}{\overline{\Theta}}\right)\right]^4 \sim 4\Theta(\tau)\overline{\Theta}^3 - \overline{\Theta}^4 \qquad (5.161)$$

2. Perturbation with result of the conduction part as zero order and solve in orders of τ/τ_0.

3. Iteration by arranging Eq. (5.159) as a nonlinear Fredholm integral equation of the second kind [V11].

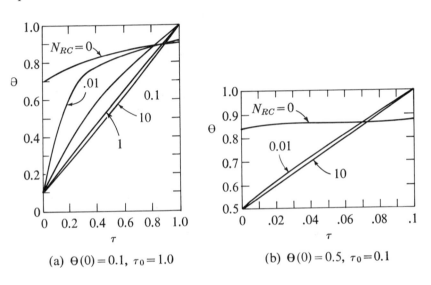

(a) $\Theta(0) = 0.1$, $\tau_0 = 1.0$ (b) $\Theta(0) = 0.5$, $\tau_0 = 0.1$

Figure 5.20 Variation of Ξ with $\Xi(0)$ and optical thickness, $\theta = T/T^*$ [V10].

The result of calculation by Viskanta is shown in Fig. 5.20, for $\Theta(0) = 0.1$ and $\tau_0 = 1.0$; and $\Theta = 0.5$ and $\tau_0 = 0.1$, showing that, for small N_{RC}, the temperature of the medium is nearly uniform, especially for small τ_0.

Approximate solutions were given by Rosseland [R38], and Milne-Eddington [M47]. The former is discussed here. For optically thick media "near" thermodynamic equilibrium, the radiant flux is given by

$$\mathbf{E} = -\frac{1}{3\alpha'_m} \operatorname{grad} \mathscr{E}'_o = -\frac{16n_m^3\sigma_r T^3}{3\alpha'_m} \operatorname{grad} T, \qquad (5.162)$$

that is, an approximation based on diffusion of radiant flux vector. Equation (5.152) now becomes

$$\operatorname{div}\left(-\kappa \operatorname{grad} T + \mathbf{E}\right) = 0, \qquad (5.163)$$

or

$$\frac{d}{dx} \kappa_{\text{eff}} \frac{dT}{dx} = 0,$$ (5.164)

with

$$\kappa_{\text{eff}} = \kappa + \kappa_{\text{rad}} = \kappa + \frac{16 n_m^2 \sigma_r T^3}{3\alpha'_m},$$ (5.165)

where κ_{rad} is the radiative conductivity. The temperature distribution is now

$$T - \frac{4 n_r^2 \sigma_r}{3\alpha_m K} T^4 = T_1\left(1 - \frac{x}{x_0}\right) + T_2\left(\frac{x}{x_0}\right)$$

$$+ \frac{4 n_m^2 \sigma_r}{3\alpha'_m K}\left[T_1^4\left(1 - \frac{x}{x_0}\right) + T_2^4\left(\frac{x}{x_0}\right)\right], \quad (5.166)$$

where

$$K = \frac{1}{4\pi} \int_{\Omega=4\pi} I\mu^2 \, d\Omega.$$ (5.167)

Parameters of Diffused Radiation—When the density of particles is so small that literally every particle sees the wall with which it exchanges heat by radiation, $\mathscr{E}_{no}$ can be represented simply as has been dealt with earlier (Sec. 4.3 p. 152).

When the particle density is high enough so that diffused radiation is the case, analogous to the case of microscopic diffusion, the absorption coefficient α'_m is given by [S46]

$$\alpha'_m = \alpha \pi a^2 n_p \,,$$ (5.168)

where α is the absorptivity of the surface. For a gas-solid system consisting of opaque solid particles, since reflection is, in general, diffused, the index of refraction of a mixture is therefore that of the gas phase alone. For transparent or partially transparent solid particles, the index of refraction depends on the surface condition of the solid particles. For rough surfaces and low transmissivity, the index of refraction will be that of the gas phase at one limiting condition, and the Lorentz relation [L56] gives

$$\frac{n_m^2 - 1}{n_m^2 + 2} \sim \frac{n_{gm}^2 - 1}{n_{gm}^2 + 2} + \frac{\rho_p}{\bar{\rho}_p} \frac{n_{pm}^2 - 1}{n_{pm}^2 + 2},$$ (5.169)

as the other limit, especially for very small transparent solid spheres. In the above relation n_{gm} is the index of refraction of the gas and n_{pm} is the index of refraction of the solid material.

The influence of particle size is seen from the fact radiative conductivity [V11] is actually a measure of transparency. In blackbody radiation, the optimum energy per unit wavelength is known to be at $\Lambda_m T \sim 3 \times 10^3 \ \mu°K.$

For $T = 3000°K$, $\Lambda_m \sim 1\ \mu$. The size of particles in the submicron range of, say, $0.1\ \mu$ renders it almost transparent to radiation. In this case the fraction of total blackbody radiation transferred to a particle of radius a is nearly

$$\alpha_a \sim \frac{15}{\pi^4}\left(\frac{hc}{2akT}\right)^3 \exp\left(\frac{-hc}{2akT}\right),$$

where h is the Planck constant, c the speed of light, and k the Boltzmann constant. For a 0.1-μ particle with $T = 3000°K$, $hc/2akT \sim 48$, $\alpha_a \sim 1.5 \times 10^{-16}$. At $2a = 1\ \mu$, $\alpha_a \sim 0.15$.

For a dense particle cloud, the Mie theory shows that, for $2a < \Lambda_m$ (mean radiation wavelength), absorptivity is independent of a. Observation by Thring [T30] showed that absorptivity may be $\pm 30\%$ or up to 2–3 times that of the predicted value.

Aspects of application of radiation from a cloud of particles were indicated by Jakob [J2] in his review of early works on luminous flames of powdered coal; Thring, Foster, McGrath, and Ashton [T30] utilized Mie theory in the determination of extinction cross section of flames. Glaser [G22] investigated radiant heat transfer in evacuated powder insulations; Larkin and Churchill [L21] treated porous insulations; in these cases, closely spaced particles will not scatter independently and diffuse radiation model may be more appropriate. Hawkins, Tang, Gary and Wikman [H26] treated radiation effects in fluidized beds but neglected scattering effects. Paint may be treated as a dispersion of particles in a semitransparent medium and was treated by Blevin and Brown [B43] as multiple scattering; the reinforced plastic heat shield of reentry vehicles has a similar nature.

Radiation to particle clouds in motion has not yet been treated extensively. Available reference of flow systems in which radiation to the flow media is accounted for includes Viskanta and Grosh [V12] and Cess [C12] including boundary layer flow, and Tien and Abu-Romia [T33] relating to rocket base flow. Flow systems involving a significant effect of radiation are treated in Chap. 8.

5.7 Particle-Size Distribution and Scattering of Light

When dealing with heat transfer, little is known about polarization of energy emitted or reflected by the bounding surface, and polarization is expected to contribute insignificantly to heat transfer [L16]. However, polarization is an important effect in the utilization of scattering for purposes of particle identification and measurement.

Chin, Sliepcevich, and Tribus [C22] formulated a method for determining size distribution in polydispersions based on the angular variation of the intensity of forward-scattered light. They derived an integral formula from the modified Bouguer-Beer light transmission equation:

$$\ln\left(\frac{\Gamma_o}{\Gamma}\right) = 2\pi x \int_0^\infty R^* K_m f_N(a) a^2 \, da, \qquad (5.170)$$

where Γ_o is the incident parallel flux, ergs/sec, Γ the flux traversing a distance x through the dispersion, K_m the Mie theory total scattering coefficient in cm^{-1}, and

$$K_m = K_m(a,\Lambda,n_m,n_p), \qquad (5.171)$$

R^* is a factor allowing for geometry of the optical system and for measuring F, $f_N(a)$ is the number distribution function of the dispersion and

$$\int f_N(a) \, da = \sum_i n_{pi}, \qquad (5.172)$$

where n_{pi} is the number of particles of size i per unit volume of the dispersion. For particles large in comparison to Λ of the incident light and for a measuring system having a small value of the forward-scattering half-angle θ, Gumprecht and Sliepcevich [G50] derived, according to the diffraction theory,

$$R^* = R^*(\alpha\theta) = (\tfrac{1}{2})[1 + J_0^2(\alpha\theta) + J_1^2(\alpha\theta)],$$

where α is still $2\pi a/\Lambda$ and J_0 and J_1 are Bessel functions of the first kind of orders 0 and 1 respectively.

Equation (5.170) may now be expressed as, by changing a to α:

$$\frac{4\pi}{x\Lambda^2} \ln\left(\frac{\Gamma_o}{\Gamma}\right) = \int_0^\infty R^*(\alpha\theta) K_m(\alpha) f_N(\alpha)\alpha^2 \, d\alpha, \qquad (5.173)$$

and Mellon transformation [S44] gives

$$K_m(\alpha) f_N(\alpha)\alpha^2 = \int_0^\infty \frac{4\pi}{x\Lambda^2} \ln\left(\frac{\Gamma_o}{\Gamma}\right) h(\alpha\theta) \, d\theta, \qquad (5.174)$$

where $h(\alpha\theta)$ is a kernel to be determined from R^*. This leads to, with the transformation procedure of Titchmarsh [T38],

$$K_m(\alpha) f_N(\alpha)\alpha^2 = 2\pi \int_0^\infty \frac{4\pi}{x\Lambda^2} \frac{d}{d\theta}\left(\theta^2 \frac{d\ln\Gamma}{d\theta}\right)[-J_1(\alpha\theta) Y_1(\alpha\theta)]\alpha\theta \, d\theta, \quad (5.175)$$

where Y_1 is the Bessel function of the second kind of order 1.

Since $(4\pi/x\Lambda^2)(d/d\theta)(\theta^2 \, d\ln\Gamma/d\theta)$ can be determined by experiment, the left hand side can be calculated from the integral in Eq. (5.175) by inserting a series values of α into the kernel; the integral must check with the left-hand side, and $f_N(\alpha)$ or $f_N(a)$ can thus be determined. Possible experimental procedures include the lens-pinhole method [G50], moving pinhole method, and microdensitometric method. The latter uses a photographic film at the focal plane of the receiving lens and a beam of parallel monochromatic light is passed through the dispersion in front of the lens. This forward-scattering gives rise to a distribution of the density on the photographic plate. The relative illumination E_m on the plate is related to Γ according to

$$d\Gamma = 2\pi r E_m \, dr, \qquad (5.176)$$

where r is the radius of the density ring of the plate. Since $r \sim l_\Gamma \theta$, where l_Γ is the focal length, the radiant flux Γ_m for a pinhole radius r_o is

$$\frac{\Gamma_m}{\pi r_o^2/4} \sim (2\pi l_\Gamma^2 \theta)\frac{d\Gamma}{d\theta} = E_m , \qquad (5.177)$$

or

$$f_N(\alpha)\alpha^2 = \frac{32\pi^2 l_\Gamma^2}{x\Lambda^2 r_o^2 \Gamma_\delta} \int_0^\infty \frac{d}{d\theta}(\theta^3 \Gamma_m)[-J_1(\alpha\theta)Y_1(\alpha\theta)]\alpha\theta \, d\theta. \qquad (5.178)$$

This integral method provides a convenient means of determining $f_N(a)$, the particle size distribution; Γ_δ is its flux falling over a very small circle of radius δ.

It is seen that the above relations point to a way of treating radiation problems in the above section involving particle-size distribution. Smoke-scattered light was also used by Rosensweig, Hottel, and Williams [R36] for determining turbulent concentration fluctuations.

The effect of anisotropic scattering on radiant transport was treated by Evans, Churchill, and Chu [E25]. The angular distribution for single scattering was represented by a finite set of Legendre polynomials.

5.8 Interaction with Sound Waves by a Suspension and a Bubbling Liquid

Propagation of sound waves through a suspension is basically a momentum-transfer phenomenon. Applications include absorption of noise by a dispersion of solid particles and liquid droplets in a gas, determination of mean particle size, and sonic agglomeration and dispersion [H63]. Another case of interest is the sonic interaction with a liquid containing a large number of gas bubbles, a significant phenomenon in underwater warfare.

Propagation of sonic and ultrasonic sound waves in aerosols has been studied by many [R14]. Sewell considered the case of small (smaller than wavelength) solid spheres under the prescription: $\omega(2a)^2/\bar{\nu}$ is large (ω is the pulsatance, $2a$ the diameter, and $\bar{\nu}$ is the kinematic viscosity of the fluid material), but neglected dispersion and the effect of relative acceleration and heat transfer between the phases [S24, T15]. Various discrepancies between Sewell's theory and experimental results were found [R14]. In terms of absorption, experiment by Laidler and Richardson [L3] shows consistently lower values than the Sewell's theory, while experimental results by Hartman and Focke [H21] are consistently higher.

Epstein and Carhart accounted for the contribution of both viscosity and heat conduction in their analysis [E17], but neglected the effects of dispersion and relaxation, as well as relative acceleration of particles. Their result compares favorably to the experimental result of Knudsen, Wilson, and Anderson [K24] in the low-frequency range, but the calculated attenuation is much smaller in the high-frequency range. In a study by Soo [S49], the effects of dispersion and relative acceleration of particles are included, but the problem is formulated and solved in one space dimension for the sake of generality of the results.

The oscillating motion of a spherical particle in a gaseous medium can be described by (in one dimension)

$$\frac{4\pi}{3}a^3\bar{\rho}_p\dot{u}_p = -X - \frac{4\pi}{3}a\bar{\mu}\left[\frac{2a}{(\pi\bar{\nu})^{1/2}}\int_{-\infty}^{t}\frac{\dot{u}_p - \dot{u}}{(t-\tau)^{1/2}}\,d\tau\right] + \frac{4\pi}{3}a^3\bar{\rho}\dot{u}, \quad (5.179)$$

where the dotted quantities are time derivatives, the bracketed term gives the fluid resistance due to the Basset force (Sec. 2.4), and p. 643 of [L5]

$$X = \frac{4\pi}{3}a^3\bar{\rho}\left[\frac{1}{2} + \frac{9}{4\sqrt{(N_{\mathrm{Re}})}}\right]\frac{d(u - u_p)}{dt}$$

$$- 3\pi a^3\bar{\rho}\frac{\omega}{\sqrt{(N_{\mathrm{Re}})}}\left[1 + \frac{1}{\sqrt{(N_{\mathrm{Re}})}}\right](u - u_p), \quad (5.180)$$

where $(N_{\mathrm{Re}}) = \omega(2a)^2/8\bar{\nu}$, giving the correction to the inertia of solid particle amounting to the fraction of the mass of fluid displaced, and the friction force varying as the velocity (Sewell considered only the last contribution). The effect of pressure gradient is negligible, since our interest is in gaseous suspensions of liquid droplets and solid particles, or $\bar{\rho}_p \gg \bar{\rho}$.

For m_p^* pound of solid per pound of gas, the equation of plane wave in the mixture can be expressed as

$$\bar{\rho}\left(\frac{\partial^2 u}{\partial t^2}\right) = \gamma P\left(\frac{\partial^2 u}{\partial x^2}\right) + \left(\frac{\frac{3}{4}m_p^*}{\pi a^3\bar{\rho}_p}\right)\left(\frac{\partial X'}{\partial t}\right), \quad (5.181)$$

where t and x are time and space coordinates, $\bar{\rho}$ and P the mean density and pressure of the gas, and γ the apparent ratio of specific heats of the mixture. X' includes the Basset force. In Eq. (5.181), the volume occupied by the solid particles is neglected, as well as scattering (10^{-6} times that due to friction) [S24]. Neglecting temperature dependence of $\bar{\mu}$ and $\bar{\rho}$, Eq. (5.179) gives, for $u = u_0 e^{i(\omega t - mx)} e^{-\alpha' x}$,

$$\frac{u_p}{u} = \frac{\beta^2 + (1 + \alpha)\left[\dfrac{\bar{\rho}}{\bar{\rho}_p} + \alpha\right] - i\left[1 - \dfrac{\bar{\rho}}{\bar{\rho}_p}\right]\beta}{(1 + \alpha)^2 + \beta^2}, \tag{5.182}$$

where α' is the absorption coefficient,

$$\alpha = G^* + H^* \qquad \beta = F^* + H^*, \tag{5.183}$$

and

$$F^* = \frac{\dfrac{9}{4}\left(\dfrac{\bar{\rho}}{\bar{\rho}_p}\right)\left\{1 + \left[\dfrac{1}{\sqrt{(N_{\mathrm{Re}})}}\right]\right\}}{\sqrt{(N_{\mathrm{Re}})}}, \tag{5.184}$$

the friction force coefficient;

$$G^* = \frac{\bar{\rho}}{\bar{\rho}_p}\left\{\frac{1}{2} + \left[\dfrac{9}{4\sqrt{(N_{\mathrm{Re}})}}\right]\right\} \tag{5.185}$$

the inertia correction; and

$$H^* = \frac{2\sqrt{2}\left(\dfrac{\bar{\rho}}{\bar{\rho}_p}\right)}{\sqrt{(N_{\mathrm{Re}})}} \tag{5.186}$$

the resistance coefficient due to the Basset force.

It was shown that, neglecting heat transfer, substitution of u and u_p into Eq. (5.181) gives:

$$\frac{a_m^2}{a_g^2} = \left[1 + m_p^*\left(1 - \frac{\bar{\rho}}{\bar{\rho}_p}\right)\frac{(1 + \alpha)\alpha + \beta^2}{(1 + \alpha)^2 + \beta^2}\right]^{-1}, \tag{5.187}$$

from the real part, for $\alpha' a_g/\omega < 1$, where $a_g = (\gamma P/\bar{\rho})^{1/2}$, the speed of sound in the pure gas, $a_m = \omega/m$ is that in the mixture and the attenuation coefficient α' given by the imaginary part:

$$2\frac{\alpha' a_g}{\omega} = m_p^* \frac{a_m}{a_g}\left(1 - \frac{\bar{\rho}}{\bar{\rho}_p}\right)\frac{\beta}{(1 + \alpha)^2 + \beta^2}, \tag{5.188}$$

which is similar to the result of Urick [U5]. For $G^* \sim H^* \sim 0$, $\bar{\rho}_p/\bar{\rho} \gg 1$, and $F^* \ll 1$,

$$2\frac{\alpha' a_g}{\omega} = m_p^* F^*, \tag{5.189}$$

similar to Sewell's result, not including scattering.

Figure 5.21 shows the dispersion for $\bar{\rho}_p/\bar{\rho}$ of 1000 and 100 with 0.3 lb magnesia per pound of air, for various values of $(2a)^2\omega/\bar{\nu}$.

The dispersion due to heat transfer [E17] is not usually felt at large $(2a)^2\omega/\bar{\nu}$, but is usually felt at low values of $(2a)^2\omega/\bar{\nu}$ (slow motion). The lower limit is that of a gaseous mixture. The solid-gas suspension gives a simple model of relaxation phenomenon in sonics [R14] as well as in shock

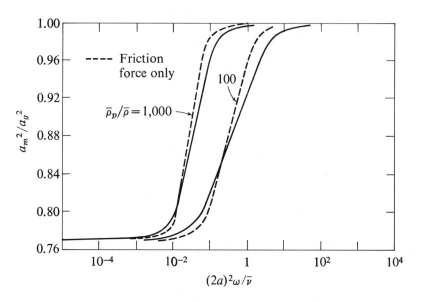

Figure 5.21 Dispersion of sound by 0.3 lb of magnesia per pound of air [S49].

waves (Sec. 7.8). This theoretical trend of dispersion is not clearly observable in gases [H63, R14].

This relaxation phenomenon is further seen in Fig. 5.22. The variation in attenuation per unit wavelength follows the same trend as the result of Leonard [R14] on carbon dioxide.

Figure 5.22 shows the attenuation in terms of $\alpha' a_g/\omega$ for $\bar{\rho}_p/\bar{\rho}$ of 1000 and 100 for 0.3 lb magnesia per pound of air, as compared to Sewell's theory. For small $(2a)^2\omega/\bar{\nu}$, the present result is smaller than his, following the experimental trend of Laidler and Richardson [L3]. As $(2a)^2\omega/\bar{\nu}$ increases, the value of $\alpha' a_g/\omega$ is greater than Sewell's, confirming the experimental trend of Hartman and Focke [H21]. Figure 5.23 shows these comparisons. The fact that, at large $(2a)^2\omega/\bar{\nu}$, resistance due to the Basset term predominating confirms the conjecture that larger actual attenuation may be due to wave phenomena. Comparison to the analytical results of Epstein and Carhart [E17] is made numerically in Fig. 5.23, together with the experimental results of Knudsen, Wilson, and Anderson [K24]. There is currently no available experimental data with low enough $(2a)^2\omega/\bar{\nu}$ to substantiate the relation in Fig. 5.22, showing peaks of $\alpha'a_g/\omega$. Experiments by Knudsen at 500 cps is

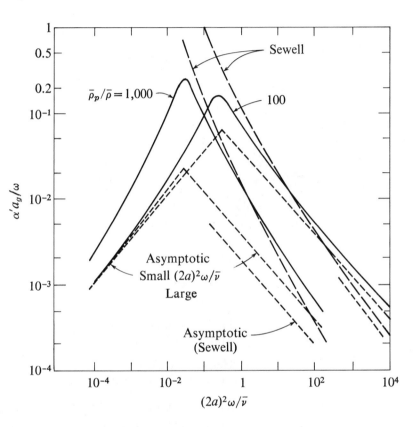

Figure 5.22 Attenuation per wavelength as compared to Sewell's theory (0.3 lb of magnesia per pound of air) [S49].

close to that range, but the observed attenuation, being averaged over various particle sizes, does not give a clear indication; the spread of $(2a)^2\omega/\bar{\nu}$ and $\alpha'a_g/\omega$ at 500 cps over the curve of present study is interesting. At high frequencies, naturally, Epstein's relation approaches Sewell's relation asymptotically.

It is also well to point out that since the sizes of aerosols always follow certain distributions, the experimental points of Laidler and Hartman in reference to $2a$ cannot be taken as exact.

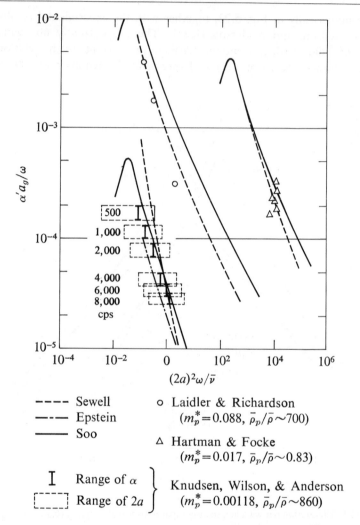

- - - - Sewell   o Laidler & Richardson
- - · - Epstein $(m_p^* = 0.088,\ \bar{\rho}_p/\bar{\rho} \sim 700)$
——— Soo
               △ Hartman & Focke
                    $(m_p^* = 0.017,\ \bar{\rho}_p/\bar{\rho} \sim 0.83)$

I Range of α ⎱
                              Knudsen, Wilson, & Anderson
⌐--¬ Range of $2a$ ⎰ $(m_p^* = 0.00118,\ \bar{\rho}_p/\bar{\rho} \sim 860)$

Figure 5.23 Attenuation per wavelength compared to experimental data [S49].

It is of interest to note the asymptotic values of $\alpha' a_g/\omega$. For very small $(2a)^2\omega/\bar{\nu}$, Eq. (5.188) reduces to

$$2\frac{\alpha' a_g}{\omega} \sim m_p^*\left(1 - \frac{\bar{\rho}}{\bar{\rho}_p}\right)\beta^{-1} \qquad (5.190)$$

This asymptotic relation as well as the following are shown in Figs. 5.22 and 5.23. The limit is the attenuation coefficient of a gaseous mixture.

At large $(2a)^2\omega/\bar{\nu}$, we get

$$2\frac{\alpha' a_g}{\omega} \sim m_p^* \beta = \frac{m_p^*(\frac{9}{4} + 2\sqrt{2})\frac{\bar{\rho}}{\rho_p}}{\sqrt{(N_{\mathrm{Re}})}}. \tag{5.191}$$

Scattering may be significant for large diameters, for unit depth of suspension [U5]:

$$2\frac{\alpha_s' a_g}{\omega} = \tfrac{1}{24}m_p^*\left(\frac{\bar{\rho}}{\bar{\rho}_p}\right)\left(\frac{\omega 2a}{a_g}\right)^3\left(\frac{a_g}{a_m}\right)^3 \tag{5.192}$$

The contribution of heat transfer does not significantly change the order of magnitude of attenuation.

Good agreement between theory and experiment was also obtained by Zink and Delsasso [Z7]. Dispersion and attenuation by suspensions of 0.1 to 0.15 volume fraction solid were computed by Urick [U5] and Byzova and Nesterov [B73]; the results do not compare favorably with experimental data. It is noted that a suspension of high concentration is a highly nonlinear system. The non-Newtonian nature (Secs. 4.1 and 5.3) the dependence of drag on concentration (Sec. 5.1) and the mutual interaction of particles (Secs. 5.3 and 5.4) should all be accounted for in dealing with concentrated suspensions.

Acoustic properties of air bubbles in water were studied by Carstensen and Foldy [C8] to determine the effect of bubbles in the wakes of ships and submarines in the propagation of sound. They made measurements on the attenuation of sound through a screen (17 × 3 in. to 6 in. various vertical lengths) of bubbles and the amount of reflection of the sound from such a screen, with various number densities of bubbles over a range of sizes. Bubbles were produced by a microdisperser. Bubble radii were measured optically and acoustically, the latter method according to the resonant angular frequency ω_o of a bubble, and

$$\omega_0 = \left(\frac{3\gamma P_0}{\bar{\rho}_p a^2}\right)^{1/2}. \tag{5.193}$$

$\bar{\rho}_p$ is the density of the vapor.

Their experiments were carried out with the system shown in Fig. 5.24. The bubble screen was produced by six microdispersers. Six feet above the microdispersers were an $\frac{1}{8}$-in. directional Brush crystal projector and two Bell Telephone Laboratories' 2A pressure gradient hydrophones. Bubble diameters ranged from 0.5 to 1 mm.

Theoretical study in this case accounted for the distribution in bubble size and number distribution in space, and change in bubble configuration. A comparison of theoretical and measured damping constant is shown in Fig. 5.25. Theoretical analysis included the losses due to viscosity and thermal

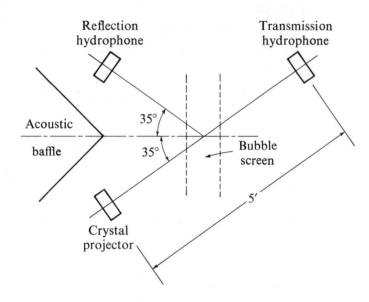

Figure 5.24 Apparatus for acoustic measurement of bubbles in liquid [C8].

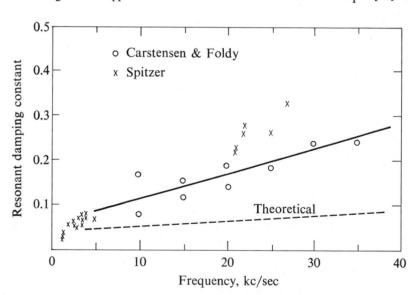

Figure 5.25 Comparison of theoretical and experimental results [C8].

conductivity. Typical trends of attenuation and reflection are shown in Fig. 5.26.

A statistical procedure introduced by Davis and Thurston [D15] consists of a distribution function $f(a)$, the number of bubbles per unit volume having

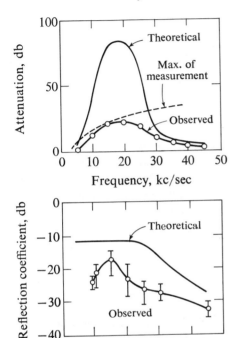

(a)   Attenuation through a continuous-flow screen.

(b)   Reflection through a continuous-flow screen.

Figure 5.26 Typical results of measurements and computation [C8].

radius lying between a and $a + \delta a$. The contribution of these bubbles to the volume of air is

$$\delta v = \left(\frac{4\pi}{3}\right) a^3 f(a) \, \mathrm{d}a = v(a) \, \delta a,$$

and the total volume per cubic centimeter of water occupied by all the bubbles is

$$\mathscr{V} = \frac{4\pi}{3} \int_0^\infty a^3 f(a) \, \mathrm{d}a. \tag{5.194}$$

The dispersion due to bubbles is given by

$$\frac{a_l^2}{a_m^2} = 1 - \frac{3}{\alpha_r^2} \int_0^\infty \frac{a_r^2}{a^2} v(a) \, \mathrm{d}a, \tag{5.195}$$

where a_l is the speed of sound when no bubbles are present, a_r is the resonant radius for a given frequency, and

$$\alpha_r = \frac{2\pi a_r}{\Lambda}. \tag{5.196}$$

It was shown that for a normal size distribution of $\Delta a = 0.1 a_r$, the dispersion effect is negligible. For bubble sizes below resonance, no dispersion occurs; the bulk compliance of the material is increased and sound velocity is decreased. For bubble sizes above that at resonance, the vibrations are out of phase; dispersion is evidenced, the group and phase velocities differ, and the phase velocity is increased.

The effect of vibrations on the motion of small gas bubbles in a liquid was studied by Bleich [B42]. Depending on the magnitude of acceleration and frequency of vibration a bubble may sink instead of rise according to buoyancy. Migration of very small bubbles in an ultrasonic field was discussed by Rosenberg [R33]. Karplus [K6] further considered the collapse of the bubbles.

A survey of the velocity of sound in two-phase mixtures was presented by Gouse and Brown [G35]. It was shown that for liquid droplets, the effect of the compressibility of liquid was small.

5.9 Brownian Motion, Coagulation, and Agglomeration

We have so far dealt with situations in which the motion of solid particles is due to fluid motion only. This is true for relatively large particles, say, greater than the order 1 μ in size. The size range of particles encountered in dispersed systems ranges from 10^{-6} m in coarse dispersions to 10^{-9} m in molecular dispersions. Due to thermal excitation, these particles experience Brownian motion, such that

$$\tfrac{1}{2} m_p \langle v_p^2 \rangle \sim \tfrac{3}{2} kT, \tag{5.197}$$

or the root-mean-square velocity of Brownian motion is given by

$$\langle v_p^2 \rangle^{1/2} = \left[\frac{3kT}{\dfrac{4\pi}{3} a^3 \bar\rho_p} \right]^{1/2}. \tag{5.198}$$

It is seen that for $T = 300°K$, $\bar\rho_p = 2500$ kg/m³, $\langle v_p^2 \rangle^{1/2} \sim 1.09 \times 10^{-3} a_\mu^{-3/2}$ m/sec, for a_μ in microns. Thus the root-mean-square velocity is to the order of 1 mm/sec for 1-μ particles and up to 10^3 m/sec for molecules where a is of the order of 1 angstrom.

The randomness of Brownian motion frequently brings individual particles into close proximity where electrostatic or polarization forces (Van der Waals forces) strongly attract them to each other. Only for the case of very small particles (10^{-9} m size) can thermal motion disrupt this attraction. Levich [L35] suggested that particles approaching each other within a distance of one diameter become bounded to each other, leading to rapid coagulations.

In the simple model due to Smoluchowski [S42], N spherical particles of equal size in a dilute dispersion were considered so that only binary encounter is significant. The probability of the binary collision due to Brownian motion or diffusion was computed.

Take one particle as stationary, imagine a sphere of radius R surrounding the particle such that any other particle entering this sphere will be attracted to the first and become bonded to it. Within this radius R the particle concentration remains zero. The diffusional flux across that surface depends on the average rate at which particles cross as a result of Brownian motion. For noninteracting particles, $R = 2a$.

The diffusional flux is given by the distribution of particles diffusing toward the sphere R. The concentration n of these particles satisfies the diffusion equation

$$\frac{\partial n}{\partial t} = D \frac{1}{r^2} \frac{\partial}{\partial r}\left(r^2 \frac{\partial n}{\partial r}\right), \tag{5.199}$$

where D is the Brownian diffusion coefficient of the dispersed particles. The boundary conditions are:

$$\left.\begin{array}{ll} n = n_o & \text{for } r > R, t = 0 \\ n = 0 & \text{at } r = R, t > 0 \\ n = n_o & \text{as } r \to \infty \end{array}\right\} \tag{5.200}$$

The solution of Eq. (5.199), satisfying (5.200) is

$$n = n_o\left[1 - \frac{R}{r} + \frac{2}{\sqrt{\pi}} \frac{R}{r} \int_0^{\frac{r-R}{2\sqrt{Dt}}} \exp\left(-z^2\right) dz\right]. \tag{5.201}$$

The flux of particles crossing the surface at R is

$$J = D\left(\frac{\partial n}{\partial r}\right)_{r=R} = \frac{Dn_o}{R}\left[1 + \frac{R}{\sqrt{\pi Dt}}\right]. \tag{5.202}$$

The total number of particles that cross the surface $r = R$ or total number of collisions per unit time is

$$\dot{N} = \int J\, dS = D \cdot 4\pi n_o R\left[1 + \frac{R}{\sqrt{\pi Dt}}\right]. \tag{5.203}$$

The rate of rapid coagulation is given by viewing t sec after its start, when $t \gg R^2/D$. In the case of usual particle dimensions, this means that the elapsed time from the start of the aggregation process exceeds 10^{-3} to 10^{-4} sec. The number of encounters per unit time after the initial period equals

$$\dot{N} = 4\pi DRn_o .$$ (5.204)

For like particles, the total number of contacts per unit volume of dispersion per second is

$$N = 8\pi DRn_o^2 = 16\pi Dan_o^2.$$ (5.205)

The rate of change of n is

$$\frac{dn}{dt} = -8\pi DRn^2.$$ (5.206)

Integration gives for constant DR

$$n = \frac{n_o}{1 + \dfrac{t}{\tau}},$$ (5.207)

where

$$\tau = \frac{1}{8\pi DRn_o},$$ (5.208)

the coagulation time; the reciprocal is the coagulation time constant

$$\frac{1}{\tau} = 8\pi DRn_o .$$ (5.209)

Since, for Brownian motion

$$D = \frac{kT}{3\pi \bar{\mu}a}$$ (5.210)

$$\frac{1}{\tau} = \frac{8kTRn_o}{3\bar{\mu}a}.$$ (5.211)

Extensive treatment of gradient coagulation, coagulation due to fluid turbulence, was given by Levich [L35]. Brownian motion and collection of particles and dusts by filters, impact collection based on individual trajectories, are treated in detail by Fuchs [F36]. Hydrodynamic collection based on continuum consideration is treated in Chap. 8; electrostatic collection is treated in Chap. 10.

Hayakawa [H27] studied the coagulation of ammonium chloride aerosols and showed that coagulation is promoted by addition of acidic polar compounds, while addition of nonpolar or neutral polar compounds would increase the stability of the aerosol system. It was also shown that vapors of carbon tetrachloride and carbon disulfide increase the stability while vapors of acetic acid and formic acid increase the coagulation rate. The change in coagulation rate of solids in the presence of a foreign vapor was considered by Green and Lane [G38]; their book includes a large number of references on this subject.

Agglomeration of fine particles also occurs due to reaction and thermal effect. The size of oxidizer particles (ammonium perchlorate, polybutadiene acrylic acid) in solid-propellant application affects the rate of agglomeration of metallic additives (such as aluminum). Povinelli [P27] showed that for aluminum of 2.2 μ mean radius, agglomeration of aluminum particles on the surface of burning propellant will not occur if the oxidizer particles are above 21 μ in diameter.

Another aspect of agglomeration is the adhesion of solid particles to solid surfaces. A survey by Corn [C41] showed that factors influencing adhesion are: London-Van der Waals forces, humidity, surfaces, constant area, time of contact, static electricity, viscous surface coating, temperature, to name a few. Studies include those of Bradley [B53, B54] on London-Van der Waals forces between particles and between a particle and a surface. The effect of humidity was attributed to a small amount of liquid interposed between surfaces by Bowden and Tabor [B51]. Kordecki and Orr [K26] determined the effects of contact area, particle size, and shape. Bowden and Tabor [B51] also dealt with the time required for full adhesion. It is not hard to visualize that adhesion and London-Van der Waals forces are electric in origin. They are discussed in Chap. 10.

SUMMARY OF BASIC CONCEPTS

Particle-Fluid Interaction
  Brownian diffusion—Brown (1828) [S42]
  Drag of a cloud of particles—(1965) [S60]
  Viscosity of suspension—Einstein (1906) [E6] Taylor (1954) [T12]

Particle-Particle Interaction
  Momentum transfer due to relative motion—Hicks (1880), Herman (1887), Basset (1887) [L5]
  Viscosity and thermal conductivity of a cloud—(1962) [S52], (1965) [S61]
  Transport between different clouds—(1965) [S60]
  Flow regime due to mutual interactions—(1962) [S52]

Interaction with Waves
  Radiation—Milne (1920) [C14, M47]
  Attenuation and dispersion of sound—Sewell (1910) [R14]
  Cutoff of wave spectrum in relation to particle size—(1964)*

* Present volume.

6 | Basic Equations of Multiphase Systems

The continuum mechanics of a single-phase fluid amount to a successful simplification of the general transport equation (Boltzmann transport equation for cases where binary collisions alone are prominent) of kinetic theory of a flow system by replacing the coordinates in the phase space (position and momentum coordinates) with configuration space (position coordinates) through the introduction of pertinent phenomenological relations and transport properties. Not only were the equations and their solutions simplified, but the equations of continuum mechanics are also applicable to fluids (such as liquids) whose microscopic details are unknown.

After the frustration of various efforts of extending the results of single particles (Chap. 2) to clouds of particles, it was natural to try to extend the continuum mechanics of a single-phase fluid to the case of a suspension. Earlier efforts were made on formulation of a two-phase system with spherical particles of one size; these include Hooyman [H52], Van Deemter and Van der Laan [V1], Hinze [H43], and Soo [S52]. Hooyman treated sedimentation in a potential field by extending the methods of irreversible thermodynamics [D18]. Marble [M6] treated the system with consideration of local slip motion of particles. Study by Edelman and Kiely [E2] included consideration of rotation of particles. Terms in equations of Van Deemter and Van der Laan which were deemed to have only formal meaning by Hinze [H43] were generalized in formulations of transport properties of the particulate phase (Chap. 5). Murray [M55] contributed to further generalization of formulation of suspensions with one size of particles.

Any realistic general formulation of multiphase (gas-solid, gas-liquid, or other combinations of a particulate phase and a fluid phase) flow (including fluidization) must account for the distribution in the size of particles in the theoretical formulation. It is well known that except in very isolated cases of large particles (millimeter size), distribution in the size of particles is an unavoidable fact in most particulate systems. Rigorous formulation of gas-solid flow with a distribution in the size of particles [S60] will be presented in this chapter.

The basic theoretical approach includes extending the earlier formulation of the flow system as a continuum with pertinent qualifications. It was recognized that, apart from the obvious definition of a multiphase system (mixture of phases of solid, liquid, and gas), from the point of view of "continuum" mechanics of a cloud of particles, particles of different sizes constitute different "phases," although a nonreactive suspension may consist of one gas and one type of solid material.

Formulations in the above cited references are largely intuitive in nature and, with the exception of the cautious definitions on the interactions among components by Soo [S60, S61], are incomplete. Before presenting the basic formulations for the specific case of a multiphase system, it is desirable to clarify first the relations of general motion of components to that of the mixture which they constitute. Both the mixture and its components are first treated as true continua in the next section. The general situation is visualized as a number of interacting systems occupying the same space; each may have its own streamlines.

6.1 General Motion of Components of a Mixture

Most of the formulations of hydrodynamics of a mixture refer to the motion of the center of mass (barycentric motion [D18]) of the system, individual motions of components are treated in terms of diffusion through the mixture [T54]. It will be demonstrated in later chapters that when dealing with a particulate system, it is often desirable and convenient to treat the motion of an individual component or species interacting with other components of the mixture. This requires clarification of the relation of the general motion of components to that of the mixture which they constitute and the relation of transport properties of components in a mixture to those of the mixture and the pure components. In order that computations on physical systems can be made, the formalism in terms of partial stress, partial energy, and partial heat flux as suggested by Truesdell and Noll [T54] must be expressed in terms of measurable properties. The conclusions are applicable to general mixtures of disparate particle (aerosols or molecules) masses.

The density of a mixture ρ_m is given by

$$\rho_m = \sum_{(q)} \rho^{(q)}, \tag{6.1}$$

where $\rho^{(q)}$ is the density of component (q) of the mixture occupying the volume of the mixture of v components $(q = 1, \ldots, v)$. The ith component of velocity of the mixture U_{mi} is given by

$$\rho_m U_{mi} = \sum_{(q)} \rho^{(q)} U_i^{(q)}. \tag{6.2}$$

Taking the general case including chemical reaction, the continuity equation of component (q) of the mixture can be expressed as

$$\frac{\partial \rho^{(q)}}{\partial t} + \frac{\partial}{\partial x_j} (\rho^{(q)} U_i^{(q)}) = \Gamma^{(q)}, \tag{6.3}$$

where t is the time, x_j is the jth component of the space coordinate, $\Gamma^{(q)}$ is the rate of generation of (q) per unit volume. Since $\sum_{(q)} \Gamma^{(q)} = 0$ over the whole mixture, we get

$$\frac{\partial \rho_m}{\partial t} + \frac{\partial}{\partial x_j} (\rho_m U_{mi}) = 0. \tag{6.4}$$

For a Newtonian fluid, with negligible effect of thermal diffusion, the equations of momentum and energy of a mixture are given by [H41, H44]:

$$\frac{\rho_m \, dU_{mi}}{dt_m} = \frac{\partial}{\partial x_j} [-P_m \, \delta_{ji} + \mu_m (\Delta_m)_{ji} + \mu_{m2} \Theta_m \, \delta_{ji}] + \rho \mathscr{F}_{mi} \tag{6.5}$$

$$\rho_m \frac{dE_m}{dt_m} = \frac{\partial}{\partial x_j} U_{mj} [-P_m \, \delta_{ji} + \mu_m (\Delta_m)_{ji} + \mu_{m2} \Theta_m \, \delta_{ji}]$$

$$+ \frac{\partial}{\partial x_j} \frac{\kappa_m \partial T_m}{\partial x_j} + \mathscr{F}_{Em}, \tag{6.6}$$

where

$$\frac{d}{dt_m} = \frac{\partial}{\partial t} + U_{mj} \frac{\partial}{\partial x_j},$$

and the deformation tensor and the dilatation:

$$(\Delta_m)_{ji} = \frac{\partial U_{mi}}{\partial x_j} + \frac{\partial U_{mj}}{\partial x_i},$$

$$\Theta_m = \tfrac{1}{2} (\Delta_m)_{kk} = \frac{\partial U_{mk}}{\partial x_k},$$

and P_m is the overall static pressure of the mixture, μ_m its viscosity, $\mu_{m2} = \zeta_m - \tfrac{2}{3}\mu_m$, ζ_m is the bulk viscosity, and the total energy $E_m = u_m + (U_m^2/2)$, u_m is the internal energy per unit mass of the mixture, κ_m is the thermal conductivity of the mixture, T_m its static temperature, $\mathscr{F}_{mi}$ is the ith component of the body force acting on the mixture, $\mathscr{F}_{Em}$ is the rate of energy generation per unit volume. The cumulative nature of energy gives

$$\rho_m E_m = \sum_{(q)} \rho^{(q)} E^{(q)}, \tag{6.7}$$

$$\rho_m c_{vm} = \sum_{(q)} \rho^{(q)} c_v^{(q)}, \tag{6.8}$$

where c_v denotes the specific heat at constant volume; the latter defined at zero mass velocity. The static temperatures T_m and $T^{(q)}$ are related according to

$$T_m = (\rho_m c_m)^{-1} \left[\sum_{(q)} \rho^{(q)} c^{(q)} T^{(q)} + \tfrac{1}{2} \sum_{(q)} \rho^{(q)} U_i^{(q)} (U_i^{(q)} - U_{mi}) \right]$$

$$= (\rho_m c_m)^{-1} \sum_{(q)} [\rho^{(q)} c^{(q)} T^{(q)} + \tfrac{1}{2} U_i^{(q)} J_i^{(q)}], \tag{6.9}$$

where c is the specific heat at constant pressure, $J_i^{(q)} = \rho^{(q)}(U_i^{(q)} - U_{mi})$ is the diffusion flow of component (q) with respect to the barycentric motion, and $\sum_{(q)} \mathbf{J}^{(q)} = 0$ for the mixture.

Equations (6.5) and (6.6) can be reduced to those of the components, since it is readily shown that derivation based on Eqs. (6.1), (6.2) and (6.7) gives:*

$$\rho_m \frac{dU_{mi}}{dt_m} = \sum_{(q)} \left[\rho^{(q)} \frac{dU_i^{(q)}}{dt^{(q)}} + (U_i^{(q)} - U_{mi}) \Gamma^{(q)} \right.$$

$$\left. - \frac{\partial}{\partial x_j} \rho^{(q)} (U_i^{(q)} - U_{mi})(U_j^{(q)} - U_{mj}) \right] \tag{6.10}$$

$$\rho_m \frac{dE_m}{dt_m} = \sum_{(q)} \left[\rho^{(q)} \frac{dE^{(q)}}{dt^{(q)}} + \Gamma^{(q)} E^{(q)} \right.$$

$$\left. - \frac{\partial}{\partial x_j} \rho^{(q)} (U_j^{(q)} - U_{mj}) E^{(q)} \right] \tag{6.11}$$

showing the contributions of the motion about the center of mass of the system, where

$$\frac{d}{dt^{(q)}} = \frac{\partial}{\partial t} + U_j^{(q)} \frac{\partial}{\partial x_j}$$

---

* These relations can be derived from "fundamental identity" of Truesdell and Toupin [T54] relating the material derivatives of the mean value to the mean value of the material derivatives.

that is, at a given point in the space coordinates each component in the mixture could have its own streamlines. Moreover

$$(\Delta_m)_{ji} = \sum_{(q)} \left[\frac{\rho^{(q)}}{\rho_m} \Delta_{ji}^{(q)} + \rho_m^{-1}(U_i^{(q)} - U_{mi}) \frac{\partial \rho^{(q)}}{\partial x_j} \right.$$

$$\left. + \rho_m^{-1}(U_j^{(q)} - U_{mj}) \frac{\partial \rho^{(q)}}{\partial x_i} \right]$$

$$= \rho_m^{-1} \sum_{(q)} \left[\rho^{(q)}(\Delta_m)_{ji} + \frac{\partial J_i^{(q)}}{\partial x_j} + \frac{\partial J_j^{(q)}}{\partial x_i} \right] \tag{6.12}$$

and

$$\frac{\partial T}{\partial x_j} = \sum_{(q)} \left[\frac{\rho^{(q)} c^{(q)}}{\rho_m c_m} \frac{\partial T^{(q)}}{\partial x_j} + T^{(q)} \frac{\partial}{\partial x_j} \frac{\rho^{(q)} c^{(q)}}{\rho_m c_m} \right.$$

$$\left. + \frac{\partial}{\partial x_j} \frac{U_j^{(q)} J_j^{(q)}}{2 \rho_m c_m} \right] \tag{6.13}$$

Substitution of Eqs. (6.10) to (6.13) into Eqs. (6.5) and (6.6), and after rearranging, gives, for component (q), the following equations of momentum

$$\frac{\rho^{(q)}}{dt^{(q)}} \frac{dU_i^{(q)}}{dt^{(q)}} = \frac{\partial}{\partial x_j} [-P^{(q)} \delta_{ji} + \mu_m^{(q)} \Delta_{ji}^{(q)} + \mu_{m2}^{(q)} \Theta^{(q)} \delta_{ji}]$$

$$+ \rho^{(q)} \mathscr{F}_i^{(q)} - (U_i^{(q)} - U_{mi}) \Gamma^{(q)}$$

$$+ \rho^{(q)} \sum_{(p)} F^{(qp)}(U_i^{(p)} - U_i^{(q)}) \tag{6.14}$$

where $\mathscr{F}_i^{(q)}$ is the body force acting on a unit mass of component (q); with $P^{(q)}$ denoting the static partial pressure of component (q),

$$P_m = \sum_{(q)} P^{(q)}. \tag{6.15}$$

The viscosity of component (q) in the mixture $\mu_m^{(q)}$ is defined by

$$\mu_m^{(q)} \Delta_{ji}^{(q)} = \mu_m \frac{\rho^{(q)}}{\rho_m} \Delta_{ji}^{(q)} + \frac{\mu_m}{\rho_m} \left[(U_i^{(q)} - U_{mi}) \frac{\partial \rho^{(q)}}{\partial x_j} \right.$$

$$\left. + (U_j^{(q)} - U_{mj}) \frac{\partial \rho^{(q)}}{\partial x_i} \right] + \rho^{(q)}(U_i^{(q)} - U_{mi})(U_j^{(q)} - U_{mj})$$

$$= \mu_m \frac{\rho^{(q)}}{\rho_m} (\Delta_m)_{ji} + \frac{\mu_m}{\rho_m} \left[\frac{\partial J_i^{(q)}}{\partial x_j} + \frac{\partial J_j^{(q)}}{\partial x_i} \right]$$

$$+ J_i^{(q)}(U_j^{(q)} - U_{mj}), \tag{6.16}$$

and

$$\mu_{m2}^{(q)}\Theta^{(q)} = \mu_{m2}\frac{\rho^{(q)}}{\rho_m}\Theta^{(q)} + \frac{\mu_{m2}}{\rho_m}(U_k^{(q)} - U_{mk})\frac{\partial\rho^{(q)}}{\partial x_k}$$

$$= \mu_{m2}\frac{\rho^{(q)}}{\rho_m}\Theta_m + \frac{\mu_{m2}}{\rho_m}\frac{\partial J_k^{(q)}}{\partial x_k}, \tag{6.17}$$

that is, the motion of a component includes mutual diffusion of momentum and convection of momentum which should be accounted for if $\mu_m^{(q)}$ is computed from μ_m. The source term in Eq. (6.14) accounts for the fact that species (q) generated will not, in general, be at $\mathbf{U}^{(q)}$. The last term of Eq. (6.14) is introduced to account for the interaction of component (q) by other components (p)'s of the mixture, with $F^{(qp)}$ denoting the time constant of their interactions, and

$$\sum_{(q)}\sum_{(p)}\rho^{(q)}F^{(qp)}(\mathbf{U}^{(p)} - \mathbf{U}^{(q)}) = 0.$$

The energy equation of component (q) can be arranged in the form

$$\frac{\rho^{(q)}\,dE^{(q)}}{dt^{(q)}} = \frac{\partial}{\partial x_j}U_j^{(q)}[-P^{(q)}\delta_{ji} + \mu_m^{(q)}\Delta_{ji}^{(q)} + \mu_{m2}^{(q)}\Theta^{(q)}\delta_{ji}]$$

$$- \Gamma^{(q)}E^{(q)} + \frac{\partial}{\partial x_j}\left[\kappa_m^{(q)}\frac{\partial T^{(q)}}{\partial x_j}\right] + \mathscr{F}_E^{(q)}$$

$$+ c^{(q)}\rho^{(q)}\sum_{(p)}G^{(qp)}(T^{(p)} - T^{(q)}), \tag{6.18}$$

where the heat flux to component (q) includes

$$\frac{\kappa_m^{(q)}\partial T^{(q)}}{\partial x_j} = \kappa_m\frac{\rho^{(q)}c^{(q)}}{\rho_m c_m}\frac{\partial T^{(q)}}{\partial x_j}$$

$$+ \kappa_m T^{(q)}\frac{\partial}{\partial x_j}\frac{\rho^{(q)}c^{(q)}}{\rho_m c_m}$$

$$+ \kappa_m\frac{\partial}{\partial x_j}\left[\frac{\rho^{(q)}U_i^{(q)}(U_i^{(q)} - U_{mi})}{\rho_m c_m}\right]$$

$$+ \rho^{(q)}(U_j^{(q)} - U_{mj})E^{(q)}$$

$$= \kappa_m\left\{\frac{\rho^{(q)}c^{(q)}}{\rho_m c_m}\frac{\partial T^{(q)}}{\partial x_j} + T^{(q)}\frac{\partial}{\partial x_j}\frac{\rho^{(q)}c^{(q)}}{\rho_m c_m}\right.$$

$$\left. + \frac{\partial}{\partial x_j}\left(\frac{U_i^{(q)}J_i^{(q)}}{\rho_m c_m}\right)\right\} + J_j^{(q)}E^{(q)}, \tag{6.19}$$

which include change in heat capacity, thermal diffusivity ($\kappa_m/\rho_m c_m$), and convection of energy. The distribution from a heat source is proportional to the heat capacity of components, and

$$\mathscr{F}_E^{(q)} = \frac{\rho^{(q)} c^{(q)}}{\rho_m c_m} \mathscr{F}_E - \frac{\partial}{\partial x_j} (U_i^{(q)} - U_i)$$

$$\times [-P^{(q)} \delta_{ji} + \mu_m^{(q)} \Delta_{ji}^{(q)} + \mu_{m2}^{(q)} \Theta^{(q)} \delta_{ji}].$$

including dissipation due to relative motion. $G^{(qp)}$'s are the time constants of energy transfer and $\sum_{(q)} \sum_{(p)} c^{(q)} \rho^{(q)} G^{(qp)}(T^{(p)} - T^{(q)}) = 0$ for the overall mixture.

The above equations (6.3), (6.14), and (6.18) of components treated components of a mixture as interacting continua and are directly applicable to mixtures of disparate molecular masses (such as a mixture of hydrogen and uranium gas). It does not incorporate specific behavior of particles in a suspension. However, the effects of shear stresses and heat flow are valid.

The above shows the care that needs to be exercised in identifying the transport properties of component (p) in the mixture when formulating equations for a component of a mixture. It is seen that for the motion of a nonreactive mixture ($\Gamma^{(q)} = 0$), with small slip to mean motion, small concentration gradients, the relations in Eqs. (6.16), (6.17), and (6.19) reduce to $\mu_m^{(q)} = (\rho^{(q)}/\rho_m)\mu_m$, $\mu_{m2}^{(q)} = (\rho^{(q)}/\rho_m)\mu_{m2}$, $\kappa_m^{(q)} = (\rho^{(q)} c^{(q)}/\rho_m c_m)\kappa_m$, as in the approximation given by Soo [S61].

Although direct determination of $\mu_m^{(q)}$ according to kinetic theory cannot be made without a knowledge of the motion of the other components, the viscosity of a gaseous (or nearly gaseous) mixture can be computed following the method by Hirschfelder, Curtiss, and Bird [H44] in the general determinant form. For a binary mixture ($q = 1,2$) we have, as an approximation [H44],

$$\frac{1}{\mu_m} \cong \left[\frac{x^{(1)2}}{\mu^{(11)}} + \frac{2x^{(1)}x^{(2)}}{\mu^{(12)}} + \frac{x^{(2)2}}{\mu^{(22)}}\right][1 + f(x^{(1)}, x^{(2)}, \mu^{(1)}, \ldots, m^{(1)}, \ldots)],$$

$$(6.20)$$

where $x^{(1)}$, $x^{(2)}$ are molefractions based on number densities of components; $m^{(1)} \cdots$ their molecular or particle masses, $\mu^{(11)}$ is the viscosity due to interaction among species (1) particles, $\mu^{(12)}$ is that due to mutual interaction of species (1) and (2). Equation (6.20) is nearly valid for a gas-solid suspension of one species of particles of particle size smaller than the mean free path of the gas.

When applied to a suspension of one species of solid particles, Eq. (6.16) gives, for such a binary mixture (subscripts p denotes particles, f or no subscript denotes the gas)

$$\mu_{pm}(\Delta_p)_{ji} = \mu_m\left[\frac{\rho_p}{\rho_p + \rho}\right](\Delta_p)_{ji} + \left[\frac{\mu_m\rho}{(\rho_p + \rho)^2}\right]\left[(U_{pi} - U_i)\frac{\partial\rho_p}{\partial x_j}\right.$$

$$\left. + (U_{pj} - U_j)\frac{\partial\rho_p}{\partial x_i}\right] + \rho^2\rho_p(\rho_p + \rho)^{-2}(U_{pi} - U_i)(U_{pj} - U_j),$$

$$\mu_{fm}\Delta_{ji} = \mu_m\left[\frac{\rho}{\rho_p + \rho}\right]\Delta_{ji} + \left[\frac{\mu_m\rho_p}{(\rho_p + \rho)^2}\right](U_i - U_{pi})\frac{\partial\rho}{\partial x_j}$$

$$+ (U_j - U_{pj})\frac{\partial\rho}{\partial x_i} + \rho\rho_p^2(\rho + \rho_p)^{-2}(U_i - U_{pi})(U_j - U_{pj}).$$

$$(6.21)$$

It is seen that for $\rho \gg \rho_p$, that is, a dilute suspension, we get

$$\mu_{pm}(\Delta_p)_{ji} \sim \frac{\mu_m}{\rho}\left[(U_{pi} - U_i)\frac{\partial\rho_p}{\partial x_j} + (U_{pj} - U_j)\frac{\partial\rho_p}{\partial x_i}\right]$$

$$+ \frac{\rho^2}{\rho_p}(U_{pi} - U_i)(U_{pj} - U_j), \qquad (6.22)$$

$$\mu_{fm}\Delta_{ji} \sim \mu_m\Delta_{ji}.$$

Equation (6.20) further gives for number densities $n_f \gg n_p$, $\mu_m \sim \mu_f = \bar{\mu}$ and $\mu_{pm} \sim 0$ and we have the case where fluid motion is unaffected by the presence of the particles. The situation is that viscous stress due to shear is contributed by the fluid phase, while corresponding momentum transfer of the particle phase is carried out by diffusion through the fluid. An alternate situation of $\rho_p \gg \rho$, but $n_f \gg n_p$ gives $\mu_{pm} \sim \mu_m \sim \bar{\mu}$. This suggests significant contribution of shear stress by the particle cloud (due to their mutual collision), with the fluid diffusing through it. The approximation in Eq. (6.20) may give $\mu_m < \bar{\mu}$, that is, loading of solid particles could reduce the apparent viscosity of the mixture, a fact substantiated experimentally by Sproull [S78] (Sec. 5.5). Application of these relations to a suspension of 0.4 volume fraction solid of 1 micron MgO in air at room conditions gives from Eqs. (5.44), (5.47), (with $r = s$): $\mu^{(11)} = \mu_p^{(ss)} = 0[10^{-9}]$, $\mu^{(12)} = \mu_p^{(sf)} = 0[10^{-6}]$, $\mu^{(22)} = \mu_f = 0[10^{-6}]$, kg/m sec $= \bar{\mu}$, with $x_p^2(m_p/m) \sim 2 \times 10^{-5}$, and from Eq. (6.20) we get $\mu_m \sim 10^{-6}$ kg/m sec $\sim \bar{\mu}$ even for a rather dense suspension. In this example, $\rho_p = 0.4\bar{\rho}_p$, $\rho = 0.6\bar{\rho}$, where the densities of materials: $\bar{\rho}_p = 3.58 \times 10^3$ kg/m³, $\bar{\rho} = 1.293$ kg/m³; we get $\mu_{pm} \sim \mu_m$ while diffusion of the gaseous phase is important. It is noted that Murray [M55] accounted for $\mu^{(22)}$ and $\mu^{(12)}$ only. The above magnitude of quantities shows that such a simplification is a possibility rather than a generally valid procedure.

The above situation is modified if we consider a dilute suspension of $\phi = 10^{-4}$ or 0.275 mass ratio of solid to gas. This still gives $\mu_m \sim 10^{-6}$ kg/m sec, but $\mu_{mp} \sim 0.21\,\mu_m$, and $\mu_{mf} \sim 0.79\,\mu_m$. For a sub-micron particle, $U_p \sim U$, the case reverts to that formulated by Hinze [H43] for shear stress.

Similar considerations are applicable to thermal conductivities. Since $\rho c / \rho_p c_p \sim n/n_p$, if $\rho c \gg \rho_p c_p$, or $n \gg n_p$, and $\rho \gg \rho_p$, Eq. (6.19) gives

$$\kappa_{fm}\frac{\partial T}{\partial x_j} \sim \kappa_m \frac{\partial T}{\partial x_j} \tag{6.23}$$

where the particle phase contributes in terms of diffusion and convection.

More rigorous development of relations for transport properties of components in a mixture remains to be accomplished via further research. For the present we have endeavored to identify the meaning of transport properties of components in a mixture. Approximation for a suspension of one species of particles is

$$\left. \begin{aligned} \mu_{fm} &\sim \left[1 - \frac{\rho_p}{\rho}\right]\mu_m, \\[2mm] \mu_{pm} &\sim \frac{\rho_p}{\rho}\,\mu_m, \end{aligned} \right\} \tag{6.24}$$

and

$$\left. \begin{aligned} \kappa_{fm} &\sim \left[1 - \frac{\rho_p c_p}{\rho c}\right]\kappa_m, \\[2mm] \kappa_{pm} &\sim \frac{\rho_p c_p}{\rho c}\,\kappa_m, \end{aligned} \right\} \tag{6.25}$$

When applied to a dilute suspension, the above gives, $\mu_m \sim \bar{\mu} \sim \mu_{fm}$, $\mu_{pm} \sim 0$, and $\kappa_m \sim \bar{\kappa} \sim \kappa_{fm}$, $\kappa_{pm} \sim 0$.

6.2 Behavior of a Suspension

We shall first formulate the case of a nonreactive gas-solid system with distribution in particle sizes or species. It is recognized that any generalized formulation of such a gas-solid system has as its basis the recognized physical concepts concerning a single particle and a cloud of particles. It must account for the following facts:

(a) The drag on a solid particle is mainly due to difference between the velocities of the particles and the stream. It is expected that the minimum size of solid particles consists of millions of molecules each (even for particles in the submicron range). Hence, the velocity of each solid particle due to its own thermal state is extremely low and the particulate phase does not contribute to the static pressure of the system. Cases involving significant Brownian diffusion of particles will be dealt with later (Chap. 8).

(b) When a large number of solid particles is present, some average properties of a cloud of similar solid particles can be spoken of.

(c) Interactions exist between the solid particles and the system, the solid particles themselves, and both with any solid boundary (Chap. 5). Heat transfer between the solid and the gas is due to the mean temperature difference. Fluctuation is expected, but each solid particle, due to its small size and high thermal conductivity (as compared to the gas), is assumed to be at a uniform temperature.

(d) Due to the inertia of solid particles, one has to identify the velocity of solid particles and that of the gas separately at any given location in space. At a solid boundary, solid particles may have finite velocity even though the gas phase attains zero velocity there except at very low pressures.

(e) When heat transfer is involved, radiation to and among particles can be significant (Secs. 5.6 and 5.7).

Recognizing that the solid particles of different size range constitute different phases from the point of view of continuum mechanics, the previous basic formulations were generalized in the following sections [S60]. Here, we illustrate with the case of nonreactive suspensions in which the solid particles are sufficiently numerous. For the sake of generality, we include the bulk viscosities (ζ) in our formulations. Note that $\zeta = 0$ for incompressible fluid and its suspension of rigid particles (Secs. 5.3 and 5.5).

For the convenience of formulation, we shall revert to the notations in Chap. 5. The particulate phase will be identified with subscript p and additional phases among particles by superscripts (s) and (r); the unsubscripted quantities denote the fluid phase, when needed for clarity, subscript f will be used to denote the fluid or gaseous phase.

We define the density of a cloud of particles of species (size and material) (s) as $\rho_p^{(s)}$ (the density of the solid material is denoted as $\bar{\rho}_p^{(s)}$),

$$\rho_p^{(s)} = n^{(s)} m^{(s)} = \phi^{(s)} \bar{\rho}_p^{(s)}, \qquad (6.26)$$

where $n^{(s)}$ is the number of solid particles per unit volume, and $m^{(s)}$ is the mass of each particle, and $\phi^{(s)}$ is the volume fraction solid of species (s); and the overall density of the cloud of solid particles is given by

$$\rho_p = \sum_{(s)} \rho_p^{(s)}. \qquad (6.27)$$

The overall density of the cloud of N solid particles is also given by

$$\rho_p = \mathscr{V}^{-1} \int_{\mathscr{V}} \sum_{(s)} m^{(s)} \, dN^{(s)},$$ (6.28)

where $\mathscr{V}$ is the volume of the suspension under consideration.
The volume $\mathscr{V}_f$ occupied by the gaseous phase is given by the relation

$$\mathscr{V} = \mathscr{V}_f + \mathscr{V}_p = \mathscr{V}_f + \mathscr{V} \sum_{(s)} \frac{\rho_p^{(s)}}{\bar{\rho}_p^{(s)}},$$ (6.29)

where $\mathscr{V}_p$ is the volume occupied by the solid particles. Multiplying Eq. (6.29) by the density of the gas $\bar{\rho}$ and dividing by the total volume $\mathscr{V}$, we get the apparent density of the gaseous phase,

$$\rho = \bar{\rho}\left[1 - \sum_{(s)} \frac{\rho_p^{(s)}}{\bar{\rho}_p^{(s)}}\right] = \bar{\rho}\left[1 - \frac{\rho_p}{\bar{\rho}_p}\right].$$ (6.30)

The last equality for $\bar{\rho}_p^{(s)} = \bar{\rho}_p$. Equations (6.28) and (6.30) represent a complete generalization from the attempt toward subdivision of flow area by Glauz [G25] and subdivision of volume by Tangren [T4] in one dimensional motion. Only for a system of extremely low fraction solid, $\rho \sim \bar{\rho}$. Note that $\rho_p/\bar{\rho}_p$ is the fraction solid ϕ of the whole particulate system. It is seen that the overall density of the suspension is given by

$$\rho_m = \rho + \sum_{(s)} \rho_p^{(s)}.$$ (6.31)

In such a nonreactive system, these solid particles, in spite of even visual discreteness, may be treated as a quasi-continuum, and the continuity relation in Eq. (6.3) gives

$$\frac{\partial \rho_p^{(s)}}{\partial t} + \frac{\partial \rho_p^{(s)} U_{pj}^{(s)}}{\partial x_j} = 0,$$ (6.32)

where $U_{pj}^{(s)}$ is the jth component of the velocity of the cloud of particles of species (s). For the gaseous or fluid phase, the continuity equation is

$$\frac{\partial \rho}{\partial t} + \frac{\partial \rho U_j}{\partial x_j} = 0,$$ (6.33)

where ρ is the density of the gas in the suspension, and U_j is the jth component of velocity of the fluid phase with the volume occupied by the particulate phase hollowed out.

It is seen that, by substituting Eq. (6.30) into Eq. (6.33), the continuity equation of the fluid phase can be expressed as

$$\frac{\partial \bar{\rho}}{\partial t} + \frac{\partial \bar{\rho} U_i}{\partial x_j} = \frac{\bar{\rho}}{1 - \phi}\left[U_j \frac{\partial \phi}{\partial x_j} - \frac{\partial \phi U_{pj}}{\partial x_j}\right],$$

for the case $\bar{\rho}_p^{(s)} = \bar{\rho}_p$, and $\phi = \rho_p/\bar{\rho}_p$. Therefore when we refer to the density of the fluid material, the right-hand side constitutes a source (or sink) term as the density of the particle cloud changes. For an incompressible fluid, we get

$$\frac{\partial U_j}{\partial x_j} = (1 - \phi)^{-1} \left[U_j \frac{\partial \phi}{\partial x_j} - \frac{\partial \phi U_{pj}}{\partial x_j} \right],$$

as a modification of the divergence theorem for a pure incompressible fluid.

6.3 Limit of Continuum Approximations

We have noted that in Eqs. (6.32) and (6.33), U_j and $U_{pj}^{(s)}$ correspond to the "free stream velocity" of the fluid and the velocity of the solid particle. For a solid particle of finite size, however, we know that there is a velocity distribution around the particle due to relative motion $(\mathbf{U} - \mathbf{U}_p^{(s)})$ and when the relative speed is high enough, the existence of a wake is expected (Sec. 2.1). Therefore, the concept of continuum mechanics when applied to the case of a particulate suspension must be properly qualified by examining the nature of the fluid flow around the particles.

In the absence of shear motion, body force, and chemical reaction, an obvious relation for the conservation of momentum of a suspension of one species of solid particles would be

$$\rho \frac{dU_i}{dt} + \rho_p \frac{dU_{pi}}{dt_p} = - \frac{\partial P}{\partial x_i}, \tag{6.34}$$

for identical solid particles. Equation (6.34) is true if we have "slow" relative motion or "high" concentration of solid particles. These qualifications are now clarified by considering transfer of momentum from particles to the fluid. It is noted that Eq. (6.34) treated the particle phase as a true continuum; that is, not only the gas imparts its momentum to the particles, the equation also implies that a cloud of solid particles can transfer its momentum to the gas. This would lead to the conclusion that in a diffuser, as solid particles are slowed down, they contribute to pressure rise also. This is obviously not always the case. Even in the laminar flow range of relative motion, Froessling [S13] showed that before separation occurs, the boundary layer thickness δ for flow over a sphere (Fig. 2.2) is given by

$$\frac{\sqrt{2\delta}}{2a} \sqrt{\frac{2a(\Delta U)}{\bar{\nu}}} \leqslant 3, \tag{6.35}$$

where $\bar{v} = \bar{\mu}/\bar{\rho}$ is the kinetic viscosity of the fluid material and (ΔU) is the relative speed. Therefore if the cloud of particles is to exert a sufficient drag on the gas, the interparticle spacing must be smaller than $(2\delta + 2a)$ given by Eq. (6.35), or the number density of solid particles n_p must give

$$n_p^{-\frac{1}{3}} < 2\delta + 2a \lessapprox 2\delta. \tag{6.36}$$

This relation leads to the condition

$$2an_p^{\frac{1}{3}} \lessapprox \frac{\sqrt{2}}{3} \sqrt{\frac{2a(\Delta U)}{\bar{v}}}, \tag{6.37}$$

for successful transfer of momentum of mass motion with the particles accelerating the gas; that is, in the same manner as the gas may accelerate the solid particles; otherwise, the gas simply acts as a free stream with the kinetic energy of the particles dissipated completely in their wakes. This physical state of affairs is depicted in Fig. 6.1a, which also leads to the conclusion that outside the Stokes' law range, drag coefficient of solid particles depends on concentration of the cloud besides the Reynolds number of relative motion (Sec. 5.1).

To account for all situations, Eq. (6.34) should be modified to the form

$$\rho \frac{dU_i}{dt} + K_m \rho_p \frac{dU_{pi}}{dt_p} = -\frac{\partial P}{\partial x_i}, \tag{6.38}$$

with the "effectiveness" $K_m = 1$ for the case when solid particles are accelerated by the gas, and $K_m < 1$ for the case when solid particles are decelerated by the gas. In the absence of experimental information, the relations may be expressed as a discontinuity as shown in Fig. 6.1b, although a smooth transition (dotted line) is expected. This modification accounts for the fact that slowing down of solid particles does not necessarily give rise to increase in static pressure of the gas. The order of magnitude is such that, for $2a(U - U_p)\bar{\rho}/\bar{\mu} \sim 1$, Eq. (6.37) requires an interparticle spacing of not too much greater than $4a$. It is noted that for magnesia particles of 1 micron diameter at interparticle spacing of 3 diameters gives $n_p \sim 3 \times 10^{16}/m^3$, $\rho_p \sim 50 \text{ kg/m}^3$. If this is in air at room condition, $\bar{\rho} \sim 1 \text{ kg/m}^3$, giving a loading of $m_p^* \sim 50$. For a loading of $m_p^* \sim 1$, the solid particles are, on the average, more than 10 diameters apart.

It is noted that the "effectiveness" K_m is in addition to the dependence of drag coefficient C_D, and therefore the time constant of momentum transfer F, on the concentration of the suspension. This suggests that the experimental results on drag coefficient presented by Ingebo [14] based on an acceleration of particles are better defined than those based on deceleration of particles [R48] (Fig. 2.1).

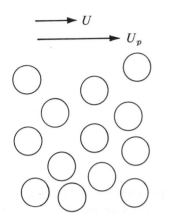 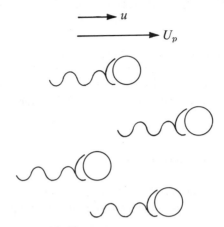

Dense cloud of solid
particles – negligible
dissipation in wakes
$(K_m \sim 1)$

Lean suspension—
dissipation in wakes
without increase in kinetic
energy of mass motion
of gas $(K_m \sim 0)$

(a) Transfer of momentum of mass motion
from cloud of solid particles to gas

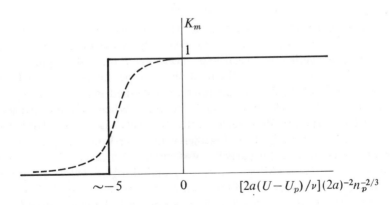

(b) "Discontinuous" representation of effectiveness
based on Froessling [S11]

Figure 6.1 Effectiveness of momentum transfer from solid particles to the gas [S58].

With this understanding of the qualified continuum approximations, the basic equations of the multiphase system should be corrected with this "effectiveness" K_m, or $K_m^{(s)}$ for the particulate phase [S56, S58].

Another limit of the continuum approximation is that the thermal state of a particle is identified by its temperature. Addition of heat to a moving particle increases the body temperature of the particle, while its velocity arises primarily from particle-fluid interaction.

6.4 Equations of Motion

Summation of corresponding terms in Eq. (6.14) with the qualification in Sec. (6.3) gives the overall momentum equation of the suspension as:*

$$
\frac{\rho \, dU_i}{dt} + \sum_{(s)} \frac{K_m^{(s)} \rho_p^{(s)} \, dU_{pi}^{(s)}}{dt_p^{(s)}} = -\frac{\partial P}{\partial x_i}
$$

$$
+ \frac{\partial}{\partial x_j} \left[\mu_{fm} \Delta_{ji} + \mu_{fm2} \Theta \, \delta_{ji} \right]
$$

$$
+ \frac{\partial}{\partial x_j} \sum_{(s)} K_m^{(s)} [\mu_{pm}^{(s)} (\Delta_p^{(s)})_{ji} + \mu_{pm2}^{(s)} \Theta_p^{(s)} \, \delta_{ji}]
$$

$$
+ \rho \mathscr{F}_i + \sum_{(s)} \frac{K_m^{(s)} \rho_p^{(s)} f_{pi}^{(s)}}{m^{(s)}} \tag{6.39}
$$

where $\mathscr{F}_i$ is the ith component of the external force per unit mass of the fluid material such as due to an electric field, $f_{pi}^{(s)}$ is the ith component of the external force acting on a particle of species (s), P is the static pressure in the fluid, μ_{fm} is the viscosity of the fluid phase in the mixture, μ_{fm2} includes the bulk viscosity of the fluid in the mixture as defined in Sec. (6.1). $\mu_{pm}^{(s)}$ is the viscosity of the particle phase (s) in the mixture. When the solid particles have negligible thermal random velocity, the "viscosity" is due to relative motion imparted by the fluid. This, together with other transport properties concerning a cloud of solid particles, was discussed in Chap. 5. Note that in Eq. (6.39), $(d/dt) = (\partial/\partial t) + U_j(\partial/\partial x_j)$ and $d/dt_p^{(s)} = (\partial/\partial t) + U_{pj}^{(s)}(\partial/\partial x_j)$. Note also that Newtonian fluid is assumed in formulating Eq. (6.39) to be consistent with Eq. (6.14). Advanced treatment yet to be made should account for the non-Newtonian nature of the particle cloud illustrated in Eq. (5.44).

Application of Eq. (6.14) to component (s) of the particulate phase must account for the exchange of momentum between a solid particle and the gas,

* In a similar equation, Hinze [H40] included $\mathscr{F}_{pi}^{(s)}$ of Eq. (6.40) instead of $f_{pi}^{(s)}$ (for $s = 1$). Specific objection was raised by Murray [M55].

and that of exchange of momentum with the mixture. Corresponding to $\mathscr{F}_i^{(q)}$ in Eq. (6.14), the force acting on spherical particles of radius a_s in a general fluid field besides drag forces of fluid and particle clouds was given by Tchen [Eq. (2.37)] as

$$\mathscr{F}_{pi}^{(s)} = - \frac{1}{\bar{\rho}_p^{(s)}} \frac{\partial P}{\partial x_i} + \frac{1}{2} \frac{\bar{\rho}}{\bar{\rho}_p^{(s)}} \frac{d}{dt_p^{(s)}} [U_i - U_{pi}^{(s)}]$$

$$+ (\tfrac{9}{2}\sqrt{\pi}a_s) \frac{\bar{\rho}}{\bar{\rho}_p^{(s)}} \sqrt{\frac{\bar{\mu}}{\bar{\rho}}} \int_{t_0}^{t_p^{(s)}} \left[\frac{d}{d\tau}(U_i - U_{pi}^{(s)}) \right](t_p^{(s)} - \tau)^{-\frac{1}{2}} d\tau$$

$$+ \frac{f_{pi}^{(s)}}{m^{(s)}}.$$

$$\tag{6.40}$$

Since the particulate phase does not contribute substantially to the static pressure of the system, Eq. (6.14) when applied to species (s) of the particulate phase therefore gives the momentum equation of particulate phase (s) as

$$\frac{\rho_p^{(s)} dU_{pi}^{(s)}}{dt_p^{(s)}} = \frac{\partial}{\partial x_j} [\mu_{pm}^{(s)}(\Delta_p^{(s)})_{ji} + \mu_{pm2}^{(s)}\Theta_p^{(s)} \delta_{ji}] + \rho_p^{(s)}\mathscr{F}_{pi}^{(s)}$$

$$+ \rho_p^{(s)}F^{(s)}(U_i - U_{pi}^{(s)}) + \rho_p^{(s)}\sum_{(r)} F_p^{(sr)}(U_{pi}^{(r)} - U_{pi}^{(s)}) \quad (6.41)$$

$F_p^{(sr)}$ is the time constant of the momentum transfer between particle clouds of species (r) and species (s) (Sec. 5.3). $F^{(s)}$ is the time constant of fluid-particle interaction, a_s is the radius; $F^{(s)} = \tfrac{3}{8}C_D(\bar{\rho}/\rho_p)(\Delta U/a_s)$, where C_D is the drag coefficient at relative speed ΔU; $F^{(s)} = 9\bar{\mu}/2a_s^2\bar{\rho}_p^{(s)}$ for spherical particles in the Stokes' range (Sec. 5.1). $\rho_p^{(s)}F_p^{(sr)} = \rho_p^{(r)}F_p^{(rs)}$ was discussed in Chap. 5.

It must be remembered that when we speak of shear tensor and dilatation of the particle phase $(\Delta_p^{(s)})_{ji}$, $\Theta_p^{(s)}$, we mean shear and dilatation of the particle cloud; we do not mean shear and dilatation of a particle. For instance, dilatation of a particle, if occurs (for instance, when we extend the present formulation to a swarm of gas bubbles in a liquid) is reflected as a transition of species (s) to another species (r), with attendant change in transport properties (Sec. 6.9).

In the case of turbulent flow, wave lengths smaller than the diameter of particles are accounted for by the time constant $F^{(s)}$ or drag coefficient (Fig. 2.1, p. 16, and Fig. 5.2, p. 188), while wave lengths greater than the diameters are accounted for by the term of relative acceleration and the Basset term. It is further seen that if the motion is steady (Basset term is negligible), and that there is no shear motion, only the third term of fluid drag is retained on the right-hand side of Eq. (6.41) for a dilute suspension. Consistency would require neglecting the volume occupied by the particulate phase; that is, taking $\rho \sim \bar{\rho}$ in Eq. (6.30), especially when $\bar{\rho}$ and $\bar{\rho}_p$ are close in magnitude.

Edelman and Kiely [E2] showed from considering particle rotation that the particle torque and fluid rotational inertia are in most cases negligible. An example of the effect of particle motion in the shear layer of the fluid is given in Sec. 8.3.

The equation of motion of the fluid phase alone is obtained by eliminating $dU_p^{(s)}/dt_p^{(s)}$ from Eqs. (6.39) and (6.41), or

$$
\begin{aligned}
\frac{\rho \, dU_i}{dt} = & -\left[1 - \sum K_m^{(s)} \frac{\rho_p^{(s)}}{\rho_p^{(s)}}\right] \frac{\partial P}{\partial x_i} \\
& + \frac{\partial}{\partial x_j}\left[\mu_{fm} \Delta_{ji} + \mu_{fm2} \Theta \, \delta_{ji}\right] + \rho \mathscr{F}_i \\
& - \tfrac{1}{2}\bar{\rho} \sum_{(s)} K_m^{(s)} \frac{\rho_p^{(s)}}{\bar{\rho}_p^{(s)}} \frac{d}{dt_p^{(s)}} (U_i - U_{pi}) \\
& - \frac{9}{2\sqrt{\pi}} \sqrt{\bar{\mu}\bar{\rho}} \sum_{(s)} K_m^{(s)} \frac{\rho_p^{(s)}}{\bar{\rho}_p^{(s)}} \int_{t_0}^{t_p^{(s)}} \\
& \times \left[\frac{d}{d\tau}(U_i - U_{pi}^{(s)})\right](t_p^{(s)} - \tau)^{-\frac{1}{2}} \, d\tau \\
& - \sum_{(s)} K_m^{(s)} \rho_p^{(s)} F^{(s)}(U_i - U_{pi}^{(s)}).
\end{aligned}
\tag{6.42}
$$

Since

$$
\sum_{(s)} \rho_p^{(s)} \sum_{(r)} F_p^{(sr)}(U_{pi}^{(r)} - U_{pi}^{(s)}) = 0,
$$

it is seen that the first term on the right-hand side of Eq. (6.42) gives a correction for volume occupied by the solid particles, the fourth term accounts for the reaction due to accelerating the apparent mass of the particles relative to the fluid, the fifth term represents the reaction due to the Basset force on the particle, and the sixth term is due to the drag of particle on the fluid. It is noted that of the Eqs. (6.39) and (6.42), only one is independent.

6.5 Energy Equations

The energy equations of a multiphase system include the relationships of exchange of energy of the mixture and the exchange of energy between a solid particle and the other particles, and the effect of radiation. When applied to a suspension, we sum Eq. (6.18) over all the components with

distinction of the fluid and the particulate phases to give the overall energy
equation of the mixture as

$$\rho \frac{d}{dt}\left[\frac{U_i^2}{2} + cT\right] + \sum_{(s)} \rho_p^{(s)} \frac{d}{dt_p^{(s)}}\left[\frac{U_{pi}^{(s)2}}{2} + c_p^{(s)} T_p^{(s)}\right]$$

$$= \frac{\partial P}{\partial t} + \frac{\partial}{\partial x_j} \kappa_{fm} \frac{\partial T}{\partial x_j} + \sum_{(s)} \frac{\partial}{\partial x_j} \kappa_{pm}^{(s)} \frac{\partial T_p^{(s)}}{\partial x_j}$$

$$+ \frac{\partial}{\partial x_j} U_i(\mu_{fm} \Delta_{ji} + \mu_{fm2}\Theta \, \delta_{ji})$$

$$+ \sum_{(s)} \frac{\partial}{\partial x_j} U_{pj}^{(s)}[\mu_{pm}^{(s)}(\Delta_p^{(s)})_{ji} + \mu_{pm2}^{(s)}\Theta_p^{(s)} \, \delta_{ji}] + \mathscr{F}_E$$

$$+ \sum_{(s)} \mathscr{F}_{pE}^{(s)}, \tag{6.43}$$

with enthalpy $h = u + (P/\rho) = cT$ in place of internal energy u, thus c, $c_p^{(s)}$
are specific heats of the phases at constant pressure, T, $T_p^{(s)}$ are absolute
temperatures of the fluid and particulate phase(s) respectively; $\kappa_m^{(f)}$, $\kappa_{pm}^{(s)}$ are
the thermal conductivities of components in the mixture discussed in Sec. (6.1)
based on Sec. (5.5); $\mathscr{F}_E$ includes heat source and radiation, the net emission
per unit volume of the mixture (Sec. 5.6)

$$\mathscr{F}_E = \mathscr{E}_n = \int_0^\infty \mathscr{E}_{n,\Lambda}(x_i) \, d\Lambda$$

$$= \int_0^\infty \left[4n_m^2\alpha_\Lambda(x_i)E_{b,\Lambda}(x_i) - \alpha_\Lambda(x_i)\int_{\Omega=4\pi} I_\Lambda(x_i,\mu_i) \, d\Omega\right] d\Lambda \tag{6.44}$$

over all the wave lengths Λ; to which the contribution of other energy sources
may be added. $\mathscr{F}_{pE}^{(s)}$ includes the heating of a particle due to viscous dissipation

$$\mathscr{F}_{pE}^{(r)} = \rho_p^{(s)}F^{(s)}(U - U_p^{(s)})^2 + \rho_p^{(s)} \sum_{(r)} F_p^{(sr)}(U_p^{(r)} - U_p^{(s)})^2. \tag{6.45}$$

The energy equation of the particulate phase (s) includes the relationships
of exchange of energy between a solid particle and the gas and other particles.
As noted in Sec. 6.3, the thermal state of a moving particle is identified by its
body temperature while its velocity is influenced primarily by particle-fluid interaction. Therefore, when applied to particle phase (s), Eq. (6.18) reduces to:

$$\rho_p^{(s)} \frac{d}{dt_p^{(s)}}\left[c_p^{(s)} T_p^{(s)}\right] = \frac{\partial}{\partial x_j} \kappa_{pm}^{(s)} \frac{\partial T_p^{(s)}}{\partial x_j} + \frac{\partial}{\partial x_j} U_{pj}^{(s)}[\mu_{pm}^{(s)}(\Delta_p^{(s)})_{ji} + \mu_{m2}^{(f)}\Theta \, \delta_{ji}]$$

$$+ \mathscr{F}_{pE}^{(s)} + \rho_p^{(s)}\frac{4\pi a_s^2}{m_p^{(s)}}\int \alpha_\Lambda\left(E_{b,\Lambda} - \int_{4\pi} I_\Lambda \, d\Omega\right) d\Lambda + c_p^{(s)}\rho_p^{(s)}G^{(s)}(T - T_p^{(s)})$$

$$+ c_p^{(s)}\rho_p^{(s)} \sum_{(r)} G_p^{(sr)}(T_p^{(r)} - T_p^{(s)}), \tag{6.46}$$

$G^{(s)}$ is the time constant of convective heat transfer between the particle and the fluid, $G^{(s)} = (N_{\mathrm{Nu}}^{(s)})\bar{\kappa}2\pi a_s/m$ (Sec. 5.4); and c_p is the specific heat of the solid material; $(N_{\mathrm{Nu}}^{(s)})$ is the Nusselt number of the solid particles in the gas, $\bar{\kappa}$ is the thermal conductivity of the gas, and T is the temperature of the gas; $G^{(s)} = 3\bar{\kappa}/c_p\bar{\rho}_p a_s^2$ for spherical particles on the Stokes' law range of relative motion; $G_p^{(sr)}$ is the time constant of heat transfer between particle clouds of species (r) and species (s) (Sec. 5.5).

Eqs. (6.32), (6.33), (6.39), (6.41), (6.43), and (6.46) account for general motion, field forces, heat transfer, and size distribution. Logical extension can be made to cases involving mass transfer, chemical reaction, etc. It might be added that the generalized "multiphase" concept is such that even for a gas-solid suspension of one type of solid material, particles of different sizes, shapes, masses, electric charges, dipole moments, or magnetism constitute different "phases" in addition to the gas phase. For non-spherical particles, the time constants F's and G's can be determined experimentally. Since particle-particle interactions have been accounted for, but not the internal stresses of particles, these relations are applicable to concentration up to the dilute phase fluidized bed, say, down to 90 per cent fraction void, but not to dense beds (Sec. 9.7). This calls for a mean interparticle spacing of 2 to 3 particle diameters as a lower limit; for interparticle spacing above 10 diameters, F_p's and G_p's can be neglected, and $\mu_m^{(1)} \sim \bar{\mu}$, $\mu_{pm}^{(s)} \sim 0$; $\zeta_m \sim 0$, $\zeta_{pm}^{(s)} = 0$.

For a multiphase system where static continuous size distribution is known, the above summations become integrals. This is illustrated in Chaps. 7 and 8.

Hinze [H43] applied Reynolds' procedure to turbulent flow of a suspension and expressed the basic equations in terms of time mean values and fluctuations.

6.6 Adiabatic Potential Flow

Some understanding of the basic nature of the multiphase flow system may be achieved by considering potential motion. For the case of a nonshear flow of a nonreactive, uncharged gas-solid suspension, the overall momentum equation takes the form

$$\rho \frac{dU_i}{dt} + \sum_{(s)} K_m^{(s)} \rho_p^{(s)} \frac{dU_{pi}^{(s)}}{dt} = -\frac{\partial P}{\partial x_i}. \tag{6.47}$$

The overall energy equation (6.43) takes the form

$$\rho \frac{d}{dt}\left[\frac{U_i^2}{2} + cT\right] + \sum_{(s)} \rho_p^{(s)} \frac{d}{dt_p^{(s)}}\left[\frac{U_{pi}^{(s)2}}{2} + c_p^{(s)}T_p^{(s)}\right] = \frac{\partial P}{\partial t}. \tag{6.48}$$

Neglecting the volume occupied by the solid particles and the relative acceleration, the momentum and energy of a particle of size (s) given by Eqs. (6.41) and (6.46) take the forms:

$$\frac{dU_{pi}^{(s)}}{dt_p^{(s)}} = F^{(s)}(U_i - U_{pi}^{(s)}) + \sum_{(r)} F_p^{(sr)}(U_{pi}^{(r)} - U_{pi}^{(s)}) \tag{6.49}$$

$$\frac{dT_p^{(s)}}{dt_p^{(s)}} = G^{(s)}(T - T_p^{(s)}) + \sum_{(r)} G_p^{(sr)}(T_p^{(r)} - T_p^{(s)}) \tag{6.50}$$

Multiplying Eq. (6.47) by U_i and subtracting that from Eq. (6.48), we get

$$\frac{dP}{dt} = \rho c \frac{dT}{dt} + \sum_{(s)} \rho_p^{(s)} \left[(U_{pi}^{(s)} - K_m^{(s)} U_i) \frac{dU_{pi}^{(s)}}{dt_p^{(s)}} + c_p^{(s)} \frac{dT_p^{(s)}}{dt_p^{(s)}} \right]. \tag{6.51}$$

Since the entropy of a given volume of the suspension is given by:

$$dS_m = \rho c \frac{dT}{T} - \rho R \frac{dP}{P} + \sum_{(s)} \rho_p^{(s)} c_p^{(s)} \frac{dT_p^{(s)}}{T_p^{(s)}},$$

the rate of entropy generation is given by substituting Eq. (6.51) as [S60]:

$$
\begin{aligned}
\dot{S} = \frac{dS_m}{dt} = \sum_{(s)} & \left[\rho_p^{(s)} c_p^{(s)} G^{(s)} (T_p^{(s)} - T) \left(\frac{1}{T} - \frac{1}{T_p^{(s)}} \right) \right] \\
+ \sum_{(s)} & \left[\frac{\rho_p^{(s)} F^{(s)} (U_{pi}^{(s)} - K_m^{(s)} U_i)(U_{pi}^{(s)} - U_i)}{T} \right] \\
+ \sum_{(s)} & \left\{ \rho_p^{(s)} c_p^{(s)} \left(\frac{1}{T} - \frac{1}{T_p^{(s)}} \right) \left[\sum_{(r)} G_p^{(sr)} (T_p^{(s)} - T_p^{(r)}) \right] \right\} \\
+ \sum_{(s)} & \left\{ \rho_p^{(s)} (U_{pi}^{(s)} - K_m^{(s)} U_i) \frac{1}{T} \left[\sum_{(r)} F_p^{(sr)} (U_{pi}^{(s)} - U_{pi}^{(r)}) \right] \right\}. \tag{6.52}
\end{aligned}
$$

It is expected that for a dissipative system such as a gas-solid suspension, $\dot{S} > 0$. The first two summations deal with gas-solid interaction only and are obviously greater than zero ($K_m = 1$ for $U_{pi} < U_i$, $K_m \leq 1$ for $U_{pi} > U_i$). The last two summations are greater than zero because, due to the relation between viscous drag and inertia of particles and the fact that smaller particles are easier to accelerate or decelerate than larger particles,

$$U_p^{(s)} > U_p^{(r)} \quad \text{for} \quad F^{(s)} > F^{(r)} \quad \text{at} \quad U > U_p$$

$$U_p^{(s)} < U_p^{(r)} \quad \text{for} \quad F^{(s)} > F^{(r)} \quad \text{at} \quad U < U_p,$$

and

$$\sum F_p^{(sr)} (U_{pi}^{(s)} - U_{pi}^{(r)}) > 0 \quad \text{for} \quad U_{pi}^{(r)} > K_m^{(r)} U_i$$

$$\sum F_p^{(sr)} (U_{pi}^{(s)} - U_{pi}^{(r)}) < 0 \quad \text{for} \quad U_{pi} < K_m^{(r)} U_i.$$

Similarly, the temperatures $T_p^{(s)}$ are determined by the relation between con vection and heat capacity, or

$$T_p^{(s)} > T_p^{(r)} \quad \text{for} \quad G^{(s)} > G^{(r)} \quad \text{at} \quad T > T_p \, ;$$

$$T_p^{(s)} < T_p^{(r)} \quad \text{for} \quad G^{(s)} > G^{(r)} \quad \text{at} \quad T < T_p \, ;$$

that is, at any moment, either all the particles have higher temperature than the fluid or they all have lower temperature. Therefore,

$$\sum_{(r)} G_p^{(sr)}(T_p^{(s)} - T_p^{(r)}) > 0 \quad \text{for} \quad T_p > T;$$

$$\sum_{(r)} G_p^{(sr)}(T_p^{(s)} - T_p^{(r)}) < 0 \quad \text{for} \quad T_p < T.$$

It is recognized that $F_p^{(sr)}$ and $G_p^{(sr)}$ are small for dilute suspension with particles at the average of 10 diameters apart. They become significant, however, when applied to, for instance, a fluidized bed. These transport parameters are not well known other than from the few references cited earlier.

6.7 Speed of Sound

Based on the above relations, particularly Eq. (6.47), the speed of sound and other apparent thermodynamic properties of a suspension of given size distribution can be computed [S58]. Here we illustrate with the case of particles of one size, and we take $K_m = 1$ for simplicity. When the fluid medium is a perfect gas, Eq. (6.50) becomes, for particles of uniform size and mass and $K_m = 1$:

$$-F\rho_p(U_i - U_{pi})^2 + \rho_p c_p G(T - T_p) = \frac{dP}{dt} - \rho c \frac{dT}{dt} \qquad (6.53)$$

which can be rearranged (with $P/\bar{\rho} = \bar{R}T$, $c = \gamma \bar{R}/(\gamma - 1)$; T is the gas con- stant, γ is the ratio of specific heats of the gaseous phase) to give:

$$\frac{d}{dt} \ln \frac{P}{T^{\gamma/\gamma - 1}} + \frac{\gamma}{\gamma - 1} \frac{\rho_p}{\bar{\rho}_p} \frac{d \ln T}{dt} = \frac{\rho_p[Gc_p(T - T_p) - F(U_i - U_{pi})^2]}{P}$$

$$(6.54)$$

which is the equation of an adiabatic process of a gas-solid system, showing that the contribution of the dissipation process is rate dependent.

For a very slow process, such that $T = T_p$, $U_i = U_{pi}$, the mass of the phases M_p, M in a given volume is related to $M_p/M_g = m_p^* = \text{constant}$, $\rho_p = m_p^*$, Eq. (6.53) reverts to

$$dP = (\rho c + \rho_p c_p) \, dT. \qquad (6.55)$$

In this case, if the simplification of $\rho = \bar{\rho}$ does not apply, then Eq. (6.55) gives, on integration

$$\left\{ T - \left[\frac{m_p^* P}{\bar{\rho}_p} (c - \bar{R} + m_p^* c_p) \right] \right\} P^{-\bar{R}/(c + m_p^* c_p)} = \text{constant}, \qquad (6.56)$$

as an exact adiabatic relation for small particles at equilibrium with the gas.

From Eq. (6.53), the speed of sound a_m through a gas-solid suspension is given by $a_m^2 = dP/d(\rho + \rho_p)$, and

$$\frac{RT}{a_m^2} = RT \frac{d(\rho + \rho_p)}{dP}$$

$$= \left[1 - \frac{d \ln T}{d \ln P} \right] \frac{d\rho}{d\bar{\rho}} + \bar{R}T \frac{d\rho_p}{dP}$$

$$= \gamma^{-1} - \frac{\rho_p}{\bar{\rho}_p} + (\gamma - 1)\gamma^{-1} \rho_p [G c_p (T - T_p)$$

$$- F(U - U_p)^2] \left(\frac{dP}{dt} \right)^{-1} + (\bar{\rho}^{-1} - \bar{\rho}_p^{-1}) \frac{d\rho_p}{d \ln P}, \qquad (6.57)$$

showing that the speed of sound is affected by the dissipative process but not the flow velocities. For similar simplification as leading to Eq. (6.56), we have

$$\frac{RT}{a_m^2} = (1 + m_p^*) \left\{ 1 - (\gamma - 1)\gamma^{-1} \left[1 + m_p^* \frac{\bar{\rho}}{\bar{\rho}_p} \right] \left[1 + m_p^* \frac{c_p}{c} \right]^{-1} \right\} \left[1 + m_p^* \frac{\bar{\rho}}{\bar{\rho}_p} \right]^{-2},$$

$$(6.58)$$

showing that due to inertia of solid particles, the sonic speed of the suspension a_m is always less than $\sqrt{\gamma \bar{R} T}$, that of clean gas.

6.8 The Meaning of Total Head Pressure

Another immediate application of the general formulation is the meaning of total pressure and its measurement [S58, S56].

Dussourd and Shapiro [D43] have investigated the characteristics of probes with droplets of a given size in a zero shear flow with uniform distribution. Contribution of particles to total head pressure was accounted for by bleeding the liquid droplets. It is interesting to determine the contribution of particles on total pressure reading in an actual pitot tube.

Formally, expressing Eq. (6.39) and (6.43) in one dimension, we get

$$U \frac{dU}{dx} + K_m \dot{m}_p^* U \frac{dU_p}{dx} = - \frac{1}{\rho} \frac{dP}{dx} \qquad (6.59)$$

$$\frac{U^2}{2} + \dot{m}_p^* \frac{U_p^2}{2} + cT + \dot{m}_p^* c_p T_p = (c + \dot{m}_p^* c_p) T', \qquad (6.60)$$

where T' is the total temperature, $\dot{m}_p^* = \rho_p U_p / \rho U$.

For $K_m \sim 1$, the total pressure can be related to the total temperature according to Eq. (6.59). For $K_m \sim 0$, we get

$$\frac{P'}{P} \cong \left(\frac{T'}{T} \right)^{(c + \dot{m}_p^* c_p)/\bar{R}}$$

$$= \left[1 + \frac{U^2}{2cT \dfrac{1 + \dot{m}_p^* c_p}{c}} \right]^{c \left(1 + \frac{\dot{m}_p^* c_p}{c} \right)/\bar{R}} \qquad (6.61)$$

For subsonic flow,

$$P' \sim P + \bar{\rho} \frac{U^2}{2} \qquad (6.62)$$

Thermodynamically the irreversibility in a gas-solid flow process can be seen in the enthalpy-entropy diagrams in Fig. 6.2. For deceleration the stagnation pressures for $K_m = 1$ and $K_m = 0$ are shown in Fig. 6.2a. For accelerating flow the increase in velocities is due to pressure drop as shown in Fig. 6.2b. Figure 6.2c shows complete dissipation of kinetic energy of solid particles in still gas.

The above considerations lead to an answer to the question: If we insert a total head tube in a stream of dusty gas, what does it indicate? Physically, we can expect that if the particle phase is extremely dense for the given relative Reynolds number, the pressure of solid particles can be felt by the pitot tube, but for $[2a(U - U_p)/\bar{\nu}](2a)^{-2} n_p^{-2/3} \ll -5$ as in the above case of $m_p^* \sim 1$, $K_m = 0$ and only the velocity head of the air is to be measured. This has been the case with our previous experiments (Sec. 4.5). The different regimes encountered by a total head tube is as shown in Fig. 6.3, ranging from the case: (a) a light gas-heavy gas mixture ($K_m = 1$, $U = U_p$); through: (b) high density of cloud of small solid particles ($K_m = 1$, $U \neq U_p$); (c) medium concentration of small particles or larger particles at high concentration ($K_m < 1$); to: (d) low concentration of particles which are not too small ($K_m = 0$). The location of stagnation of the gas is also described with corresponding enthalpy-entropy (H-S) diagrams. Almost all experiments so far on gas-solid suspensions are in the regime (d). Therefore, Eq. (6.59) holds

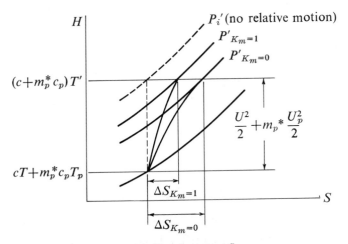

(a) Decelerating flow

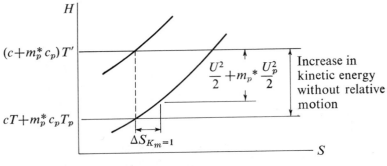

(b) Accelerating flow

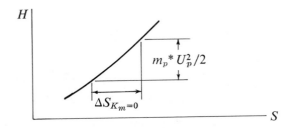

(c) Dissipation of kinetic energy of
a cloud of solid particles

Figure 6.2 Irreversibility in gas-solid flow [S56, S58].

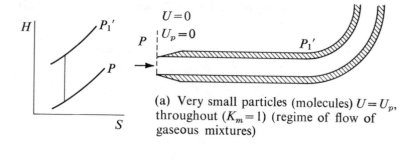

(a) Very small particles (molecules) $U = U_p$, throughout ($K_m = 1$) (regime of flow of gaseous mixtures)

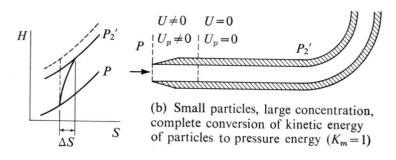

(b) Small particles, large concentration, complete conversion of kinetic energy of particles to pressure energy ($K_m = 1$)

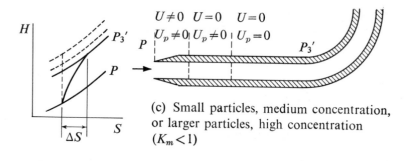

(c) Small particles, medium concentration, or larger particles, high concentration ($K_m < 1$)

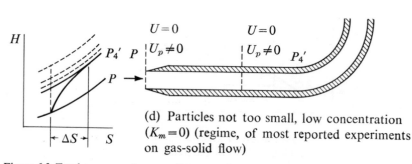

(d) Particles not too small, low concentration ($K_m = 0$) (regime, of most reported experiments on gas-solid flow)

Figure 6.3 Total pressure of a gas-solid suspension as seen by an actual pitot tube [S58].

272

for, for instance, subsonic measurement with a pitot tube in a gas-solid flow. In this regime, the average velocity distribution of the gaseous phase is unaffected by the presence of particles.

6.9 Reactive Suspensions

With the above clarification of the outstanding fluid dynamic behavior of a nonreactive suspension, we may now consider modifications needed for treating the general situation of the reactive (including phase change [S51]) suspension. Fluid mechanics of multicomponent (not multiphase) systems with chemical reactions were formulated by Penner [P8] and Truesdell [T54]. Sauerwein and Fendell [S5] treated the distribution of particle size in a condensing vapor. When applied to a reactive suspension, all the considerations in these references should be taken into account. In this general situation, the fluid phase may consist of a reacting gaseous mixture or a reacting solution, and the particulate phase may consist of solid particles or liquid droplets. Physical instances are liquid droplets in a vapor in a condensation process (Sec. 7.6); gases, metal vapor, metal droplets, solid particles of oxide in the combustion of metal (Secs. 3.3, 7.7); and liquid globules in a solution in an extraction process.

It is seen that in addition to identification of particulate clouds as species by superscripts (s) and (r), we identify the molecular species in the fluid phase by superscripts (q) and (p). The continuity relation in the fluid phase has to be represented by [H44]

$$\frac{\partial \rho^{(q)}}{\partial t} + \frac{\partial}{\partial x_i} [\rho^{(q)}(U_i + V_i^{(q)})] = -\Gamma^{(q)} + K^{(q)}, \qquad (6.63)$$

where $V_i^{(q)}$ is the ith component of the diffusion velocity of species (q), $\Gamma^{(q)}$ is the rate of generation (mass per unit volume, time) of species (q) going into the particulate phase of condensed phase, $K^{(q)}$ is the rate of species (q) generated by reaction in gaseous phase. Treating the gaseous mixture as a single phase, the flux due to diffusional flow of species (q) is given by Hirschfelder, Curtiss, and Bird [H44] as the mass flux vector:

$$\mathbf{J}^{(q)} = \rho^{(q)} \mathbf{V}^{(q)}$$

$$= \frac{n^2}{\rho} \sum_{(p)} m^{(p)} m^{(q)} D^{(qp)} \mathbf{d}^{(p)} - D_{(q)}^T \frac{\partial \ln T}{\partial \mathbf{r}}, \qquad (6.64)$$

where n, ρ are overall number density and mass density of the fluid phase,

$D^{(qp)}$ is the multicomponent diffusion coefficient, $D_{(q)}^T$ is the multicomponent thermal diffusion coefficient of species (q), $\mathbf{d}^{(p)}$ is given by

$$\mathbf{d}^{(p)} = \frac{\partial}{\partial \mathbf{r}}\left(\frac{n^{(p)}}{n}\right) + \left(\frac{n^{(p)}}{n} + \frac{n^{(p)}m^{(p)}}{\rho}\right)\frac{\partial \ln P}{\partial \mathbf{r}}$$

$$- \frac{n^{(p)}m^{(p)}}{P\rho}\left[\frac{\rho}{m^{(p)}}\mathscr{F}^{(q)} - \sum_{k=1}^{v} n^{(k)}\mathscr{F}^{(k)}\right], \qquad (6.65)$$

where $n^{(p)}$, $m^{(p)}$ are the number density and molecular mass of the (p) species, $\mathscr{F}^{(q)}$ is the external force acting on the (q) species of molecules. Noting that the number density of the (q) component is given by

$$\rho^{(q)} = n^{(q)}m^{(q)} = \bar{\rho}^{(q)}(1 - \sum_{(s)} \phi^{(s)}), \qquad (6.66)$$

where $\phi^{(s)}$ is the volume fraction solid of the (s) species of the condensed phase, while the overall number density in the fluid phase is given by

$$\sum_{(q)} n^{(q)} = n. \qquad (6.67)$$

It is noted that the total rate of generation to the particulate phase is given by

$$\sum_{(q)} \Gamma^{(q)} = \Gamma, \qquad (6.68)$$

and for the net conversion in the vapor phase

$$\sum_{(q)} K^{(q)} = 0, \qquad \sum \mathbf{J}^{(q)} = 0. \qquad (6.69)$$

Therefore, for the fluid or gaseous phase, assuming the fluid phase has only one mass velocity, the overall continuity equation of the fluid phase is

$$\frac{\partial \rho}{\partial t} + \frac{\partial}{\partial x_i} \rho U_i = -\Gamma, \qquad (6.70)$$

with

$$\rho = \bar{\rho}(1 - \sum_{(s)} \phi^{(s)}), \qquad (6.71)$$

as before.

For the particulate phases, it is readily seen that, including Brownian diffusion, the continuity equation for particulate species (s) is given by

$$\frac{\partial \rho_p^{(s)}}{\partial t} + \frac{\partial}{\partial x_i}[\rho_p^{(s)}U_{pi}^{(s)}] = \Gamma^{(s)} + K_p^{(s)}, \qquad (6.72)$$

where $U_{pi}^{(s)}$ includes ith component of the diffusion velocity of species (s) due to Brownian diffusion (Sec. 2.9) as well as that due to temperature and pressure gradients (Sec. 2.3); analogous relations as Eqs. (6.64) and (6.65) are readily derived. $K_p^{(s)}$ is the rate of generation of the (s) species by breakup or coalescence of other particulate species. Therefore, in the general sense of the "multiphase" system transition from species (s) to species (r) through change in particle size by evaporation or condensation is in itself a "phase" change. Thus

$$\sum_{(s)} \Gamma^{(s)} = \Gamma = \sum_{(q)} \Gamma^{(q)}, \tag{6.73}$$

the latter equality by combining with Eq. (6.68), and

$$\sum_{(s)} K_p^{(s)} = 0, \tag{6.74}$$

since the mass of the particulate phase is not altered due to $K_p^{(s)}$. Assuming binary collisions only, by analogy with Friedlander [F27], we have

$$\frac{K_p^{(s)}}{m_p^{(s)}} = \frac{1}{2} \sum_{(m)+(n)=(s)} N^{(mn)} + \sum_{(m)=1}^{(m)=\infty} S^{(ms)}$$

$$- \sum_{(m)=1}^{(m)=\infty} N^{(ms)} - \frac{1}{2} \sum_{(m)+(n)=(s)} S^{(mn)}, \tag{6.75}$$

where $N_{ij}^{(mn)}$ is the number of effective collisions per unit (time) (volume) between the two classes of particles (or embryos) of species (m) and (n) to form (s) particles; $S^{(mn)}$ is the number of (s) species splitting into (m) and (n) species per unit (time)(volume). The other two terms represent all other collision and splitting leading to formation and removal of species (s). The rate $\Gamma^{(s)}$, by the same token is given by

$$\frac{\Gamma^{(s)}}{m_p^{(s)}} = \frac{1}{2} \sum_{(i)+(j)=(s)} N^{(ij)} + \sum_{i=1}^{i=\infty} S^{(is)}$$

$$- \sum_{i=1}^{i=\infty} N^{(is)} - \frac{1}{2} \sum_{(i)+(j)=(s)} S^{(ij)}, \tag{6.76}$$

where the first and last terms on the right-hand side represent the formation of (s) species by collision of (i) and (j) molecular species and the removal by splitting of the (s) species to (i) and (j) molecules or embryos; the other two terms include collision by (i) molecules and (s) species of particles and splitting into (i) molecules and (s) particles. Determination of $\Gamma^{(s)}$ and $K_p^{(s)}$ in special cases was given by Friedlander [F27].

It is further seen that $\Gamma^{(s)}$ and $K_p^{(s)}$ contribute to the momentum equation of the particulate phase (s) by adding the terms

$$\Gamma^{(s)}(U_i - U_{pi}^{(s)}) + \langle K_p^{(s)} \Delta U_{pi}^{(s)} \rangle$$

to the right-hand side of Eq. (6.11), where

$$\langle K_p^{(s)} \Delta U_{pi}^{(s)} \rangle = \frac{1}{2} \sum_{(m)+(n)=(s)} N^{(mn)}(m_p^{(m)} U_{pi}^{(m)} + m_p^{(n)} U_{pi}^{(n)} - m_p^{(s)} U_{pi}^{(s)})$$

$$+ \sum_{(m)=1}^{(m)=\infty} S^{(ms)}(m_p^{(ms)} U_{pi}^{(ms)} - m_p^{(m)} U_{pi}^{(m)} - m_p^{(s)} U_{pi}^{(s)})$$

$$- \sum_{(m)=1}^{(m)=\infty} N^{(mn)} m_p^{(s)} U_{pi}^{(s)} - \frac{1}{2} \sum_{(m)+(n)=(s)} S^{(mn)} m_p^{(s)} U_{pi}^{(s)},$$

accounts for the change of momentum of the cloud of (s) particles due to agglomeration and breakup.

Analogous modification on the energy equation should also include taking into account latent heat and heat of reaction. Details are not given here. The above relations are applicable to condensation such as illustrated in Sec. 7.6, and to chemical reaction as illustrated in Sec. 9.6. These later sections illustrate simplified application of the basic concepts outlined here. The above indicates that multiphase-multicomponent reactive systems can be formulated rigorously for predicting their dynamic behaviors.

SUMMARY OF BASIC CONCEPTS

Multiplicity of Streamlines—(1962) [S52]
Limit of Continuum Approximation—(1964) [S58]
Generalized Multiphase Representation—(1964) [S60]
Transport Properties of Components in a Suspension—(1965) [S60, S61]

Gas Dynamics of a Suspension

One-dimensional dynamics of gas-particle suspensions were studied because of applications in metallized propellant rocket flow [A9] and gas dynamic diffusers with evaporative cooling [E20]. The basic methods are also applicable to jet type dust collectors [S22]. Moreover, the apparent thermodynamic properties of a suspension can be seen clearly through steady one-dimensional motion.

Shock relaxation of a dusty gas is pertinent to calculation of blast waves in a dusty atmosphere.

Basic discussion in this chapter concerns gas-solid suspensions only. Extensions to cases involving mass transfer and chemical reaction are treated as additional details.

7.1 One-Dimensional Steady Motion

One-dimensional steady motion of a gas-solid suspension through a duct of variable area was given by Glauz [G25], Kliegel [K19], Rannie [R1], Soo [S50], and by Bailey, Nilson, Serra, and Zupnik [B6] for solid particles of one size, with the following assumptions:

1. The motion is one-dimensional and steady; effect of turbulence enters only in characteristic parameters.

2. The solid particles are uniformly distributed over each cross section, although it is understood that they are suspended by turbulence and interactions exist between components.

3. The solid particles are uniform in diameter and physical properties. Variations again can be accounted for with characteristic parameters in the following.

4. The drag on the particles is mainly due to difference between the mean velocities of particles and stream. It is expected that the minimum size of solid particles consists of millions of molecules each (even in the submicron range). Hence the velocity of each solid particle due to its thermal state is extremely low. Slip flow, if it occurs, again can be accounted for by an appropriate characteristic parameter.

5. The heat transfer between the gas and the solid is basically due to their mean temperature difference. Effect of fluctuation in temperature will be accounted for by proper characteristic parameters.

6. The solid particles, due to their small size and high thermal conductivity (as compared to that of the gas), are assumed to be at uniform temperatures.

Glauz [G25] and Kliegel [K19] attempted to account for the volume occupied by solid particles in terms of flow area occupied by the particles. Rannie [R1] introduced variable particle mass fraction with density of mixture. All these studies neglected the volume of the virtual mass of fluid subjected to the acceleration of the particles relative to the ambient fluid. Another independent study by Stockel [S89] takes specific account of the volume occupied by solid particles and drag as given by the Ergun's drag equation (Sec. 5.1), but neglected the momentum of the fluid in the momentum equation and the heat transfer between the phases. Stockel made extensive measurements of the dense suspension through a converging-diverging nozzle. Apparently unaware of the work of Stockel, Rudinger [R50] considered the volume occupied by the solid particle but did not account for the Ergun's drag relation nor the consistent contribution to the particle momentum equation (Secs. 5.1, 6.4).

In the following, consistent formulations are given, taking into account distribution in particle (spherical) radii extending the study by Soo [S50].

It was shown in Sec. 6.2 that, through introduction of density ρ_p and ρ pertaining to the cloud, the continuity relation gives the flow rate of gas as

$$\dot{M} = \rho u A, \tag{7.1}$$

where u is the axial flow velocity of the gas in the x-direction and A is the cross-sectional area. $\rho = \bar{\rho}$ when the volume occupied by solids is neglected. The flow rate of solid particles is

$$\dot{M}_p = \sum_{(s)} \rho_p^{(s)} u_p^{(s)} A = A \sum_{(s)} \rho_p^{(s)} u_p^{(s)}. \tag{7.2}$$

Steady-flow condition gives the mass flow ratio as

$$\dot{m}_p^* = \frac{\dot{M}_p}{\dot{M}} = \frac{\sum\limits_{(s)} \rho_p^{(s)} u_p^{(s)}}{\rho u} = \text{const.,} \tag{7.3}$$

as well as

$$\dot{m}_p^{*(s)} = \frac{\rho_p^{(s)} u_p^{(s)}}{\rho u} = \text{const.,} \tag{7.4}$$

when there is no reaction or phase change, and the mass ratio is given by $\dot{m}_p^{*(s)} u_p^{(s)} / u$. It is seen when $u = u_p^{(s)} = 0$,

$$\dot{m}_p^* = \frac{\sum\limits_{(s)} \rho_p^{(s)}}{\rho} . \tag{7.5}$$

The momentum equations of the particulate phase from Eq. (6.41), neglecting the volume occupied by solid particles and relative acceleration, are given by

$$u_p^{(s)} \frac{du_p^{(s)}}{dx} = F^{(s)}(u - u_p^{(s)}) + \sum_{(r)} F^{(sr)}(u_p^{(r)} - u_p^{(s)}). \tag{7.6}$$

In deriving the overall momentum equation, we account for the shear stress terms with boundary friction [S25], shear stress at the wall τ_w, and Eq. (6.39) becomes

$$\rho u \frac{du}{dx} + \sum_{(s)} \rho_p^{(s)} u_p^{(s)} \frac{du_p^{(s)}}{dx} = -\frac{dP}{dx} - \frac{\tau_w \mathscr{P}}{A}, \tag{7.7}$$

where $\mathscr{P}$ is the perimeter of the duct at area A, and τ_w is given by

$$C_f = \frac{\tau_w}{\rho u^2 / 2} \tag{7.8}$$

When the stress due to impact of particles with the wall is neglected, and the perimeter $\mathscr{P}$ is related to A via the hydraulic diameter

$$D_H = \frac{4A}{\mathscr{P}} . \tag{7.9}$$

Equation (7.7), after substitution of Eqs. (7.8) and (7.9) and rearranging, becomes (take $\rho = \bar{\rho}$, and $\bar{\rho} = P/\bar{R}T$):

$$\frac{u}{T} \frac{du}{dx} + \frac{u}{\bar{R}T} \sum_{(s)} \dot{m}_p^{*(s)} \frac{du_p^{(s)}}{dx} + \frac{dP}{P \, dx} + \frac{2C_f u^2}{\bar{R}T D_H} = 0. \tag{7.10}$$

The energy equation of particles includes heat input into a particle of size (s) by convection from the gas and radiation from the wall, or, neglecting transfer of heat between particles and wall due to impact,

$$\frac{q_p^{(s)}}{A_p^{(s)}} = h_p^{(s)}(T - T_p^{(s)}) + \sum_{(r)} h_p^{(sr)}(T_p^{(r)} - T_p^{(s)}) + \epsilon_p^{(s)}\sigma_r(T_w^4 - T_p^{(s)4}), \quad (7.11)$$

where $A_p^{(s)}$ is the heat-transfer area of a sphere, $A_p^{(s)} = 4\pi a_s^2$; $h_p^{(s)}$ is the heat-transfer coefficient of convection from the gas, $h_p^{(sr)}$ is the heat transfer by collision with other particles, ϵ_p is the emissivity of the surface of the (s) particle, σ_r is the Stefan-Boltzmann constant of radiation, T_w is the temperature of the wall. The last term in Eq. (7.11) is for cases where the number density of particles is low enough that the effect of diffuse radiation is insignificant. With this relation, the energy equation of a solid particle is

$$u_p^{(s)}\frac{dT_p^{(s)}}{dx} = G^{(s)}(T - T_p) + \sum_{(r)} G^{(sr)}(T_p^{(r)} - T_p^{(s)}) + \frac{3\epsilon_p\sigma_r}{c_p\bar{\rho}_p a_s}(T_w^4 - T_p^{(s)4}). \tag{7.12}$$

The overall energy equation should account for the heat transfer, if any, at the wall of amount

$$h\mathscr{P}\left[T_w - \left(T + \frac{u^2}{2c}\right)\right]dx,$$

over length dx, and by radiation from the wall to the particles, since $dx = u_p^{(s)} dt$ for (s) particles, or

$$d\left(cT + \frac{u^2}{2} + \sum_{(s)} \dot{m}_p^{*(s)}c_p^{(s)}T_p^{(s)} + \sum \dot{m}_p^{*(s)}\frac{u_p^{(s)2}}{2}\right)$$

$$= \frac{4(N_{\text{Nu}})_{DH}\bar{\kappa}A}{D_H^2\dot{M}}\left[T_w - \left(T + \frac{u^2}{2c}\right)\right]dx$$

$$+ \frac{3\sigma_r}{\rho_p}\sum_{(s)} \frac{\epsilon_p^{(s)}}{a_s}(T_w^4 - T_p^{(s)4})\frac{dx}{u_p^{(s)}}. \tag{7.13}$$

The above equations are basic to all one-dimensional gas dynamic systems in steady flow. The latter include nozzle flow, Fanno flow, and shock waves. Detailed treatment is illustrated with nozzle flows. Fanno flow or flow of a suspension in a pipe of uniform flow area with wall friction was studied analytically and experimentally by Trezek and Soo [T57, T58].

7.2 Adiabatic Flow Through a Nozzle

First, let us consider the nature of gas-solid nozzle flow with particles of one size, leaving the case with size distribution to a later section.

The intentional addition of solids in the gas of a rocket nozzle was discussed by Altman and Curtis [A9]. Whether the solids in the gas are introduced intentionally or are accidentally, the result is a decrease in the efficiency of the nozzle when operating with a gas-solid suspension in comparison to operation with gas only.

Glassman [G23] suggests that the addition of solids to a gas be corrected for by modifying γ, the ratio of specific heats, and by modifying the molecular weight. The modification to the ratio of specific heats depends only on the specific heats and the amount of the phases present. The modification to the molecular weight depends only on the molecular weights of the components and the number of moles of each that are present. This method gives satisfactory approximation only for small mass ratios of solid to gas.

In most of the studies cited in the above, the critical flow conditions at the throat were not clarified [G25, K19, K21]. This condition is significant to correct solution of flow through a convergent-divergent nozzle.

Speed of Sound and Throat Condition [S58]—When applied to one-dimensional nozzle flow, Eq. (6.57) gives, for $\dot{m}_p^* = \rho_p u_p / \rho u$, the ratio of mass flow of phases and one size of solid particles.

$$\frac{\gamma \bar{R} T}{a_m^2}\left[1 + \dot{m}_p^* \frac{du_p}{du}\right] = \left\{1 + \dot{m}_p^*\left[\gamma \frac{du_p}{du} - (\gamma - 1)\frac{u_p \, du_p}{u \, du} - (\gamma - 1)\frac{c_p \, dT_p}{u \, du}\right]\right\}$$

$$\times \left[1 + \dot{m}_p^* \frac{u}{u_p}\right] + \frac{\gamma \bar{R} T}{u_p^2}\left[\frac{u_p}{u} - \frac{du_p}{du}\right], \tag{7.14}$$

taking $\rho \sim \bar{\rho}$. In the case of a frictionless adiabatic nozzle handling a pure gas, it is well known that the critical flow is at sonic velocity. Due to internal friction between the phases in the gas-solid system, a different result is expected. The flow through an area A is given by

$$\frac{\dot{M}}{A} = \rho u (1 + \dot{m}_p^*), \tag{7.15}$$

which has a maximum at

$$\rho \frac{du}{dx} = -u \frac{d\rho}{dx}. \tag{7.16}$$

Equations (7.10), (7.13), and (7.14) give for adiabatic flow without wall friction, at critical flow (subscript c):

$$\frac{\bar{R} T_c}{u_c^2} = \frac{\bar{R} T_c}{a_m^2}\left[1 + \dot{m}_p^* \frac{du_p}{du}\right]. \tag{7.17}$$

The Mach number of the gas at the throat based on the sonic velocity of the mixture is therefore

$$(N_M)_g^2 = \left[1 + \dot{m}_p^* \frac{du_p}{du}\right]^{-1}, \tag{7.18}$$

and that of the solid particles is

$$(N_M)_p^2 = \left(\frac{u_p}{u}\right)_c^2 \left[1 + \dot{m}_p^*\left(\frac{du_p}{du}\right)\right]^{-1} \tag{7.19}$$

Hence, both phases are subsonic at the throat which is in conformity with the fact that a gas-solid suspension is a dissipative system even in the absence of wall friction.

When wall friction is involved, the momentum equation in one dimension takes the form

$$\frac{dP}{P} = -(\bar{R}T)^{-1}\left[u\frac{du}{dx} + \dot{m}_p^*u\frac{du_p}{dx} + 2\frac{C_fL}{D_H}u^2\right], \tag{7.20}$$

where C_f is the friction factor, L is the characteristic length and D_H is the hydraulic diameter. The Mach number of the gas phase at the throat is now

$$(N_M)_g^2 = \left[1 + \dot{m}_p^* \frac{du_p}{du} + 2\frac{C_f}{D_H}u\left(\frac{du}{dx}\right)^{-1}\right]^{-1}. \tag{7.21}$$

Thus, the throat Mach number is still lower if wall friction is significant. Kliegel and Nickerson [K21] in his theoretical analysis, took the gas velocity at the throat at a Mach number of 0.8 based on the sonic speed of the gas.

The above considerations further show that for the nozzles of similar inlet, throat, and exit areas operated at similar inlet temperature, pressure and exit pressure, the throat and sonic speeds for a given gas-solid mixture are different for different lengths and shapes of nozzles.

Nondimensionalizing of Basic Equations—The usual method of non-dimensionalizing Eqs. (7.3), (7.6), (7.7), (7.10), (7.12), and (7.13) in terms of Mach number is used by Kliegel and Nickerson [K21] and Glauz [G25]. For a two-phase gas-solid system this technique may give misleading results. The simple relationship for the velocity of sound of a clean gas is no longer valid for a gas-solid suspension. Although the basic equations may still be nondimensionalized in terms of the gas phase Mach number, care must be exercised in interpreting the results. It must be remembered that the Mach number will be incorrect except for light solid particle loadings.

Rannie [R1] and Soo [S50] recognized this problem and chose to nondimensionalize without the use of Mach number. The equations are made nondimensional according to inlet or stagnation conditions (subscript zero below) and length of nozzle L. The nondimensional variables have a superscript $*$.

$$A^* = \frac{A}{\dot{M}}\frac{U_o}{v_o} = \frac{AU_oP_o}{\dot{M}\bar{R}T_o}, \quad x^* = \frac{x}{L}, \quad P^* = \frac{P}{P_o}$$

$$T^* = \frac{T}{T_o}, \quad T_p^* = \frac{T_p}{T_o}, \quad T_w^* = \frac{T_w}{T_o}, \quad u^* = \frac{u}{U_o}\Biggr\} \tag{7.22}$$

$$u_p^* = \frac{u_p}{U_o}, \quad U_o = \sqrt{2cT_o}$$

Equation (7.1) becomes:
$$A^*u^*P^* = T^*. \tag{7.23}$$

Equation (7.6) rewritten in dimensionless form becomes

$$u_p^* \frac{du_p^*}{dx^*} = E^*(u^* - u_p^*). \tag{7.24}$$

Introducing

$$E^* = \frac{FL}{U_o}. \tag{7.25}$$

Equation (7.12) rewritten in dimensionless form becomes

$$u_p^* \frac{dT_p^*}{dx^*} = B^*(T^* - T_p^*) + D^*(T_w^{*4} - T_p^{*4}), \tag{7.26}$$

where

$$B^* = \frac{3(N_{\mathrm{Nu}})_p \bar{\kappa}L}{2c_p\bar{\rho}_p a^2 U_o}, \tag{7.27}$$

and

$$D^* = \frac{3\epsilon_p\sigma_r T_o^3 L}{c_p\bar{\rho}_p a U_o}. \tag{7.28}$$

Equation (7.10) rewritten in dimensionless form becomes

$$\frac{dP^*}{P^*} + \frac{2c}{\bar{R}}\frac{u^*}{T^*}du^* + \frac{\dot{m}_p^*c}{\bar{R}}\frac{u^*}{T^*}du_p^* + \frac{4C_fL}{\bar{R}D_H}\frac{u^{*2}}{T^*}dx^* = 0 \tag{7.29}$$

Equation (7.13) rewritten in dimensionless form becomes

$$d\left(T^* + u^{*2} + \frac{\dot{m}_p^*c_p}{c}T_p^* + \dot{m}_p^*u_p^{*2}\right)$$

$$= B_w^*A^*[T_w^* - (T^* - u^{*2})]\,dx^* + \frac{c_p}{c}D^*\frac{\dot{m}_p^*}{u_p^*}(T_w^{*4} - T_p^{*4})\,dx^*, \tag{7.30}$$

where

$$B_w^* = \frac{4(N_{\mathrm{Nu}})_{D_H}\bar{\kappa}L\bar{R}T_o}{D_H^2 cU_oP_o}. \tag{7.31}$$

These five equations, (7.23), (7.24), (7.26), (7.29), and (7.30), are the governing equations for a gas-solid suspension derived under the assumption previously mentioned.

Adiabatic Nozzle Flow Without Wall Friction—When it is assumed that radiation, wall friction, and heat transfer from the wall to the gas may be neglected, $(N_{\text{Nu}})_p = 2$, and Stokes' law drag is applicable, then Eqs. (7.26), (7.29), and (7.30) take the following form:

$$u_p^* \frac{dT_p^*}{dx^*} = B^*(T^* - T_p^*) \tag{7.32}$$

$$\frac{1}{P^*} \frac{dP^*}{dx^*} + \frac{2cu^*}{\bar{R}T^*} \frac{du^*}{dx^*} + \frac{2\dot{m}_p^* cu^*}{\bar{R}T^*} \frac{du_p^*}{dx^*} = 0, \tag{7.33}$$

and

$$d\left[T^* + u^{*2} + \frac{\dot{m}_p^* c_p}{c} T_p^* + \dot{m}_p^* u_p^{*2} \right] = 0, \tag{7.34}$$

integrating,

$$T^* + u^{*2} + \frac{\dot{m}_p^* c_p}{c} T_p^* + \dot{m}_p^* u_p^{*\,2} = \text{constant.} \tag{7.35}$$

The initial boundary conditions may now be applied to evaluate the constant. The boundary conditions at $x^* = 0$ are:

$$
\begin{aligned}
T &= T_o & T^* &= 1 & T_p &= T_o & T_p^* &= 1 \\
u &= 0 & u^* &= 0 & u_p &= 0 & u_p^* &= 0.
\end{aligned}
\tag{7.36}
$$

Thus Eq. (7.35) becomes

$$T^* + u^{*2} + \frac{\dot{m}_p^* c_p}{c} T_p^* + \dot{m}_p^* u_p^{*2} = 1 + \frac{\dot{m}_p^* c_p}{c}. \tag{7.37}$$

These five equations, (7.23), (7.24), (7.32), (7.33), and (7.37), are the governing equations for $B_w^* = D^* = C_f = 0$, $(N_{\text{Nu}})_p = 2$, and $C_D = 24/(N_{\text{Re}})_p$. They constitute a set of ordinary, nonlinear, first-order, differential equations. Their solution is complicated by the fact that the velocity of the gas is almost equal to the velocity of the particles and the temperature of the gas is almost equal to the temperature of the particles near the stagnation condition. The speed of sound and the mixture and the throat condition must be accounted for.

Uniform Acceleration of the Gas—Although the solution of the above equations for arbitrary area distribution is of interest, analytical solution can be obtained only with prescribed velocities [K19, S50, H25]. A simple solution may be obtained if

$$u^* = \alpha x^*, \tag{7.38}$$

where α is a positive arbitrary constant less than one. Equation (7.38) may be substituted in Eq. (7.24) to obtain $u_p^*(x)$. This yields

$$u_p^* = \tfrac{1}{2}(\sqrt{E^{*2} + 4E^*\alpha} - E^*)x^* = \beta x^*. \tag{7.39}$$

Now Eqs. (7.34) and (7.32) may be combined to give

$$\frac{dT_p^*}{dx^*} + \frac{B^*}{u_p^*}\left(1 + \frac{\dot{m}_p^* c_p}{c}\right)T_p^* = \frac{-B^*}{u_p^*}(u^{*2} + \dot{m}_p^* u_p^{*2} - \text{const.}). \tag{7.40}$$

This is of the form $(dy/dx) + P(x)y = Q(x)$. Applying the integrating factor

$$\exp\left\{\int B^*\left[\frac{1 + \dfrac{\dot{m}_p^* c_p}{c}}{u_p^*}\right] dx\right\},$$

and remembering that $u^* = \alpha x^*$ and $u_p^* = \beta x^*$, gives

$$T_p^* = \frac{B^*}{\beta}\left[\frac{\text{const.}}{\dfrac{B^*}{\beta}\left(1 + \dfrac{\dot{m}_p^* c_p}{c}\right)} - \frac{x^{*2}(\alpha^2 + \dot{m}_p^*\beta^2)}{\dfrac{B^*}{\beta}\left(1 + \dot{m}_p^*\dfrac{c_p}{c}\right) + 2}\right] + \begin{array}{l}(\text{const. of}\\ \text{integration}).\end{array}$$

The initial boundary condition at $x^* = 0$ is $T_p^* = 1.0$. Therefore, const. $= 1 + (\dot{m}_p^* c_p)/c$ and the constant of integration is zero. This gives:

$$T_p^* = 1 - \frac{B^*}{\beta}\left[\frac{\alpha^2 + \dot{m}_p^*\beta^2}{\dfrac{B^*}{\beta}\left(1 + \dfrac{\dot{m}_p^* c_p}{c}\right) + 2}\right]x^{*2}. \tag{7.41}$$

Equations (7.34), (7.38), (7.39), and (7.41) may now be solved for T^*, giving

$$T^* = 1 - \alpha^2 x^{*2}\frac{c}{c_e}, \tag{7.42}$$

where c_e is the apparent specific heat (at constant pressure) of the suspension,

$$\frac{c_e}{c} = \frac{\dfrac{B^*}{\alpha}\left(1 + \dfrac{\dot{m}_p^* c_p}{c}\right) + 2\left(\dfrac{\beta}{\alpha}\right)}{\left[1 + \dot{m}_p^*\dfrac{\beta^2}{\alpha^2}\right]\left[\dfrac{B^*}{\alpha} + 2\left(\dfrac{\beta}{\alpha}\right)\right]}. \tag{7.43}$$

It is interesting to note that specific heat, normally a thermodynamic property, is dependent on the transport process in the case of the gas-solid suspension because of nonequilibrium between the two phases. The solid is at different temperatures of the gas. The limiting cases are (corresponding to cases outlined in the above):

(a)

$$E^* \to \infty, \quad \frac{\beta}{\alpha} \to 1, \quad B^* \to \infty, \quad c_e = \frac{c + \dot{m}_p^* c_p}{1 + \dot{m}_p^*},$$

like a heavy gas-light gas mixture. When there is no heat transfer between phases, we have

(b)

$$E^* \to \infty, \quad \frac{\beta}{\alpha} \to 1, \quad B^* \to 0, \quad c_e = \frac{c}{1 + \dot{m}_p^*},$$

with the solid particles simply contributing to inertia.

(c)

$$E^* \to 0, \quad \frac{\beta}{\alpha} \to 0, \quad B^* \to \infty$$

gives, for (1) $\dot{m}_p^*$ finite, $c_e = c + \dot{m}_p^* c_p$, with solid particles left behind; and (2) $\dot{m}_p^* = \infty$, $c_e \to \infty$, with a large quantity of solid particles trickling out at very low velocity and heating the gas phase. The expansion is at constant temperature, with solid particles heating the gas continuously.

(d)

$$E^* \to 0, \quad \frac{\beta}{\alpha} \to 0, \quad B^* \to 0, \quad c_e = c,$$

in the case of a clean gas [G23, D28].

Now $P^*(x^*)$ may be found from Eq. (7.33):

$$P^* = \left(1 - \alpha^2 x^{*2} \frac{c}{c_e}\right)^{(c_e/\bar{R})[1 + \dot{m}_p^*(\beta/\alpha)]} \tag{7.44}$$

Equation (7.41) may be written to include T^*:

$$T_p^* = T^* + \left\{ \frac{2\frac{\beta}{\alpha} \frac{c}{c_e}}{\left(\frac{B^*}{\alpha} + 2\frac{\beta}{\alpha}\right)} \frac{c}{c_e} \alpha^2 \right\} x^{*2}. \tag{7.45}$$

In general, for E^* and B^* both greater than 1000, the approximation of $u = u_p$, $T = T_p$, should be quite accurate.

The speed of sound of the mixture, Eq. (7.14), for the case of uniform acceleration, gives

$$a_m = \left\{ \frac{\gamma \bar{R} T \left(1 + \dot{m}_p^* \frac{\beta}{\alpha}\right)}{\left(1 + \dot{m}_p^* \frac{\alpha}{\beta}\right)\left[\gamma - (\gamma - 1)\frac{c}{c_e} + \gamma \dot{m}_p^* \frac{\beta}{\alpha}\right]} \right\}^{1/2}. \tag{7.46}$$

The throat condition gives the Mach number at the throat. Equations (7.18) and (7.19) for this case give

$$N_M = \left(1 + \dot{m}_p^* \frac{\beta}{\alpha}\right)^{-\frac{1}{2}}, \tag{7.47}$$

and

$$(N_M)_p = \frac{\beta}{\alpha}\left(1 + \dot{m}_p^* \frac{\beta}{\alpha}\right)^{-\frac{1}{2}}. \tag{7.48}$$

Now, from Eq. (7.23), $A^*(x)$ may be found. This is actually a solution to the equations; however, it depends on the fact that the gas must have uniform acceleration. The solution is useful because it is an exact solution to the equations.

It is difficult to draw conclusions from this solution because the area distribution cannot be held constant for a study of parameters. For typical parameters of: $c_p = 0.118$ Btu/lb °R, $c = 0.24$ Btu/lb °R air, $\dot{m}_p^* = 0.30$ lb solid/lb gas, $\bar{R} = 53.35$ ft lb/lb °R air, $E^* = 100.0$, $B^* = 10.0$, and $a = 0.9$, the solutions for $A^*(x)$, $P^*(x)$, $T^*(x)$, $T_p^*(x)$, $u^*(x)$, and $N_M(x)$ are shown in Figs. 7.1 through 7.6. The nozzle in Fig. 7.1 was computed for linear acceleration with $\dot{m}_p^* = 0.3$ with the above parameters. The calculation for $\dot{m}_p^* = 0$ is well known. For other values of $\dot{m}_p^*$'s, the numerical method in Sec. 7.3 was used to obtain various values of P^*, T^*, etc., for A^* given in Fig. 7.1.

For this numerical example, the general character of c_e/c given by Eq. (7.43) is shown in Fig. 7.7. The speed of sound of the mixture a_m as influenced by the transport processes is now expressed in terms of its ratio to speed of sound a_g in the gas alone:

$$\frac{a_m^2}{a_g^2} = \left[\left(\frac{B^*}{E^*}\right)\left(\frac{\beta}{\alpha}\right)\left(\frac{c + \dot{m}_p^* c_p}{c}\right) + 2\left(1 - \frac{\beta}{\alpha}\right)\right]$$
$$\times \left\{\left(\frac{B^*}{E^*}\right)\left(\frac{\beta}{\alpha}\right)\left[\left(1 + \dot{m}_p^* \frac{\beta}{\alpha}\right)\left(\frac{c + \dot{m}_p^* c_p}{c - \bar{R}}\right) - \left(\frac{\bar{R}}{c - \bar{R}}\right)\left(1 + \dot{m}_p^* \frac{\beta^2}{\alpha^2}\right)\right]\right.$$
$$\left. + 2\left(1 - \frac{\beta}{\alpha}\right)\left[\left(\frac{c}{c - \bar{R}}\right)\left(1 + \dot{m}_p^* \frac{\beta}{\alpha}\right) - \frac{\bar{R}}{c - \bar{R}}\left(1 + \dot{m}_p^* \frac{\beta^2}{\alpha^2}\right)\right]\right\}^{-1}. \tag{7.49}$$

This relation is shown in Fig. 7.8 for the same numerical example.

From consideration of this simple case, we have seen that, in flow through nozzles, the previous results [A9, D28, G23] are confirmed as limiting cases. It has been generalized that it is not just a matter of small particles and dense gas that will produce small momentum and thermal lag. It calls for a large heat-transfer parameter:

$$B^* = \tfrac{3}{2}(N_{Nu})_p \frac{\bar{\kappa}}{c_p \bar{\rho}_p} \frac{L}{a^2 U_o},$$

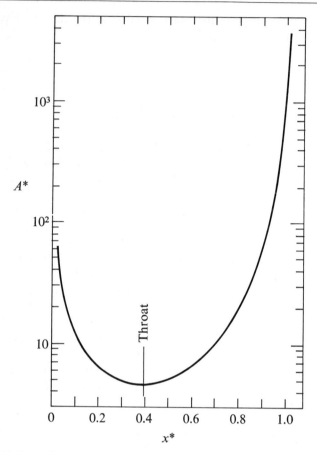

Figure 7.1 Area distribution of nozzle designed for linear acceleration with $\dot{m}_p^* = 0.3$ [H68].

U_o here is the characteristic velocity, and large drag parameter

$$E^* = \frac{3}{8} \frac{C_D}{a} \frac{\bar{\rho}_p}{\rho} \frac{|u - u_p|}{U_o} L \sim \frac{9\bar{\mu}L}{2\bar{\rho}_p a^2 U_o} \cdot$$

The ratio

$$\frac{B^*}{E^*} = \frac{2}{3} \frac{c\rho}{c_p \bar{\rho}_p} \bigg/ N_{\text{Pr}} \,,$$

being usually small, thermal lag is usually more significant than momentum lag, although the latter might be quite large at the exit of a nozzle. For particle size smaller than the mean free path Λ, modifications given by Eqs. (2.9) and (2.14) have to be made.

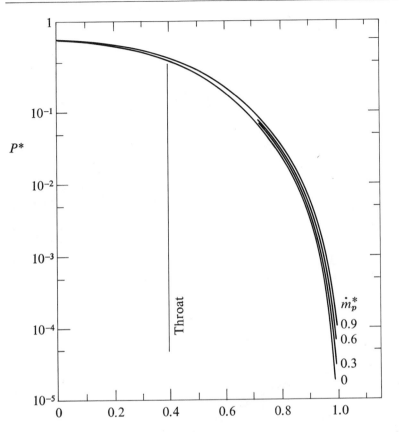

Figure 7.2 Pressure distribution in nozzle designed for linear acceleration at $\dot{m}_p^* = 0.3$ [H68].

The speed of sound through a gas-solid suspension is another point of interest. This velocity is affected by the heat and momentum transfer between the two phases. For large drag and small heat transfer, the solid contributes only as added molecular weight. If the heat-transfer rate is also large, the situation of a heavy gas mixture arises. If the drag is very small, the solid particles do not contribute to the speed of sound. Therefore, any gas dynamic analysis referring to the speed of sound of the gas phase alone is inadequate.

Turbulence, when present, tends to increase the value of B^*. It also affects the value C_f in Eq. (7.29).

These results indicate that, even without wall friction, the shape of the nozzle affects its thrust. For a nozzle operating with very low exit pressure, the expansion should be as complete as possible, because the particles do not contribute to pressure thrust (Sec. 6.2).

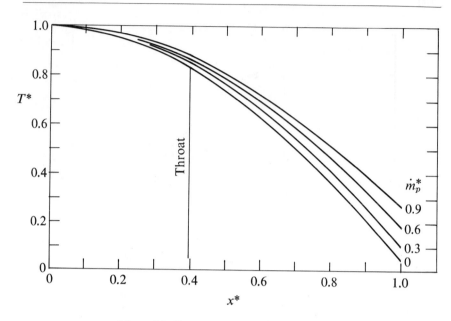

Figure 7.3 Gas-temperature distribution [H68].

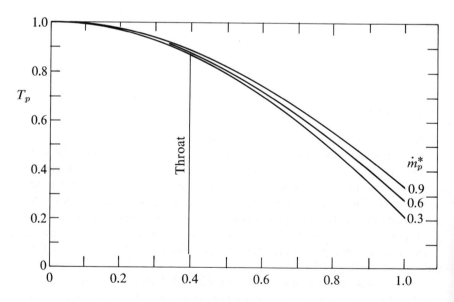

Figure 7.4 Particle-temperature distribution [H68].

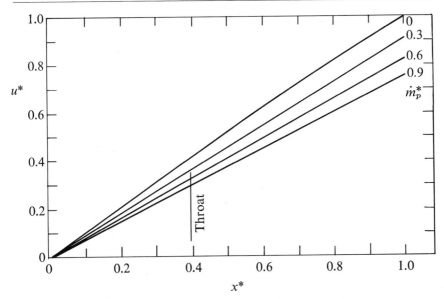

Figure 7.5 Gas velocity (linear for $\dot{m}_p^* = 0.3$) [H68].

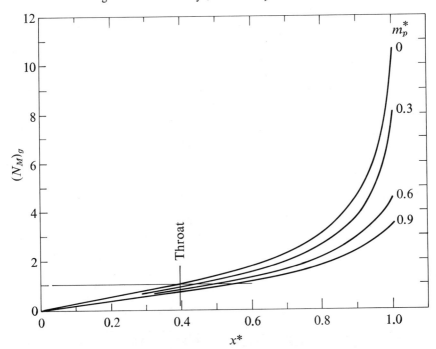

Figure 7.6 Mach number of the gas phase [H68].

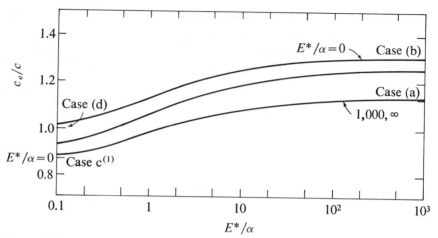

Figure 7.7 Apparent specific heat of a suspension as affected by transport processes ($\dot{m}_p^* = 0.3$ MgO in air).

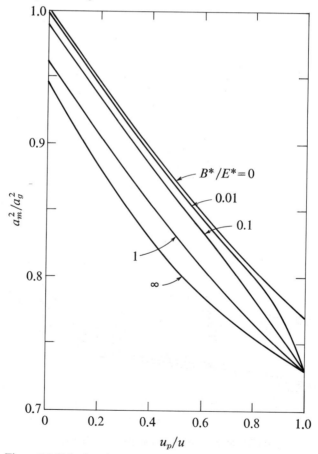

Figure 7.8 Velocity of sound through a gas-solid suspension ($\dot{m}_p^* = 0.3$).

When applied to a rocket nozzle, the specific impulse is given by

$$I = \frac{\alpha\sqrt{2cT_o}}{g_c(1 + \dot{m}_p^*)}\left[1 + \dot{m}_p^*\frac{\beta}{\alpha}\right], \tag{7.50}$$

where g_c is the gravitational constant. Hence, for the same exit velocity from the nozzle, the specific impulse of a gas-solid system is always the same as that of a pure gas of similar composition as the gas phase, regardless of the exit velocity and concentration of the solid phase. For the same impulse, the inlet pressure to the nozzle usually has to be higher when solid particles are

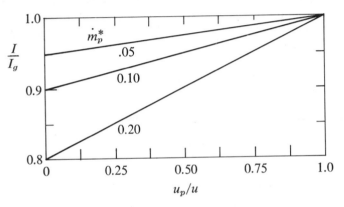

Figure 7.9 Effect of nonequilibrium particle velocity on specific impulse (I_g for gas alone) [O4].

present. Since B^* and E^* are primarily dependent on the length of the passage, and E^* actually decreases toward the exit, thus, even without wall friction, the final state of expansion is affected by the shape and size of the nozzle. Although thermal lag is greater than the velocity lag in most actual cases, the effect of thermal lag on performance of a rocket is far less than that of velocity lag [A9, G23]. Figure 7.9 illustrates the trend of effect of velocity lag, with the ratio of specific impulse including particles to that of pure gas [O4].

7.3 Numerical Solution for Given Area Distribution

The problem of the gas dynamic flow of a gas-solid suspension through a converging-diverging nozzle of given area distribution has a significant bearing on the design of a rocket. Since a number of results were published [G25,

K20, M6], but none identified fully the initial and critical conditions [H68], it is useful to discuss the numerical method by Hultberg in some detail [H66, H68].

In this numerical method, the complete initial and throat conditions for a unique solution were taken into account. The fact that flow with negligible wall friction gives rise to subsonic flow at the throat based on the speed of sound of the mixture, and the fact that the sonic point occurs after the throat, constituting a singularity, were accounted for. The convergence of the solution and the usefulness of the Runge-Kutta-Gill method [G16] were thoroughly treated and the digital program was thoroughly proved.

A numerical solution must be used for the solution of an arbitrary area distribution. Generally, total differential equations are arranged in the following form for solution on digital computers:

$$\frac{\mathrm{d}y_i}{\mathrm{d}x} = f_i(x, y_1, y_2, \ldots, y_n). \tag{7.51}$$

The momentum equation of the particles becomes

$$\frac{\mathrm{d}u_p^*}{\mathrm{d}x^*} = \frac{E^*(u^* - u_p^*)}{u_p^*}, \tag{7.52}$$

and the energy equation of the particles becomes

$$\frac{\mathrm{d}T_p^*}{\mathrm{d}x^*} = \frac{-B^*(T_p^* - T^*)}{u_p^*}. \tag{7.53}$$

Since there are two algebraic equations, two variables may be eliminated. The energy equation of the mixture is

$$\frac{\mathrm{d}T^*}{\mathrm{d}x^*} = -2u^* \frac{\mathrm{d}u^*}{\mathrm{d}x^*} - \frac{\dot{m}_p^* c_p^*}{c} \frac{\mathrm{d}T_p^*}{\mathrm{d}x^*} - 2\dot{m}_p^* u_p^* \frac{\mathrm{d}u_p^*}{\mathrm{d}x^*}, \tag{7.54}$$

and the overall continuity equation is

$$\frac{T^*}{A^*} \frac{\mathrm{d}A^*}{\mathrm{d}x^*} + \frac{T^*}{u^*} \frac{\mathrm{d}u^*}{\mathrm{d}x^*} + \frac{T^*}{P^*} \frac{\mathrm{d}P^*}{\mathrm{d}x^*} = \frac{\mathrm{d}T^*}{\mathrm{d}x^*}. \tag{7.55}$$

Equations (7.54), (7.55), and the momentum equation of the mixture may be solved for $\mathrm{d}u^*/\mathrm{d}x^*$, giving

$$\frac{\mathrm{d}u^*}{\mathrm{d}x^*} = \frac{-\dfrac{T^*}{A^*} \dfrac{\mathrm{d}A^*}{\mathrm{d}x^*} + \left(\dfrac{2\dot{m}_p^* c u^*}{\bar{R}} - 2\dot{m}_p^* u_p^*\right)\dfrac{\mathrm{d}u_p^*}{\mathrm{d}x^*} - \dfrac{\dot{m}_p^* c_p}{c} \dfrac{\mathrm{d}T_p^*}{\mathrm{d}x^*}}{\dfrac{T^*}{u^*} - \dfrac{2c u^*}{\bar{R}} + 2u^*}. \tag{7.56}$$

These three equations, (7.52), (7.53), and (7.56), together with $dx^*/dx^* = 1$, constitute the set of equations which must be solved numerically. Introducing

$$\frac{u^{*2}}{T^*} = (N_M)_g^2 \frac{\gamma \bar{R}}{2c}, \tag{7.57}$$

the denominator of Eq. (7.56) becomes

$$u^* \left[\frac{T^*}{u^{*2}} - 2 \left(\frac{c}{\bar{R}} - 1 \right) \right] = \frac{2u^*}{\gamma - 1} \left[\frac{1}{(N_M)_g^2} - 1 \right]$$

$$= \frac{2u^*}{(N_M)_g^2 (1 - \gamma)} [(N_M)_g^2 - 1]. \tag{7.58}$$

Introducing [G25]

$$Z = \tfrac{1}{2} [(N_M)_g^2 - 1]^2, \tag{7.59}$$

then

$$\frac{dZ}{dx^*} = [(N_M)_g^2 - 1] \frac{d(N_M)_g^2}{dx^*}, \tag{7.60}$$

and

$$(N_M)_g^2 = 1 \mp \sqrt{2Z}, \tag{7.61}$$

where the minus sign is for subsonic flow.

Differentiation of Eq. (7.57) and combining Eqs. (7.54) and (7.60) together with Eq. (7.56) gives

$$\frac{dZ}{dx^*} = 2(N_M)_g^2 \left(\frac{1}{T^*} + \frac{u^{*2}}{T^{*2}} \right) \left[\frac{T^*}{A^*} \frac{dA^*}{dx^*} - \left(\frac{2\dot{m}_p^* c u^*}{\bar{R}} - 2\dot{m}_p^* u_p^* \right) \frac{du_p^*}{dx^*} + \frac{\dot{m}_p^* c_p}{c} \frac{dT_p^*}{dx^*} \right]$$

$$+ [(N_M)_g^2 - 1] \frac{2c}{\gamma \bar{R}} \frac{u^{*2}}{T^{*2}} \left[\frac{\dot{m}_p^* c_p}{c} \frac{dT^*}{dx^*} + 2\dot{m}_p^* u_p^* \frac{du_p^*}{dx^*} \right], \tag{7.62}$$

removing $(N_M)_g^2 - 1$ term from the denominator. Thus the solution may be continued to supersonic flow. The minus sign in Eq. (7.61) is changed to positive when the flow, based on the velocity of sound in the gas only, becomes supersonic. It is important to note that the sign is to be changed only when $Z = 0$. It would be improper to change the sign in Eq. (7.61) during a step of the solution. The exact point where $Z = 0$ is found by varying the step size.

If dP^*/dx^* or dT^*/dx^* had been used as one of the variables, the singularity would still be present in either expression. The form of the denominator changes but $(N_M)_g^2 - 1$ may still be factored out. The du^*/dx^* expression was used because it was of the simplest form. The basic equations have now been transformed and rearranged in such a manner that they are suitable for solution of a digital computer.

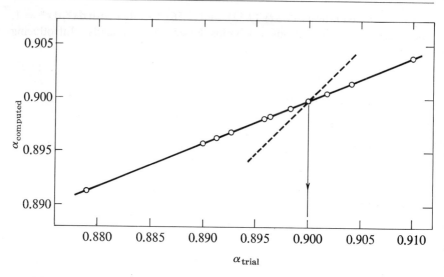

Figure 7.10 Iteration at throat condition for critical flow (case $\dot{m}_p^* = 0.30$) [H68].

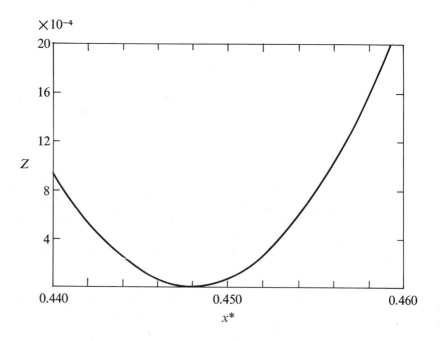

Figure 7.11 Z near the sonic (gas-phase) point [H68].

Initial Conditions—Since theoretical examples have initial conditions at $x^* = 0$, $P^* = T^* = T_p^* = 1.0$, $u^* = u_p^* = 0$, the area approaches infinity. In applying the theory to actual cases these conditions may also be used. Obviously a numerical solution cannot start at $x^* = 0$. It is therefore necessary to use an approximate solution until all of the values lie within machine range. The solution for uniform acceleration of the gas phase is well suited for this purpose. It is used as an approximate solution for $x^* = 0$ to $x^* = 0.03$.

In the uniform acceleration solution ($u^* = \alpha x^*$) [K19, S50], once the acceleration constant α is given, the values for A^*, P^*, T^*, T_p^*, u^*, and u_p^* are easily obtained. When applying this solution as an approximate solution the constant α must be properly selected. Initially, α is determined by an educated guess. Its value is checked at the throat.

Throat Condition—Once the constant α is selected, the initial conditions are determined. The solution is continued to the throat where the throat condition must be satisfied. The velocity of sound of the mixture may now be determined. Then the critical velocity of the gas at the throat u_c^* is determined by optimum flow rate. If the constant α was selected properly then u_c^* as determined at the throat by the numerical solution will agree with u_c^* determined by the throat condition. If u_c^* calculated by both methods does not agree, then a correction is applied to the constant α and the solution is tried again. The correction used is

$$\alpha_{\text{correction}} = 0.5 \frac{u_{c_{\text{throat condition}}}^* - u_{c_{\text{Runge-Kutta-Gill}}}^*}{x_{\text{throat}}^*}. \tag{7.63}$$

Since each time a new value for α is computed all the initial conditions change, it is difficult to develop a correction formula for α that would work in all cases. If a better correction formula would be developed, the final answer would not change; only the total time would be less because fewer iterations would be required (Fig. 7.10). The constant 0.5 in the above equation was used so that the constant α would not be overcorrected.

For the numerical solution the Runge-Kutta method with the Gill modification was used [G16, M39]. The Gill modification to the Runge-Kutta method was used to minimize the effect of roundoff error. The solution was programmed on the automatic double precision IBM-7094. High accuracy was maintained by seventeen decimal places. Typical results of computation are shown in Figs. 7.10 and 7.11, and the accuracy is shown in Fig. 7.12 by comparing with the check case of constant acceleration. Details of programming are given in the report by Hultberg [H66].

An attempt toward designing a nozzle contour for minimum loss due to particle lag was made by Marble [M6]. In his study, particular attention was paid to the need of an elongated throat.

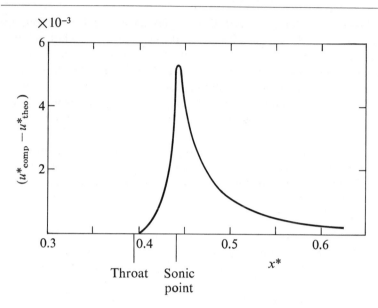

Figure 7.12 Error of computation [H68].

7.4 Experimental Studies on Nozzle Flow

Experimental studies were made in a converging nozzle and a Mach 2.3 nozzle by Hulberg and Soo [H67, H68]. The measurements on a 10-sec blow-down system included pressures, exit gas velocity, and a shadowgraph determination of the solids concentration. The particles were fed by a ram in a cylinder with screw feed.

The test nozzle was made of 7075-T6 aluminum. Experimental nozzle I was a convergent nozzle. Nozzle II was made from arcs of a circle and its area was as shown in Fig. 7.13. This had the advantage that the derivative of the area was easily determined.

Tests were performed first with air alone in order to determine the deviation of the experimental data from one-dimensional theory. It would be expected that the deviation of the one-dimensional two-phase theory from the experimental data would be in the same direction and would be of approximately the same magnitude as the deviation for air only.

Tests with air only were performed under the following test condition. Experimental nozzle I:

Stagnation pressure = 29.022 in. Hg = barometric pressure

Stagnation temperature = 72°F = room temperature

Experimental nozzle II:

Stagnation pressure = 29.898 in. Hg = barometric pressure

Stagnation temperature = 76°F = room temperature

$$c = 0.24 \text{ Btu/lb }°R$$

The nozzles used for the tests with particles were the same ones that were used for the tests with air only. The glass particles had values of specific heat and density of

$$c_p = 0.20 \text{ Btu/lb }°R \quad \bar{\rho}_p = 139 \text{ lb/ft}^3 \quad 2a = 230 \, \mu$$

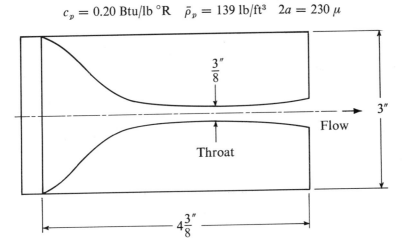

Figure 7.13 Experimental nozzle II [H68].

For experimental nozzle I, the bead feeder was run with a 60-tooth sprocket on the motor and a 12-tooth sprocket on the lead screw. The particle feed rate was 0.2653 lb/sec. The mass flow rate of air, calculated in the same manner as for the tests with no particles, was 0.1405 lb/sec. The predicted mass flow rate was 0.1478 lb/sec, or an error compared with theory of 5 per cent. This gives a loading ratio, $\dot{m}_p^*$, of 1.89 lb solid/lb gas.

For experimental nozzle II, the loading ratios thus obtained were 2.86 and 1.39, respectively. Results are shown in Fig. 7.14 and 7.15. The calculated gas-velocity data points and the theory for $\dot{m}_p^* = 1.39$ and $\dot{m}_p^* = 2.86$ are shown in Fig. 7.15.

The optical density of a negative of a view of the system of particles in the test section was determined with a Weston densitometer. Since the optical density is directly proportional to the particle density ρ_p, and since the loading ratio $\dot{m}_p^*$ and the velocity of the gas are known, then the velocity of the particles may be determined.

Comparison of the results at the experiment and computation shows that

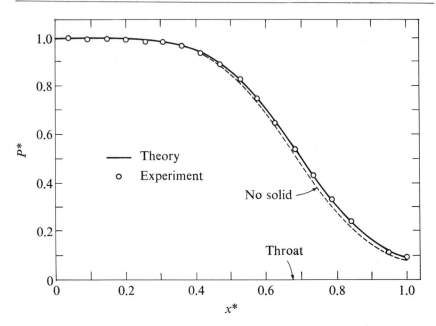

Figure 7.14 Pressure distribution at $\dot{m}_p^* = 1.39$, experimental nozzle II [H68].

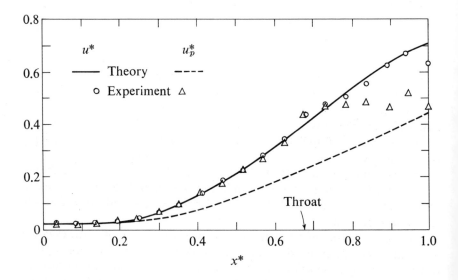

Figure 7.15 Velocities at $\dot{m}_p^* = 1.39$, experimental nozzle II [H68].

the one-dimensional computation is useful for the system. Two- and three-dimensional gas dynamic effects [K21] tend to be overshadowed by electrostatic effects [S57, S58, S72]. The flow was not one-dimensional. As was noted previously, the static pressure profile across the last three measuring stations next to the throat was not uniform.

The relatively large deviation between the theory and the data for the particle velocity was attributed to deviations from one-dimensional flow of the particles and the slip of the particles at the wall of the nozzle [S53, S72]. Although the nozzle was designed for uniform distribution of the solid particles across any cross section, the buildup of solid particles at the wall of the nozzle was due to electrostatic charge on the particles [S58]. It is further noted that the worst deviation between the theory and experimental data was when the rate of change of area was the largest. The rapid rate of change of area of the test nozzle rendered the basic assumptions of one-dimensional flow inadequate. Correction for the transverse concentration distribution may be made according to the boundary-layer theory (Sec. 8.5).

Extensive measurements were made on nozzle flow of a dense suspension (silica-alumina spheres 64.2 μ in diameter) by Stockel [S89] with fraction void down to 0.6. Due to the simplification of his theoretical analysis (Sec. 7.1), his results show a lack of agreement with measurements. The fact that his solution shows correctness of trend substantiates the significance of Ergun's drag equation for a dense cloud (Sec. 5.1) and the volume occupied by the solid particles as overriding factors. Shock due to overexpansion of the nozzle was not evaluated.

Experiments on metallized (aluminum) propellant rockets were made by Brown and McArty [B63], who presented data on the particle-size distribution of metal oxides. Two kinds of observation were made: (1) Particles were collected on microscope slides exposed to the exhaust of motors burning double base composite propellant. It was found that the location of the slide has no effect on the results. Countings were made on samples of thousands of particles. (2) Optical absorption of the flame was determined from photographs of a steel cone exposed to the exhaust jet. The film density of photographs taken through the flame at 750 frames per second was compared with film density of photographs taken immediately after burning, but before the cone cooled appreciably, and a particle size was again computed.

All of the measurements made on motors having various pressures, metal particle sizes, propellant compositions, expansion ratios, residence times, and exit pressures, point to a mass average diameter between 2 and 3 μ. Approximately 5 per cent loss in specific impulse in these rockets was measured.

Brown [B62] also measured the velocity of the condensed phase at the nozzle exit plane by streak photography. These velocities are related to calculated gas velocities and plotted as shown in Fig. 7.16 against specific impulse ratio. The theoretical curve was calculated by assuming equilibrium at the nozzle entrance and isentropic expansion [A9], and lowering 1 per cent to account for heat loss. Nozzles A, B, C, have the following shape:

Nozzle	$\dfrac{I_{exp}}{I_{calc}}$	Entrance Angle	Radius Throat Wall / Throat Dia	Length cm	Exit Angle	Area Ratio
A	0.91	30°	2	13	15°	3.5
B	0.93	30°	2	21	15°	3.5
C	0.95	5°	2	24	15°	

The longer nozzles and gradual contour produced higher particle exit velocities, conforming to theoretical prediction.

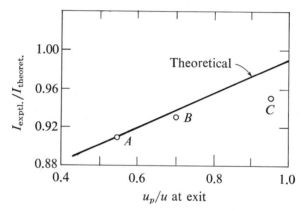

Figure 7.16 Effect of particle velocity at nozzle exit on thrust [B62].

Measurements of thermal lag in rockets were reported by Carlson [C4, C3]. The method consists of measuring both the gas and particle temperature independently at a single location within the nozzle. Spectral emissions were observed at two narrow bands of wavelength. The first is centered on one of the sodium D-lines, which gives the magnitude of total emission from the gas and the particles; the second, chosen at a wavelength where emission of atomic sodium is not observed, yields the magnitude of particle emission alone. Simultaneously, the transmitted continuum from a tungsten ribbon-filament lamp yields absorptivities of the flame at both wavelengths. After corrected for mutual absorption, the static temperature of the gas and the temperature of the particles were determined—with the assumption that the effects of radiation and scattering are negligible and that the system is one-dimensional.

Carlson [C4] used a rocket motor of 1000-lb thrust and 400 psia chamber

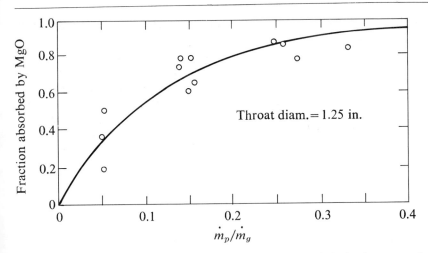

Figure 7.17 Absorptivity of rocket exhaust due to presence of MgO cloud; measured at
5911 Å [C3].

pressure, burning a slurry of MgO particles suspended in RP-1 fuel, using
gaseous oxygen as oxidizer. Sodium atoms for spectral measurement were
provided by salt with measurement optical area ratio of 5. The absorptivity
of the product is given in Fig. 7.17; gas and particle temperatures were as
shown in Fig. 7.18. Measurement of velocity lag further gives distribution
in particle size as shown in Fig. 7.19.

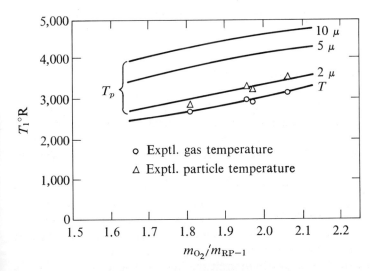

Figure 7.18 Experimental and theoretical gas and particle temperature at mass-flow ratio
of particle to gas of 0.275 [C4].

Radiation effects in rockets were studied by Joerg and McFarland [J11] without specific consideration of particles.

Measurement of individual particle velocities in a simulated rocket exhaust were made by Fulmer and Wirtz [F38]. They used a double-pulsed explosive-krypton light source to provide intense and precisely controlled light pulses. The particle images were recorded on a film as pairs of streaks. Helium stream at 2900 fps carried aluminum powder of 3 μ to 50 μ size at velocities up to 2600 fps. Accuracy of measurement was 1.5 to 3.2 per cent.

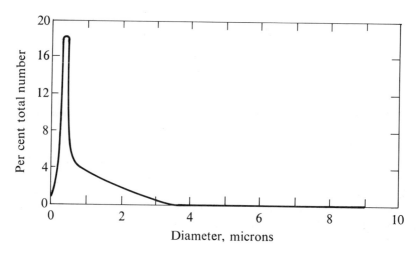

Figure 7.19 Distribution of MgO particle sizes in velocity tests [C4].

7.5 Nozzle Flow with Distribution in Particle Size

The above sections show that with the amount of effort engaged in the study of nozzle flow of a gas-solid suspension, still the contribution of particle-size distribution remains to be determined. Brown and McArty [B63] reported alumina particles collected from rocket engines are essentially spheres with mean particle size nearly 1 μ diameter; the mean particle mass corresponds to between 2 and 3 μ in diameter. There is limited evidence that the condensed particles in the rocket chamber are appreciably smaller than those obtained beyond the nozzle exit, implying condensation or agglomeration in the rocket nozzle. A theoretical model for predicting alumina particle size distributions in rocket exhausts was proposed by Fein [F8].

For given particle size distribution at the inlet, the general case of given area distribution of a nozzle requires solution of the basic equations as a self-consistent problem with particles of different sizes at different velocities and at different temperatures at an axial location along the nozzle.

Applying the multiphase concept [S60] to one-dimensional motion, the basic equations for adiabatic $(D^* = B_w^* = 0)$ flow without wall friction $(C_f = 0)$ and radiation effects $(\epsilon_p = 0)$, and for low number density of particles $(F^{(sr)} = 0, G^{(sr)} = 0)$ and negligible volume occupied by the particles $(\rho = \bar{\rho} = P/\bar{R}T)$, now become, in dimensionless form:

$$A^* u^* P^* = T^* \tag{7.64}$$

$$u_p^{*(s)} \frac{du_p^{*(s)}}{dx^*} = E^{*(s)}(u^* - u_p^{*(s)}) \tag{7.65}$$

$$u_p^{*(s)} \frac{dT_p^{*(s)}}{dx^*} = B^{*(s)}(T^* - T_p^{*(s)}) \tag{7.66}$$

$$\frac{dP^*}{P^*} + \frac{2c}{\bar{R}} \frac{u^*}{T^*} du^* + \frac{2c}{RT^*} \sum_{(s)} \dot{m}_p^{*(s)} du_p^{*(s)} = 0 \tag{7.67}$$

$$T^* + u^{*2} + \frac{c_p}{c} \sum_{(s)} \dot{m}_p^{*(s)} T_p^{*(s)} + \sum_{(s)} \dot{m}_p^{*(s)} u_p^{*(s)2} = \frac{c + \dot{m}_p^* c_p}{c}, \tag{7.68}$$

where

$$E^{*(s)} = \frac{F^{(s)} L}{U_o} \tag{7.69}$$

$$B^{*(s)} = \frac{G^{(s)} L}{U_o}. \tag{7.70}$$

Due to smaller lag of smaller particles than that of larger particles, we expect that distribution in particle concentration at any given axial location will differ from static concentration, or, if a distribution is given at static condition

$$\dot{m}_p^{*(s)} = \frac{\rho_p^{(s)} u_p^{(s)}}{\rho u} = \frac{\rho_p}{\rho}\bigg|_{u, u_p = 0} = \dot{m}_p^* f_M \, \Delta a, \tag{7.71}$$

where f_M is the fraction mass distribution over a range of radius a. Further:

$$\sum_{(s)} \dot{m}_p^{*(s)} = \dot{m}_p^* = \int f_M \, da. \tag{7.72}$$

To obtain a solution in analytical form for our discussions, it is seen that in spite of the complexity of the above equation, a solution exists for the case with given

$$u^* = \alpha x^*. \tag{7.73}$$

This leads to

$$u_p^{*(s)} = \beta^{(s)} x^*, \tag{7.74}$$

where

$$\beta^{(s)} = \tfrac{1}{2}\sqrt{E^{*(s)2} + 4E^{*(s)}\alpha} - E^{*(s)}. \tag{7.75}$$

It is seen that Eqs. (7.66) and (7.68) are self-consistent. This general complexity is avoided because Eq. (7.68) is satisfied by a relation analogous to Eq. (7.42), or,

$$T^* = 1 - \alpha^2 x^{*2}\left(\frac{c}{c_e}\right). \tag{7.76}$$

Substitution of Eq. (7.76) into (7.66) and integrating gives

$$T_p^{*(s)} = 1 - \frac{B^{*(s)}}{\beta}\frac{c}{c_e}\alpha^2\frac{x^{*2}}{\dfrac{B^{*(s)}}{\beta} + 2}. \tag{7.77}$$

Substitution of Eqs. (7.76) and (7.77) in Eq. (7.68) gives:

$$-\frac{c}{c_e} + 1 - \left(\frac{c_p}{c}\right)\left(\frac{c}{c_e}\right)\sum_{(s)}\dot{m}_p^{*(s)}\frac{\dfrac{B^{*(s)}}{\beta^{(s)}}}{\dfrac{B^{*(s)}}{\beta^{(s)}} + 2} + \sum_{(s)}\dot{m}_p^{*(s)}\frac{\beta^{(s)2}}{\alpha^2} = 0. \tag{7.78}$$

Equation (7.78) reverts to Eq. (7.43) for $s = 1$. These two summations can be evaluated by integration for given f_M from Eq. (7.71)

$$\sum_{(s)}\dot{m}_p^{*(s)}\frac{\dfrac{B^{*(s)}}{\beta^{(s)}}}{\dfrac{B^{*(s)}}{\beta^{(s)}} + 2} = \dot{m}_p^*\int f_M\left[1 + 2\left(\frac{\beta^{(s)}}{B^{*(s)}}\right)\right]^{-1} da$$

$$\sum_{(s)}\frac{\dot{m}_p^{*(s)}\beta^{(s)2}}{\alpha^2} = \frac{\dot{m}_p^*}{\alpha^2}\int f_M\beta^{(s)2}\, da.$$

For small particles,

$$F^{(s)} \sim \frac{9\bar{\mu}}{2a_s^2\bar{\rho}_p}$$

$$G^{(s)} \sim \frac{3\bar{\kappa}}{c_p\bar{\rho}_p a_s^2}.$$

It is readily shown that

$$\left[1 + 2\left(\frac{\beta^{(s)}}{B^{*(s)}}\right)\right] = (1 - \tfrac{3}{2}N'_{\text{Pr}}) + \tfrac{3}{2}N'_{\text{Pr}}\left(1 + 4N'_{\text{Re}}\frac{a^2}{a_o^2}\right)^{1/2}, \qquad (7.79)$$

and

$$\frac{\beta^{(s)}}{\alpha} = \frac{1}{2}\left(\frac{a}{a_o}\right)^{-2} N'^{-1}_{\text{Re}}\left[\left(1 + 4N'_{\text{Re}}\frac{a^2}{a_o^2}\right)^{1/2} - 1\right], \qquad (7.80)$$

where

$$N'_{\text{Pr}} = \frac{c\bar{\mu}}{\bar{\kappa}}\frac{c_p}{c}$$

$$N'_{\text{Re}} = \frac{2}{9}\frac{\alpha U_o \bar{\rho} L}{\bar{\mu}}\frac{\bar{p}_p}{\rho}\left(\frac{a_o}{L}\right)^2.$$

For f_M following normal distribution, and for small mean deviation $(\Delta a/a_o)$, Eq. (1.13) gives

$$f_M = \frac{1}{\sqrt{\pi}\, a_o}\left[\frac{3}{2} + \left(\frac{a_o}{\sqrt{2}\,\Delta a}\right)^2\right]^{-1}\frac{a^3}{(\sqrt{2}\,\Delta a)^3}\exp\left[-\frac{(a - a_o)^2}{2(\Delta a)^2}\right]. \qquad (7.81)$$

The above integrals can be evaluated, with the following approximation for small particle lag:

$$\left[1 + 2\left(\frac{\beta^{(s)}}{B^{*(s)}}\right)\right]^{-1} \cong 1 - 3N'_{\text{Pr}}N'_{\text{Re}}\left(\frac{a^2}{a_o^2}\right) - \cdots$$

$$\frac{\beta^{(s)2}}{\alpha^2} \cong \left[1 - N'_{\text{Re}}\left(\frac{a^2}{a_o^2}\right)\right]^2$$

$$\sim 1 - 2N'_{\text{Re}}\left(\frac{a^2}{a_o^2}\right).$$

The above integrals give, for

$$\frac{c}{c_e} \cong \frac{1 + \dot{m}_p^*(1 - 2N'_{\text{Re}}g)}{1 + \dfrac{c_p}{c}\dot{m}_p^*(1 - 3N'_{\text{Pr}}N'_{\text{Re}}g)}, \qquad (7.82)$$

where

$$g\left(\frac{\sqrt{2}\,\Delta a}{a_o}\right) = \frac{1 + 5\left(\dfrac{\sqrt{2}\,\Delta a}{a_o}\right)^2 + \dfrac{15}{4}\left(\dfrac{\sqrt{2}\,\Delta a}{a_o}\right)^4}{1 + \dfrac{3}{2}\left(\dfrac{\sqrt{2}\,\Delta a}{a_o}\right)^2}$$

$$\sim 1 + \frac{7}{2}\left(\frac{\sqrt{2}\,\Delta a}{a_o}\right)^2 - \frac{3}{2}\left(\frac{\sqrt{2}\,\Delta a}{a_o}\right)^4, \qquad (7.83)$$

(Fig. 7.20), showing the primary effect of particle size distribution on the gas dynamics of a suspension. The above relations are valid for small N'_{Re} and small mean deviation. $g(0) = 1$ gives the value of c/c_e for uniform particle size distribution. For the previous example of air-magnesia suspension, c/c_e decreases slightly for increased mean deviation and increased value of N'_{Re}.

Further, since $[1 + 2\beta^{(s)}/B^{*(s)}]^{-1} \sim [1 - 3N'_{\mathrm{Re}}N'_{\mathrm{Pr}}(a^2/a_o^2)]$ is larger for smaller a, $T_p^{(s)}$ for smaller particles follows the stream temperature T more closely than larger a.

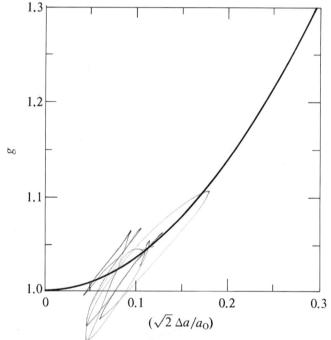

Figure 7.20 Effect of particle-size distribution given in Eq. (7.83).

The integral pertaining to pressure drop in adiabatic flow is

$$\dot{m}_p^* \int_{-\infty}^{\infty} \frac{\beta^{(s)}}{\alpha} f_M \, da \sim 1 - N'_{\mathrm{Re}} g. \qquad (7.84)$$

The pressure variation is given by

$$P^* \cong \left[1 - \alpha^2 x^{*2} \left(\frac{c}{c_e} \right) \right]^{c_e/\bar{R}[1 + \dot{m}_p^*(1 - N'_{\mathrm{Re}} g)]}, \qquad (7.85)$$

which indicates that for the same α, the pressure drop from inlet to a given x^* is smaller for larger mean deviation. This again conforms with the fact that smaller particles behave more like a gas than do the larger particles. For similar weight fraction, greater number of smaller particles are available than larger particles.

For given area distribution $A^*(x^*)$ and given continuum distribution of particle size, Eqs. (7.67) and (7.68) take the form

$$\frac{dP^*}{P^*} + \frac{2cu^*}{RT^*}\,du^* + \frac{2c}{RT^*}\,\dot{m}_p^*\left[\int_{a_1}^{a_2} f_M \frac{du_p^*}{dx^*}\,da\right]dx^* = 0 \qquad (7.86)$$

$$T^* + u^{*2} + \frac{c_p}{c}\,\dot{m}_p^*\int_{a_1}^{a_2} f_M T_p^*\,da + \dot{m}_p^*\int_{a_1}^{a_2} f_M u_p^{*2}\,da = \frac{c + \dot{m}_p^* c_p}{c}, \qquad (7.87)$$

together with Eqs. (7.64), (7.65), and (7.66), with superscript (s) dropped from the latter two equations. Simultaneous solution of these equations for given A^* remains challenging.

7.6 Gas-Liquid System and Condensation

Tangren, Dodge, and Seifert [T4] investigated a gas-water system for the possibility of applying it to the propulsion of underwater devices in which a gas is injected into the water, the working fluid. It was assumed in the analysis that the gas and liquid have the same temperature. The only property of the gas that enters into the analysis is the volume ratio. In the analysis of a gas-in-water system the volume ratio is a more significant parameter than the mass ratio which is used in the analysis of the gas-solid suspensions. A modified γ approach was used to correct for the addition of gas in the water.

The velocity of sound in the gas-in-water system is of considerable interest because when a relatively small amount of gas is introduced into the water the velocity of sound of the mixture is considerably reduced from that of pure water. It was correctly assumed in the analysis that a pressure pulse is transmitted through the mixture with a definite sonic velocity. However, it was incorrectly implied that the bulk velocity at the throat is equal to this sonic velocity and the Mach number is therefore unity at the throat of the nozzle. The velocity of sound of the mixture is much lower when compared with that in either the gas or the liquid. This was attributed to the fact that the gas acts as a weak spring when coupled with a large mass, the liquid.

In comparing the experiment with the theory, errors of from three to thirteen per cent were noted in the pressure ratio at the throat for various stagnation pressures and various volume ratios. The discrepancy between theory and experiment for the pressure ratio and the large discrepancy in the case of the velocity of sound of the mixture are largely due to the fact that in the former heat or momentum transfer between the gas bubbles and the water was not taken into account.

Netzer [N4] analyzed two-phase flow consisting of water droplets in a gas stream expanding through an angular converging-diverging nozzle. The momentum transfer between the two phases which was considered is calculated by methods similar to those in Sec. 7.2. The flow rate of the liquid was quite large, being approximately ten times the flow rate of the gas by weight. In order to avoid calculation of the heat transferred from the liquid droplets to the gas, two limiting cases of heat transfer between the phases were considered. The first case was thermal equilibrium between the phases in which the temperature of the liquid was assumed to be at the same temperature as the surrounding gas. In the second case it was assumed that the temperature of the liquid remained unchanged from its stagnation temperature. These two cases are similar to those investigated by Altman and Curtis [A9] for the gas-solid suspension, except that the momentum transfer between the liquid droplets and the gas was not neglected. It was pointed out that experimental work shows the heat transfer between the phases is closer to that of thermal equilibrium than to that of no heat transfer between the phases. The case of a heat-transfer coefficient lying between the two limiting cases would be a better solution. The velocity of sound or Mach number in the mixture was not discussed. Some detail was given on the method and nature of the numerical solution. Only a first-order method of solving the equations was used. The consideration of a singularity at or near the throat, which is a possibility in a problem of this nature, was not discussed.

Erickson [E20] in his study of the aerothermopressor, treated the singularity at the throat of a converging-diverging nozzle of the aerothermopressor. The singularity arises from the $1 - N_M^2$ terms in the denominator of expressions when the Mach number is equal to one at the throat of the nozzle. The Mach number was defined based on the properties of the gas only. The singularity was passed by holding dN_M/dZ constant until the Mach number crossed unity. (N_M is the Mach number and Z is the longitudinal distance from the inlet plane.) A method of iteration was used to determine the value of the Mach number at the inlet plane. For various initial Mach numbers the Mach numbers at the throat were found. The resulting values were interpolated for a throat Mach number of 1. The process approached the second boundary rapidly. It is important to note the assumption that the Mach number based on the gas properties was equal to the one at the throat of the nozzle introduced inaccuracy.

Studies on condensation in supersonic nozzles were made due to interests in nucleation in condensation and problems of condensation shock. Binnie and Green [B37] studied condensation of steam, Willmarth and Nagamatsu [W28] and Faro, Small, and Hill [F6] studied that of nitrogen; Wegener [W9] studied condensation from humidified air in supersonic nozzles. Duff and Hill [D38] studied the case of condensation of carbon dioxide.

The use of a supersonic nozzle makes possible experimental investigation of homogeneous nucleation and condensation because it allows a maximum relaxation rate in the simplest possible manner compared to other methods of sudden expansion. Static pressure measurements along the nozzle serve as a sensitive indicator of heat released by condensation [K37]. Duff [D38] further measured gas density by interferometry.

Duff developed the drop growth equations from consideration of incident and evaporating molecules due to Stodola [S90] and Oswatitsch [O8], and temperature, mass, and energy equations. The nucleation rate equation for condensation from supersaturated vapor was given by Frenkel [F22]:

$$\Gamma = \left(\frac{P}{kT}\right)^2 \frac{m}{\bar{\rho}} \sqrt{\frac{2\sigma}{\pi m}} \exp\left[-\frac{4\pi\sigma r^{*2}}{3kT}\right], \tag{7.88}$$

where Γ is the nucleation rate in nuclei/ft^3 sec, σ the surface tension of the drop, $\bar{\rho}$ the density of the vapor, r^* the Kelvin-Helmholtz initial radius at which a liquid is at equilibrium with its vapor, and m the molecular mass. The drop temperature is given by, for N_g complexes consisting of g simple molecules of similar structure, and $\xi = (N_g)^{1/g}$,

$$\frac{\xi}{2\bar{R}T}[U_{fg} + \tfrac{1}{2}\bar{R}T_p]\left[1 - \frac{P_\infty}{P}\exp\left(\frac{2\sigma}{\bar{\rho}\bar{R}T_p}\right)\left(\frac{T}{T_p}\right)^{\frac{1}{2}}\right] = \frac{T_p}{T} - 1, \tag{7.89}$$

where U_{fg} is the potential energy in the absence of rotation and vibration, T_p is the droplet temperature, P_∞ is the flat surface vapor pressure; this equation gives the droplet temperature T_p. The rate of drop growth is given by:

$$\frac{dr}{dt} = \frac{2P}{\bar{\rho}\sqrt{2\pi\bar{R}T}}\left[\frac{\bar{R}T_p - \bar{R}T}{U_{fg} + \tfrac{1}{2}\bar{R}T_p}\right]. \tag{7.90}$$

The gas dynamic relations are now†

$$\frac{dP}{dx} = P\frac{\gamma(N_M)^2}{(N_M)^2 - 1}\left[\left(\frac{h_{fg}}{cT} - \frac{1}{1 + m_p^*}\right)\frac{dm_p^*}{dx} - \frac{1}{A}\frac{dA}{dx}\right], \tag{7.91}$$

where (N_M) is the Mach number of the vapor phase, h_{fg} is the latent heat, c is the specific heat at constant pressure of the vapor, m_p^* is the mass fraction of liquid; the velocity u is given by

$$\frac{1}{u}\frac{du}{dx} = -\left(\frac{1}{\gamma(N_M)^2}\right)\left(\frac{1}{P}\frac{dP}{dx}\right), \tag{7.92}$$

† Note that

$$\dot{m} = A(\rho u + \rho_p u_p) = A\bar{\rho}(u + m_p^* u_p)\left(1 + \frac{\bar{\rho}}{\bar{\rho}_p} m_p^*\right) \sim A\bar{\rho}u(1 + m_p^*)$$

for $u \sim u_p$, $\bar{\rho}_p \gg \bar{\rho}$.

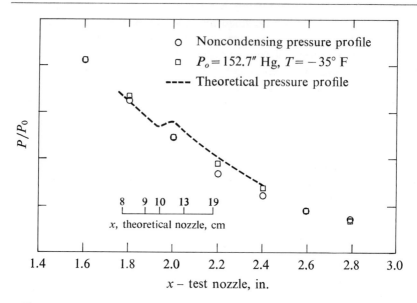

Figure 7.21 Comparison of experimental results to theoretical pressure profile [D38].

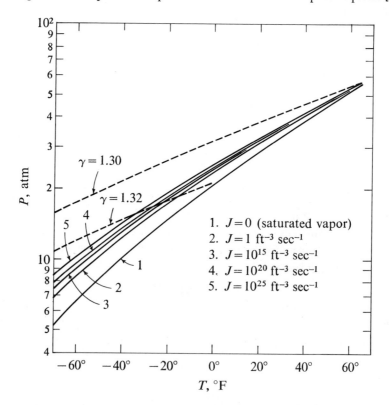

Figure 7.22 Predicted nucleation rates for CO_2 [D38].

with the contribution of droplets neglected, and

$$\frac{dT}{dx} = T\left(\frac{\gamma - 1}{\gamma}\right)\frac{1}{P}\frac{dP}{dx} + \frac{h_{fg}}{c}\frac{dm_p^*}{dx}, \tag{7.93}$$

change in m_p^* is given by Eqs. (7.88) and (7.90).

A comparison of theoretical and measured pressure profile is shown in Fig. 7.21 showing the occurrence of condensation shock. The predicted nucleation rate is given in Fig. 7.22 showing that greater supersaturation is required at lower temperatures to obtain a given nucleation rate. The supersaturation ratios steadily increase prior to the occurrence of rapid condensation.

Expansion of steam near saturation through a convergent-divergent nozzle and orifices was studied by Bottomley [B49], Hodkinson [H48], Silver and Mitchell [S33], Linning [L46]; Isbin, Moy, and Da Cruz [I9]; Isbin and Gavalas [I8]. In general, the phenomena include annular flow, bubble flow, slug flow, frothing flow, and flow of liquid droplet in vapor, as identified in gas-liquid pipe flow (Sec. 3.7). The simplest, but unrealistic, computation

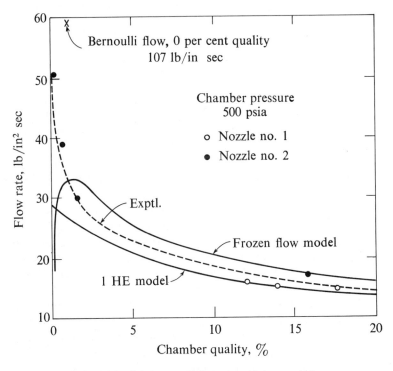

Figure 7.23 Comparison of experimental flow rate with isentropic-homogeneous expansion (IHE) and frozen-flow models [S84].

assumes isentropic-homogeneous expansion. Another method for approximation utilizes a frozen flow model—that is, with no heat or mass transfer between the phases (constant steam quality). A comparison of these methods was given by Starkman, Schrock, Neusen, and Maneely [S84] as shown in Fig. 7.23. It was also shown that shock due to two-phase overexpansion is much weaker than shock in a gas.

Edelman and Rosenbaum [E3] studied the finite rate evaporation of a cryogenic propellant in a binary two-phase mixture of hydrogen and air. Time-history calculations were performed for a variety of initial states.

Detailed analysis including particle-size distribution, particle velocity lag, etc., should follow the method in Sec. 6.9.

7.7 Effects of Chemical Reaction and Radiation

The above methods of computations and experimental evaluations of rockets are, of course, idealized. When metals or their compounds are used in fuels or propellants in a rocket, condensation of certain combustion products may occur during adiabatic expansion. Heat will be released and the number of moles of gas will decrease. Equilibrium conditions will not be maintained due to high flow rate. To predict various losses in addition to velocity and thermal lag requires knowledge of the rate of nucleation, condensation (Sec. 3.2), and reaction (Sec. 3.3). These rates, however, are not generally known for substances and conditions in rockets. This is the major difficulty of comparing predicted and actual performances of rockets.

Reaction rate including a particulate phase was discussed before (Chap. 3). However, studies in nozzle expansion of a reacting medium have only been made on a clean gas [O4], or two-phase expansion such as combustion products of boron-containing fuel with phase equilibrium as presented by Tower [T46]. Extension of the case of reaction including phases is a clear possibility.

To account for the effects of heat transfer in nozzle flow of clean exhaust gases, a simplified method of estimating convection heat transfer was presented by Bartz [B20]; a study of local fluxes was given by Welsh and Witte [W11]. An analytical method of computing configuration factor for radiant heat transfer in a conical nozzle was given by Joerg and McFarland [J11]; a numerical method was developed by Robbins [R23]. These methods have to be modified with considerations in previous chapters when applied to a nozzle with multiphase exhaust.

Combustion in liquid propellant system is also influenced by the relative motion of the fuel droplet and gas. Analytical studies were made by Probert [P30], Spalding [S74], and Williams, Penner, Gill, and Eckel [W26]. Vaporization was treated as rate control process.

Hershkowitz [H34] studied the propagation of combustion front in a pyrotechnic mixture; the mixture consists of two components in granular form (nearly 15 μ diameter): a light metal, such as aluminum or magnesium, and an oxidizer, such as potassium perchlorate.

Combustion and detonation of fuel sprays were studied by Williams [W24, W25].

7.8 Shock Waves in Dusty Gas

The nature of passage of a dusty gas through a shock wave is interesting to the determination of losses due to overexpansion of a suspension in a nozzle, and to the determination of strength of a nuclear blast, and as a possibility of determining drag coefficient of dust particles (Sec. 2.1). Studies were made by Hoenig [H49], Carrier [C7], Soo [S50], Rudinger [R49], and Kriebel [K39]. The present discussion is based on the comprehensive study by Kriebel using a method suggested by Carrier [C7].

For standing shock wave, similar sets of basic equations as in one-dimensional nozzle flow with distribution in particle size apply to normal shock except that the continuity equation is replaced by

$$(\rho_1 + \rho_{p1})u_1 = (\rho_\infty + \rho_{p\infty})u_\infty , \qquad (7.94)$$

for the upstream of shock at condition 1 and far downstream when equilibrium is again reached at condition with subscript ∞. The large-particle Reynolds-number effect was accounted for in the time constants for momentum and heat transfer to particles. Typical results of machine computation are shown in Fig. 7.24 for upstream Mach number of 2.0 and mass-flow ratio of particle to gas of 0.4, mean particle radius of 1.5 μ, $c = 0.60$ Btu/lb °R, $c_p = 0.34$ Btu/lb °R, $\bar{\kappa} = 0.158$ Btu/ft hr °R. $\bar{\mu} = 4.3 \times 10^{-5}$ lb/ft sec, $\bar{\rho}_p = 240$ lb/ft³, for distribution in particle sizes represented by a/a_m of $\frac{1}{3}$, 1, and $\frac{5}{3}$ (subscripts 1, 2, 3 in Fig. 7.24). Figure 7.24 shows the nature of relaxation of particles after traversing through the shock front. Realistic modifications of these results should include the forces on the particles due to pressure gradient (Sec. 2.3) and the irreversibility in the conversion of kinetic energy of particles to static pressure [S56]; a reduced pressure rise in shock is expected.

Kriebel [K39] also considered oblique shock problems and the application of a method of characteristics. These aspects were also treated by Rudinger and Chang [R51] and Kliegel [K21]. Chu and Chow [C27] attempted to formulate the system based on free paths of particles in reference to those of other interactions.

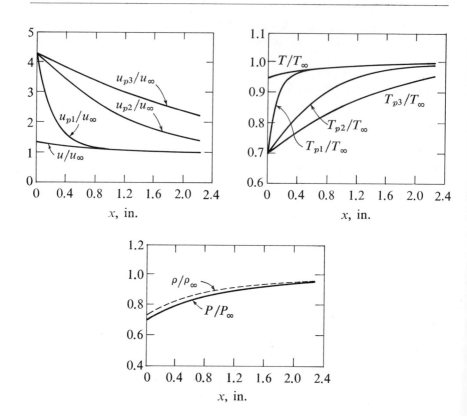

Figure 7.24 Typical shock structure of dusty gas [K39].

SUMMARY OF BASIC CONCEPTS

Apparent Thermodynamic Properties—Tangren (1949) [T4], (1961) [S50, S58]

Throat Condition in Adiabatic Nozzle Flow—(1962) [S58]

Shock Waves in Dusty Gas—Carrier (1958) [C7]

Hydrodynamics of a Suspension

8

In previous chapters we have accounted for the basic aspects of multiphase systems through the steps of recognition of the basic phenomena, development of instrumentations, and mathematical representations of physical concepts. We have just seen some of the methods of solution in the case of one-dimensional motion. Now we want to take up the more general case of two- and three-dimensional flow based on the qualified continuum approximations. These are, of course, the stages along which the mechanics of single-phase fluid has progressed to the present level.

We are concerned with motion and accumulation of particles in a hydrodynamic flow field, and the interaction of a suspension with a boundary. This scope encompasses phenomena in dust collectors, ejector scrubbers, spray evaporation, ablation, fluidized beds, and boiling. Although at the present time we can only look into a few simplest nontrivial solutions, we shall take up at first cases where rigorous computations can be made— namely, potential and laminar motions—and then extend to other situations where semiempirical methods will be introduced. An important aspect treated in this chapter is the basis of similar solutions of fluid mechanics of suspensions.

8.1 Vortex Motion

First, we consider cases in which viscosity at the solid boundary of the system is neglected, but retaining the viscous interaction between the phases. Solutions on trajectories of particles flowing over an obstacle (Sec. 5.2) belong to this category. Other calculations of particle trajectories were made by Shepherd and Lapple [S28] and ter Linden [T17] on motion of solid particles in a swirling flow field of a cyclone dust separator. All made the assumption that solid particles have acquired fluid velocity when the mixture is injected tangentially at the top of the collector. Uematu, Munekazi, and Fuzisawa [U2] treated the system for any tangential fluid-velocity distribution, but neglected tangential accelerations on the particle. Kriebel [K38] treated the problem as one of solid-body flow without axial-velocity component. Hirschkron and Ehrich [H45] accounted for the case of fluid in free vortex motion and uniform axial-flow velocity of both phases but omitted variations of tangential and radial velocities of particles in the axial direction. Since all computed particle trajectories only, Lagrangian coordinate system was used, which itself is a unique case in fluid mechanics. All these studies do not include density distribution and collection rate.

   Particle Trajectories in Swirling Flow—In the Lagrangian frame of reference, Eq. (6.41) becomes

$$\frac{du_p}{dt} - \frac{v_p^2}{r} = F(u - u_p) \tag{8.1}$$

$$\frac{dv_p}{dt} + \frac{u_p v_p}{r} = F(v - v_p) \tag{8.2}$$

$$\frac{dw_p}{dt} = F(w - w_p), \tag{8.3}$$

where t is the time, u, v, w, and u_p, v_p, w_p are the components of velocity in the radial (r), tangential (θ), and axial (z) directions. With the fluid-flow field given to be in concentric cylinders such that

$$u = 0, \quad w = w_0, \quad \text{and} \quad v = \frac{C}{r}$$

(the last specifies free vortex motion with vorticity C). For particle position given by r, θ, and z,

$$u_p = \frac{dr}{dt}.$$

Equations (8.1) to (8.3) become

$$\frac{d^2 r}{dt^2} - \frac{v_p^2}{r} = -F \frac{dr}{dt} \tag{8.4}$$

$$\frac{dr v_p}{dt} + F r v_p = FC \tag{8.5}$$

$$\frac{dw_p}{dt} + F w_p = F w_0. \tag{8.6}$$

If the inlet condition at z_0 for particles is

$$u_p = u_{p0}, \quad v_p(r_0) = v_{p0}, \quad \text{and} \quad w_p = w_{p0} . \tag{8.7}$$

Equations (8.4) to (8.6) now integrate to give

$$v_p = \frac{C}{r} + \frac{r_0 v_{p0} - C}{r} e^{-Ft} = r \frac{d\theta}{dt} \tag{8.8}$$

$$w_p = w_0 + (w_{p0} - w_0)e^{-Ft} = \frac{dz}{dt} , \tag{8.9}$$

with u_p given by

$$\frac{d^2 r}{dt^2} + F \frac{dr}{dt} - \frac{[(r_0 v_{p0} - C)e^{-Ft} + C]^2}{r^3} = 0, \tag{8.10}$$

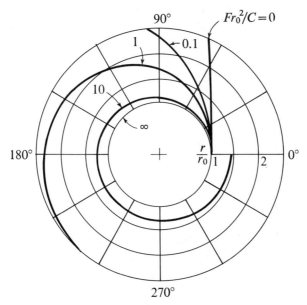

Figure 8.1 Spiral path, zero deviation of injection velocity.

as given by Hirschkron and Ehrich [H45]. Equation (8.9) is readily integrated to give $z(t)$, but Eqs. (8.8) and (8.10), being nonlinear, have to be integrated numerically.

For the case $v_{p0} = v_0$, $w_{p0} = w_0$

$$v_p = \frac{C}{r} , \quad w_p = w_0. \tag{8.11}$$

Some simplification is feasible and the dimensionless time coordinate is $t^* = tC^2/r_0^2$, and radial coordinate $r^* = r/r_0$; the drag effect is generalized in terms of the drag parameter: Fr_0^2/C. Figure 8.1 gives the particle paths in a z-plane and the time trace at various radii r/r_0. Solution was also given for the case with $v_p = 0$ at the inlet. It is seen that when applied to the case where the fluid is turbulent, solution in the Lagrangian system of coordinates calls for solution of Eq. (2.37). Even so, the individual particle path and streamline of particle cloud is not directly known. However, solution in the Eulerian system would, in general, eliminate the need for determining individual particle path. This is illustrated next.

Collection and Distribution of Particles in Vortex Motion—In order to determine the distribution of particles, and, conceptually, to account for cases where random motion of particles exists, the following solution is proposed. With the above simplifications in the Eulerian system of coordinates, we have, from Eqs. (6.32) and (6.41):

$$\frac{\partial r \rho_p u_p}{\partial r} + \frac{\partial r \rho_p w_0}{\partial z} = 0, \tag{8.12}$$

and

$$u_p \frac{\partial u_p}{\partial r} + w_0 \frac{\partial u_p}{\partial z} - \frac{v_p^2}{r} = -F u_p, \tag{8.13}$$

while the momentum equations in the θ and z directions vanish, and F may account for turbulence.

These are first-order differential equations and solution is feasible for given conditions at z_0, together with the above conditions.

Introducing stream function ψ_p for the particle phase such that

$$r \rho_p w_0 = \left(\frac{\partial \psi_p}{\partial r}\right)_z, \quad r \rho_p u_p = -\left(\frac{\partial \psi_p}{\partial z}\right)_r, \tag{8.14}$$

which satisfies Eq. (8.12), and changing the independent variable from r and z to ψ_p and z, we get, from Eq. (8.13),

$$\left(\frac{\partial u_p}{\partial z}\right)_{\psi_p} + \frac{F}{w_0} u_p = \frac{C^2}{w_0 r^3}, \tag{8.15}$$

r is now a dependent variable. Integration gives, for $u_p = 0$ at $z = 0$, along a streamline ψ_p,

$$u_p = e^{-\frac{F}{w_0}z} \int_0^z \frac{C^2}{w_0 r^3} e^{\frac{F}{w_0}z} \, dz. \tag{8.16}$$

Also along a streamline, Eqs. (8.14) give

$$\frac{u_p}{w_0} = \frac{\left(\frac{\partial \psi_p}{\partial z}\right)_r}{\left(\frac{\partial \psi_p}{\partial r}\right)_z} = \left(\frac{\partial r}{\partial z}\right)_{\psi_p}. \tag{8.17}$$

Substitution of Eq. (8.16) and differentiating gives

$$\frac{d^2 r}{dz^2} + \frac{F}{w_0}\frac{dr}{dz} = \frac{C^2}{w_0^2 r^3},\tag{8.18}$$

whose solution is also given by Fig. 8.2, with $z^* = (z/w_0)(C/r_0^2)$, and

$$\frac{d^2 r^*}{dz^{*2}} + \frac{Fr_1^2}{C}\frac{dr^*}{dz^*} = \frac{1}{r^{*3}}.\tag{8.19}$$

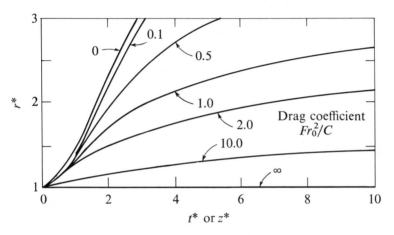

Figure 8.2 Displacement at zero deviation of injection velocity.

The usefulness of this solution is seen in Fig. 8.3a for the case of a uniform inlet mixture with $Fr_1^2/C = 10$ for the streamline starting at $r = r_1$, $r^+ = r/r_1 = r^*$, and $\psi_p^* = r^2\rho_{p0}w_0/r_1^2\rho_{p0}w_0$ at $z^* = 0$. For other streamlines starting at r_1', $r^+ = (r_1'/r_1)r^*$, $z^+ = z^*(r_1'/r_1)^2$, $Fr_1'^2/C = [Fr_1^2/C](r_1'/r_1)^2$. The dashed parts of streamlines indicate particles colliding with the wall. If the particles hitting the wall do not become reentrained, the rate of collection is now obtained as shown in Fig. 8.3b, or, the flux of particles hitting the wall is given by

$$2\pi\psi_p = 2\pi r_1 \int_0^z \rho_p u_p\, dz,\tag{8.20}$$

that is, the intercept of particle streamlines at the wall. Hughes [H64] discussed the secondary flow patterns in a cyclone separator. Schowalter and Johnstone [S16], from measurements of flow structure over a pipe with involute entry and a cyclone separator, showed that the angular velocity of the flow is nearly constant at radius less than one-half the radius of the wall. They found that the dynamic center line was shaped like a helix and the

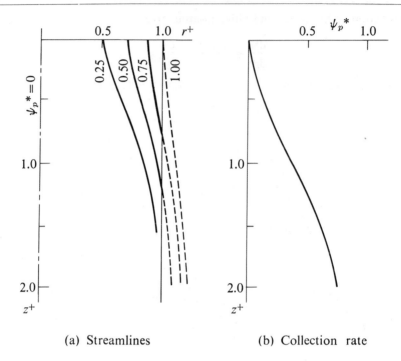

(a) Streamlines   (b) Collection rate

Figure 8.3 Flow and collection rate of particles in vortex flow ($Fr_1^2/C = 10$).

longitudinal intensity of turbulence increases sharply near the center of the
vortex tube due to abrupt decrease in mean velocity near the center. Overall
measurements on mechanical dust collectors were made recently by Gallaer
and Schindeler [G1]. Extensive details on cyclone separators were compiled
by Van der Kolk [V4] and Rietema and Verner [R20]. Cyclone separation
of liquid and solid was analyzed by Rietema [R19]; Goldberg, Watkins,
Baerke, and Chatigny [G28] studied the collection of aerosols with a rotating
drum.

8.2 Trajectories of Solid Particles in a Supersonic Flow Field

Computation of motion of solid particles in a symmetric three-dimensional
supersonic nozzle was made by Kliegel and Nickerson [K21]. They applied
the method of characteristics to regions of flow downstream of points where
the gas-phase Mach number is unity. In spite of the criticism of Hoglund
[H51] of the rough approximation in the subsonic region, it is noted that

accurate solution can be carried out in the subsonic region as in the above paragraph. Moreover, their method has the merit of being one of a few attempts toward studying supersonic gas-particle flows in more than one dimension. Using similar coordinates as in the above, without swirling flow ($v = v_p = 0$), but accounting for the gas-phase compressibility, Kliegel and Nickerson gave the complete systems of characteristics of the basic equations (obtainable from Chap. 6) as, along the gas streamlines ψ:

$$\frac{dr}{dz} = \frac{u}{w} \tag{8.21}$$

$$\bar{\rho}[w\,dw + u\,du] + dP = -F[(w - w_p)\,dz + (u - u_p)\,dr] \tag{8.22}$$

$$\frac{dP}{P} - \gamma\frac{d\bar{\rho}}{\bar{\rho}} = -F\frac{(\gamma - 1)}{Pw}[F(w - w_p)^2 + F(u - u_p)^2 - G(T - T_p)]\,dz, \tag{8.23}$$

along the gas Mach lines

$$\frac{dr}{dz} = \frac{uw \pm \bar{R}T\sqrt{(N_M)_g^2 - 1}}{w^2 - \gamma\bar{R}T} \tag{8.24}$$

$$\left(w\frac{dr}{dz} - u\right)\{(\gamma - 1)[F(w - w_p)^2 + F(u - u_p)^2 - G(T - T_p)]\,dz - w\,dP\}$$

$$+ \bar{R}T\Big\{[F(w - w_p)\,dr - F(u - u_p)\,dz]$$

$$+ \bar{\rho}\Big[u\,dw - w\,du - \frac{u}{r}(w\,dr - u\,dz)\Big] + \frac{dr}{dz}dP\Big\} = 0, \tag{8.25}$$

and along particle streamlines ψ_p

$$\frac{dr}{dz} = \frac{u_p}{w_p} \tag{8.26}$$

$$w_p\,dw_p = F(w - w_p)\,dz \tag{8.27}$$

$$u_p\,du_p = F(u - u_p)\,dr \tag{8.28}$$

$$w_p\,dT_p = G(T - T_p)\,dz. \tag{8.29}$$

For supersonic flow, the characteristics are real and the method of characteristics as given by Sauer [S6] can be applied to solve the above equations. The transonic condition near the throat was approximated by extending the method of Sauer [S6]. It is believed that accurate solution can be obtained in the light of recent findings as given in Secs. 7.2 and 7.3. Again, we have to treat the continuum approximation with the qualification: characteristics exist only for $(N_M)_g > 1$.

Other studies involving supersonic gas-particle flows are those of Kriebel [K39] on oblique shock problem, Morgenthaler [M44] on the deflection of gas-particle flow by a wedge. Studies on method of characteristics in two-phase flow were reported by Rudinger and Chang [R51], and Sauerwein and Fendell [S5].

8.3 Laminar Boundary-Layer Motion over a Flat Plate

Although most gas-solid systems encountered in practice are turbulent, the case of laminar boundary layer motion of a gas-solid suspension over a flat plate was treated [S58, S61, S62] to develop some basic understanding, via mathematical procedures, of interaction of a gas-solid suspension with a boundary. This was done for the same reason laminar boundary-layer motion of a gas was studied in spite of the fact that almost all flow machineries involve turbulent flow. We leave out the electrostatic effects (Chap. 10) for the present.

A simplest nontrivial case of two-dimensional motion of a gas-solid suspension over a flat plate consists of an incompressible gas phase with uniform solid concentration ρ_p of particles of one size in the free stream only. Based on the coordinates as shown in Fig. 8.4 (coordinate x and velocity component u along the plate, coordinate y and velocity component v normal to the plate), we have the following boundary-layer equations:

$$\frac{\partial u}{\partial x} + \frac{\partial v}{\partial y} = 0 \tag{8.30}$$

$$\frac{\partial}{\partial x}\,\rho_p u_p + \frac{\partial}{\partial y}\,\rho_p v_p = 0 \tag{8.31}$$

$$\rho u \frac{\partial u}{\partial x} + \rho v \frac{\partial u}{\partial y} = -\frac{\partial P}{\partial x} + \frac{\partial}{\partial y}\,\bar{\mu}\frac{\partial u}{\partial y} - K_m \rho_p F(u - u_p) \tag{8.32}$$

$$u_p \frac{\partial u_p}{\partial x} + v_p \frac{\partial u_p}{\partial y} = F(u - u_p). \tag{8.33}$$

Under the boundary layer assumptions, the equations of the y-component of momentum of the fluid is dropped [S13]. The equation of the y-component of momentum of the particles

$$u_p \frac{\partial v_p}{\partial x} + v_p \frac{\partial v_p}{\partial y} = F(v - v_p),$$

gives, for the present system $v_p \lesssim 0[v]$ even for large F, hence this equation is dropped, consistent with the boundary layer assumption.

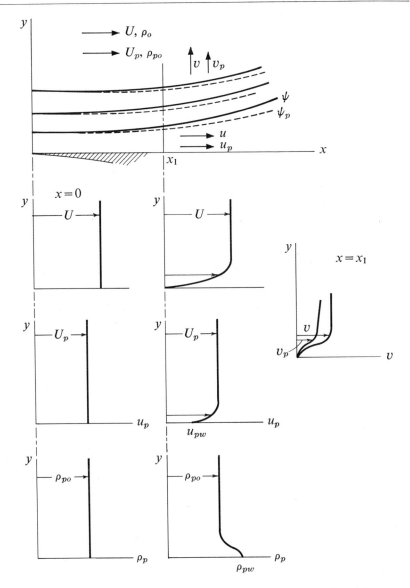

Figure 8.4 Coordinates and notations for laminar flow over a flat plate.

The energy equation is independent because we are considering the case of an incompressible gas. The formulation of general (all magnitudes of flow velocities) compressible boundary layer motion is complicated because of the functional dependence of speed of sound as given by Eq. (6.57).

Equations (8.30) to (8.33) have the following primary boundary conditions as in the case of a simple fluid:

$$y = 0, \quad u = v = 0, \\ y = \infty, \quad u = U, \quad \left.\right\} \quad (8.34a)$$

The obvious boundary conditions for the particle phase are

$$y = 0, \quad v_p = 0, \\ y = \infty, \quad u_p = U_p, \quad \rho_p = \rho_{po}. \quad \left.\right\} \quad (8.34b)$$

It is seen that for given U, U_p at $x = 0$, subsequent U_p is given by Eq. (8.33). The condition that no particle penetrates the wall is given by:

$$y = 0, \quad \left.\frac{\partial \rho_p}{\partial y}\right]_w = 0. \quad (8.34c)$$

The above conditions are no more than extensions of those of mechanics of simple phase fluids. It is noted that additional conditions must be clarified for the simplest nontrivial solution. Since there is negligible mutual collision among the particles and that the definition of laminar motion rules out collision with the wall, the particles adjacent to the wall slide along it. Detailed consideration of sliding motion of particles along the wall calls for a knowledge of dry friction. The simplest assumption is to neglect such dry friction, but consider the braking of particle motion by the fluid which is slowed down to zero velocity at the wall. Equation (8.33) gives, at the wall ($v_p = 0, u = 0$), $(\partial u_p/\partial x)_w = -F$. Integration gives

$$u_{pw} = U_p - Fx, \quad (8.35)$$

for $x \lesssim U_p/F$. At $x \gtrsim U_p/F$ deposition starts and the above equation is no longer descriptive of the problem; the latter range as well as the physical meaning of the ($\sim$) sign will be discussed in the next section. Consistent with Eq. (8.35), the last boundary condition of Eq. (8.34) is not adequate, the total flow rate is accounted for by

$$\rho_{po}U_p = \lim_{Y \to \infty} \frac{1}{Y} \int_0^Y \rho_p u_p \, dy. \quad (8.36)$$

The concentration variation along the wall still remains to be determined. Since $y = 0$, $u = 0$, hence $\partial u/\partial x]_w = 0$, and Eq. (8.30) gives $\partial v/\partial y]_w = 0$. The earlier relation $v_p \lesssim 0[v]$ thus gives $\partial v_p/\partial y]_w = 0$. Together with Eq. (8.34b) we have from Eq. (8.31) $\partial \rho_p u_p/\partial x]_w = 0$, or $\rho_p u_p]_w = \rho_{po}U_p$, or with Eq. (8.35)

$$\frac{\rho_{pw}}{\rho_{po}} = \left[1 - \left(\frac{Fx}{U_p}\right)\right]^{-1} \quad (8.37)$$

A basic feature of gas-particle flow, that is, as the particle cloud is slowed down, in the absence of transport normal to the wall, its concentration must increase.

We are interested in, from the solution of this problem, determining the velocity distributions and concentration distribution in the boundary layer. It is seen that for large F or small particles, the distance from the leading edge within which the above relations are valid might be extremely small.

It is noted that the variation of ρ_p has to be accounted for in order that the solution be nontrivial. The function $\rho_p(x,y)$ here may be regarded as a special "compressibility". Moreover, it is readily seen in Fig. 8.4 that the well-known methods such as the Howarth [H57] transformation offer no advantage because we have to account for two sets of streamlines ψ and ψ_p for the fluid and the particle cloud [S58]. Some understanding can be achieved, however, by considering an approximate solution.

Momentum-Integral Method—To develop some physical understanding of the interactions among the phases and the wall, the momentum-integral method is applied to the problem of laminar flow over a flat plate. It was noted that the boundary-layer integrals serve also as correlation functions of the interactions [S52]. With the simplification of the laminar motion, density and velocity distributions and the magnitude of boundary layers of phases can be computed.

The concept of boundary-layer thickness δ of flow of a fluid over a flat plate was discussed thoroughly by Schlichting [S13]. From considering the case of impulse motion of a flat plate it was shown that $\delta \sim \sqrt{\bar{\nu}t}$ where $\bar{\nu}$ is the kinematic viscosity. Solution of the same problem for a suspension would be quite complicated. However, the order of relative magnitude of displacement of the phase can be seen from considering the case of a solid particle starting from rest in an accelerating fluid of velocity $v = b_1 t$. For time constant F, the displacement of the particle y_p is given by

$$\frac{d^2 y_p}{dt^2} = \frac{dv_p}{dt} = F(v - v_p), \tag{8.38}$$

which gives

$$y_p = \frac{b_1 F t^3}{6} + \cdots, \tag{8.39}$$

for small Ft. Since the corresponding displacement y of the fluid is

$$y = \frac{b_1 t^2}{2}. \tag{8.40}$$

It is seen that

$$\frac{y_p}{y} \sim \frac{Ft}{3}. \tag{8.41}$$

Thus corresponding to $\delta \sim \sqrt{\bar{\nu}t}$, we have

$$\delta_p \sim \delta F t, \tag{8.42}$$

for the particle phase in the case of a suddenly accelerated plate in a suspension.

When applied to the present problem, it is readily seen that

$$\delta \sim \sqrt{\frac{\bar{\nu}x}{U}}, \tag{8.43}$$

and

$$\delta_p \sim \sqrt{\frac{\bar{\nu}x}{U}\left(\frac{Fx}{U}\right)}. \tag{8.44}$$

For the dimensionless coordinate $\eta = y/\delta$, or

$$\eta \sim y \sqrt{\frac{U}{\bar{\nu}x}}, \tag{8.45}$$

we have, denoting $x^* = Fx/U$,

$$\eta_p \sim \frac{y\sqrt{U/\bar{\nu}x}}{x^*} = \frac{\eta}{x^*}. \tag{8.46}$$

To apply the momentum-integral method, we consider the general relation and boundary conditions given by Eqs. (8.30) to (8.37). It is seen that, from Eq. (8.32), the free-stream condition is given by

$$-\left(\frac{dP}{dx}\right) = \rho_o U\left(\frac{dU}{dx}\right) + K_m F \rho_{po}(U - U_p), \tag{8.47}$$

and, from Eq. (8.33),

$$\rho_{po} U_p\left(\frac{dU_p}{dx}\right) = F\rho_{po}(U - U_p). \tag{8.48}$$

Equation (8.36) is given by particle boundary-layer thickness δ_p

$$\int_0^{\delta_p} \rho_p u_p \, dy = \rho_{po} U_p \delta_p, \tag{8.49}$$

noting that physically $\delta > \delta_p$ at $x^* < 1$ due to the inertia of the solid particles. With the transformation

$$\rho v = -\int\left(\frac{\partial}{\partial x}\right)\rho u \, dy, \qquad \rho_p v_p = -\int\left(\frac{\partial}{\partial x}\right)\rho_p u_p \, dy, \tag{8.50}$$

reduction of momentum Eqs. (8.32) and (8.33) is accomplished by introducing the displacement thicknesses δ^*, δ_p^*, and δ_{pg} as given by

$$\rho U \delta^* = \int_0^\delta \rho(U - u)\,\mathrm{d}y \qquad (8.51)$$

$$\rho_{po} U_p \delta_p^* = \int_0^{\delta_p} \rho_p(U_p - u_p)\,\mathrm{d}y, \qquad (8.52)$$

and the interaction between phases is accounted for by

$$\rho_{po} U \delta_{pg} = \int_0^\delta \rho_p(U - u)\,\mathrm{d}y, \qquad (8.53)$$

a step made simple by taking $\rho = $ constant; the momentum thicknesses θ and θ_p given by

$$\rho U^2 \theta = \int_0^\delta \rho u(U - u)\,\mathrm{d}y \qquad (8.54)$$

$$\rho_{po} U_p^2 \theta_p = \int_0^{\delta_p} \rho_p u_p(U_p - u_p)\,\mathrm{d}y. \qquad (8.55)$$

Equations (8.32) and (8.33) now take the form

$$\frac{\mathrm{d}}{\mathrm{d}x}(U^2\theta) + \delta^* U \frac{\mathrm{d}U}{\mathrm{d}x} + K_m F \frac{\rho_{po}}{\rho} U(\delta_{pg} - \delta_p^*) = \frac{\tau_o}{\rho} \qquad (8.56)$$

$$\frac{\mathrm{d}}{\mathrm{d}x}(\rho_{po} U_p^2 \theta_p) + \rho_{po} \delta_p^* U_p \frac{\mathrm{d}U_p}{\mathrm{d}x} = F\rho_{po} U(\delta_{pg} - \delta_p^*), \qquad (8.57)$$

where τ_o is the shear stress at the wall. When a dilute suspension is slowed down, $K_m = 0$.

Solution of these simultaneous equations is facilitated by introducing coordinates η and η_p instead of y, or

$$\mathrm{d}\eta = \frac{\mathrm{d}y}{\delta(x)} \qquad (8.58)$$

$$\mathrm{d}\eta_p = \left(\frac{\rho_p}{\rho_{po}}\right) \frac{\mathrm{d}y}{\delta_{p1}(x)}, \qquad (8.59)$$

where

$$\delta_{p1} = \int_0^{\delta_p} \frac{\rho_p}{\rho_{po}}\,\mathrm{d}y. \qquad (8.60)$$

Following von Kármán [S13], we set

$$\frac{u}{U} = f(\eta). \qquad (8.61)$$

Consistent extension of the above approximation leads to

$$\frac{u_p}{U_p} = (1 - x^*) + x^* g(\eta_p),$$ (8.62)

for $U_p = $ constant, according to Eq. (8.35), and setting

$$\frac{\rho_p}{\rho_{po}} = (1 - x^*)^{-1} - x^*(1 - x^*)^{-1} h(\eta_p).$$ (8.63)

Equations (8.52) and (8.55) relate the distributions of velocity and concentration of the particle phase. Equation (8.53) now gives

$$\delta_{pg} = \delta(x) \int_0^1 \frac{\rho_p}{\rho_{po}} [1 - f(\eta)] \, d\eta.$$ (8.64)

The necessary relations for the solution are complete with given shear stress at the wall, which is obtained from Eqs. (8.58) and (8.61) as

$$\tau_w(x) = \bar{\mu} \left(\frac{\partial u}{\partial y} \right)_{y=0} = \frac{\bar{\mu} U f'(\eta)}{\delta(x)},$$ (8.65)

since collision of solid particles with the wall can be neglected in laminar motion.

In the calculation of boundary-layer behavior of a single-phase fluid, various velocity distributions $f(\eta)$ have been tried and the degrees of approximation were known. The postulate of a linear velocity distribution in the boundary layer was shown to provide the simplest realistic approximation (although somewhat optimistic in its estimate of friction) [S13]. We postulate the following distributions:

$$f(\eta) = \eta$$ (8.66)

$$g(\eta_p) = \eta_p$$ (8.67)

$$h(\eta) = \eta_p^2.$$ (8.68)

For these approximations it is seen from substitution into Eq. (8.33) that, at $\eta_p \to 0$, but arbitrary values of $x^* \eta_p$,

$$\eta_p \sim \frac{2\eta}{x^*}.$$ (8.69)

We further take the simple case of $U = U_p$, and consider the case where the stream velocity distribution is unaffected by the presence of the solid particles (that is, the case of light loading and $K_m = 0$). The problem is now simplified with elimination of Eq. (8.56) and from the exact value of τ_w [S13],

$$\delta = \sqrt{12 \frac{\bar{\nu} x}{U}}.$$ (8.70)

Substitution of Eqs. (8.66) to (8.68) into Eq. (8.52), (8.53), and (8.55) gives, with Eq. (8.57) at small x^*,

$$\frac{d}{dx^*} (x^* \delta_{p1}) = \delta x^*. \tag{8.71}$$

Integration gives

$$\delta_{p1} \sim \frac{2 \sqrt{\dfrac{3\bar{\nu}}{F}} x^{*5/2}}{\frac{5}{2} x^*}$$

$$\sim \tfrac{2}{5} \delta x^*. \tag{8.72}$$

The normal component of velocities is zero for the above linear approximation. However for the given value outside the boundary layer

$$V = 0.865 U \sqrt{\frac{\bar{\nu}}{xU}}. \tag{8.73}$$

The viscous drag on the solid particles gives

$$U \frac{dV_p}{dx} = F(V - V_p), \tag{8.74}$$

leading to

$$V_p \sim 1.73 U \sqrt{\frac{\bar{\nu}}{xU} \frac{Fx}{U}} \left[1 - \frac{Fx}{U} \right]. \tag{8.75}$$

The trend of the above results is shown in Fig. 8.5, for flow over a flat plate not too far from the leading edge; that is, for $Fx/U \ll 1$. Figure 8.5 shows that as the suspension proceeds along the flat plate, the slip velocity U_{pw} of solid particles decreases, the concentration at the wall increases, the boundary-layer thickness of solid particles increases, as the solid particles develop a normal component of velocity V_p by the viscous drag of the velocity V of the fluid. $V_p < V$ even where $U = U_p$. The trend of increase in concentration of solid particles suggests the possibility of deposition of solid particles at a distance downstream from the leading edge; this is discussed in Sec. 8.4.

It is pertinent to investigate the contribution of the shear layer to particle motion. Equation (2.22) with Eq. (2.23) gives

$$\frac{dv_p}{dt} = F(v - v_p) + K \frac{\bar{u}}{m} U \left(\frac{U}{\delta} \right)^{1/2} a^2 \bar{\nu}^{-1/2},$$

where $K = 81.2$, $m = (4\pi/3)\bar{\rho}_p a^3$, the last term accounts for the effect of shear motion on particle lift. The ratio of the lift force to the drag force is, since $F(v - v_p) \sim Fv$,

$$\frac{K\bar{u}(U - U_{pw}) \left(\dfrac{U}{\delta} \right)^{1/2} a^2 \bar{\nu}^{-1/2}}{mFv} = \frac{3K}{4\pi(12)^{1/4} 0.865} \left(\frac{Ux}{\bar{\nu}} \right)^{1/4} \left(\frac{x}{a} \right) \left(\frac{\bar{\rho}}{\bar{\rho}_p} \right),$$

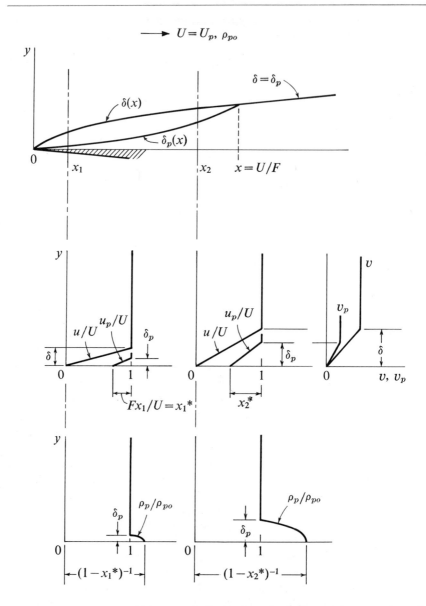

Figure 8.5 Boundary-layer thickness and distribution of velocity and concentration of laminar flow over a flat plate at $x^* < 1$.

from substitution of Eqs. (8.70)–(8.73), and $F = 9\bar{\mu}/2a^2\bar{\rho}_p$ for the Stokes' regime. In other words, in spite of large shear rate at the leading edge, it takes time for the spinning of the particle to take place so as to give rise to substantial lift force. Therefore for small a, the lift due to shear motion is negligible in comparison to that due to induced normal component of fluid velocity. At the limiting value of $x = U/F$, the above ratio is

$$\left[\frac{K}{6\pi}(0.865)2^{1/4}3^{3/4}\right]\left(\frac{Ua}{\bar{\nu}}\right)^{3/2}\left(\frac{\bar{\rho}_p}{\rho}\right)^{1/4}.$$

It is seen that although the lift force due to shear flow near the leading edge is usually small, its effect further downstream could be quite substantial. This is the extent to which the present boundary layer results should be modified.

It is also seen that the above correlation of gas-solid motion is influenced by the dimensionless quantity

$$N_m = \frac{U}{Fx} = x^* = \frac{2a^2\bar{\rho}_p U}{9\bar{\mu}x} \tag{8.76}$$

$$= \text{inertia force of solid/viscous force of gas,}$$

which we might call a "gas-solid momentum number." The magnitude of N_m affects the flow characteristics of a gas-solid suspension in addition to the gas-phase Reynolds number:

$$(N_{\text{Re}})_x = \frac{Ux}{\bar{\nu}}, \tag{8.77}$$

much as $(N_{\text{Re}})_x$ above affects the flow characteristics of a single phase fluid. The above boundary layer approximation for large N_m means that the solid particles are sufficiently large. Large F or $N_m \to 0$ means that the gas-solid suspension reverts to a gaseous mixture.

A similar study of flow of a suspension over a flat plate was made by Marble [M8], who assumed $\rho_p = \rho_{po}$ at $y = 0$, which does not satisfy the conditions given by Eqs. (8.35) and (8.37). Singleton [S38] followed basically the procedure of Marble.

Effect of Distribution in Particle Size—When applied to incompressible (gas) laminar boundary-layer motion of an uncharged suspension of spherical solid particles with distribution in size, the basic equations for steady flow over a flat plate are simplified for a dilute suspension with $F_p^{(sr)} = 0$, $K_m^{(s)} = 0$, $P = \text{constant}$, velocities $U = U_p = \text{constant}$, and $\rho_{po} = \text{constant}$ for the free stream. The above solution is readily extended by specifying x_s^* as

$$x_s^* = \frac{F^{(s)}x}{U}, \tag{8.78}$$

and clouds of different particle size s have different thicknesses $\delta_p^{(s)}$.

This suggests that the distribution of sizes of particles at the wall will be quite different from that in the free stream. For given size distribution of particle radius a, in the free stream the numbers of particles in a given volume $\mathscr{V}$ are $N^{(s)}$ and N,

$$\frac{d\left(\dfrac{N^{(s)}}{N}\right)}{da} = Af_o(a), \tag{8.79}$$

where A is a normalizing factor and $f_o(a)$ is the distribution function of radius a, or

$$1 = A \int_0^{a_m} f_o(a), \tag{8.80}$$

where a_m is the maximum radius of particles in the distribution. The density of the particle cloud in the free stream is thus

$$\rho_{po} = \mathscr{V}^{-1} \int m^{(s)} \, dN^{(s)}$$

$$= \frac{N}{\mathscr{V}} \frac{4\pi}{3} \bar\rho_p A \int_0^{a_m} a^3 f_o(a) \, da, \tag{8.81}$$

where $m^{(s)} \, dN^{(s)}/\mathscr{V} = d\rho_p^{(s)}$. From Eq. (8.63) the density at the wall is

$$\rho_{pw} = \frac{N}{\mathscr{V}} \frac{4\pi}{3} \bar\rho_p A \int_0^{a_m} a^3 f_o(a) \left[1 - x_o^* \left(\frac{a_o}{a} \right)^2 \right]^{-1} da, \tag{8.82}$$

and m_o is the madd of a particle of characteristic or mean radius a_o, $x_o = F^{(o)}x/U$, and

$$F^{(o)} = \frac{9\bar\mu}{2\bar\rho_p a_o^2}. \tag{8.83}$$

The corresponding distribution in size at the wall is

$$\frac{d\left(\dfrac{N_w^{(s)}}{N_w}\right)}{da} = A_w f_o(a) \left[1 - x_o^* \left(\frac{a_o}{a} \right)^2 \right]^{-1}, \tag{8.84}$$

namely, more small particles at the wall than in the free stream; A_w is the normalizing constant at the wall. $(F^{(o)}x/U)$ is the gas-particle momentum number $(N_m)_x$ based on dimension x and mean size a_o.

As an example, we take a distribution in particle size in the free stream as given by

$$f_o(a) = A \exp\left[-\frac{(a - a_o)^2}{(\Delta a)^2}\right], \tag{8.85}$$

where a_o is a characteristic or nearly mean particle radius, Δa is the range of size variation. For small a/a_o, or sufficiently narrow size distribution such that

$$\frac{\Delta a}{a_o} \leq 0[10^{-1}], \tag{8.86}$$

the integral

$$\int_0^{a_m} f_o(a)\, da \cong \int_{-\infty}^{\infty} f_o(a)\, da, \tag{8.87}$$

and

$$A = \frac{1}{(\Delta a)\sqrt{\pi}}, \tag{8.88}$$

or, the distribution is given by

$$\frac{d\left(\frac{N^{(s)}}{N}\right)}{d\left(\frac{a}{a_o}\right)} = \pi^{-\frac{1}{2}}\left(\frac{a_o}{\Delta a}\right)\exp\left[-\frac{(a - a_o)^2}{(\Delta a)^2}\right], \tag{8.89}$$

which gives, from Eq. (8.81),

$$\rho_{po} = \frac{N}{\mathcal{V}}\frac{4\pi}{3}\bar{\rho}_p a_o^3\left[1 + \frac{3}{2}\left(\frac{\Delta a}{a_o}\right)\right], \tag{8.90}$$

which shows the deviation in particle density if a_o is used without considering distribution in size.

The density of particles at the wall is now given by

$$\frac{\rho_{pw}}{\rho_{po}} \sim 1 + x_o^*\left(\frac{\Delta a}{a_o}\right)\left[1 + \frac{3}{2}\left(\frac{\Delta a}{a_o}\right)\right]^{-1}, \tag{8.91}$$

rather than $\rho_{pw}/\rho_{po} \sim 1 + x_o^*$ showing that the ratio ρ_{pw}/ρ_{po} is greater than estimation by taking a_o as the only size present, and that solution based on mean radius a_o may introduce a substantial error.

A theoretical study of the effect of solid particles on the stability of laminar flow was reported by Michael [M27] extending an earlier method due to Saffman [S1]. A characteristic relaxation time $\tau(= 1/F)$ for the velocity of a dust particle to adjust to changes in the gas velocity was used to describe the system. It was shown that if τ is small compared with a characteristic time scale associated with the flow, the addition of dust destabilized the gas flow; whereas coarse dust or small τ stabilizes the flow. The Orr-Sommerfeld equation for plane parallel flow was derived for a suspension and was used to illustrate some features of the presence of the dust particles.

8.4 Laminar Motion with Accumulation or Diffusion of Particles [S62]

It is noted that for 1 μ spherical particles of magnesia in air at room condition, $F \sim 9\bar{\mu}/2\bar{\rho}_p a^2 \sim 10^5$ sec^{-1}. The distance x from the leading edge within which the flow condition $(Fx/U \leqslant 1)$ in Sec. 8.3 applies is extremely small. It is therefore pertinent to ask what happens when $x^* = Fx/U \geqslant 1$.

Equation (8.37) suggests that at $x^* = 1$, $\rho_{pw} \to \infty$. This, of course, is not a realistic conclusion. However, at or before this condition, deposition of particles is expected at $u_{pw} \sim 0$ when Brownian motion of particles is negligible. Let us consider this case first. We know from Sec. 5.1 that the limit for ρ_{pw} is the maximum volume fraction solid ϕ_{max} that can be realized by packing of a particular material ($\phi_{max} = 1$ for liquid droplets). Therefore the limit for ρ_{pw} is $\rho_{ps} = \phi_{max}\bar{\rho}_p$, or

$$\frac{\rho_{ps}}{\rho_{po}} = \frac{\phi_{max}\bar{\rho}_p}{\rho_{po}} = (1 - x^*)^{-1}. \tag{8.92}$$

That is, a different flow regime is expected for

$$x^*_{max} = x^* \leq 1 - \frac{\phi_o}{\phi_{max}}, \tag{8.93}$$

where $\phi_o = \rho_{po}/\bar{\rho}_p$, that is, beyond x^*_m there is a layer of high concentration near the wall which moves or settles like a packed bed. Although the latter is discussed in Sec. 9.7, it is interesting to discuss, at this point, the interaction of such a layer with the free stream. The velocity at which such a layer moves is expected to be small, or

$$\frac{U_s}{U} \sim \frac{\phi_o}{\phi_{max}}, \tag{8.94}$$

but, depending on the materials and surfaces of the particles and the wall, the layer may build up or erode away. We want to explore a simple case at steady state.

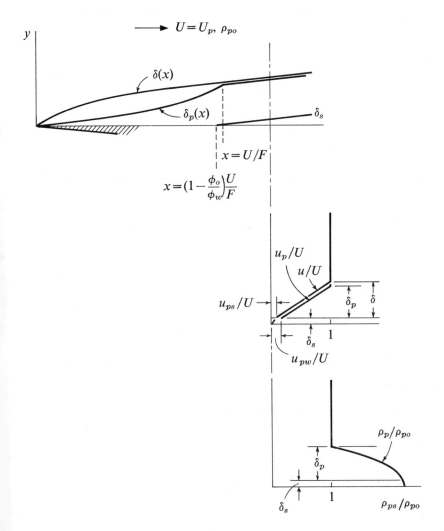

Figure 8.6 Boundary-layer motion with deposited layer of particles; Brownian motion of particles negligible.

Consider the situation where there is a layer of solids of thickness δ_s (Fig. 8.6), which does not affect the velocity distribution of the fluid substantially. Steady condition is reached when the shear instances are equalized:

$$\tau_s = \frac{\mu_s U_s}{\delta_s} = \tau_w = \frac{\bar{\mu} U}{\delta}, \tag{8.95}$$

the latter given by Eq. (8.65) for small U_{pw}, μ_s is the viscosity due to shear motion of the solid layer at $U_{pw}/U > \phi_o/\phi_m$. When $\tau_s < \tau_w$, the layer will be eroded (see ablation, Sec. 8.7), at $\tau_s > \tau_w$, the layer will increase in its thickness by deposition. The general situation would also include a density gradient in the layer δ_s.

With U_s given by Eq. (8.94), δ_s can be expressed as

$$\delta_s = \frac{\mu_s}{\bar{\mu}} \frac{\phi_o}{\phi_{\max}} \delta. \tag{8.96}$$

In general, $U_{pw} \gtrsim U_s$, contribution of particles to τ_w (Sec. 5.3, p. 202) may also be significant. Deposition is not expected to be uniform, but in periodic dunes (Sec. 9.2).

Effect of Brownian Motion of Particles—As was indicated in Sec. 5.9, even though the magnitude of Brownian motion of submicron particles may still be quite small, it is not negligible at the wall where the fluid velocity goes to zero. Before ρ_{ps} in Eq. (8.92) is reached, diffusion due to Brownian motion sets in according to

$$D\nabla^2 \rho_p = \left(\frac{d\rho_p}{dt}\right)_A + \left(\frac{d\rho_p}{dt}\right)_B, \tag{8.97}$$

where D is the Brownian diffusion coefficient, subscript A denotes increase in density due to transport and subscript B indicates increase in density due to slowing down of the particle cloud. When applied to the case of steady flow over a flat plate, the source term for the increase in density in the boundary layer is given by the approximation from Eq. (8.49), or

$$\rho_p u_p = \rho_{po} U, \tag{8.98}$$

and

$$\left(\frac{d\rho_p}{dt}\right)_B = -\left(\frac{\rho_{po} U}{u_p^2}\right)\frac{du_p}{dt}$$

$$= -\left(\frac{\rho_{po} U}{u_p}\right)\frac{\partial u_p}{\partial x}. \tag{8.99}$$

We may also neglect the effects of diffusion in the x-direction, Eq. (8.97) now becomes:

$$D\frac{\partial^2 \rho_p}{\partial x^2} = u_p \frac{\partial \rho_p}{\partial x} + v_p \frac{\partial \rho_p}{\partial y} - \left(\frac{\rho_{po} U}{u_p}\right)\frac{\partial u_p}{\partial x}, \tag{8.100}$$

with the boundary condition:

$$\frac{\partial \rho_p}{\partial y}\bigg]_w = 0. \tag{8.101}$$

Further when $x^* = 1$, $u_p \sim u$ and $\eta_p \sim \eta$. Solution of Eq. (8.100) can be obtained by applying the Blasius solution [S13] of the flat-plate problem in an analogous manner as the Chapman-Rubesin solution [S13] of the case of adiabatic compressible flow over a flat plate.

The Blasius solution to Eq. (8.32) at $K_m = 0$ takes the form, for $\eta = y\sqrt{U/\bar{\nu}x}$

$$\left. \begin{aligned} u &= Uf_1'(\eta) \\ v &= \frac{1}{2}\sqrt{\frac{\bar{\nu}U}{x}}\,(\eta f_1' - f_1) \end{aligned} \right\}, \tag{8.102}$$

and

$$f_1 f_1'' + 2f_1''' = 0. \tag{8.103}$$

When applied to Eq. (8.100) with

$$\rho_p = \rho_{po}h_1(\eta), \tag{8.104}$$

we get

$$h_1'' + \frac{\bar{\nu}}{2D}f_1 h_1' = -\frac{\bar{\nu}}{2D}\frac{\eta f_1''}{f_1'}, \tag{8.105}$$

where $\bar{\nu}/D$ is the Schmidt number N_{Sc}. The boundary conditions are

$$\left. \begin{aligned} \eta = 0, \quad f_1 = 0, \quad f_1' = 0, \quad h_1' = 0 \\ \eta = \infty, \quad f_1' = 1, \quad h_1 = 1 \end{aligned} \right\}. \tag{8.106}$$

Eq. (8.105) is readily integrated by substituting Eq. (8.103) according to:

$$\int f_1 \, d\eta = -2\int \frac{f_1'''}{f_1''} \, d\eta = -2\ln f_1'', \tag{8.107}$$

and

$$h_1 = -\tfrac{1}{2}N_{\text{Sc}}\int_\infty^\eta \left[f_1''^{(N_{\text{Sc}})}\int_0^\eta f_1'^{-1}f_1''^{(1-N_{\text{Sc}})}\eta \, d\eta \right] d\eta + 1. \tag{8.108}$$

Exact integration according to the Blasius formula for $f_1(\eta)$ is feasible but complicated. We may, however, apply the boundary-layer approximation in Eq. (8.66) or $f_1'(\eta) = \eta$ and

$$h_1 \cong 1 - \tfrac{1}{2}N_{\text{Sc}}\int_\infty^\eta f''^{(N_{\text{Sc}})}\int_0^\eta f'^{-1}f''^{(1-N_{\text{Sc}})}\eta \, d\eta$$

$$= 1 + \tfrac{1}{4}N_{\text{Sc}}(1 - \eta^2). \tag{8.109}$$

Equation (8.109) indicates that for very small particles, D becomes larger, $N_{\text{Sc}} \to 0$, the solution reverts to the case of incompressible flow of a gaseous mixture; ρ_p is then uniform. The relations for boundary-layer thicknesses, density and velocity distribution for the case including Brownian motion of particles are shown in Fig. 8.7.

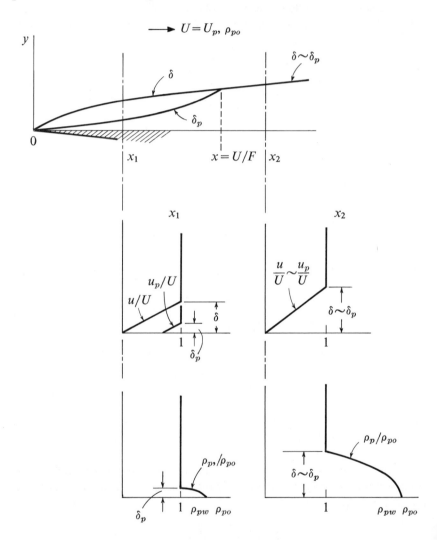

Figure 8.7 Boundary-layer motion with significant Brownian diffusion of particles.

The general case including a deposited layer, Brownian motion and continuous variation is illustrated in Fig. 8.8. Where there is a distribution in particle sizes (s) and (r), more smaller particles than larger particles will be

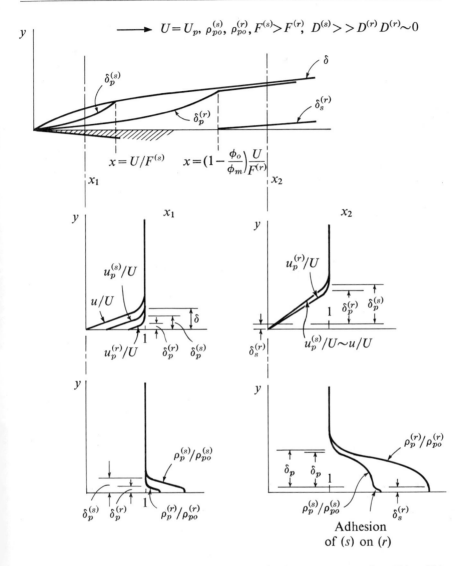

Figure 8.8 Boundary-layer motion with particles of different sizes or species. $F^{(s)} > F^{(r)}$, $D^{(s)} \gg D^{(r)}$, $D^{(r)} \sim 0$.

found at the wall near the leading edge. However, at a distance x downstream such as all $x^* > 1$, more larger particles than smaller particles will be found near the wall as suggested by Eq. (8.109). This is also true in the deposited layer.

8.5 Turbulent Flow over a Flat Plate

When applied to turbulent flow, the feasibility of applying the momentum integral method was discussed by Soo [S52], extending the semiempirical procedure as in the case of turbulent boundary-layer flow of a single-phase fluid. At the present time, only simple cases have been treated.

We shall consider the limiting case of an isothermal incompressible system with small particle density. In the isothermal incompressible system we further specify that the free stream has uniform velocity ($U_p = U$); and the particle motion is in the "free-particle" range. The momentum integral method leads to

$$\frac{d}{dx} [\rho_{po}\theta_p + \rho_o\theta]U^2 = \tau + \tau_p. \tag{8.110}$$

For the velocity profile of the stream [S13]:

$$u = U\left(\frac{y}{\delta}\right)^{1/n}, \tag{8.111}$$

and, extending from measurements made on pipe flow (Sec. 4.5) [S53]:

$$u_p = U_{pw} + (U_p - U_{pw})\left(\frac{y}{\delta}\right)^{1/m} \tag{8.112}$$

$$\rho_p = \rho_{po} - (\rho_{po} - \rho_{pw})\left(1 - \frac{y}{\delta}\right)^{\alpha}, \tag{8.113}$$

we have (Eqs. 8.54 and 8.55)

$$\frac{\theta}{\delta} = \frac{n}{(1 + n)(2 + n)} \tag{8.114}$$

$$\frac{\theta_p}{\delta} = \left(\frac{U_p - U_{pw}}{U_p}\right)^2 \frac{m}{(1 + m)(2 + m)} - \left(\frac{\rho_{po} - \rho_{pw}}{\rho_{po}}\right)\frac{U_{pw}}{U_p}\frac{1}{\alpha + 1}$$

$$+ \left(\frac{\rho_{po} - \rho_{pw}}{\rho_{po}}\right)\left(\frac{U_p - U_{pw}}{U_p}\right)^2$$

$$\times \left[\frac{\Gamma\left(\frac{2}{m} + 1\right)(\alpha + 1)}{\Gamma\left(\frac{2}{m} + \alpha + 2\right)} - \frac{\Gamma\left(\frac{1}{m} + 1\right)\Gamma(\alpha + 1)}{\Gamma\left(\frac{1}{m} + \alpha + 2\right)}\right]. \tag{8.115}$$

The shear stress due to the stream is given [S13] by:

$$\frac{\tau}{\bar{\rho} U^2} = 0.0225 \left(\frac{\bar{\mu}}{U \delta \bar{\rho}} \right)^{\frac{1}{4}},$$ (8.116)

and that due to collision of particles with the wall is

$$\tau_{pw} \sim \frac{1}{2\sqrt{\pi}} \rho_{pw} U_{pw} \sqrt{\langle u_{pw}^2 \rangle}$$

$$\sim \frac{1}{2\sqrt{\pi}} \rho_{po} U_{pw} \sqrt{\langle u_{po}^2 \rangle},$$ (8.117)

as an approximation. Taking

$$n = 7, \quad m = 1.25, \quad \alpha = 2.30, \quad \frac{U_p - U_{pw}}{U_p} = 0.812, \quad \frac{\rho_{pw}}{\rho_{po}} = 1.451$$

for the case of glass beads of 100 and 200 μ in diameter in air at room conditions at velocity of 50 to 100 fps [S53] (in the range of free particles, as in Fig. 5.13), we get

$$\frac{\theta}{\delta} = \frac{7}{72} = 0.0972, \quad \frac{\theta_p}{\delta} = 0.1402.$$

Equation (8.110) gives

$$\frac{d}{dx} \left[\frac{\rho_{po}}{\rho_o} \theta_p + \theta \right] = 0.0225 \left(\frac{\bar{\mu}}{U \delta \rho_o} \right)^{\frac{1}{4}} + \frac{1}{2\sqrt{\pi}} \frac{\rho_{po}}{\rho_o} \frac{U_{pw} \sqrt{\langle u_{po}^2 \rangle}}{U^2},$$ (8.118)

or,

$$\left(\frac{\rho_{po}}{\rho_o} 0.1402 + 0.0972 \right) \frac{d\delta}{dx} = 0.0225 \left(\frac{\bar{\mu}}{U \delta \rho_o} \right)^{\frac{1}{4}} + \frac{1}{2\sqrt{\pi}} \frac{\rho_{po}}{\rho_o} \frac{U_{pw} \sqrt{\langle u_{po}^2 \rangle}}{U^2},$$

                    (8.119)

which is readily integrated to give

$$a = \left(\frac{a}{b} \right) \left(\frac{\delta}{x} \right) - \frac{4a^3}{3b^2} \left(\frac{\delta}{x} \right)^{\frac{3}{4}} + \frac{4a^3}{3b^3} \left(\frac{\delta}{x} \right)^{\frac{1}{2}} - \frac{4a^4}{b^4} \left(\frac{\delta}{x} \right)^{\frac{1}{4}}$$

$$+ \frac{4a^5}{b^5} \ln \left| 1 + \frac{b}{a} \left(\frac{\delta}{x} \right)^{\frac{1}{4}} \right|,$$ (8.120)

from which δ/x can be calculated where (Fig. 8.9 for $\rho_{po}/\rho_o = 0.10$)

$$a = \frac{0.0225\left(\dfrac{\bar{\mu}}{U\rho_o x}\right)^{1/4}}{0.1402\dfrac{\rho_{po}}{\rho_o} + 0.0972}$$

$$b = \frac{\dfrac{1}{2\sqrt{\pi}}\dfrac{\rho_{po}}{\rho_o}\dfrac{U_{pw}\sqrt{\langle u_{pw}^2\rangle}}{U^2}}{\left(0.1402\dfrac{\rho_{po}}{\rho_o} + 0.0972\right)}. \tag{8.121}$$

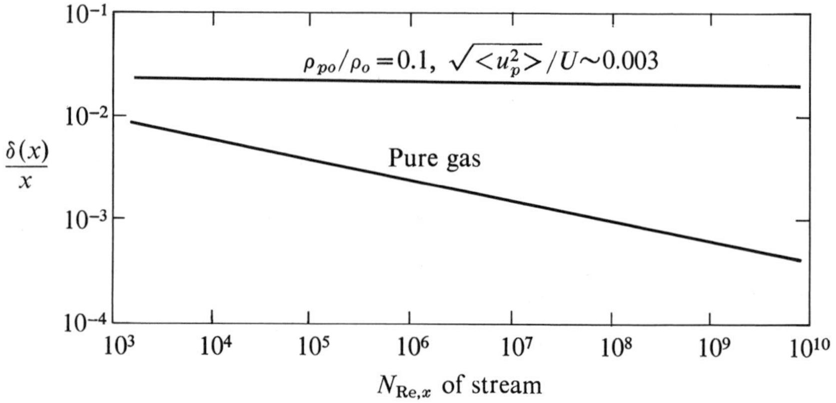

Figure 8.9 Boundary-layer thickness due to presence of solid particles.

It can be shown that

$$\frac{\delta}{x} = \frac{0.37\left(\dfrac{Ux\rho_o}{\bar{\mu}}\right)^{1/5}}{\left(1 + 1.442\dfrac{\rho_{po}}{\rho_o}\right)^{4/5}}, \tag{8.122}$$

for $b = 0$ as a limit; i.e., neglect shear due to impact of solid particles. In other words, due to inertia of particles alone, the tendency of their presence is to suppress the growth of boundary-layer thickness. It is interesting to note that this would lead to smaller friction factor in the inlet length. Therefore, depending on the turbulence of the free stream (which affects $\sqrt{\langle u_p^2\rangle}$), the thickness δ may fall anywhere between the curves of Eqs. (8.120) and (8.122). The resultant friction factor or shear stress exerted on the flat plate will follow similar relations which can be computed from $\delta(x)$ and $\theta(x)$.

It is interesting to consider the thickness θ_D due to particle diffusion; continue from the above numerical example.

$$
\frac{\theta_D}{\delta} = -\frac{\rho_{pw} U_{pw}}{\rho_{po} U_p} - \frac{U_{pw}}{U_p}\left(1 - \frac{\rho_{pw}^2}{\rho_{po}^2}\right)\frac{1}{\alpha + 1}
$$

$$
+ \left(1 - \frac{\rho_{pw}}{\rho_{po}}\right)^2 \frac{U_{pw}}{U_p}\frac{1}{2\alpha + 1} + \left(1 - \frac{U_{pw}}{U_p}\right)\left(\frac{\rho_{pw}}{\rho_{po}}\right)\frac{1}{\frac{1}{m} + 1}
$$

$$
- \left(1 - \frac{U_{pw}}{U_{po}}\right)\left(1 - \frac{\rho_{pw}^2}{\rho_{po}^2}\right)\frac{\Gamma\left(\frac{1}{m} + 1\right)\Gamma(\alpha + 1)}{\Gamma\left(\frac{1}{m} + \alpha + 2\right)} \qquad (8.123)
$$

$$
+ \left(1 - \frac{U_{pw}}{U_{po}}\right)\left(1 - \frac{\rho_{pw}}{\rho_{po}}\right)^2 \frac{\Gamma\left(\frac{1}{m} + 1\right)\Gamma(2\alpha + 1)}{\Gamma\left(\frac{1}{m} + 2\alpha + 2\right)}
$$

$$
= 1.042.
$$

That is, to the same order of δ, greater number of particles will be slowed down as the mixture proceeds downstream.

The nature of turbulent boundary layer of a suspension is seen in the case of flow through a nozzle (Sec. 7.4 p. 299). Shadowgraph records show a dense (fraction of a millimeter thick) but moving layer of solid particles along the wall of the nozzle [S58]. A typical set of results is shown in Fig. 8.10, which is a comparison of experimental and computed (one-dimensional) results for the case of glass particles in air with a given area (A_f) distribution. (Data points of stream velocities, u, were computed from pressure, P; particle velocities, u_r, from u; and mass ratio, m_s, of solid to gas; subscript 1 is for inlet or stagnation conditions.) Figure 8.10 shows that until a point approximately 2 in. from the inlet, experimental values of u_p and m_s are consistent (indicating that the drag parameter of solid particles was taken correctly). From there on, the particle concentration m_s in the core was observed to be uniform, but the concentration of solid particles began to increase significantly at the wall (the curve of Δm_{sw} shows the increase). Although the thickness of this moving layer of solid particles cannot be measured accurately from the shadowgraph record, the data of Δm_{sw} shows, for the case in Fig. 8.10, that at $x = 2.5$ in., 40 per cent of the area of the wall was covered with solid particles; the thickness increases to that of two particles at $x = 3$ in.; to three particles at $x = 4$ in.; and decreases to two particles at $x = 4.5$ in. as the average velocity of solid particles increases. Results as in this example

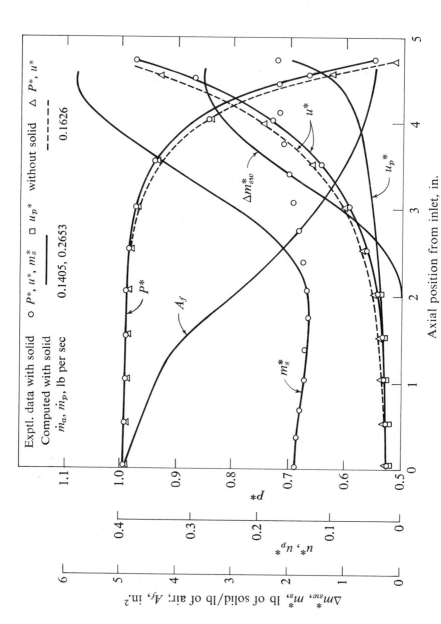

Figure 8.10 Experimental and computed results of nozzle flow of a gas-solid suspension (case $P_1 = 29.022$ in. Hg, $T_1 = 72°$F, $c = 0.24$, $c_p = 0.20$, $2a = 230\ \mu$, nozzle height, 1 in. $P^* = P/P_1$, $u^* = u/u_o$, $u_p^* = u_p/u_o$, $u_o = 2525$ fps.)

show the significance of the contribution of electrostatic forces (to be treated in Chap. 10) as well as hydrodynamic forces. The particles sliding along the wall will be deficient in velocity but will be effective in heat transfer at the wall with respect to the case of uniform concentration at each cross section. The actual thrust of a nozzle based on one-dimensional computation will be

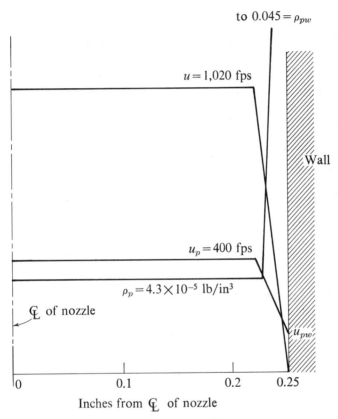

to $0.045 = \rho_{pw}$

$u = 1,020$ fps

Wall

$u_p = 400$ fps

$\rho_p = 4.3 \times 10^{-5}$ lb/in^3

₵ of nozzle

u_{pw}

0   0.1   0.2   0.25

Inches from ₵ of nozzle

Figure 8.11 Estimated velocity and concentration profiles of case shown in Fig. 8.10 ($x = 4.5$ in.).

lower, while the cooling requirement of the nozzle wall might be higher than predicted—especially when the system is reactive.

The above nozzle flow experiment is computed to have a gas-phase boundary-layer thickness of no more than 10^{-3} in. near the throat, based on the method of Buri and Gruschwitz [S13], which is even smaller than the thickness of the layer of solid particles. Therefore, for high velocity flow we have the trend as in Fig. 8.11 for the condition near the throat (Reynolds number of gas phase at the throat is 7.5×10^4) given in Fig. 8.10.

Another aspect of high-velocity flow involving phases is the influence of condensation of water vapor in wind tunnels on heat-transfer and recovery temperature. A survey was given by Stever [S88]; recent measurements were reported by Thomann [T20].

8.6 Boundary-Layer Motion with Thermal Radiation [S52]

When particle density is high enough so that the free-stream condition is not affected by the heat transfer from a heated flat plate, and diffuse radiation is active only within a thickness to the order of magnitude of that of the boundary layer, we have the condition $T_{po} = T_o$, $U_p = U$, and the mixture acts together in the turbulent motion like a gaseous mixture (Sec. 5.6). Application of the momentum-integral method to the energy equation for the temperature thickness

$$\theta'_T = \int_o^\delta \frac{u}{U}\left(1 - \frac{T}{T_o}\right) dy, \qquad (8.124)$$

gives

$$(cp_o + c_p \rho_{po}) T_o \frac{d}{dx} \theta'_T = (\kappa_m + \kappa_r) \frac{\partial T_p}{\partial y}\bigg]_w, \qquad (8.125)$$

κ_m is the thermal conductivity of the mixture and κ_r is the radiative conductivity [V10]. Solution of Eq. (8.125) corresponds [E1] to:

$$N_{\mathrm{Nu},x} = \frac{hx}{\kappa_m + \kappa_r} = 0.007(N_{\mathrm{Pr}})^{1/3}(N_{\mathrm{Re},x})^{0.8}. \qquad (8.126)$$

Here

$$\kappa_r \sim \frac{16 n_m^2 \sigma_r T^3}{3 \alpha'_m}, \qquad (8.127)$$

where α'_m is the absorption coefficient and

$$\kappa_m \sim \kappa_p, \quad \mu_m \sim \mu_p \qquad (8.128)$$

$$\alpha'_m \sim \alpha' \pi a^2 n_p. \qquad (8.129)$$

Where α' is the absorptivity of the surface. For 1 lb of 100-μ glass beads per pound of air at room conditions,

$$\alpha'_m \sim 30\alpha' \ \mathrm{ft}^{-1}, \qquad (8.130)$$

and, from Sec. 5.6,

$$\kappa_r \sim \frac{16 n_m^2 \sigma_r T^3}{3 \alpha'_m} \qquad (8.131)$$

is nearly 3 Btu/ft hr °F for $T \sim 2000°R$; this is much greater than the conductivity of the air or the mixture. To apply the result in Sec. 5.6, which does not involve motion, the value of the parameter for the present case is, from Eq. (5.148),

$$N_{\text{Rc}} = \frac{\kappa_m \alpha_m'}{4\sigma_r T^3} \sim \frac{2 \times 10^8}{T^3}. \tag{8.132}$$

The Prandtl number of the mixture is now

$$N_{\text{Pr}} \sim \frac{c\rho_o + c_p \rho_{po}}{\rho_o + \rho_{po}} \frac{\mu_m}{\kappa_r}, \tag{8.133}$$

and becomes strongly temperature-dependent.

To see the ranges where diffusion of radiation or particle-wall radiation [S52] is effective, we compute the particle temperature at 0.1 ft from a wall at 2000°R, gas at 1000°R, with glass beads of 100-μ diameter but at various particle densities. At the limiting condition of steady particle temperature, equation of particle temperature (Sec. 6.5) gives:

$$\frac{\alpha_m'}{a\alpha' \sigma_r T_w^3} \left(\frac{T_p}{T_w} - \frac{T_g}{T_w} \right) = 1 - \frac{T_p^4}{T_w^4}, \tag{8.134}$$

(T_g is the gas temperature) for the case of low particle density and radiation from wall to particle only. The condition of diffusion of radiation for high particle density is, for radiative conductivity derived from Eq. (8.132),

$$\frac{9}{64} \frac{\alpha_m' y \alpha'}{a^2 n_m^2 \sigma_r T_w^3} \frac{\rho_p}{\bar{\rho}_p} \left(\frac{T_p}{T_w} - \frac{T}{T_w} \right) \cong \left(1 - \frac{T_p}{T_w} \right), \tag{8.135}$$

where y is the distance from the wall. Equations (8.134) and (8.135) are plotted for this limiting case in Fig. 8.12, which shows that diffusion of radiation becomes significant for this case at $\rho_p > 0.5$ lb/cu ft.

Transition from blackbody to Rosseland formulations in optically thick flow was studied by Tien and Greif [T34]. Boundary layer in thermal radiation absorbing media was formulated by Viskanta and Grosh [V12], and by Cess [C12]. Other studies of boundary-layer motion of a radiative medium (gas alone) are those of Howe on the laminar boundary layer in chemical equilibrium in the stagnation region [H59] and possibility of shielding by transpiration of an absorbing gas [H58], radiative heat transfer during reentry was measured by Kivel [K17]. These results are not directly applicable to a multiphase system, but offer a variety of methods of approach which are worth considering when dealing with multiphase systems.

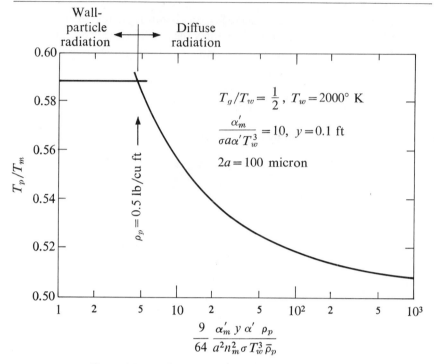

Figure 8.12 Particle temperature due to radiation [S52].

8.7 Boundary Layer with Ablation

The condition of reentry of spacecraft into atmospheres at hypersonic speeds led to the consideration of material ablation as a means of alleviating the high heat flux. In the class of materials such as Teflon®, the solid material sublimes in the severely high enthalpy environment, and boundary layer is similar to that of transpiration cooling with reaction. Reinforced plastics, such as phenolic resin reinforced with nylon or foamed polyurethane, produces a charred layer under the above condition. This layer is produced by depolymerization process with generation of gases such as methane and hydrogen.

Multiphase boundary layer flow condition occurs with refractory material such as quartz, which, when exposed to high enthalpy environment, gradually softens, melts, and flows under the influence of gas-shearing action and may evaporate in the boundary layer. Refractory material such as graphite ablates by oxidation process as in the case of combustion of a solid material. A survey of all these ablations was made by Steg and Lew [S85]. It is expected that, at the high rate of heating encountered at reentry, due to high thermal stress, the refractory layer may become flaked and we would get gas-solid boundary-layer flow with evaporation or chemical reaction.

The effects of ablation on heat transfer to arbitrary axisymmetric body were studied by Swann and South [S102] with consideration of mass (gas) injection and approximation of radiation from the hot gas layer. The case typified by Teflon® was treated by Sutton [S99, S100], who accounted for heat transfer and reaction rate. Sutton [S101] studied the pyrolysis of reinforced plastics and found the phenomenological behavior varies significantly with time and magnitude of heating. The heat blocked due to mass transfer was formulated by Scala [S8].

Melting and vaporization of silica may include dissociation. The heated solid silica softens and forms a liquid layer which vaporizes and injects the gaseous dioxide, monoxide, and oxygen into the gaseous boundary layer. An analysis was made by Fanucci and Lew [F2] on the effect of mass transfer and body forces on two-phase boundary layer. The liquid layer and shedding in droplets is influenced by the conditions for drop and jet scattering (studied by Morrell [M45], based on Hinze [H42] and Taylor [T10]). Ablation of graphite involves combustion reactions with dissociated air. For surfaces below 5000°R, nitrogen atoms of the dissociated air are expected to recombine in the gaseous phase. A simple model was employed for the analysis of the C-O-N system by Scala [S9].

A comparison of the above systems is shown in Fig. 8.13, for the ablation rate for spacecraft reentry. Ablation rate for ballistic trajectory is considerably higher and over much shorter duration.

Reacting two-phase particle-gas flow in the boundary layer of an ablative hypersonic body was studied in detail by Choudhury [C24]. His modifications of the multiphase boundary-layer flow formulated in the above sections include the burning time of a solid particle and the heat of evaporation or reaction. The surface reaction rate $\dot{m}_r$ is given by Langmuir as [G24]:

$$\dot{m}_r = \frac{k_a k_d [A]_s}{k_a [A]_s + k_d}, \tag{8.136}$$

where $\dot{m}_r$ is in rate of mass reacted/surface area, time; k_a is the velocity constant for absorption, and k_d is that for desorption from the surface; $[A]_s$ is the concentration of the oxidant in the vicinity of the surface in mass per unit volume. At high temperature, $k_d \gg k_a[A]_s$, and $k_s \sim k_a[A]$, which is largely confirmed by Essenhigh's measurements [E23]. This leads to, for the C-F (fluorine from Teflon®)

$$\dot{m}_r = 3.5 \frac{\mathscr{M}}{\sqrt{T_g}} m_F^* e^{-E_c/\bar{R}T} \tag{8.137}$$

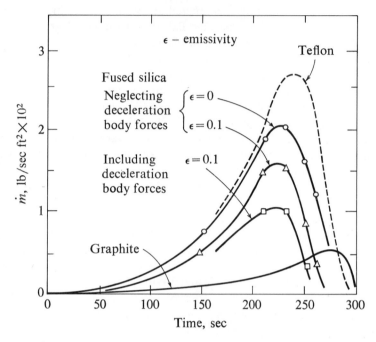

Figure 8.13 Material ablation rates for reentry satellite trajectory [S85].

where $\bar{\mathcal{M}}$ is the mean molecular weight of the gas mixture, m_F^* is the mass fraction of the F atoms, T is the temperature of the gas, E_c is the activation energy, $\bar{R}$ is the gas constant. Thus, in addition to the other basic equations, the change in particle radius for rate of sublimation $\dot{m}_s$ is given by

$$-\frac{da}{dt} = \frac{\dot{m}_s}{\bar{\rho}_p},$$ (8.138)

and the particle-energy equation now becomes

$$h(T - T_p) - \epsilon_p \sigma_r(T_p^4 - \tfrac{1}{2}T_w^4) - \dot{m}_r \Delta H - \frac{\dot{m}_s}{A_s} h_{sg} = \frac{\bar{\rho}_p}{3} ca \frac{dT_p}{dt},$$ (8.139)

where h is the heat-transfer coefficient, ϵ_p the emissivity of the carbon particle, σ_r the Stefan-Boltzmann constant, ΔH the heat of chemisorption, and h_{sg} the heat of sublimation. Choudhury applied the boundary-layer method to this system and computed numerically the velocity and temperature variations for flow over a cone.

The use of ablative thrust chambers for space propulsion was studied by Lafazan and Siegel [L2].

8.8 Jets and Sprays

Jets of multiphase systems exist in air-cleaning systems, such as the ejector venturi scrubbers [H17], air-atomizing systems, and exhaust of metallized propellant rockets, to name a few. In all these applications, distribution of particulate matter in the jet is a quantity of interest [S62].

Laminar Circular Jet—Laminar flow of a jet of single-phase fluid was studied by many. Extensive surveys on jets were made by Forstall and Shapiro [F15], Alexander, Baron, and Comings [A7], and Krzywoblocki [K42]. The case of incompressible laminar circular jet was studied by Schlichting [S13], who gave, from solution of the boundary-layer equations, the radial (r) component of velocity (u), and the axial (z) component of velocity (w) as

$$u = \frac{\bar{\nu}}{z}\gamma(\xi - \tfrac{1}{4}\xi^2)(1 + \tfrac{1}{4}\xi^2)^{-3} = \frac{\bar{\nu}}{z\eta}[\eta f'(\eta) - f(\eta)], \qquad (8.140)$$

and

$$w = \frac{\bar{\nu}}{z}2\gamma^2(1 + \tfrac{1}{4}\xi^2)^{-2} = \frac{\bar{\nu}}{z\eta}f'(\eta), \qquad (8.141)$$

where $\xi = \gamma r/z$, $\eta = r/z$, $\bar{\nu}$ is the kinematic viscosity, and γ is given by the momentum of the jet J as

$$J = 2\pi\rho \int_0^\infty w^2 r\, dr = \tfrac{16}{3}\pi\rho\gamma^2\bar{\nu}^2 = \rho\pi r_1^2 w_1^2 . \qquad (8.142)$$

It is seen that $\gamma = (\sqrt{3}/8)(N_{\text{Re}})_1$, where $(N_{\text{Re}})_1$ is the Reynolds number at the exit of the jet nozzle $2r_1 w_1/\bar{\nu}$.

Again we take the case of a dilute suspension of particles above micron size. Thus the velocity distribution in the fluid is not significantly affected by the presence to the particles, and the Brownian diffusion of particles is negligible. It is seen that (1) the spread of the particles in the jet is due to fluid motion, (2) as the particle cloud is slowed down, its concentration increases and eventually settles down, and (3) the overall momentum of the system is conserved as in a jet of single-phase fluid, but the momenta of the particles are being dissipated. The method in the previous sections can be applied, and the continuity and momentum equations of the particulate phase take the form

$$\frac{\partial(r\rho_p u_p)}{\partial r} + \frac{\partial(r\rho_p w_p)}{\partial z} = 0 \qquad (8.143)$$

$$w_p\frac{\partial w_p}{\partial z} + u_p\frac{\partial w_p}{\partial r} = F(w - w_p), \qquad (8.144)$$

with the boundary conditions $z = 0$, $w = w_p = w_1$, $\rho_p = \rho_{p1}$; $r = 0$, $u_p = 0$, $\partial w_p / \partial r = 0$, $\partial \rho_p / \partial r = 0$; $r = \infty$, $w_p = 0$. Equation (8.143) further gives at $r = 0$, $\rho_p w_p = $ constant.

Equation (8.144) gives at $r = 0$, $w = \alpha/z$, $\alpha = 2\gamma^2 \bar{\nu}$,

$$w_{po} = \frac{\alpha}{z}\left[1 + \left(\frac{\alpha}{Fz^2}\right) + 4\left(\frac{\alpha}{Fz^2}\right)^2 + \cdots\right].\tag{8.145}$$

where the nature of coupling of the phase is seen via

$$\left(\frac{\alpha}{Fz^2}\right) = 3\left(\frac{2\bar{\nu}}{Fz^2}\right)(N_{\mathrm{Re}})_1^2 \equiv \zeta,\tag{8.146}$$

$Fz^2/\bar{\nu}$ corresponds to the gas-solid momentum number of the present problem. Further

$$\rho_{po} = \frac{\rho_{p1}w_{p1}}{\alpha}z\left[1 - \left(\frac{\alpha}{Fz^2}\right) - 3\left(\frac{\alpha}{Fz^2}\right)^2 - \cdots\right],\tag{8.147}$$

where subscript 1 denotes conditions at the outlet of the jet nozzle.

The boundary condition suggests ζ as the pertinent similarity parameter for a perturbation solution of Eqs. (8.143) and (8.144), or, corresponding to Eqs. (8.140) and (8.141), we postulate

$$w_p = \frac{\bar{\nu}}{z\eta}[g_0'(\eta) + \zeta g_1'(\eta) + \zeta^2 g_2'(\eta) + \cdots]\tag{8.148}$$

$$u_p = \frac{\bar{\nu}}{z\eta}[m_0(\eta) + \zeta m_1(\eta) + \zeta^2 m_2(\eta) + \cdots]\tag{8.149}$$

$$\rho_p = \left(\frac{\rho_{p1}w_{p1}}{\alpha}\right)z[h_0(\eta) + \zeta h_1(\eta) + \zeta^2 h_2(\eta) + \cdots].\tag{8.150}$$

Substitution of Eqs. (8.148) and (8.149) in Eq. (8.144) and that of the r-component gives

$$\left.\begin{aligned}
g_0' &= f' \\
g_1' &= \frac{1}{2\gamma^2}\left(\frac{f'}{\eta} - f''\right)' \\
m_0 &= \eta f' - f \\
m_1 &= \frac{1}{2\gamma^2}\eta\left[\left(\frac{f'}{\eta} - f''\right)' + \frac{f^2}{\eta^2}\right]
\end{aligned}\right\}\tag{8.151}$$

Substitution of Eqs. (8.148) to (8.150) into Eq. (8.143) gives

$$\left.\begin{aligned}
h_0 &= g_0 = f + 1 \\
h_1 &= \frac{f^2}{2\gamma^2\eta} - \frac{1}{g_0}
\end{aligned}\right\}\tag{8.152}$$

with boundary conditions

$$\eta \to 0, \quad g_0' = 2\gamma^2\eta, \quad g_1' = 2\gamma^2\eta, \quad g_2' = 8\gamma^2\eta, \ldots$$

$$h_0 = 1, \quad h_1 = -1, \quad h_2 = -3 \cdots$$

Solution of these equations gives, for $\xi = \gamma\eta$

$$\left.\begin{array}{l} g_0' = 2\gamma\xi(1 + \tfrac{1}{4}\xi^2)^{-2} = f' \\ g_1' = 2\gamma\xi(1 - \tfrac{1}{2}\xi^2)(1 + \tfrac{1}{4}\xi^2)^{-4} \end{array}\right\} \tag{8.153}$$

$$\left.\begin{array}{l} h_0 = g_0 = \xi^2(1 + \tfrac{1}{4}\xi^2)^{-1} + 1 \\ h_1 = \dfrac{\xi^3}{2\gamma}(1 + \tfrac{1}{4}\xi^2)^{-2} - (1 + \tfrac{1}{4}\xi^2)(1 + \tfrac{5}{4}\xi^2)^{-1} \end{array}\right\} \tag{8.154}$$

The results can be expressed in the general forms:

$$w^* = \frac{wz}{2\gamma^2\bar{\nu}} \tag{8.155}$$

$$\Delta w^* = \frac{(w_p - w)Fz^3}{2\gamma^2\bar{\nu}^2} + \cdots$$

$$= (w_p^* - w^*)\frac{Fz^2}{\bar{\nu}} + \cdots \tag{8.156}$$

$$\rho_p^* = \frac{\rho_p}{\rho_{p1}}\sqrt{3}\frac{r_1}{z}\gamma = h_1^*(\xi)\{1 - \zeta h_2^*(\xi,\gamma) - \cdots\}, \tag{8.157}$$

where

$$h_1^*(\xi) = 1 + \xi^2(1 + \tfrac{1}{4}\xi^2)^{-1}$$

$$h_2^*(\xi,\gamma) = \frac{\xi^2}{2\gamma}(1 + \tfrac{1}{4}\xi^2)^{-1}(1 + \tfrac{5}{4}\xi^2)^{-1} - (1 + \tfrac{1}{4}\xi^2)^2(1 + \tfrac{5}{4}\xi^2)^{-2}.$$

The above functions w^*, Δw^*, h_1^*, h_2^* are illustrated in Fig. 8.14, for $\gamma = 1$.

When applying these results, it is seen that we have two possible cases: (1) there is no solid particle in the receiving or background fluid of the jet, and (2) when there are similar solid particles in the background fluid.

The behavior of the jet in case (1) can be seen from the fact that when we have a single-phase fluid alone, the background fluid is also set in motion, with the jet momentum conserved, but the spread of the original jet is given by the total flow rate:

$$\pi r_1^2 \rho w_1 = 2\pi\rho\int_0^{r_s} wr \, dr, \tag{8.158}$$

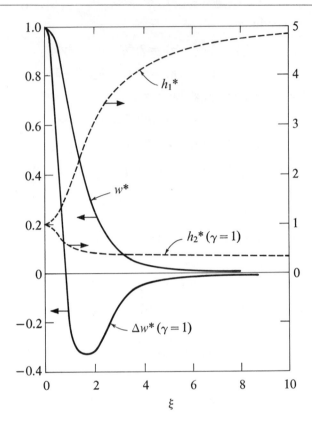

Figure 8.14 Functions w^*, Δw^*, h_1^*, h_2^* of a laminar circular jet of a suspension.

where r_s is the radius to which the original jet has spread. Substitution of Eq. (8.141) and integration gives

$$\frac{w_1 r_1^2}{8\bar{\nu}z} = \frac{\gamma}{2\sqrt{3}}\frac{r_1}{z} = \frac{\xi_s^2}{4}\left(1 + \frac{\xi_s^2}{4}\right)^{-1}, \qquad (8.159)$$

where $\xi_s = \gamma r_s/z$. Similarly, the spread of the particle cloud is given by

$$\pi r_1^2 \rho_{p1} w_1 = 2\pi \int_0^{r_{ps}} \rho_p w_p r \, dr. \qquad (8.160)$$

As an illustration of the nature of the problem, Fig. 8.15 shows the case of a jet with w, w_p, and ρ_p plotted for $\gamma = 1$, $\zeta = 0.2$ at $Fz^2/\bar{\nu} = 10$. It is seen that based on the original assumptions w of fluid phase is as given before [S13], shown by the dotted lines at two stations along the jet and the jet boundary. The motion of the particle phase is seen limited within the jet boundary of

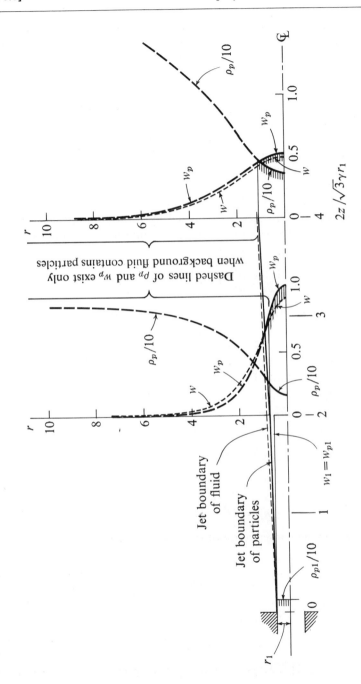

Figure 8.15 Velocity and concentration profiles, and jet boundaries of a laminar circular jet of a suspension ($\gamma = 1$, $F = 10$).

the particle cloud. The velocity w_p and concentration distributions ρ_p are shown by solid lines accented by the horizontal hatch lines. The effect of inertia of the solid particles is seen. In this case, no particle exists outside the jet boundary of the particle cloud.

In case (2), the present solution gives velocity and concentration distribution including dashed lines in Fig. 8.15. This case represents an idealized situation of a spouted fluidized bed (Sec. 9.4).

The present solution has similar limitations as that of a single-phase jet, that is, it applies to downstream away from the nozzle. Results in Sec. 8.3 suggest that right at the nozzle exit w, w_p, and ρ_p cannot be uniform; separated flow has to be treated locally.

For the submicron particles, Brownian motion can be significant, the concentration distribution will then be modified by Brownian diffusion. Take the case where particles exist only in the jet, the diffusion equation takes the form

$$Dr^{-1}\frac{\partial}{\partial r}\,r\,\frac{\partial \rho_p}{\partial r} = u_p\frac{\partial \rho_p}{\partial r} + w_p\frac{\partial \rho_p}{\partial z}. \tag{8.161}$$

We further take $\zeta^{-1} > 0$[1], or $u_p \sim u$, $w_p \sim w$, and postulate

$$\rho_p = \beta z^{-1}h_B(\eta), \tag{8.162}$$

where β is a constant to be determined. Substitution of Eq. (8.162) with Eqs. (8.140) and (8.141) into Eq. (8.161) gives

$$\eta h_B'' + h_B' = \frac{\bar{\nu}}{D}\,(fh_B' + f'h_B), \tag{8.163}$$

or, for $N_{\text{Sc}} = \bar{\nu}/D$,

$$(\eta h_B')' = -N_{\text{Sc}}(fh_B)'. \tag{8.164}$$

The boundary conditions are $h_B'(0) = 0$, $h_B(\infty) = 0$. Integration of Eq. (8.164) gives,

$$h_B = (1 + \tfrac{1}{4}\xi^2)^{-2N_{\text{Sc}}}, \tag{8.165}$$

β is determined by the conservation of total particle flow, or

$$\rho_{p1}w_1\pi r_1^2 = 2\pi\int_0^\infty \rho_p wr\,dr,$$

which gives

$$\beta = \frac{\rho_{p1}w_1 r_1^2(1 + 2N_{\text{Sc}})}{8\bar{\nu}}, \tag{8.166}$$

or

$$\frac{\rho_p}{\rho_{p1}} = \frac{1}{8}\left(\frac{\rho w_1 r_1}{\bar{\nu}}\right)\frac{r_1}{z}\,(1 + 2N_{\text{Sc}})(1 + \tfrac{1}{4}\xi^2)^{-2N_{\text{Sc}}}. \tag{8.167}$$

Therefore the concentration profile is similar to the fluid velocity profile for $N_{Sc} = 1$, that is, the diffusion of particles is completely similar to the diffusion of momentum of the fluid. The particle density then behave identically as a tracer of fluid velocity. For extremely small particles, $N_{Sc} \to \infty$, ρ_p = constant, thus reverting to the condition of a gaseous mixture.

Elperin, Lepeshinsky, and Pavlovsky [E11] studied the motion of particles in two impinging jets. Their experiments were conducted with the impingement of a jet of suspension on a wall. Their analysis was carried out by assuming potential flow of the impinging jet. The criterion of oscillating motion of particles was determined to be

$$\frac{128 W \bar{\rho}_p a^2}{3 \alpha \bar{\mu} H} > 1$$

where W is the initial jet velocity, $\bar{\rho}_p$ is the density of the particle material, α is the coefficient of the drag formula $C_D = \alpha/(N_{Re})_p$ as a modification of Eq. (2.4), H is the distance between the ends of the tubes (or twice the distance between the tube and the plate). Note that they neglected impact and rebound from the flat plate.

It is seen that the above method of solution based in ζ as the similarity parameter can be applied to the flat plate problem in Sec. 8.3; the pertinent similarity parameter is then x^*.

Turbulent Jet—The case of a turbulent jet was treated by Tollmien [T39], extending the mixing-length theory of Prandtl [S13]; and by Howarth [H56], using the vorticity theory of turbulent mixing. Lewis, Petersen, Acrivos, and Tao [L36] made measurements on a gas-solid jet using air and particles of 0.0116 to 0.0058-in. diameter. They treated the problem as one of turbulent diffusion and applied Tollmien's method, and showed that best fit was obtained with the spreading coefficient, C = mixing length/$z \sim 0.0086$, and $\xi = r/zC^{3/2}$. A comparison to their experimental results is shown in Fig. 8.16, for the mass flow ratio $(\rho_p w_p)_r/(\rho_p w_p)_{r=0}$. They showed that

$$\Phi = \frac{(\rho_p w_p)_r}{(\rho_p w_p)_0} \sim (1 + 0.24\xi^{3/2})^{-2(\gamma+1)\gamma}, \qquad (8.168)$$

with $\gamma \sim 2$ as shown in Fig. 8.17.

Sprays—In the category of mass transfer in a jet with liquid droplets is the case of evaporation from a liquid spray. For small liquid-gas ratios, the concept of evaporation from a single droplet can be applied. Studies based on this premise include those of Hsu, Sato, and Sage [H60] on material transfer in turbulent gas streams, Ingebo on evaporation rates [I2, I3]. Droplet-size distribution in sprays was determined by Mugele and Evans [M49]. Tribus, Klein, and Rembowski [T51] studies the rate of evaporation

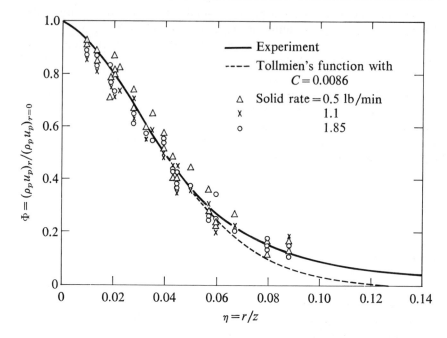

Figure 8.16 Mass flow of solid in a jet [L36].

and the change in drop-size distribution for pure sprays in unsaturated air. Daskin [D8] proposed a method based on equivalent uniform spray. An analytical solution was obtained by Probert [P30].

The evaporation of liquid sprays was studied by Probert [P30], based on the distribution in sizes of droplets given by the Rosin-Rammler relation:

$$f = e^{-(a/\bar{a})^n} \qquad (8.169)$$

where f is the volume or weight fraction of the spray composed of drops greater in diameter than a, $\bar{a}$ the size constant, and n the distribution constant. A spray is defined by $\bar{a}$ and n. The rate of evaporation $\dot{m}_v$ was approximated as

$$\dot{m}_v = \frac{4\pi a D}{K(P_s - P_o)}, \qquad (8.170)$$

where D is the diffusion constant, P_s the saturation pressure, P_o the vapor pressure of the surrounding air, and K a constant depending on air temperature and density. A typical case is that of evaporation of water drops smaller than 0.2 mm in diameter, where

$$\frac{da^2}{dt} = -(A - B e^{-\alpha v}), \qquad (8.171)$$

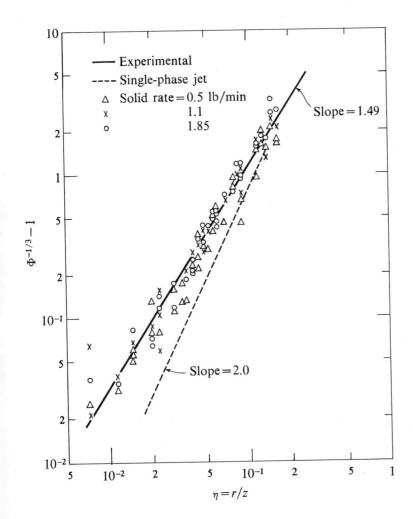

Figure 8.17 Correlation of mass flow in a jet [L36].

where A, B, α, are constants for given temperature and humidity, v the relative velocity to air.

The mean diameter in a spray was given as

$$2a_m = \left[\sum \frac{\phi_n}{4a_n^2}\right]^{-\frac{1}{2}}, \tag{8.172}$$

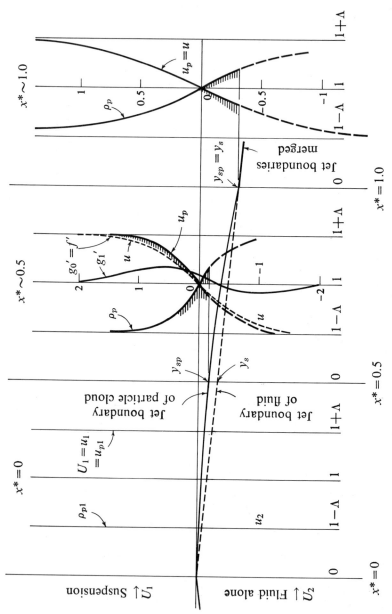

Figure 8.18 Jet boundary, velocity, and density distribution of a suspension and a clean fluid.

where ϕ_n is the volume fraction of the spray. For the distribution given by Eq. (8.169), it is readily shown that

$$a_m = \frac{\bar{a}}{\sqrt{\Gamma\left(1 - \frac{2}{n}\right)}}.$$

(8.173)

The evaporation rate of a drop at time t is

$$\frac{\mathrm{d}}{\mathrm{d}t} a^3 = -Ka,$$

(8.174)

which gives, for evaporation constant $\Lambda = \frac{2}{3}K$,

$$a^2 = a_o^2 - \Lambda t.$$

(8.175)

The possibility of incomplete evaporation and the influence of combustion processes was also treated.

Heat-transfer rates between flames of freely burning hydrocarbon fires and water sprays were studied by Rasbash [R6].

8.9 Free Jet Boundary and Separated Flow [S62]

Near the exit of a jet nozzle, or in the general case of separated flow, smoothing out of velocity discontinuity must be taken into consideration. Even in the case of small characteristic Reynolds numbers, say, based on the length of the nozzle, the laminar-flow velocity profile in the wake of the nozzle possesses a point of inflexion, and is extremely unstable [S13]. Therefore it is appropriate to treat separated flow as involving turbulent mixing in general. The method here in dealing with separated flow of a dilute suspension extends from that due to Goertler [S13], who gave for a meeting of two fluid streams of velocities U_1 and U_2 at $x = 0$, with $U_1 > U_2$,

$$u = \bar{U}(1 + \Lambda \operatorname{erf} \xi) = \bar{U}f'(\xi),$$

(8.176)

where $\bar{U} = (U_1 + U_2)/2$ and $\Lambda = (U_1 - U_2)/(U_1 + U_2)$, and $\xi = \sigma y/x$, $\sigma \sim 13.5$ is an empirical constant, x is along the direction of U and u, and y is normal to x (Fig. 8.18). It is readily shown that

$$v = -\frac{\bar{U}}{\sigma}\Lambda\left[\int_\xi^\infty (1 - \operatorname{erf} x)\,\mathrm{d}x - \xi(1 - \operatorname{erf} \xi)\right]$$

$$= \frac{\bar{U}}{\sigma}[f - \xi f'].$$

(8.177)

Now we want to consider the case with the particulate phase suspended in U_1 and at $x = 0$, $u_p = U_1$, $\rho_p = \rho_{p1}$. The continuity and momentum equations of the particulate phase are

$$\frac{\partial(\rho_p u_p)}{\partial x} + \frac{\partial(\rho_p v_p)}{\partial y} = 0 \tag{8.178}$$

$$u_p \frac{\partial u_p}{\partial x} + v_p \frac{\partial u_p}{\partial y} = F(u - u_p), \tag{8.179}$$

with additional boundary conditions $y = \pm\infty$, $u_p = \bar{U}(1 \pm \Lambda)$, $v_p = 0$; $y = \infty$, $\rho_p = \rho_{p1}$.

As when dealing with a circular jet, for a suspension, it is desirable to identify the jet boundary of stream 1, which is given by

$$\xi_s(1 - \Lambda) = \Lambda \int_{-\infty}^{\xi_s} (1 - \operatorname{erf} x) \, dx, \tag{8.180}$$

for example, at $\Lambda = \frac{1}{2}$, $\xi_B = -0.314$, or $y_s = \xi_s x / \sigma$ in the physical coordinate (Fig. 8.18, dotted line). From similar considerations as when dealing with flat-plate flow, it is seen that for $x^* = Fx/U_1 \lesssim 0[1]$, $y_{sp} \sim x^* y_s = (\xi_s/\sigma)(F/U_1)x^2$, y_s and y_{sp} merge at $x^* \geq 0[1]$ and the jet boundary of the particle phase is shown by solid line in Fig. 8.18. It is further seen that

$$f(\xi) = \xi - \xi_s + \Lambda \int_{\xi_s}^{\xi} \operatorname{erf} \xi' \, d\xi'$$

$$= (1 + \Lambda)\xi - \Lambda \int_{\infty}^{\xi} (1 - \operatorname{erf} x) \, dx. \tag{8.181}$$

Pertinent solutions of the motion and density of the particulate phase are given by

$$u_p = \bar{U}[g_0' + x^{*-1}g_1' + x^{*-2}g_2' + \cdots] \tag{8.182}$$

$$v_p = -\frac{\bar{U}}{\sigma}[m_0 + x^{*-1}m_1 + x^{*-2}m_2 + \cdots] \tag{8.183}$$

$$\rho_p = \rho_{p1}\left[1 + \frac{1 + \Lambda}{1 - \Lambda}x^*(h_0 + x^{*-1}h_1 + \cdots)\right]. \tag{8.184}$$

Substitution into Eqs. (8.178) and (8.179) and that of the y-component gives

$$g_0' = f', \qquad g_0 = f$$
$$g_1' = ff'', \ldots \tag{8.185}$$
$$h_0 = (\text{const.})f, \qquad m_0 = f - \xi f', \ldots,$$

following similar procedures as when dealing with the case of circular jet. $g_0' = f'$, and g_1' are shown in Fig. 8.18.

Figure 8.18 further shows that at $x^* \lesssim 0[1] \sim 0.5$, $u_p > u$. It is seen that a fluid particle and a solid particle starting from $x = 0$, $y = 0$ reaches y_s and y_{sp} respectively ($x_{sp} \gtrsim x_s$). The jet boundary of the particulate cloud and velocity profiles are shown in solid lines with horizontal hatch lines. At $x^* \sim 1$, $u_p \sim u$ and we have the profiles of u_p, u, and ρ_p as shown.

When significant effect of Brownian diffusion is present and $\rho_{p2} = 0$, the density distribution of particles is again given by

$$D \frac{\partial^2 \rho_p}{\partial y^2} = u_p \frac{\partial \rho_p}{\partial x} + v_p \frac{\partial \rho_p}{\partial y}, \tag{8.186}$$

at $x^* > 1$, $u_p \sim u$, $v_p \sim v$, for

$$\rho_p = \rho_{p1} h_B(\xi), \tag{8.187}$$

we get

$$h_B'' + \frac{2\epsilon}{D} f h_B' = 0, \tag{8.188}$$

where ϵ is the eddy diffusivity of the fluid given by $\epsilon = \bar{U}x/2\sigma^2$, and

$$N_{\text{Sc}} = \frac{\epsilon}{D} = \frac{\bar{U}x}{2\sigma^2 D}, \tag{8.189}$$

following Goertler [S13]; N_{Sc} is the Schmidt number of Brownian diffusion.

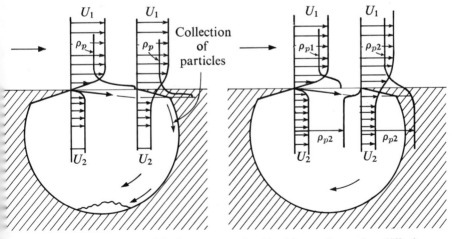

(a) Negligible Brownian diffusion   (b) Significant Brownian diffusion

Figure 8.19 Cavity flow of a suspension.

The boundary conditions are $x \le 0, y \ge 0, h_B = 1$; $x \le 0, y < 0, h_B = 0$; $\xi = \infty, h_B = 1$; $\xi = -\infty, h_B = 0$.

Since $f''' + 2ff'' = 0$, Eq. (8.188) is integrated to

$$h_B = \tfrac{1}{2}[\text{erf}(\sqrt{N_{\text{Sc}}}\xi) + 1].\tag{8.190}$$

where $\sqrt{N_{\text{Sc}}}\xi = y\sqrt{\bar{U}/2Dx}$. Again similarity of mass to momentum transfer is seen when $N_{\text{Sc}} \sim 1$.

When applied to the more general case where the particle cloud has a high concentration as given in Sec. 8.3, the layer of high particle density will be thrown along the curve of y_{sp} vs. x, and the peak of the concentration profile decreases with greater x. It is readily seen that in the case of cavity flow [K28] as shown in Fig. 8.19a the cavity will be plugged rapidly by the solid particles when Brownian diffusion is negligible (or can serve as a bleeding point of the particulate phase). When Brownian diffusion of particles is significant, the profiles will be as shown in Fig. 8.19b.

Extension of the above explanations to the case of suspensions in both streams is obvious. The dashed line in Fig. 8.18 applies to the case ($\rho_{p2} = \rho_{p1}U_1/U_2$) [S62].

SUMMARY OF BASIC CONCEPTS

Integral of Phase Interaction as Correlation—(1962) [S52]

Interaction with a Wall (Packing and Diffusion)—(1965) [S62]

Similar Solutions—(1965) [S62]

Sedimentation, Fluidization, and Packed Beds

With various excellent texts available on the subjects of sedimentation, fluidization, and packed beds, it is not intended to make a thorough coverage of these subjects in this chapter. Rather, it is intended to include the basic concepts and methods of approach in research, and to discuss the possibilities and difficulties of application of rigorous procedures outlined in the previous chapters.

Atmospheric fallout is treated in this chapter as a special case of sedimentation or the dynamics of particulate matter in the gravitational field.

9.1 Batch Settling [S61]

Batch sedimentation or settling of an initially homogeneous and quiescent suspension in the gravitational field can be formulated according to the basic relations as [S61]

$$\frac{\partial \rho}{\partial t} + \frac{\partial \rho w}{\partial z} = 0 \tag{9.1}$$

$$\frac{\partial \rho_p}{\partial t} + \frac{\partial \rho_p w_p}{\partial z} = 0 \tag{9.2}$$

$$\frac{\rho_p}{\partial t}\frac{\partial w_p}{\partial t} + \frac{\rho_p w_p}{\partial z}\frac{\partial w_p}{\partial z} = -\rho_p\left(1 - \frac{\bar{\rho}}{\bar{\rho}_p}\right)g + \rho_p F(w - w_p) - \frac{\rho_p}{\bar{\rho}_p}\frac{\partial P}{\partial z} \tag{9.3}$$

$$\frac{\rho}{\partial t}\frac{\partial w}{\partial t} + \frac{\rho w}{\partial z}\frac{\partial w}{\partial z} + \frac{\rho_p}{\partial t}\frac{\partial w_p}{\partial t} + \frac{\rho_p w_p}{\partial z}\frac{\partial w_p}{\partial z} = -\frac{\partial P}{\partial z} - (\rho_p + \rho)g, \tag{9.4}$$

with velocities w, w_p and coordinate z in the opposite direction of gravitational acceleration g. These equations apply to the case of solid particles of uniform size and we have neglected viscous forces due to dilatation. We further take the case where the fluid is incompressible such that

$$\rho = \bar{\rho}\epsilon, \quad \rho_p = \bar{\rho}_p(1 - \epsilon), \tag{9.5}$$

ϵ being the fraction void.

It is seen that Eqs. (9.1) and (9.2) account for the fact that, as solids of finite volume settle, the fluid is displaced upward. Equation (9.3) accounts for the forces acting on the solid particles due to buoyancy, fluid drag, and pressure gradient. Equation (9.4) accounts for the overall momentum of the system. Equations (9.1) and (9.2) give with Eq. (9.5),

$$w_p = -\frac{w\epsilon}{(1 - \epsilon)}, \tag{9.6}$$

meaning that as particles settle downward, the fluid moves upward. Elimination of $\partial P/\partial z$ from Eqs. (9.3) and (9.4) gives, with Eq. (9.6)

$$\left[1 + \frac{\bar{\rho}}{\bar{\rho}_p}\left(\frac{1 - \epsilon}{\epsilon}\right)\right]\frac{\partial w_p}{\partial t} + \left[1 - \frac{\bar{\rho}}{\bar{\rho}_p}\left(\frac{1 - \epsilon}{\epsilon}\right)^2\right]w_p\frac{\partial w_p}{\partial z}$$

$$-\frac{\bar{\rho}}{\bar{\rho}_p}\frac{w_p}{\epsilon^2}\left[\frac{\partial\epsilon}{\partial t} - \left(\frac{1 - \epsilon}{\epsilon}\right)w_p\frac{\partial\epsilon}{\partial z}\right] = \left[\frac{\bar{\rho}}{\bar{\rho}_p\epsilon} - \left(1 - \frac{\bar{\rho}}{\bar{\rho}_p}\right)\right]g - \frac{F}{\epsilon^2}w_p, \tag{9.7}$$

which, with Eq. (9.2) in the form

$$\frac{\partial\epsilon}{\partial t} + \frac{w_p}{\partial z}\frac{\partial\epsilon}{} = (1 - \epsilon)\frac{\partial w_p}{\partial z}, \tag{9.8}$$

are two independent equations which determine $\epsilon(z,t)$ and $w_p(z,t)$ for given initial conditions and limiting value of ϵ at the bottom of the bed; F is known as given by Ergun's extension of Stokes' law (Eq. 5.5, p. 186)

$$F \sim \frac{75}{2}\frac{1 - \epsilon}{\epsilon^2}\frac{\bar{\mu}}{\bar{\rho}_p a^2}. \tag{9.9}$$

It is seen that Eqs. (9.7) and (9.8) can only be solved numerically.

Analytical solution is feasible if we take the simple case in which $\bar{\rho}_p \gg \bar{\rho}$ (such as settling of a gas-solid suspension), $F/\epsilon^2 = F' = $ constant, and inelastic collision of the particles with the bottom of the vessel and other particles at the bottom. Equation (9.7) becomes

$$\frac{\partial w_p}{\partial t} + \frac{w_p}{\partial z}\frac{\partial w_p}{} = -g - F'w_p = \frac{dw_p}{dt}. \tag{9.10}$$

For an initially ($t = 0$) homogeneous suspension of height z_0 and volume fraction solid $\phi_0 = 1 - \epsilon_0$, and complete settling to ϕ_f at some time later, $z_f = z_0\phi_0/\phi_f$. The settling velocity w_p and fluid velocity w are given by

$$-\frac{w_p F'}{g} = (1 - e^{-F't}) = \frac{wF'(1 - \phi_0)}{\phi_0 g},$$

and the position of a particle starting at z_{01} at $t = 0$ is given by

$$\frac{z}{z_0} = \frac{z_{01}}{z_0} - \left(\frac{g}{F'z_0}\right)t + \frac{g}{F'^2 z_0}(1 - e^{-F't}). \qquad (9.11)$$

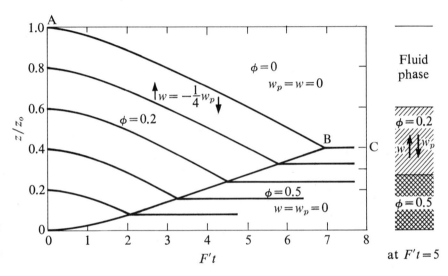

Figure 9.1 Simple sedimentation, $F' = F/\epsilon^2 = 10$, $\phi_o = 0.2$, $\phi_f = 0.5$, $g/F'z_o = 1$.

These relations are shown in Fig. 9.1 for $\phi_0 = 0.2$, $\phi_f = 0.5$, $g/F'z_0 = 1$, and $F' = 10$ sec^{-1}. In this simple case the area AOB in this diagram retains a constant ϕ of 0.20; in this area the particles settle downward at velocity w_p while the fluid is displaced upward at velocity w. Above ABC we have clean fluid and $w = 0$, below ABC the particles settle to $\phi = 0.50$ and $w = w_p = 0$. The time for complete settling is 0.694 sec. This diagram shows that at $t = 0.5$, for instance, the top 40 per cent of the overall height of the column is filled with clean fluid, below which we have 16.5 per cent of the column of a suspension of $\phi = 0.2$, and the bottom 13.5 per cent is filled with a settled bed of $\phi = 0.5$.

The above illustrates the simplest nontrivial situation. In reality, the relation in Eq. (9.9) and scattering motion of particles must be accounted for.

Without attempting to solve rigorous formulations, a number of methods of approximation is available.

In terms of a one-dimensional consideration, the vertical two-component flow is usually characterized by a slip velocity Δw_p which is the difference between the average velocities of the components and represents an average particle velocity relative to the fluid, or

$$\Delta w_p = \frac{w}{\phi} - \frac{w_p}{(1 - \phi)}, \tag{9.12}$$

where w, w_p are superficial velocities of the phases. It is seen that Δw_p is a function of ϕ, the volume fraction solid, and fluid properties. Equation (9.12) makes possible representation of the system over the whole range of cocurrent and countercurrent, upward and downward flows of components. Wallis [W4], extending the method of Kynch [K46], proposed a characteristic velocity w_m such that

$$w_m = \Delta w_p \phi(1 - \phi)$$
$$= w_p(1 - \phi) - w\phi, \tag{9.13}$$

which is also an invariant of the motion for a given pair of components and ϕ. For empirical correlation, he proposed

$$\Delta w_p = w_{p\infty}(1 - \phi)^n, \tag{9.14}$$

where n is an empirical exponent, and suggested as a means of generalizing extensive results given by Lapidus and Elgin [L17], and Lapidus, Quinn, and Elgin [L18], that the slip velocity obtained by Leva [L32] takes the form

$$w_m^* = \frac{w_m}{w_{p\infty}} = \phi(1 - \phi)(1 - 1.209\phi^{2/3}). \tag{9.15}$$

For unsteady flow, Wallis gave the "shock" velocity

$$w_m = \frac{dw_m}{d\phi}, \tag{9.16}$$

as the slope of the curve shown in Fig. 9.2. For unsteady flow in fluidized beds,

$$w_w = [(n + 1)(1 - \phi)^n - (n + 2)(1 - \phi)^{n+1}]w_{p\infty} + w_{fl}, \tag{9.17}$$

given by Richardson and Zaki [R18] belong to a similar type of equation.

For the gas-liquid system such as treated by Wallis [W3] and liquid-liquid system such as treated by Pratt, Dell, Gaylor, Jones, and Lewis [P28, P29] in the bubble or drop regime $n = 1$. Miles, Shedlovsky, and Ross [M34] gave, for drainage of water through foams, $n \sim 0.6$ to 0.9 for stable foams, and Griffith and Wallis [G41] gave $n = -1$ for fully developed slug flow.

Application of the above relations to batch sedimentation is shown in corresponding curves in Figs. 9.3. Figure 9.3a gives the interface history from

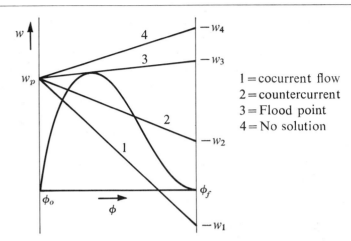

Figure 9.2 General representation of one-dimensional vertical two-phase flow [W4].

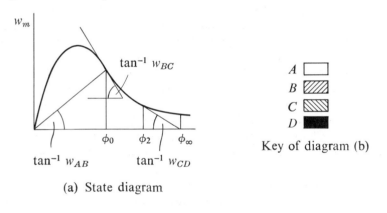

1 = cocurrent flow
2 = countercurrent
3 = Flood point
4 = No solution

Key of diagram (b)

(a) State diagram

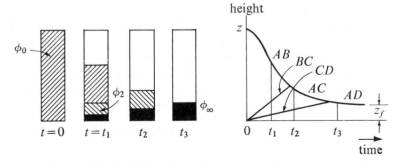

(b) Stages of sedimedation

(c) Variation of height of interface with time

Figure 9.3 Typical stages of batch sedimentation.

the range of uniform suspension B of fraction solid ϕ_0, settling with velocity w_{AB} such that clear liquid A appears at the top of the column. As this takes place, strata C and D appear at t, in Fig. 9.3b, the interface BC travels at velocity w_{BC}; and the interface CD travels at velocity w_{CD} as shown in corresponding diagrams, until final fraction solid is reached after t_3. The validity of this general procedure was further shown in a study of gas-liquid countercurrent flow systems by Bridge, Lapidus, and Elgin [B61]. A similar method of correlation was used by Robins [R24] in his study of the effect of immersed bodies on sedimentation of a suspension. Extensive details are given in the book by Larian [L20]. Pearce [P4] treated the problem of settling of dust in the presence of downward-facing surfaces.

9.2 Flow with Sedimentation

Extending from the introduction in Sec. 9.1, it is seen that sedimentation concerns a number of fields of study. Sedimentation concerns hydraulic engineering when dealing with rivers and harbors. A summary of studies prior to 1955 was given by Chien [C20]; comprehensive discussions were given by Anderson [A12], Chow [C25], and Leliavsky [L31].

In treating sedimentation, earlier discussions show that the mechanism is complicated by the variation in settling velocity due to variation in drag coefficient with concentration of solid particles (Sec. 5.1). Rigorous formulation based on Chap. 6 is feasible but more complicated than in Sec. 9.1. We shall consider the following two cases which are indicative of available methods of approach.

For a distribution in particle size, limiting deposit velocities were correlated empirically by Sinclair [S35]. Sedimentation in turbulent flow through horizontal pipes was studied by Newitt, Richardson, and Shook [N6]. They made measurements on the sedimentation flow of coarse solids such as coarse sand, gravel, and Perspex; and fine solids such as fine sand and zircon sand, in water in pipes of 1-in. diameter; pumping was done by a Vacseal grit pump. Mean water velocity was measured by salt injection; velocity distribution was measured by a pitot tube; solids were sampled with a flow divider consisting of a knife edge and baffle. It was observed that solid particles are hindered in their sedimentation by three principal lifting mechanisms:

1. Those random velocity components greater than the terminal velocity of the particle;
2. The Magnus effect as particles are spun in the shear layer (Sec. 2.3);
3. The dispersive force set up as a result of flow through a bed of particles which displaces the fluid upward, a mechanism analyzed by Bagnold [B3, B5].

The concentration distribution in the pipe, for all five materials and a variety of loadings, was found to be well correlated by

$$\frac{1}{\rho_p}\frac{d\rho_p}{dy} = -1.66\frac{v_{to}}{v_*}\left(\frac{C_D}{2a}\right)^{1/2}, \tag{9.18}$$

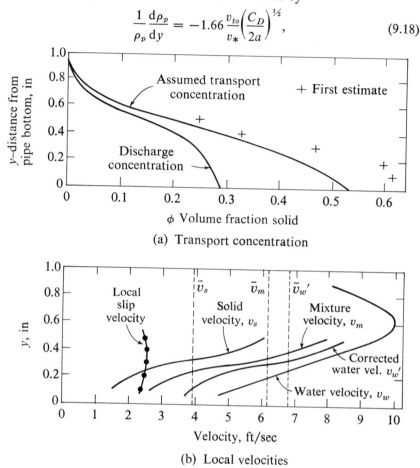

(a) Transport concentration

(b) Local velocities

Figure 9.4 Typical sedimentation flow (hydraulic gradient: 0.28 ft/ft, mean $\phi = 0.10$) [N6].

where a is in in., y is the distance normal to the bottom of the pipe in in., v_{to} is the free fall velocity in ft/sec, v_* is the shear-stress velocity in ft/sec, $v_* = \sqrt{\tau_o/\bar{\rho}}$, τ_o is the mean shear stress at the wall in poundal per ft². Figures 9.4a and 9.4b show typical results of their measurement.

For mean volume fraction solid ϕ at height y above the bottom of the pipe, at steady state, the rate of sedimentation will be equal to that due to eddy diffusion:

$$v_t\phi \, dy = -l'v_*' \, d\phi, \tag{9.19}$$

where v_t is the sedimentation velocity at a given ϕ, l' is the equivalent mixing length in the suspension, v'_* is the vertical component of the eddy velocity. Based on Laufer [L23], the vertical component of the velocity fluctuation is nearly equal to the friction velocity $(\tau_o/\bar{\rho})^{1/2} = v'_*$ outside the laminar sublayer

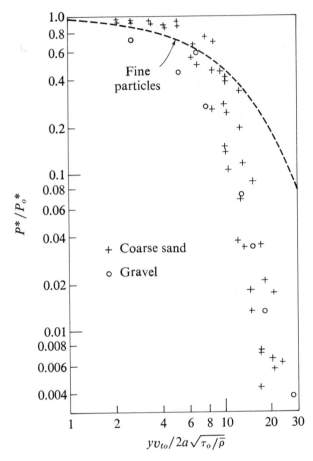

Figure 9.5 Concentration profile [N6].

and take $l' = k(2a)$, k being a constant. Further, an approximation as suggested by Richardson and Zaki [R18] is applied:

$$\frac{v_t}{v_{to}} \simeq (1 - \phi)^2. \tag{9.20}$$

Substitution of these quantities into Eq. (9.19) gives

$$\frac{d\phi}{\phi(1-\phi)^2} = -\frac{v_{to}}{k(2a)\sqrt{\frac{\tau_o}{\rho}}}\, dy, \qquad (9.21)$$

with the boundary condition $\phi = \phi_o$ at $y = 0$, we get

$$\frac{P_y^*}{P_o^*} = \exp\left[\frac{-v_{to}y}{k(2a)\sqrt{\frac{\tau_o}{\rho}}}\right], \qquad (9.22)$$

with

$$P^* = \frac{\phi}{1-\phi}\exp\left[(1-\phi)^{-1}\right]. \qquad (9.23)$$

This correlation is compared to experimental results in Fig. 9.5.

Many studies [L31] have been made on the deposition and erosion of bed deposit which follow wave motion with removal and formation of dunes. Reynolds [R11] treated the problem of waves on an erodible bed semi-empirically by extending the study of fluid flow with wavy wall by Benjamin [B32] and the idea of lag between velocity variations and erosive process due to Kennedy [K15]. His correlation confirms the primary relations that the rate of deposit is proportional to velocity gradient.

9.3 Atmospheric Fallout

A special case of sedimentation is the descent of small particles or heavy molecules through an exponential (density) atmosphere. These small particles may include nuclear fallout, micrometeorites, and cosmic dusts. Aerosols of sulfur compounds, which constitute a source of air pollution, have been detected at about 20 km above the earth's surface. An earlier study by Banister [B13] treated the descent of small particles through a stagnant isothermal atmosphere and accounted for gravitational forces only. The case of diffusion under the influence of external force in a uniform medium was given by Kennard [K13] and Chandrasekhar [C13]. Subsequently, Banister and Davis [B14] took into account both gravitational fall and molecular diffusion. They formulated the problem with the following assumptions:

1. The atmosphere is stagnant and isothermal; the ARDC model atmosphere [U4] suggests that vertical turbulence would be minimized or absent between 15 and 50 km and above 85 km.

2. The concentration of contaminant particles is sufficiently dilute such that only their interactions with air is significant; mutual interactions are negligible.

3. The initial injection is widely spread, say, by horizontal turbulence, such that the problem may be treated as one-dimensional; the divergence of geometry and gravitational forces can be neglected.

The flux J of a contaminant across a unit horizontal surface with concentration ρ_p is given by:

$$J = -\frac{K_1}{\rho}\frac{\partial \rho_p}{\partial x} - \frac{K_2}{\rho}\rho_p, \qquad (9.24)$$

where K_1/ρ is the diffusion coefficient, ρ is the density of the air, K_2/ρ is the fall velocity and x is the altitude with an upward positive direction. The change in concentration is given by:

$$\frac{\partial \rho_p}{\partial t} = -\frac{\partial J}{\partial x} = \frac{\partial}{\partial x}\left[\frac{K_1}{\rho}\frac{\partial \rho_p}{\partial x} + \frac{K_2}{\rho}\rho_p\right], \qquad (9.25)$$

a diffusion equation with drift. For spherical particles,

$$\frac{K_1}{\rho} = \frac{\frac{3}{8}\left[\dfrac{\pi(m_a + m_p)kT}{2m_a m_p}\right]^{\frac{1}{2}}}{n\pi(a_a + a)^2}, \qquad (9.26)$$

where n is the number density of air molecules, m_a its mass, a_a its radius, and a and m_p mass and radius, respectively, of the particles, k the Boltzmann constant, and T the absolute temperature [K13]. Since $m_a n = \rho$,

$$K_1 = \frac{\frac{3}{8}\left[\left(1 + \dfrac{m_a}{m_p}\right)\left(\dfrac{m_a kT}{2\pi}\right)\right]^{\frac{1}{2}}}{(a_a + a)^2}, \qquad (9.27)$$

and

$$\rho = \rho_o \exp\left(-\frac{x}{\Lambda}\right), \qquad (9.28)$$

where Λ is the e-fold distance $kT/m_a g$ of the isothermal atmosphere, g is the gravitational acceleration. The velocity of fall is given by the condition $J = 0$, or, from Eq. (9.25)

$$K_2 = K_1 \frac{m_p g}{kT} = \frac{\frac{3}{8}g\left[\dfrac{m_a m_p(m_a + m_p)}{2\pi kT}\right]^{\frac{1}{2}}}{(a_a + a)^2}, \qquad (9.29)$$

and at equilibrium, for $K_1/K_2 = \Lambda'$,

$$\rho_p = \rho_{po} \exp\left(-\frac{x}{\Lambda'}\right), \qquad (9.30)$$

as in the case of exponential atmosphere. Unlike in the case of a uniform medium, it is expected that as the altitude decreases, both particle fall and diffusion are inhibited by the increasing air density. The contaminant profile would approach the steady-state distribution in the upper portions and a decrease in concentration at the downward side of the profile. A substantial distortion of the expanding and moving Gaussian distribution is expected for an initial plane or delta function type distribution.

It is noted that a particle whose position is identified as $x = x_o$ moves with a velocity

$$\frac{dx_o}{d\tau} = -\frac{K_2}{\rho_o} \exp\left(\frac{x_o}{\Lambda}\right),$$
(9.31)

and integration gives

$$x_o = -\Lambda \ln\left(\frac{K_2 \tau}{\rho_o \Lambda}\right),$$
(9.32)

where $\tau = t + \tau_o$, $\tau_o = (\rho_o \Lambda / K_2) \exp(-A/\Lambda)$ and $A = x_o|_{t=0}$. With this moving coordinate system, Granzow [G37] proposed the following change of variables:

$$z = \frac{\Lambda}{\Lambda'} \exp\left[-\frac{(x - x_o)}{\Lambda}\right] = \frac{\Lambda^2 \rho_o}{K_1(t + \tau_o)} \exp\left(-\frac{x}{\Lambda}\right)$$
(9.33)

$$\tau = t + \tau_o,$$
(9.34)

and

$$\rho_p = z^{\Lambda/\Lambda'} e^{-z} u(z,\tau).$$
(9.35)

Equation (9.25) now becomes

$$z^2 \frac{\partial^2 u}{\partial z^2} + \left(\frac{\Lambda}{\Lambda'} - z\right)\frac{\partial u}{\partial z} - \tau \frac{\partial u}{\partial \tau} = 0.$$
(9.36)

The concentration distributions which are constant with respect to time in this moving coordinate system are given by $\partial u/\partial \tau = 0$ in the above equation, or

$$u = C_1 \int z^{-\Lambda/\Lambda'} e^z \, dz + C_2,$$
(9.37)

where C_1 and C_2 are constants of integration. $C_1 = 0$ if the distribution of matter is finite; that is, the concentration approaches zero far from the origin. The solution $u = C_2$ gives a constant profile.

Equation (9.36) can be solved by separation of variables with

$$u = Z(z)T(\tau).$$
(9.38)

We get

$$z \frac{d^2 Z}{dz^2} + \left(\frac{\Lambda}{\Lambda'} - z\right)\frac{dZ}{dz} + \xi Z = 0,$$
(9.39)

and

$$\frac{\tau}{T}\frac{dT}{d\tau} = -\xi, \tag{9.40}$$

giving

$$T = C\tau^{-\xi}, \tag{9.41}$$

choosing ξ as nonnegative integers. Equation (9.39) is an associated Laguerre equation with a complete orthogonal set of solutions, $L_\xi^b(z)$, with $b = (\Lambda/\Lambda') - 1$, and

$$u = \sum_{\xi=0}^{\infty} a_\xi \tau^{-\xi} L_\xi^b(z), \tag{9.42}$$

and ρ_p is given by

$$\frac{\rho_p}{z} = z^b e^{-z} u = z^b e^{-z} \sum_{\xi=0}^{\infty} a_\xi \tau^{-\xi} L_\xi^b(z). \tag{9.43}$$

For given distribution of particles at $t = 0$ ($\tau = \tau_o$) denoted by $f(x)$ and x given by

$$x = -\Lambda \ln\left(\frac{K_1 \tau_o z}{\Lambda^2 \rho_o}\right). \tag{9.44}$$

Denoting

$$g(z) = f(x)\left[-\Lambda \ln\left(\frac{K_1 \tau_o z}{\Lambda^2 \rho_o}\right)\right]. \tag{9.45}$$

Equation (9.43) becomes

$$\frac{g(z)}{z} = z^b e^{-z} \sum_{\xi=0}^{\infty} a_\xi \tau_o^{-\xi} L_\xi^b(z). \tag{9.46}$$

The Laguerre polynomial is given by, from Morse and Feshbach [M47]

$$L_n^a(z) = \frac{\Gamma(a + n + 1)}{\Gamma(n + 1)} \frac{e^z}{z^a} \frac{d^n}{dz^n} [z^{a+n} e^{-z}], \tag{9.47}$$

and

$$\int_0^\infty z^a e^{-z} L_m^a(z) L_n^a(z)\, dz = \delta_{mn} \frac{[\Gamma(a + n + 1)]^3}{\Gamma(n + 1)}. \tag{9.48}$$

Multiplying both sides of Eq. (9.46) by $L_\xi^b(z)$, we get

$$a_\xi = \tau_o^\xi \frac{\Gamma(\xi + 1)}{[\Gamma(b + \xi + 1)]^3} \int_0^\infty \frac{g(z)}{z} L_\xi^b(z)\, dz$$

$$= \tau_o^\xi \frac{\Gamma(\xi + 1)}{[\Gamma(b + \xi + 1)]^3} \frac{1}{\Lambda} \int_{-\infty}^\infty f(x) L_\xi^b\left(\frac{\Lambda^2 \rho_o e^{-x/\Lambda}}{K_1 \tau_o}\right) dx. \tag{9.49}$$

It is seen from Eq. (9.43) that the first term of the expansion of ρ_p is just the constant profile solution. After a long time, higher order terms become negligible. Hence any initial distribution (which can be expressed in terms of Laguerre polynomials) will approach the constant profile solution. The properties of the Laguerre polynomials are such that for $m = 0$ in Eq. (9.48)

$$\int_0^\infty z^a e^{-z} L_n^a(z)\, dz = \begin{cases} [\Gamma(a + 1)]^2, & \text{for } n = 0 \\ 0 & , & \text{for } n \neq 0 \end{cases}. \qquad (9.50)$$

Thus the total mass of a distribution of particles at t_o is

$$\int_{-\infty}^\infty \rho_p(x,t_o)\, dx = \Lambda \int_0^\infty \frac{\rho_p(z,t_o)}{z}\, dz$$

$$= \Lambda \int_0^\infty z^b e^{-z} \sum_{\xi=0}^\infty a_\xi (t_o + \tau_o)^{-\xi} L_\xi^b(z)\, dz, \qquad (9.51)$$

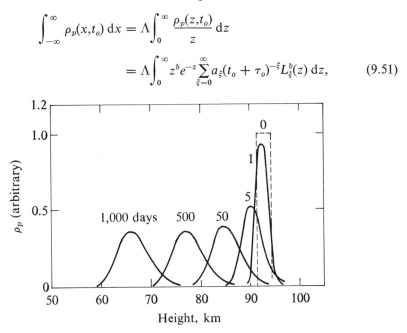

Figure 9.6 Time history of contaminant profile for a square distribution injected at between 91.44 and 94.49 km, molecular weight 150, $\bar{\rho}_p = 6$ g/cm³ [B14].

$\xi = 0$ gives the total mass, or

$$\int_{-\infty}^\infty \rho_p(x,t_o)\, dx = a_o \Lambda [\Gamma(b + 1)]^2. \qquad (9.52)$$

Typical results of computations are shown in Figs. 9.6 and 9.7. Figure 9.6 shows the calculated time history of the contaminant profile for a square distribution injected between 91.44 and 94.49 km. The contaminant was taken to have a molecular weight of 150 and a bulk density of 6 g/cm³; profiles were given at 5 to 1000 days after the injection. The air was taken to be at 245°K, $\rho_o = 1.72 \times 10^{-5}$ g/cm³ and $\Lambda = 7.18$ km. The time-altitude history in Fig. 9.7 of maximum concentration points (initially at 92.97 km)

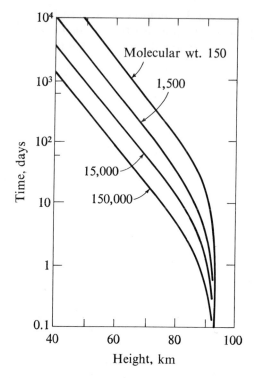

Figure 9.7 Time vs. altitude history of the maximum concentration points, initial maximum points at 92.97 km, various molecular weights $\bar{\rho}_p = 6$ g/cm³ [B14].

for various masses of particles of density $\bar{\rho}_p = 6$ g/cm³ shows results which were obtained by numerical solution of Eq. (9.25) by Banister and Davis [B14] with the properties of solution confirmed by Granzow [G37].

In general, for any initial profile, diffusion transforms it rapidly into a profile which remains stationary and descends through the atmosphere at diminishing rate and amplitude. The net transport time was found to be not seriously affected by intervening layers of turbulence, although entrance into a turbulent layer achieves an abrupt downward transport of material.

Dust deposition on various surfaces was studied by Owen [O10]. Motion of air borne microorganisms was studied by Harper, Hood, and Morton [H16].

9.4 Motion in Fluidized Beds

With the availability of treatises by Leva [L32], Othmer [O9], and Zenz [Z5] on fluidized beds, we shall cover only the basic aspects and methods here. Fluidized beds, due to their important applications as devices for mixing

and heat and mass transfer, and as chemical reactors, particularly in the field
of petroleum refining, have been the subject of many intensive studies. Still,
among gas-solid and gas-liquid systems, the fluidized bed is at present least
susceptible to rigorous treatment.

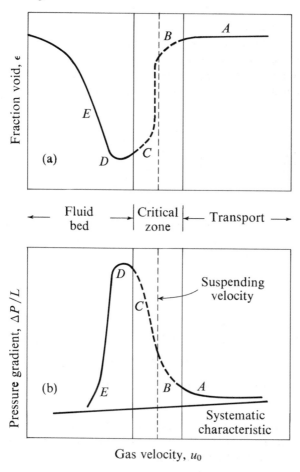

Figure 9.8 Typical trend of fraction void and pressure gradient at given feed rate [M22].

Continuous transition from the regimes of packed bed, fluidized bed, to
transport flow was studied by Wilhelm and Kwauk [W20] and Wilhelm and
Valentine [W22]. McCune and Wilhelm [M22] treated the mass and momentum transfer in fixed and fluidized beds, and gave the trend for transition from
fluidization to transport as shown in Fig. 9.8, showing the relation between
gas velocity, fraction void, and transport. Some regular behaviors have been
observed when a stable homogeneous bed is maintained, and a summary was

presented by Gohr [G27]. In the representation of May and Rossell [M18], three steps of the fluidizing process were recognized, and are summarized in Fig. 9.9. In Range A, low velocity gas percolates through the bed without agitation of individual particles, the gas phase is in viscous flow, and the pressure drop increases linearly with velocity, but less than the weight of the bed. Sufficient increase in gas velocity (to 0.01 to 0.02 fps) leads to transition to Range B; the solids are suspended by the gas and there is a substantial increase in the bed volume; the pressure drop becomes equal to or slightly in excess of the weight of the solids present. Above 0.02 fps, we have Range C. Further increase in gas flow is accompanied by "bubble" flow.

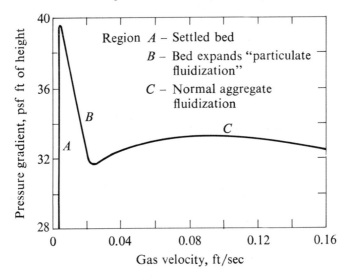

Figure 9.9 Fluidization of cracking catalyst [M18].

The density of a fluidized bed changes due to expansion of the bed. A large bed expansion in the "particulate" flow region is characteristic of smooth fluidization. The effects of particle characteristics and of gas velocity on bed density are shown by the typical relationship in Fig. 9.10; that is, for similar superficial velocity, larger particles give rise to higher bed density.

Since the study of Gilliland and Mason [G20, G21] on gas mixing in a fluidized bed, the flow patterns in a stable fluidized bed are relatively well understood. Leva [L33] showed that at relatively low fluid velocity, the bed amounts to two beds in series, with the bottom part acting as a packed bed with very little solid motion while the top bed is in intensely fluidized state (Fig. 9.11). In the upper bed, the solids move upward in the center and downward near the wall. At the interface between and the top and bottom beds,

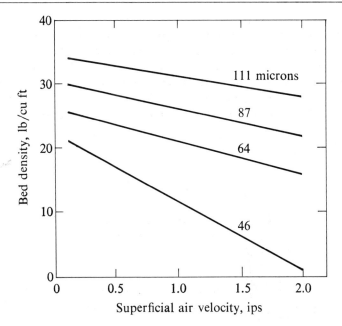

Figure 9.10 Effect of gas velocity on fluid-bed density of cracking catalyst [G27].

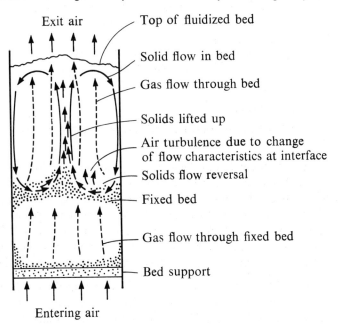

Figure 9.11 Flow model of fluidized bed [L33].

the solids move radially inward. As the fluid velocity is increased, the bottom bed may become nearly depleted other than a stagnant zone at the corner (Fig. 9.12). It is seen that a stable fluidized bed consists essentially of two portions, one in which the particles are transported by the fluid, and one in which the bed is extremely dense and motion is very slow such that internal stresses in the bed become significant. This flow mechanism was confirmed by DeMaria and Longfield [D22], from a study of point age distribution of the gas phase.

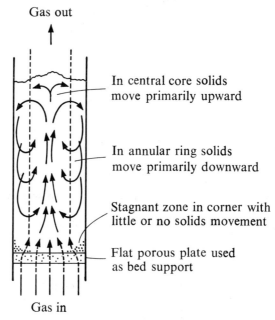

Figure 9.12 Simplified flow pattern in small diameter gas-fluidized bed [L33].

In his thorough discussion of the state of motion in a fluidized bed, Rowe [R39] suggested that large density difference $(\bar{\rho}_p - \bar{\rho})$ between the particle and the fluid will tend to damp out turbulence. At low $(\bar{\rho}_p - \bar{\rho})$, the particles will be carried around the bed by fluid eddies in a random manner. Hence, liquid fluidized beds are often turbulent although the flow may be laminar and the particles are barely mobile at low rates of flow. Gas fluidized beds are generally laminar, but turbulence may break through at high flow rates.

Laminar Flow Model [S61]—As a way of bringing up the basic problems involved, let us first consider the possibility of a steady "laminar" flow fluidized bed. We further simplify by taking the case of a pipe flow model; that is, a section of fluidized bed of radius R of infinite height. With these specifications, it is readily seen that the momentum equations (6.39) and (6.42), pp. 262–4, become (for velocities w, u in the axial z and radial r directions):

$$0 = -\frac{\partial P}{\partial z} + \frac{1}{r}\frac{\partial}{\partial r}\,r\mu'\frac{\partial w}{\partial r} + \frac{1}{r}\frac{\partial}{\partial r}\,r\mu_p'\frac{\partial w_p}{\partial r} - (\rho + \rho_p)g \qquad (9.53)$$

$$0 = -\rho_p F(w - w_p) - \frac{\partial P}{\partial z}\left(1 - \frac{\rho_p}{\bar\rho_p}\right) - \bar\rho g + \frac{1}{r}\frac{\partial}{\partial r}\,r\mu'\frac{\partial w}{\partial r} \qquad (9.54)$$

where μ' is the viscosity of the fluid in the mixture, μ_p' is the viscosity of the particle cloud in the mixture (Sec. 6.1), based on μ_p the viscosity of the particle phase from Eqs. (5.44) and (5.47). F is given by Eq. (5.5) p. 186. The continuity condition is satisfied by $u = u_p = 0$ for fully developed flow, and $w = w(r)$, $w_p = w_p(r)$ and $\rho_p = $ constant, $\rho = $ constant. Further, within the range of fluidization, there is no net transport of particles, $\int_0^R w_p r\,dr = 0$, and $\partial w/\partial r = 0$, $\partial w_p/\partial r = 0$ at $r = 0$, $w = 0$ at $r = R$, and $\partial P/\partial z = dP/dz = $ constant. In order to get a closed form solution for our discussion, we further assume $\mu' = $ constant, and $\mu_p' = $ constant, (note the non-Newtonian nature of the particle cloud—Sec. 5.3, p. 202). The solution is carried out by first eliminating w_p from Eqs. (9.53) and (9.54), or, from Eq. (9.54),

$$w_p = w - \frac{\mu'}{F\rho_p}\frac{1}{r}\frac{d}{dr}\,r\frac{dw}{dr} + \frac{1}{F\rho_p}\frac{dP}{dz}\left(1 - \frac{\rho_p}{\bar\rho_p}\right) + \frac{g\bar\rho}{F\rho_p}, \qquad (9.55)$$

and Eq. (9.53) becomes

$$\frac{1}{r}\frac{d}{dr}\,r\frac{dZ}{dr} - \alpha^2 Z = \beta, \qquad (9.56)$$

with

$$Z = \frac{1}{r}\frac{d}{dr}\,r\frac{dw}{dr} \qquad (9.57)$$

$$\alpha^2 = \frac{F\rho_p(\mu' + \mu_p')}{\mu_p'\mu'} \qquad (9.58)$$

$$\beta = \left[-\frac{dP}{dz} - (\rho + \rho_p)g\right]\frac{F\rho_p}{\mu_p'\mu'}. \qquad (9.59)$$

Equation (9.56) is a modified Bessels equation of order zero which gives for the boundary condition $Z(0) = 0$,

$$Z = AI_0(\alpha r) - \frac{\beta}{\alpha^2}, \qquad (9.60)$$

where A is the constant of integration and I_0 is the modified Bessels function of order zero. Integration of Eq. (9.57) gives, with the previously stated boundary conditions,

$$\frac{AF}{\alpha^2 g} = \frac{A\mu'\mu'_p}{\rho_p g(\mu' + \mu'_p)}$$

$$= \frac{\dfrac{F\beta R^2}{8\alpha^2 g} + \dfrac{1}{\rho_p g}\left(1 - \dfrac{\rho_p}{\bar{\rho}_p}\right)\dfrac{dP}{dz} + \dfrac{\bar{\rho}}{\rho_p} + \dfrac{\mu'\beta}{\rho_p \alpha^2 g}}{I_0(\alpha R) - 2\left(1 - \dfrac{\mu'\alpha^2}{F\rho_p'}\right)\dfrac{I_1(\alpha R)}{\alpha R}}, \qquad (9.61)$$

and

$$\frac{wF}{g} = -\frac{AF}{\alpha^2 g}[I_0(\alpha R) - I_0(\alpha r)] + \frac{\beta R^2 F}{4\alpha^2 g}\left(1 - \frac{r^2}{R^2}\right) \qquad (9.62)$$

$$\frac{w_p F}{g} = \frac{wF}{g} - \left(\frac{AF}{\alpha^2 g}\right)\left(\frac{\mu'\alpha^2}{\rho_p F}\right)I_0(\alpha r) + \frac{1}{\rho_p g}\left(1 - \frac{\rho_p}{\bar{\rho}_p}\right)\frac{dP}{dz} + \frac{\bar{\rho}}{\rho_p} + \frac{\mu'\beta}{\rho_p g\alpha^2}. \quad (9.63)$$

The mean velocity w of the fluid phase is given by

$$\frac{\bar{w}R^2}{2} = \int_0^R wr\, dr, \qquad (9.64)$$

which gives

$$\frac{\bar{w}F}{g} = \frac{\beta R^2 F}{8\alpha^2 g} - \frac{AF}{\alpha^2 g}\left(I_0(\alpha R) - \frac{2I_1(\alpha R)}{\alpha R\cdot}\right). \qquad (9.65)$$

These relations become obvious if we consider the limiting situation of a very dilute (ideal) fluidized bed; that is, $\mu' = \bar{\mu}$, $\mu'_p = 0$. We see then, that $A = 0$, and the conditions at the wall ($r = R$) are $w_w = 0$ and

$$\frac{w_{pw}F}{g} = -\left(1 - \frac{\bar{\rho}}{\bar{\rho}_p}\right) - \frac{1}{\bar{\rho}_p g}\frac{dP}{dz}, \qquad (9.66)$$

which is the terminal velocity of the particles in a pressure gradient. With this simplification, the no-transport condition of particles gives

$$\frac{\beta R^2 F}{8\alpha^2 g} = \left(1 - \frac{\bar{\rho}}{\bar{\rho}_p}\right) + \frac{1}{g\bar{\rho}_p}\frac{dP}{dz} = \frac{\bar{w}F}{g}. \qquad (9.67)$$

The velocity profiles are now

$$\frac{wF}{g} = \frac{\beta F R^2}{4\alpha^2 g}\left(1 - \frac{r^2}{R^2}\right) = \frac{2\bar{w}F}{g}\left(1 - \frac{r^2}{R^2}\right), \qquad (9.68)$$

as in laminar pipe flow, and

$$\frac{w_p F}{g} = \frac{wF}{g} - \left(1 - \frac{\bar{\rho}}{\rho_p}\right) - \frac{1}{g\bar{\rho}_p}\frac{dP}{dz} = \frac{2\bar{w}F}{g}\left(1 - \frac{r^2}{R^2}\right) - \frac{\bar{w}F}{g} \qquad (9.69)$$

which are parabolic profiles as shown in Fig. 9.13, with $w_p = 0$ at $r/R = 1/\sqrt{2}$. It is seen that the flow of particles is upward for $r/R < 1/\sqrt{2}$ and

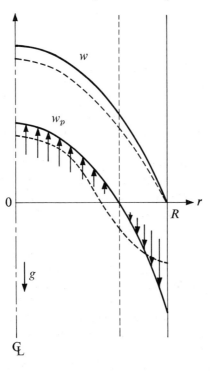

——— Simple laminar flow

– – – – Corrected for interactions

Figure 9.13 Laminar-flow profiles in a fluidized bed.

downward in the region $1 > r/R > 1/\sqrt{2}$; this magnitude agrees qualitatively with the above cited observations; Lewis, Gilliland, and Girouard [L39] actually took this ratio as 0.70 in their study. For this simple situation, the pressure drop can be expressed explicitly as

$$-\frac{dP}{dz} = \frac{8\bar{\mu}\bar{w}}{R^2} + g(\rho + \rho_p). \qquad (9.70)$$

The above relations can be expressed in terms of fraction void ϵ with $\rho = \bar{\rho}\epsilon$, $\rho_p = \bar{\rho}_p(1 - \epsilon)$, and Ergun's extension of Stokes' law in Eq. (9.9), for $\epsilon < 0.917$. It is seen that, at relatively large fraction void, Eq. (9.70) gives:

$$-\frac{dP}{dz} = \frac{g\bar{\rho}_p\left[\epsilon\dfrac{\bar{\rho}}{\bar{\rho}_p} + (1-\epsilon)\right]\left\{1 + \dfrac{32}{75}\left(1 - \dfrac{\bar{\rho}}{\bar{\rho}_p}\right)\left[\dfrac{\bar{\rho}}{\bar{\rho}_p}\epsilon + (1-\epsilon)\right]^{-1}\dfrac{a^2}{R^2}\dfrac{\epsilon^2}{1-\epsilon}\right\}}{1 + \dfrac{32}{75}\dfrac{\epsilon^2}{1-\epsilon}\dfrac{a^2}{R^2}},$$

$$(9.71)$$

and

$$\frac{\bar{w}a\bar{\rho}}{\bar{\mu}} = \frac{4}{75}\frac{\epsilon^2}{1-\epsilon}\left(\frac{g\bar{\rho}^2a^3}{\bar{\mu}^2}\right)\left(\frac{\bar{\rho}_p}{\bar{\rho}}\right)\left[\left(1 - \frac{\bar{\rho}}{\bar{\rho}_p}\right) + \frac{1}{g\bar{\rho}_p}\frac{dP}{dz}\right]. \qquad (9.72)$$

Both relations conform to the trend obtained from measurements by Wilhelm and Valentine [W22]; who also studied the transition from fluidization to transport.

Following the examples in the previous sections, fluidization and sedimentation of particles of a given size distribution can be treated based on equations in Chap. 6 with transport properties in Chap. 5. Published works, however, utilize mainly semiempirical correlation. An example is a study of stratification by size in fluidization and settling by Pruden and Epstein [P33].

Random Motion—Even in a liquid-solid fluidized bed, where the flow pattern is relatively quiescent, shear motion as dealt with in the above would set the particles (and the fluid) in continuous motion. Systematic eddies exist ranging from sizes which are large with respect to particle dimensions to those due to the wakes of these particles. Measurements of eddy diffusivity of the fluid phase were made with tracers of dyes and electrolytes in liquid-solid systems and helium in gas-solid systems.

Kramers, Westermann, de Groot, and Dupont [K35] made measurements of longitudinal eddy diffusivities (D_l) in a liquid-solid fluidized bed with diffusivity evaluated according to

$$\frac{C_z - C_1}{C_2 - C_1} = \frac{1}{2}\left[1 - \exp\left(\frac{z - Wt}{\sqrt{4D_l t}}\right)\right], \qquad (9.73)$$

where z is the axial location, W the mean velocity, t the time, C's are the electrolyte concentration at the bottom changing suddenly from C_1 to C_2 and at z. With glass spheres of 1 and 0.5-mm diameter in water, the fluidizing velocities were shown to correlate according to

$$\frac{W}{W_s} = \epsilon^{1.81}, \qquad (9.74)$$

for 1-mm diameter spheres, W_s is the flow velocity for $\epsilon = 1$, and

$$\frac{W}{W_s} = \epsilon^{2.09}, \tag{9.75}$$

for 0.5-mm diameter spheres with tube diameter below 25 times the particle diameter and bed height up to 400 times the particle diameter. The results are shown in Fig. 9.14. The variation in the dependency of D_l on ϵ near

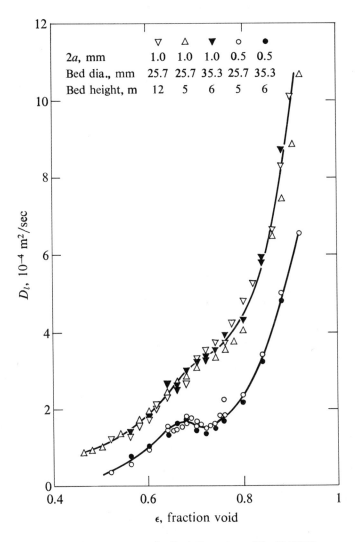

Figure 9.14 Longitudinal dispersion of liquid [K35].

$\epsilon = 0.7$ was interpreted as due to the variation of the velocity on the scale of one particle (wake); a fact confirmed by McHenry and Wilhelm [M24] from measurements on fixed beds. Rapid increase of D_l at high porosity was thought to be due to agglomeration of particles. At still higher ϵ, D_l decreases due to low concentration of particles. Hanratty, Latinen, and Wilhelm [H9], using the method cited in Sec. 2.8, showed that both longitudinal (D_l) and transverse (D_t) diffusivities pass through a maximum at $0.7 < \epsilon < 0.8$. Using a semiempirical procedure, Beek [B29] suggested that

$$\frac{D_l}{2aW_s} = 5.2\epsilon^{2.08} + 9.0(4.08\epsilon - 2.08)(3.08\epsilon - 2.08)\epsilon^{2.08}, \qquad (9.76)$$

ϵ being the average fraction void. Using a sand (0.2 to 0.3 mm in diameter) water system with 0.1 to 1.0 m internal diameter, Bruinzeel, Reman, and van der Laan [B66] concluded the correlation:

$$(N_{Pe})_p = 4.3 \times 10^{-3}(N_{Re})_p, \qquad (9.77)$$

where $(N_{Pe})_p$ is the particle Peclet number:

$$(N_{Pe})_p = \frac{2aW_s}{\epsilon D_l}, \qquad (9.78)$$

and $(N_{Re})_p$ is the particle Reynolds number, and

$$(N_{Re})_p = \frac{2a\bar{\rho}W_s}{\epsilon\mu}. \qquad (9.79)$$

Spouted Bed or Fluidized Bed with a Conical Vessel—A technique of contacting a fluid with solids proposed by Mathur and Gishler [M16] is called a spouted bed. As a modification of the fluidized bed, a spouted bed is a packed bed agitated by a centrally located jet which spouts upward, bringing the particles in its path upward while the particles near the wall of the vessel move downward. Becker [B26, B28] studied heat transfer and velocity profiles in such a system. Madonna and Lama [M3] made energy balance to correlate pressure drop and spout diameter of the system. The use of spouted beds and fluidized beds for solid mixing was discussed by Littman [L50]. The blending mechanism in an aerated conical vessel with or without stirrer was evaluated by Leva [L33]. The method in Sec. 8.8 is applicable to a dilute spouted bed.

9.5 Instabilities and Bubble Formation

As generalized by Zenz [Z2], liquid-solid fluidized beds maintain homogeneous mixtures over the complete range of the dense phase (normal loose-packed bulk density of solid particles) to disperse or dilute phase (densities commonly ranging from 0 to 10 per cent of the bulk density). In systems of gases and fine solid catalyst materials, however, homogeneous mixtures can be achieved only at these two extremes; in between, nonhomogeneous condition tends to prevail. This includes bubbles of gas within a fluidized mass of solids; further decrease in density of bed leads to alternate steps of gas and loose-packed solids. Zenz gave a complete discussion over the complete range from packed bed to transport or transfer-line operation.

Wilhelm and Rice [W21] applied the theory of interface stability of Taylor [T8] and proposed two models from consideration of stabilities: Liquid-solid fluidization in a homogeneous bed with both the density and viscosity of the dense bed nearly the same as those of the support fluid, and gas-solid fluidization where the dense region behaves as an emulsion, with bed density taken as a weighted average of solid and fluid and bed viscosity much higher than that of the fluid. The wave number of disturbance can be expressed in terms of a density ratio $[(1 - \epsilon)\bar{\rho}_p \sim \bar{\rho}]/\bar{\rho}$ and other empirical parameters.

Murray [M55] treated various aspects of instabilities in fluidized beds including propagation of small disturbances, surface wave propagation, hot (compressible fluid) beds, centrifugal beds, and electromagnetic effects in detail. His method of approach is seen considering the propagation of small disturbances in a two-dimensional (x,y-coordinates and unit vectors $\mathbf{i}$, $\mathbf{j}$) incompressible beds for the case $\bar{\rho}_p/\bar{\rho} \gg 1$, and consider only the gravity effect (y-direction). The steady state is represented by

$$
\left.
\begin{aligned}
\mathbf{v}_p &= 0, \quad \mathbf{v} = (0,v_o), \\
\phi &= \phi_o \\
P &= P_o - g\rho_p y = P_o - Fv_o y
\end{aligned}
\right\}, \tag{9.80}
$$

subscript o represents constant reference quantities; $y = 0$ at bottom of bed. Equations (6.32, 6.33, 6.41, and 6.42) become:

$$
\left.
\begin{aligned}
\nabla \cdot \rho_p \mathbf{v}_p &= -\frac{\partial \rho_p}{\partial t} \\[6pt]
\nabla \cdot \rho \mathbf{v} &= -\frac{\partial \rho}{\partial t} \\[6pt]
\frac{\rho_p \, d\mathbf{v}_p}{dt} &= -g\rho_p \mathbf{j} + \rho_p F(\mathbf{v} - \mathbf{v}_p) + \frac{C\bar{\rho}\phi \, d(\mathbf{v} - \mathbf{v}_p)}{dt} \\[6pt]
\rho \frac{d\mathbf{v}}{dt} &= -\nabla P - F(\mathbf{v} - \mathbf{v}_p)
\end{aligned}
\right\}, \tag{9.81}
$$

where $\rho = \bar{\rho}(1 - \phi)$, $\rho_p = \bar{\rho}_p \phi$, C is a proportionality for the apparent mass term ($C = \frac{1}{2}$ for $\phi \to 0$, namely, a single particle in an infinite fluid medium, $C \sim 1$ in general). The viscous stresses are neglected in the present example.

Murray considered small perturbations about the steady state given by Eq. (9.80)

$$\mathbf{v}_p = v_o \mathbf{v}_p^* E^*, \qquad \mathbf{v} = v_o[\mathbf{j} + \mathbf{v}^* E^*]$$

$$\phi = \phi_o[1 + \phi^* E^*], \qquad P = P_o[1 + P^* E^*], \qquad (9.82)$$

$$E^* = \exp\left[i\kappa_x(x - ct) + \kappa_y(y - y_o)\right]$$

where the starred quantities are dimensionless perturbations, κ_x, κ_y are the wave members, c the wave velocity, and t the time. Substitution of Eqs. (9.82) into (9.81) with Eq. (9.80) gives the following dimensionless first-order perturbation equations: (taking v^* as the real and u^* as the imaginary components of $\mathbf{v}^*$)

$$iu_p^* + zv_p^* - i\omega N\phi^* = 0 \qquad (9.83)$$

$$iu^* + zv^* - D(z - i\omega N)\phi^* = 0 \qquad (9.84)$$

$$u^*\left[\left(\frac{z}{N}\right) - i\omega\right]\mathbf{i} + v^*\left[\left(\frac{z}{N}\right) - i\omega\right]\mathbf{j}$$

$$- u_p^* RDi\omega\mathbf{i} - v_p^* RDi\omega\mathbf{j} + (R - 1)ND\phi^*\mathbf{j} + [z\mathbf{j} + i\mathbf{i}]P^*P = 0 \quad (9.85)$$

$$-\mathbf{v}^*\left[N + C(R - 1)^{-1}\left(\frac{z}{N} - i\omega\right)\right]$$

$$+ u_p^*\left[N - i(R - 1)^{-1}\omega R + C(R - 1)^{-1}\left(\frac{z}{N} - i\omega\right)\right]\mathbf{i}$$

$$+ v_p^*\left[N - i(R - 1)^{-1}\omega R + C(R - 1)^{-1}\left(\frac{z}{N} - i\omega\right)\right]\mathbf{j} = 0, \quad (9.86)$$

with the substitution of relation given by particle momentum equation in Eq. (9.81) at steady state:

$$g(\bar{\rho}_p - \bar{\rho}) = F\bar{\rho}_p v_o, \qquad (9.87)$$

and taking $F \sim$ constant. The dimensionless parameters are

$$z = \frac{\kappa_y}{\kappa_x}, \quad \omega = \frac{\kappa_x c}{(\kappa_x g)^{1/2}}, \quad D = \phi_o(1 - \phi_o)^{-1},$$

$$N = \frac{g}{\kappa_x v_o^2}, \quad P = \left(\frac{\kappa_x}{g}\right)^{1/2}\frac{P_o}{\bar{\rho}(1 - \phi_o)v_o}, \quad R = \frac{\bar{\rho}_p}{\bar{\rho}}$$

$$(9.88)$$

The dispersion relationship for Eqs. (9.83) to (9.86) reduces to

$$(z^2 - 1)L_1(\omega,z)L_2(\omega,z) = 0, \tag{9.89}$$

with

$$L_1(\omega,z) = \omega^2\left[1 + \frac{C(1 + D)}{R}\right] + i\omega\left[N(D + 1)\frac{R - 1}{R} + \frac{C(1 + 2D)z}{RN}\right]$$
$$- z\frac{R - 1}{R}\left[D + \frac{CDz}{N^2(R - 1)}\right] \tag{9.90}$$

$$L_2(\omega,z) = \omega^2\left[\frac{C(RD + 1) + R}{(R - 1)RD}\right] + \frac{i\omega}{(R - 1)RD}\left[\frac{z}{N}(R + 2C + RCD)\right]$$
$$+ N(R - 1)(1 + RD)\right] - \frac{1}{RD}\left[z + \frac{Cz^2}{N^2(R - 1)}\right]. \tag{9.91}$$

Physically possible motions are given by

$$L_1(\omega,z) = 0, \quad L_2(\omega,z) = 0, \tag{9.92}$$

z is effectively the dimensionless y-component of wave number. If z is known and imaginary, Eqs. (9.92) give ω's and the wave speeds and growth rates of small disturbances propagated in the interior of the bed. Equations (9.92) each give two values of ω, say L_1 gives ω_{01} and ω_{11}, and L_2 gives ω_{11} and ω_{12}. It is seen that as $R \to \infty$, $C \to 0$ [C15], ω_{01} is given by

$$\omega_{01} \sim \frac{izD}{N(D + 1)}, \tag{9.93}$$

while

$$\omega_{11} \sim -iN(D + 1), \tag{9.94}$$

and ω_{02} disappears, on $R \geqslant 1$, ω_{02} persists and ω_{01} disappears. ω_{11} or ω_{12} gives only stable oscillations. It is seen that as $R \to \infty$, $\omega_{12} = 0$; ω_{12} is related to shear stresses in the bed. $R > 10$ in general tends to lead to unstable motion and growth bubbles in a fluidized bed. Murray's conclusions conform with experimental findings of Rowe [R39] in the following.

Rowe [R39] suggested that at low $(\bar{\rho}_p - \bar{\rho})$ both particle and fluid flow are disturbed, bubbles cannot persist because a constant through flow of fluid does not exist. What appears to be a temporary space free of particles may be produced by centrifugal force of a turbulent vortex, but this is not a bubble in the sense of the present discussion. Liquid fluidized beds generally have low $(\bar{\rho}_p - \bar{\rho})$. When fluidized by water at rates that cause considerable expansion, temporarily empty vortices often resemble bubbles. Gas-fluidized beds are most susceptible to bubble formation. Toomey and Johnstone [T41] postulated that in aggregative fluidization all gas in excess of minimum fluidization requirements bypasses the bed as bubbles. Zenz [Z3] further associated the growth of bubbles to the slugging as bubbles of the size of column diameters. Romero and Johanson [R30] tested these theories by correlating empirically the bubble formation and bubble frequency; the average bubble thickness y correlates approximately to

$$y \sim \left[\frac{w - w_{mf}}{10\pi\bar{\rho}f} \right]^{\frac{1}{3}}, \qquad (9.95)$$

where w_{mf} is the minimum fluidization velocity and f the bubble frequency.

Studies of bubble formation and bubble dynamics have been largely observational. These include studies of the quality of fluidization in terms of change of capacitance by Bakkar and Heertjen [B8], fluctuation of pressure strain by Shuster and Kisliak [S32], X-ray transmission by Baumgarten and Pigford [B25], and light transmission by Yasui and Johanson [Y1].

A number of studies have been made, using a bubble injector, on the mechanism of formation and shape of bubbles in a fluidized bed. Rowe [R39] at first treated the bubble as spherical shaped and estimated the flow pattern from photographic records. Further details were obtained by Rowe and Partridge [R42], outlining the stages of particle movement caused by a bubble as shown in Fig. 9.15. The development of a bubble and its subsequent transitions are as follows. In Fig. 9.15a, the stable fluidized bed consists of a dense phase and a fluidized phase. In (b), a bubble is formed in the dense phase and rises in (c). It leaves the dense phase in (d), drawing a spout of particles behind it, and also forms a wake which it leaves behind. In (e), the wake rotates about its circular axis and grows in size as a result of the viscous forces until it becomes unstable; the particles flowing in streamline motion around the bubble and its attached wake "slice off" a portion of the rotating torus which remains behind in the now stationary particles. In (f), particles are stripped from the wake, and the latter appears to be a distorted torus filling the concave hollow in the rear of the bubble. Subsequently, Rowe and Partridge [R43], Rowe, Partridge, and Lyall [R44] recognized the cloud formation around bubbles in gas-fluidized beds. A bubble in a gas fluidized bed is a roughly spherical region of space that rises by having particles flowing around it as if it were a solid object moving through a liquid; gas flows continuously through the bubble from the bottom and out at the top due to pressure gradient in the bed and permeability of the bubble. At high gas velocity, the gas short circuits due to high permeability. At low gas velocity, the gas circulates through the bubble due to the drag of particles flowing around the bubble; the gas flowing out at the top is dragged down again.

On the basis of various observed bubble shapes, Murray [M55] studied motions in fluidized beds and their stability. He showed that fluidized beds are unstable to small internal disturbances and in general stable to small surface oscillations [M55]. Based on observed bubble shapes, he treated the case of steady motion of the phases for the case of large solid-to-fluid density ratio, or $\bar{\rho}_p \gg \bar{\rho}$, and neglected the inertia of the fluid phase. Equations (6.32,

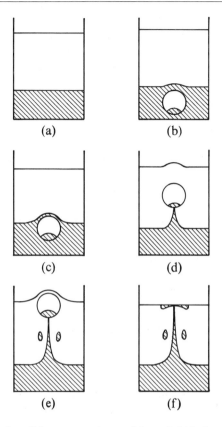

Figure 9.15 Stages of particle movement caused by a bubble in a fluidized bed [R42].

6.33, 6.41, 6.42, 6.30, 6.26) take the form in vectorial representation [M56]:

$$\left.\begin{aligned} \nabla \cdot \rho \mathbf{v} = 0, \quad \nabla \cdot \rho_p \mathbf{v}_p = 0 \\ \rho_p \mathbf{v}_p \cdot \nabla \mathbf{v}_p = -g\rho_p \mathbf{i} + F(\mathbf{v} - \mathbf{v}_p) \\ \nabla P = -F(\mathbf{v} - \mathbf{v}_p) \\ \rho = \bar{\rho}(1 - \phi), \quad \rho_p = \bar{\rho}_p \phi \end{aligned}\right\}, \tag{9.96}$$

where $\mathbf{i}$ is the unit vector in the vertical $(x\text{-})$direction, with the boundary condition far away from the bubble,

$$\left.\begin{aligned} \mathbf{v} = u_o \mathbf{i}, \quad \mathbf{v}_p = 0, \quad \phi = \phi_o \\ N_{\mathrm{Fr}} = \frac{u_o^2}{gl}, \quad P_o = \rho_{po} u_o^2 = \bar{\rho}_p \phi_o u_o^2 \\ P = P_o - x\rho_{po}g \end{aligned}\right\}, \tag{9.97}$$

u_o is the fluid flow velocity, l is a characteristic length of the fluidized bed and N_{Fr} is the Froude number aligning the bubble with coordinates x in the vertical direction and y in normal direction with radial coordinate r, for the convenience of applying complex variable solution. Introducing dimensionless variables such that

$$
\left.
\begin{aligned}
&\mathbf{v} = u_o\mathbf{v}^*, \quad \mathbf{v}_p = u\mathbf{v}_p^*, \\
&y = y^*l, \quad x = x^*l, \quad r = r^*l \\
&P = P^*(\bar{\rho}_p\phi_o u_o^2), \quad \phi = \phi^*\phi_o, \quad F(\phi) = \left(\frac{\bar{\rho}_p\phi_o u_o}{l}\right)F^* \\
&\epsilon^* = \frac{(1-\phi)}{\phi_o}, \quad U^* = \frac{U_B}{u_o}
\end{aligned}
\right\}, \qquad (9.98)
$$

ϵ^* is a dimensionless voidage, U_B is the bubble velocity. Motion far from the bubble is given by

$$
\left.
\begin{aligned}
&\mathbf{v}^* = (1-U^*)\mathbf{i} + \mathbf{v}^+, \quad \mathbf{v}_p^* = -U^*\mathbf{i} + \mathbf{v}_p^+ \\
&\phi^* = 1 + \phi^+, \quad P^* = P_o^+ - zN_{Fr}^{-1} + P^+ \\
&\epsilon^* = F^{*-1} - \phi^+,
\end{aligned}
\right\}. \qquad (9.99)
$$

For small solid particle velocities relative to bubble velocity,

$$
\phi^*(\mathbf{v}_p^* \cdot \nabla)\mathbf{v}_p^* \sim -cU^*\frac{\partial v_p^+}{\partial x^*}, \qquad (9.100)
$$

is justified when $v_p^+ < U^*$ and c is a constant with respect to independent variables, but in general, $c = c(N_{Fr}, U^*, \dots)$. The basic equations (9.96) now take the form

$$
\left.
\begin{aligned}
&\nabla \cdot \mathbf{v}_p^+ = U^*\frac{\partial\phi^+}{\partial x^*} \\
&\nabla \cdot \mathbf{v}^+ = F^*(1-U^*)\frac{\partial\phi^+}{\partial x^*} \\
&cU^*\frac{\partial\mathbf{v}_p^+}{\partial x^*} = \phi^+N_{Fr}^{-1}\mathbf{i} - (\mathbf{v}^+ - \mathbf{v}_p^+)N_{Fr}^{-1} - \phi^+F^{*\prime}(1)\mathbf{i} \\
&\nabla P^+ = -\phi^+F^{*\prime}(1)\mathbf{i} - (\mathbf{v}^+ - \mathbf{v}_p^+)N_{Fr}^{-1}
\end{aligned}
\right\} \qquad (9.101)
$$

when $F^{*\prime}(1) = (\partial F^*/\partial\phi^*)_{\phi^*=1}$. Equations (9.101) can be reduced to

$$
\frac{\partial^2\phi^+}{\partial x^{*2}} + (cN_{Fr}U^*)^{-1}[N_{Fr}F^{*\prime}(1) + F^*(1-U^*) - U^* - 1]\frac{\partial\phi^+}{\partial x^*} = 0, \qquad (9.102)
$$

with the limit $r^* \to \infty$, $\phi^+ = 0$ or $\phi^* = 1$. Equation (9.102) gives the discontinuity of ϕ around a bubble much in the nature of boundary layer.

Murray therefore sought a solution with stepwise change in particle concentration by analogy to inviscid flow. Equation (9.101) now becomes

$$\left.\begin{aligned}
\nabla \cdot \mathbf{v}_p^* &= 0 \\[4pt]
\nabla \cdot \mathbf{v}^* &= 0 \\[4pt]
cU^* \frac{\partial \mathbf{v}_p^*}{\partial x^*} &= N_{\mathrm{Fr}}^{-1}\mathbf{i} - (\mathbf{v}^* - \mathbf{v}_p^*)F^{*-1} \\[4pt]
\nabla P^* &= -(\mathbf{v}^* - \mathbf{v}_p^*)F^{*-1}
\end{aligned}\right\}, \qquad (9.103)$$

and as $r^* \to \infty$

$$\mathbf{v}^* \to (1 - U^*)\mathbf{i}, \quad \mathbf{v}_p^* \to -U^*\mathbf{i},$$
$$P^* \to P_o^* - x^* F^{*-1}$$

along a streamline, with constant ϕ^*

$$P^* + \tfrac{1}{2}\mathbf{v}_p^{*2} = \text{const.} \qquad (9.104)$$

To gain some idea of the trend of fluid and particle motion around a bubble, Murray obtained two-dimensional solution by applying the method of complex variables with $Z_p(z)$, $Z(z)$ as complex potentials for $\mathbf{v}_p^*$ and $\mathbf{v}^*$, and $z^* = x^* + iy^* = r^* e^{i\theta}$. Integration of the last two of Eqs. (9.103) gives

$$\left.\begin{aligned}
Z(z^*) &= z^* + Z_p(z^*) - cN_{\mathrm{Fr}}U^*\left[U^* + \frac{dZ_p(z^*)}{dz^*}\right] \\[6pt]
P^*(z) - P_o^* &= -\frac{[Z(z^*) - Z_p(z^*)]}{N_{\mathrm{Fr}}}
\end{aligned}\right\}, \qquad (9.105)$$

the bubble shape $Z_p(z^*)$ and U^* remains to be prescribed from observations made.

For the case of a circular (two-dimensional) bubble,

$$Z_p(z^*) = -U^*[z^* + z^{*-1}]. \qquad (9.106)$$

Equation (9.105) gives

$$Z(z^*) = (1 - U^*)\left[z^* - \frac{U^*}{(1 - U^*)z^*}\right] - cN_{\mathrm{Fr}}\frac{U^{*2}}{z^{*2}},$$

and

$$P^*(z^*) - P_o^* = -\frac{z^*}{N_{\mathrm{Fr}}} + c\frac{U^{*2}}{z^{*2}}.$$

Requirements of constant P^* in the vicinity of the leading edge can be satisfied by expanding P^* in terms of θ and set θ^2 terms to be zero. This gives

or

$$\left.\begin{aligned}
U^* &= \tfrac{1}{2}(cN_{\mathrm{Fr}})^{-\frac{1}{2}} \\[6pt]
U_B &= \frac{1}{2}\left(\frac{gl}{c}\right)^{\frac{1}{2}}
\end{aligned}\right\}, \qquad (9.107)$$

leading to

$$Z(z^*) = (1 - U^*)\left[z^* - \frac{U^*}{(1 - U^*)z^*}\right] - \tfrac{1}{4}z^{*-2}$$

and

$$P^*(z^*) - P_o^* = -\frac{z^*}{N_{\mathrm{Fr}}} + \frac{1}{4}\frac{1}{N_{\mathrm{Fr}}z^{*2}}$$

(9.108)

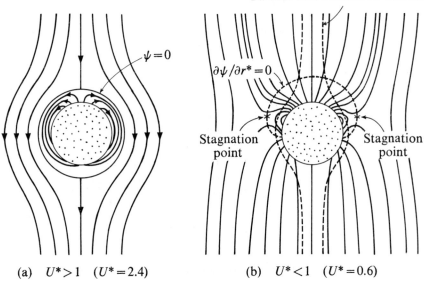

(a) $U^* > 1$ $(U^* = 2.4)$ (b) $U^* < 1$ $(U^* = 0.6)$

Figure 9.16 Gas flow relative to the bubble (two-dimensional) [M56].

Noting that $c = 1$ gives U_B the same as bubble rising in a liquid [D13]. Substitution of Eq. (9.108) into original equation of Z_p and averaging gives $c = \tfrac{2}{3}$. From Eq. (9.108) the stream function ψ is given by

$$\psi = (1 - U^*) \sin \theta \left\{r^* + \frac{U^*}{(1 - U^*)r^*}\right\} + \frac{\sin 2\theta}{4r^{*2}}.$$

(9.109)

The different values of flow configuration given by Eqs. (9.108) and (9.109) for $U^* > 1$ and $U^* < 1$ are shown in Fig. 9.16.

The distinctive feature when the bubble rises faster than free stream interstitial velocity (Fig. 9.16a) is shown by the $\psi = 0$ streamline. This circulating cloud between $\psi = 0$ streamline and the bubble moves with the bubble and in the actual case slightly ahead of it [D10]. Equation (9.109) shows that the radius r_c of the cloud is given by

$$r_c = r \sin \theta \sim r_{\theta=\pi/2} = r_B \left[\frac{U^*}{(U^* - 1)} \right]^{1/2}, \tag{9.110}$$

with

$$\cos \theta = 2[(U^* - 1)r^{*3} - U^*r^*],$$

r_B is bubble radius; which compares favorably with the result of Davidson.

In the range $U^* < 1$, the effect of the particle flow on the gas amounts to increase the apparent region of the void with flow through it evidenced by the dashed line in Fig. 9.16b. Murray also computed for cases for kidney-shaped bubbles and bubbles with cusped free-streamline wake. The trend of the circular bubble is representative.

For the three-dimensional case, Murray gave scalar potentials Φ^* and Φ_p^* for the fluid and solid, excluding the free stream:

$$\left. \begin{array}{c} \Phi^* \\ \Phi_p^* \\ P^* \end{array} \right\} = \sum_0^\infty \left. \begin{array}{c} f_m^* \\ p_m^* \\ P_m^* \end{array} \right\} \frac{P_m(\cos \theta)}{r^{m+1}}, \tag{9.111}$$

where P_m is the Legendre polynomial of order m and f_m^*, p_m^*, P_m^* are constants, determined by the last two equations of (9.103). For circular bubble $r^* = 1$

$$\Phi_p^* = -U^* \cos \theta \left[r^* + \frac{1}{2r^{*2}} \right],$$

and

$$\Phi^* = (1 - U^*) \cos \theta \left(r^* - \frac{U^*}{2(1 - U^*)r^{*2}} \right) - c N_{\mathrm{Fr}} U^{*2} P_2(\cos \theta) r^{*-3} \right\} \tag{9.112}$$

$$P^* - P_o^* = - \frac{r^* \cos \theta}{N_{\mathrm{Fr}}} + \frac{c U^* P_2(\cos \theta)}{r^{*3}},$$

for coefficient of θ^2 in $P_o^* - P^*$ is zero,

$$c N_{\mathrm{Fr}} U^{*2} = \tfrac{1}{3}, \tag{9.113}$$

similar procedure as in the above leads to $c = \tfrac{3}{5}$.

Results compare favorably with experiments by Rowe [R42]. It was shown that

$$r_c \sim r_B \left(\frac{U^*}{U^* - 1} \right)^{1/3}, \tag{9.114}$$

for $U^* > 1$. Davidson and Harrison [D11] proposed a relation for the approximate cloud radius r_c to bubble radius r_B as

$$\frac{r_c}{r_B} = \left[\frac{U^* + 1}{U^* - 1} \right]^{1/2}, \tag{9.115}$$

where U^* is the ratio of gas velocity to bubble velocity. Pressure variation through a bubble was studied by Reuter [R10]. Harrison and Leung [H18] made observations on the coalescence of bubbles in fluidized beds. From considering a number of references, Orcutt, Davidson, and Pigford [O5] suggested an average bubble velocity of

$$w_b = w - w_f + 0.711\sqrt{gD_e}, \qquad (9.116)$$

where w is the fluidizing velocity, w_f is the incipient fluidization velocity, D_e the equivalent bubble diameter, $D_e = (6v/\pi)^{\frac{1}{3}}$, v the bubble volume.

In spite of the lack of information for generalization on bubble formation and stability, it is well recognized that there is very little particle mixing when a fluidized bed is bubble free. Rowe [R39] suggested a parameter that should distinguish between bubbling and nonbubbling fluidized systems as $(\bar{\rho}_p - \bar{\rho})/\bar{\mu}$. This is evidenced by the following examples.

System	$(\bar{\rho}_p - \bar{\rho})/\bar{\mu}$, sec/cm^2	
	Imminent bubbling	Vigorous bubbling
$\frac{1}{2}$-mm Copper shots in water	1000	1300
$\frac{1}{2}$-mm Lead shots in water	800	
Phenolic resin in CO_2 gas	800	1600
Other liquid-solid systems	500	

The rate of exchange of particles between the bubbles and the dense phase was measured by Szekely [S104]. Entrainment or elutriation rates of particles in the exit stream from the fluidized bed was measured by Lewis, Gilliland, and Lang [L40].

9.6 Heat and Mass Transfer, and Chemical Reaction

One of the outstanding characteristics of a fluidized bed is that it tends to maintain uniform temperature even with nonuniform heat release. The relatively uniform temperature results from the rapid circulation of the solid in the bed. The magnitude of the effective thermal conductivity of the batch fluidized system in the vertical direction was between 100 and 25,000 Btu/hr ft^2 °/ft, depending on the condition and physical proportion of the gases and solids.

Measurement and correlation of heat transfer coefficients of internally heated bed, externally heated bed, and that along the immersed axial surface were summarized by Chu [C29]. Experiments by Mickley and Trilling [M29] have shown that the bed maintains essentially uniform temperature for an internally heated bed. They also showed that for particle size range of 0.00275 to 0.178 in. and in 4-in. and 1-in. columns, the heat transfer coefficient for an

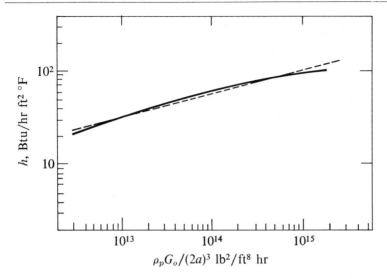

Figure 9.17 Correlation of heat-transfer coefficient in externally heated fluidized bed [M29].

externally heated bed is as shown in Fig. 9.17, correlated with $\rho_p G_o/(2a)^3$; G_o is the mass velocity of air flow, based on the cross-sectional area of empty tube; for nonspherical particles, $2a = 6/(\text{surface per unit volume})$. Figure 9.18 gives relations for internally heated bed (particle-size range 0.0016 to

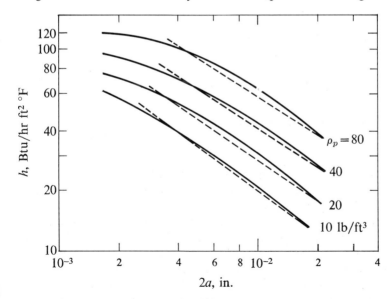

Figure 9.18 Heat-transfer coefficient with particle diameter and ρ_p in internally heated fluidized bed [M29].

0.0178 in.). Corrections by Toomey and Johnstone [T42] and by Mickley and Trilling [M29] for heat transfer coefficient h along an immersed axial surface is shown in Fig. 9.19. u_{mf} is the minimum fluidizing velocity and u is the actual velocity. Heat transfer between fluidized beds with boundary surfaces was measured and correlated by Wender and Cooper [W13].

Due to the lack of accurate description for momentum transfer in a fluidized bed, other transport processes necessarily must be treated with some form of logical approximation.

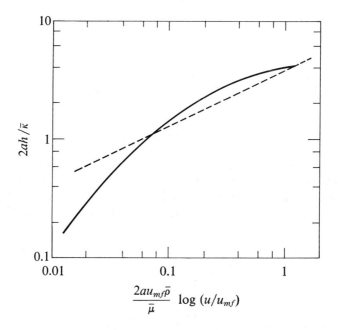

Figure 9.19 Correlation of h along immersed axial surface [T42].

Amundson and Aris [A10] proposed formulation of heat transfer in fluidized and moving beds in terms of an average thermal diffusivity and a joint probability distribution of particles.

Lewis, Gilliland, and Girouard [L39] made measurements on the radial and longitudinal heat transfer from a concentric 0.5 in. O.D. ($2r_2$) calrod heater in a fluidized bed of 2.94 in. I.D. ($2r_1$) with glass beads or petroleum cracking catalyst (microspheres 100 to 200 Tyler mesh) suspended in air or other gases (Freon-12, He, CO_2, C_3H_8, H_2). The effective thermal conductivity in the longitudinal direction K was estimated according to the temperature rise (ΔT) in the direction of the bed height L and heat flow $\dot{q}$ over area A:

$$K = \frac{\dfrac{\dot{q}}{A}}{\dfrac{\Delta T}{L}}, \tag{9.117}$$

and the effective thermal conductivity in the radial direction K_r was estimated according to

$$K_r = \frac{\dfrac{\dot{q}}{L}\ln\dfrac{r_1}{r_2}}{2\pi(T_2 - T_1)}. \tag{9.118}$$

For superficial velocities ranging from 0.3 to 1.1 ft/sec, K ranging from 4000 to 95,000 Btu/hr ft °F were measured, for bed height to diameter ratios of 2.2 to 5.5. K_r was nearly 2 per cent of K.

To determine the relation between K and K_r, they accounted for the fact that solids rise near the center and fall near the wall. Estimation of K_r was refined as follows: taking a core radius r_c within which the mean velocity of the solids is w_c and temperature T_c and average bed density ρ_m, over a height dL,

$$(w_c\rho_m\pi r_c^2)c_p T_c = (w_c\rho_m\pi r_c^2)c_p\left(T_c + \frac{dT_c}{dL}\,dL\right) + \dot{q}_w, \tag{9.119}$$

where c_p is the specific heat of the solid. $\dot{q}_w$ is the heat flow at the boundary of T_w, or

$$\dot{q}_w = -K_r 2\pi r_c\left(\frac{dT}{dr}\right)_{r=r_c} dL. \tag{9.120}$$

The net vertical heat flux is

$$w_c\rho_m\pi r_c^2 c_p(T_c - T_w) = -K\pi r_o^2 \frac{dT_c}{dL} = \dot{q}, \tag{9.121}$$

where r_o is the outer radius of the bed. Hence

$$K_r = \frac{K r_o^2\left(\dfrac{dT_c}{dL}\right)^2}{2r_c(T_c - T_w)\left(\dfrac{dT_c}{dr}\right)_{r=r_c}}$$

$$= \frac{\dot{q}\,\dfrac{dT}{dL}}{2\pi r_c(T_c - T_w)\left(\dfrac{dT}{dr}\right)_{r=r_c}}. \tag{9.122}$$

For $r_c = 0.7r_o$, $r_o = 0.125$ ft, $T_c - T_w = 4°F$, $dT_c/dL = 10.5$ F/ft, $\rho_m = 25$ lb/cu ft, $dT/dr = 60$ F/ft, $K_r = 0.04K$. A further relation is

$$w_c = \frac{\dfrac{K}{\rho_m c_p}\dfrac{dT_c}{dL}\left(\dfrac{r_o}{r_c}\right)^2}{T_c - T_w} = \frac{\dot{q}}{\rho_m c_p \pi r^2 (T_c - T_w)}. \tag{9.123}$$

Correlation for mass and momentum transfer in solid-liquid systems was made by McCune and Wilhelm [M22]. Richardson and Szekely [R17] found that equilibrium within the particulate phase tends to be rapidly obtained in fluidized beds. Mass transfer in fluidized beds as applied to drying of granular materials was studied by Vaneček, Drbohlav, and Markvart [V5]; measurement was made on the drying of wet slag. Elgin and Foust [E8] treated the case with counter current flow including liquid droplets and packed beds representing limiting situations of zero-particle velocity. A recent report on liquid-liquid extraction in countercurrent contactor with droplet size distribution was made by Olney [O3].

Chemical Reaction—The fluidized bed as a chemical reactor was treated by Wynkoop and Wilhelm [W33], and showed excellent agreement with the concept of reaction rate.

Reaction time distributions in fluidized catalytic reactors were studied by Orcutt, Davidson, and Pigford [O5]. Experiments with a bed of iron oxide particles fluidized by a mixture of ozone and air, and the degree of decomposition of the ozone in passing through the bed was measured. In comparison to a number of references cited by these authors, their method is unique because reaction persists only when the gaseous mixture is in contact with the particles. The fraction of reactants unconverted is given by

$$-\frac{d\Phi}{dt} = k_r RT\left(\frac{1-\epsilon}{\epsilon}\right)\Phi, \tag{9.124}$$

where k_r is the rate constant (on the basis of mass of catalyst-partial pressure), R is the universal gas constant, T is the absolute temperature. Defining the dimensionless reaction time,

$$\zeta = \frac{RT\rho_p \dot{M}_g}{PM_p}\int_0^t \left(\frac{1-\epsilon}{\epsilon}\right)dt', \tag{9.125}$$

where P is the overall pressure, M_p is the mass of the catalyst, and $\dot{M}_g$ is the molar feed rate. Equation (9.124) integrates to

$$\Phi = \exp\left[\frac{-k_r \zeta P M_p}{\dot{M}_g}\right]. \tag{9.126}$$

The random nature of the process was accounted for by assuming a probability density function $f(\zeta)$; then the mass fraction of reactant remaining at the exit of the bed is

$$\Phi(K) = \int_0^\infty e^{-K\zeta} f(\zeta) \, d\zeta, \tag{9.127}$$

when $K = k_r P M_p / \dot{M}_g$; thus $\Phi(K)$ is the moment-generating function of $f(\zeta)$, with the limits

$$\operatorname*{Lim}_{K \to \infty} \Phi(K) = \mu_o = \int_0^\infty f(\zeta) \, d\zeta = 1 \tag{9.128}$$

and

$$\operatorname*{Lim}_{K \to \infty} \frac{d\Phi(K)}{dK} = \mu_1 = -\int_0^\infty \zeta f(\zeta) \, d\zeta = -1. \tag{9.129}$$

Since ζ was normalized with respect to $M_p / \dot{M}_g$, the average contact time, $f(\zeta)$, satisfies the requirements for the density function of a random variable with unit mean. Equation (9.127) gives a basis for experimental determination of $f(\zeta)$ or an estimate of its lower moments. Numerical values of $f(\zeta)$ can be obtained from measuring the fraction of reactants remaining by varying K.

(a) The case of piston flow is given by $f(\zeta) = \delta(1 - \zeta)$ and

$$\Phi(K) = \int_0^\infty e^{-K\zeta} \delta(1 - \zeta) \, d\zeta = e^{-K}. \tag{9.130}$$

(b) The case of perfect mixing is given by $f(\zeta) = e^{-\zeta}$ and

$$\Phi(K) = \int_0^\infty e^{-K\zeta} e^{-\zeta} \, d\zeta = (1 + K)^{-1}. \tag{9.131}$$

(c) When a fraction of the reactant bypasses the bed, such as in the case of bubble flow, a general representation is

$$f(\zeta) = f_b \delta(\zeta) + (1 - f_b) g(\zeta), \tag{9.132}$$

when f_b is the fraction of fluid bypassing the bed; $0 \le f_b \le 1$, and $g(\zeta)$ is a continuous density function such that

$$\int_0^\infty g(\zeta) \, d\zeta = 1. \tag{9.133}$$

In this case,

$$\Phi(K) = f_b + (1 - f_b) \int_0^\infty e^{-K\zeta} g(\zeta) \, d\zeta. \tag{9.134}$$

For the bubble-flow model, they applied the relation given by Eq. (9.116), and gave, at the exit of the bed,

$$C_l = \left(1 - \frac{w_f}{w}\right)C_{b1} + \frac{w_f}{w}\,C_1 \,, \qquad (9.135)$$

where C_l, C_{b1}, and C_1 are the concentrations in the mixed gas leaving the bed, in the bubble leaving the bed, and in the dense phase respectively. For uniformly distributed n_b bubbles per unit volume, each having volume v_b,

$$n_b v_b w_b = w - w_f \,, \qquad (9.136)$$

and volumetric flow rate q into a bubble

$$q(C_1 - C_b) = v_b\,\frac{dC_b}{dt} = w_b v_b\,\frac{dC_b}{dz} \,, \qquad (9.137)$$

where C_b is the concentration in bubble at height z, we have

$$C_b = C_1 + (C_o - C_1)\exp\left(-\frac{qz}{w_b v_b}\right) \,, \qquad (9.138)$$

where C_o is the concentration entering the bed. Material balance of the dense, or particulate, phase gives

$$n_b q \int_0^{z_0}\left[C_1 + (C_o - C_1)\exp\left(-\frac{qz}{w_b v_b}\right)\right]dz + w_f C_o$$

$$= nqz_o C_1 + w_f C_1 + k_c z_o(1 - n_b v_b)C_1 \,, \qquad (9.139)$$

where k_c is the rate constant on the volume-concentration basis, and z_o is the bed height of which a fraction $(1 - n_b v_b)$ is occupied by the particulate phase.

The bed expansion $z_o - z_f$ is assumed to be due to the bubbles; z_f is the height at minimum fluidization. We have

$$n_b v_b z_o = z_o - z_f \,. \qquad (9.140)$$

Combining Eqs. (9.135), (9.139), and (9.140) gives

$$\Phi(K) = \beta e^{-n^*} + (1 - \beta e^{-n^*})\left(\frac{K}{1 - \beta e^{-n^*}} + 1\right)^{-1} \,, \qquad (9.141)$$

where $\beta = 1 - (w_f/w)$, $n^* = qz_o/w_b v_b$, and $K = k_c z_f/w = k_r PM_p/\dot{M}_g$. A comparison of these correlations is shown in Fig. 9.20.

Rowe [R40] studied batch reaction of UO_2 fluidized by HF to produce UF_4 and water (50 kcal per gm mole UO_2), and found that the reaction rate can be influenced by increasing solid particle size, thus reducing the bubble

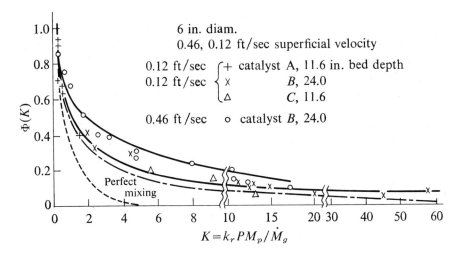

Figure 9.20 Reaction-time distribution in fluidized catalytic reactor [O5].

size and improving the contacting efficiency of phases. Design choice among particle size, gas velocity bed height, and reactor diameter was reviewed by Rowe [R41].

9.7 Stresses in Moving Beds

At high concentration of the particulate phase, appreciable normal and shear stress due to collision and saltation was shown to exist by Bagnold [B2, B4]. The problem may then be treated as one approximated by solid mechanics. This includes mixtures of large particles (such as grains and sand) in turbulent motion.

Flow of granular solids as a consolidated or dense phase is involved in Houdry flow and catalytic cracking units, and countercurrent contractors for ion exchange. Difficulty in achieving a stable condition for countercurrent flow of resin and fluid prompted studies of the solid stresses that develop during both cocurrent and countercurrent flow. Hancher and Jury [H8] analyzed the forces required for resin movement in a bed through which fluid is flowing. Delaplaine [D21] studied the forces acting in granular solids flowing downwind under gravity, neglecting the flow of a fluid. Hydrodynamic interactions in a dense system were treated by Krieger and Dougherty [K40]; the phenomena of dilatancy were treated by Metzner and Whitlock [M26].

Brandt and Johnson [B55] considered the resistance to flow of one particle past another or past the stationary wall of the container due to solid friction, and the pressure drop of the fluid as contributing an additional body force similar to gravity. In the representation in a cylindrical coordinate system (Fig. 9.21), they identified three normal compressive stresses σ_z, σ_θ, σ_r, normal to the planes and six shear stresses τ_{rz}, $\tau_{r\theta}$, etc., along the planes of the stress. Stress is distributed by particle-to-particle friction (cf. Sec. 5.3), and no equilibrium shear stress can be higher than that determined by internal friction. For example, if $\tau_{zr}/\sigma_z \geq \mu$, the coefficient of internal friction, slipping will

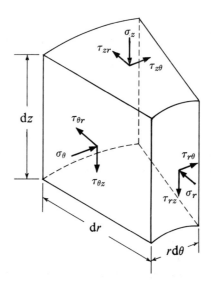

Figure 9.21 Forces acting in a moving bed [B55].

occur along the z-plane and the stress pattern will change over the whole system. The forces acting on the boundaries of a bed are the radial and shear stresses at the wall and the average vertical stress over the cross section of the containing vessel, as shown in Fig. 9.22. Delaplaine [D21] measured the stresses acting both at the boundaries and within downward flowing bed of sand, glass and bead catalyst. He showed that the stresses are not proportional to bed depth but increase asymptotically to constant values at bed depths greater than 4 to 6 tube diameters. Force balance of the system in Fig. 9.22 gives, for average vertical stress $(\sigma_z)_a$ and wall shear stress $(\tau_{rz})_w$

$$\frac{d(\sigma_z)_a}{dz} = g\rho_p - \frac{4(\tau_{rz})_w}{D_t}, \tag{9.142}$$

where D_t is the tube diameter. Substitution of the stress ratios

$$\mu^* = \frac{(\tau_{rz})_w}{(\sigma_r)_w} \qquad (9.143)$$

$$k_a = \frac{(\sigma_r)_w}{(\sigma_z)_a}, \qquad (9.144)$$

gives

$$\frac{d(\sigma_z)_a}{dz} = g\rho_p - \frac{4k_a\mu^*(\sigma_z)_a}{D_t} . \qquad (9.145)$$

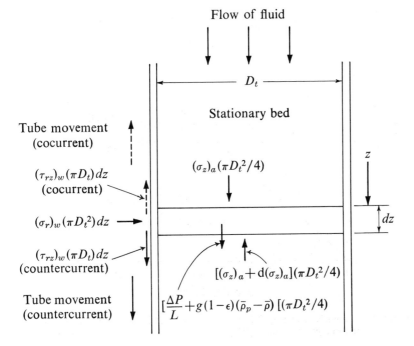

Figure 9.22 Force balance of boundary and average stresses in moving bed [B55].

Assuming k_a and μ^* as constants, Janssen [J3] gave

$$(\sigma_z)_a = \frac{g\rho_p D_t}{4k_a\mu^*}\left[1 - \exp\left(-\frac{4k_a\mu^* z}{D_t}\right)\right]. \qquad (9.146)$$

Thus $(\sigma_z)_a$ approaches $g\rho_p D_t/4k_a\mu^*$ in deep beds.
When fluid flow occurs, Hancher and Jury [H8] gave

$$(\sigma_z)_a = \pm \frac{A D_t}{4k_a\mu^*}\left[1 - \exp\left(-\frac{4k_a\mu^* z}{D_t}\right)\right], \qquad (9.147)$$

the $(+)$ sign for cocurrent movement and $(-)$ sign for countercurrent movement, and

$$A = \frac{\Delta P}{L} + (1 - \epsilon)(\bar{\rho}_p - \bar{\rho})g, \qquad (9.148)$$

$(\Delta P/L)$ being the pressure drop, $k_a \sim 1$ and $\mu^* = $ constant. The gradient of compressive stress is

$$\frac{d(\sigma_z)_a}{dz} = A \mp \frac{4k_a\mu^*(\sigma_z)_a}{D_t}. \qquad (9.149)$$

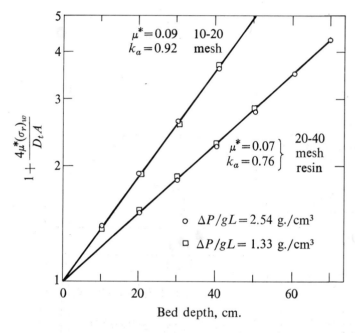

Figure 9.23 Comparison of Eq. (9.150) with experimental results (radial stress in moving bed in countercurrent) [B55].

Brandt and Johnson [B55] made measurements of the average vertical stress and radial stress at the wall of the tube containing the bed, with cocurrent or countercurrent motion (at 1 to 30 cm/min) relative to the fluid (water), by a balance and pressure transducer at the tube wall. Experiments were carried out with particle sizes in various ranges between 10 to 100 mesh. The coefficient of friction depends on solid velocity and particle size. Considerable internal friction was found in a bed of glass beads but not in that of resins. In countercurrent flow, close correlation was made with integrated equation of force balance in the cross section of the bed, but in cocurrent flow, only 20 to 40 mesh resin was represented by the same equation. Fraction void of the bed was not reported. Figure 9.23 shows a typical comparison of Eq. (9.147) for countercurrent movement with experimental results, in which case Eq. (9.147) is expressed as

$$\ln \left[1 + \frac{(\sigma_r)_w}{A} \frac{4\mu^*}{D_t} \right] = \frac{4\mu^*}{D_t} k_a z. \tag{9.150}$$

It is possible that diffusion of particles may occur for small particles in co-current motion.

Flow of frictional, cohesive solids was formulated by Jenike and Shield [J9] based on the concepts of soil mechanics and plasticity. Johanson [J12] applied their method to the computation of stress and velocity fields of the steady gravity flow of bulk solids in converging channels. Johanson [J13] formulated a method of calculating rate of discharge from hoppers and bins.

9.8 Packed Bed and Porous Solid

A limiting situation of fluidized beds and sedimentation is a packed bed. A basic macroscopic property of a packed bed is its permeability, k_p. The Kozeny-Carman [C5] equation gave

$$k_p = \frac{\epsilon^3}{S^2 a}, \tag{9.151}$$

where ϵ is the fraction void called porosity, S the surface area, and a a constant including a tortuosity factor and a shape factor; $a \sim 5$. Marshall [M12] gave

$$k_p = \tfrac{1}{8}\epsilon^2 n^{-2} \sum_{i=1}^{n} (2i - 1) r_i^2, \tag{9.152}$$

for $r_i > r_{i+1}$, and $r_1, r_2, \ldots, r_i, \ldots, r_n$ represent the mean radius of the pores in decreasing order of size in each of n equal fractions of the pore space. A comparison of the computed and measured values of k_p is shown in Fig. 9.24. $k_p < 10^{-5}$ m^{-2} is usually considered to be large.

The velocity of flow through a statistically homogeneous and isotropic packed bed is given by

$$\mathbf{v} = \frac{-k_p(\nabla P - \mathscr{F})}{\mu_d}, \tag{9.153}$$

where P is the pressure, $\mathscr{F}$ a vector body force, and μ_d the dynamic viscosity. The general aspects of flow through porous media are presented in a number of treatises; recent ones are those by Scheidegger [S12], Carman [C6], and Collins [C37].

Measurements and bibliography on heat transfer and flow friction through porous media and packed beds are given in papers by Coppage and London

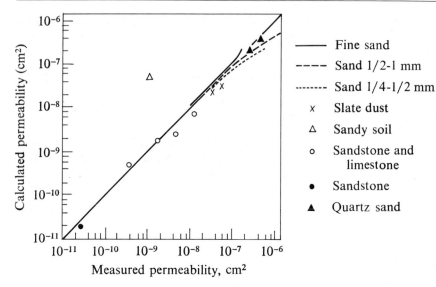

Figure 9.24 Comparison of measured and calculated permeability by Eq. (9.151) [M12].

[C39] and Lancashire, Lezberg, and Morris [L8]. Recent articles in this area are: gas-liquid flow by Weekman and Myers [W8]; cocurrent flow of immiscible liquids by Riggs and Churchill [R22] extending Ergun-Orning Equation (Sec. 5.1); Sherman [S29] on mass transfer in the washing of a packed bed.

Flow through porous media is significant to isotope separation by gaseous diffusion. Prager [P34] formulated the viscous flow through porous media by minimizing the rate of energy dissipation for a class of trial stress distributions, with or without slip at the pore walls.

SUMMARY OF BASIC CONCEPTS

Flow Mechanism in Fluidized Bed—Gilliland (1952) [G20]

Stability of Fluidized Bed—Wilhelm and Rice (1958) [W21], Rowe (1962) [R39], Murray (1965) [M55]

Bubble and Cloud Formation—Rowe and Partridge (1962) [R42, R43], Davidson and Harrison (1963) [D11], Murray (1965) [M56]

Average Bubble Velocity—Orcutt, Davidson, and Pigford (1962) [O5]

Reaction Rate and Flow Regime—Orcutt, Davidson, and Pigford (1962) [O5]

Stresses in Moving Bed—Hancher and Jury (1959) [H8]

Permeability of Bed—Kozeny and Carman (1937) [C5]

Electrodynamics of a Suspension

10

We have so far deferred the discussion of the effect of electrostatic charges on the dynamics of a multiphase system for the sake of simplicity. In reality, electrostatic charges are almost always present in a multiphase system, and, in some cases, have an overshadowing effect on transport processes (Secs. 2.8, 4.5, and 8.5).

Atmospheric dusts are normally charged; after all, ceilings do get dusty. In fair weather, the atmosphere at room condition has a space charge (positive) of 60 electronic charges per cubic centimeter [M15].

Moreover, in important applications such as electrostatic precipitation, xerography, colloidal propulsion, and among ways and means of controlling radio-wave attenuation due to intense aerodynamic heating during reentry and due to ionization in the plume of a metalized-propellant rocket, electric charges become the major concern.

Although magnetic effects will not be discussed in this volume, for the sake of completeness, it might be useful to point out the study of hydrodynamics of magnetically polarizable fluids (ferrohydrodynamics) in the presence of magnetic field by Neuringer and Rosensweig [N5] and the magnetic-field interaction with a moving metal slug reported by Wilen [W19].

10.1 Charging by Surface Contact

A thorough review of the static electrification of solids was given by Montgomery [M40]. Historically, charging by surface contact led to the

413

formulation of the whole field of study of electricity. A triboelectric series was given by Wilcke in 1757 as follows.

> Polished glass
> Wool flock
> Writer's quill
> Wood
> Paper
> Sealing wax
> White wax
> Unpolished glass
> Lead
> Sulfur
> Other metals

Upon rubbing any two of them together, the one listed higher acquires a positive charge and the other a negative charge.

Charges on atmospheric dust were first studied by Rudger [R46, R47]. He reported that a dust storm in the Sahara desert is normally below 200 v/m, and is usually positively charged. Yet the dust cloud may reverse in polarity (become negative) and exceed 500 v/m, or even as much as 10^4 v/m. At a given place, both atmospheric dust and the earth tend to be negative. Whitman [W18] studied fused-quartz particles of 100 to 0.1 μ size falling between electrically charged plates and found, for various plate materials, different charge on the cloud as follows (0.13 g of dust):

Wall Material	Charge, coulombs/kg
Aluminum	-2×10^{-4}
Copper	-1.4×10^{-4}
Platinum	-2.3×10^{-4}
Steel	-1.6×10^{-4}
Nickel	-1.2×10^{-4}

His experiments of blowing various dust materials through a brass tube give:

Dust Material	Weight, g	Charge on Cloud, coulombs/kg
Borax	0.15	-3.3×10^{-6}
Sodium bicarbonate	0.17	$+4 \times 10^{-6}$
Lime	0.07	$+3.8 \times 10^{-6}$
Fused quartz	0.13	-2.9×10^{-6}
Ammonium chloride	0.19	-3.4×10^{-6}
Sodium carbonate	0.12	-2.3×10^{-6}
Sodium fluoride	0.13	$+1.7 \times 10^{-6}$

Vollrath [V13] proposed a Van de Graaff generator using powdered material circulated by blowing with air and estimated a potential of 260 kv as an alternate of generation by friction.

The energy-level diagram of the materials of the two bodies before and after contact are shown in Fig. 10.1. In each, the Fermi energy is denoted by ζ, v_o is the energy necessary to remove an electron from the highest level of the uppermost nearly filled band, and χ_o is the energy released when an electron at rest outside the crystal is taken into the lowest level in the lowermost nearly empty band. When the two surfaces are brought into contact,

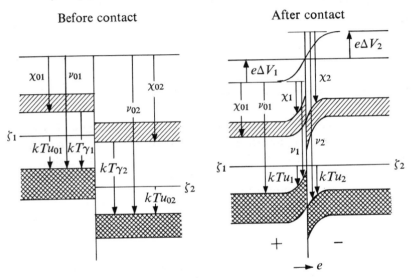

Figure 10.1 Potential diagram of charge transfer by contact [M40].

and after equilibrium is reached, the Fermi levels ζ_1 and ζ_2 equalize due to charge transferred, q_o, giving rise to modification of χ_o's and v_o's to χ_1, χ_2, v_1, and v_2 at the junction, and contact potential $|\Delta V_1| + |\Delta V_2|$. Rapid separation of these two bodies will leave Surface 1 positively charged and Surface 2 negatively charged. The basic relations outlined by Montgomery [M40] for estimating charge distribution are outlined as follows:

For net charge q upon separation to large distances of the above bodies, which amounts to a fraction f_q of q_o, q_o can be of either sign depending on the energy-band structure of the materials, their state of strain, and geometry. Introducing a band-structure factor b_q and a mechanical factor g_q as a function of one-dimension and normal and shear stresses, or $q_o = b_q g_q$ and $q = f_q q_o$, the charge-distribution potential V is given by Poisson's equation, or

$$\frac{\partial^2 V}{\partial x^2} = -\frac{\rho_q}{\epsilon_o}, \tag{10.1}$$

where ρ_q is the volume charge density, ϵ_o is the permittivity. The charge density is given by

$$\rho_q(t) = \rho_q(0) \exp\left(-\frac{t}{\tau}\right), \qquad (10.2)$$

where $\tau = \epsilon_o/\sigma_e$, σ_e being the electrical conductivity. Conditions of electric breakdown are given by relations of gaseous discharge [C33].

For measurement of charges on small particles, the electrostatic probe was developed by Batch, Dalmon, and Hignett [B22], and capacitance probes were developed by Chao, Min, and Wyman [M37] and Daniel and Brackett [D6].

10.2 Corona Charging and Scattering of an Ionized Gas

Extensive details of corona discharge and corona charging of particulate matter at low temperatures (therefore thermionic emission can be neglected) are presented in treatises by Cobine [C33] and White [W16].

When a conducting sphere of radius a is placed in a uniform electric field E_o with an initially uniform unipolar ion density n_o, the potential (V) distribution is given by Poisson's equation:

$$\nabla^2 V = -\frac{q n_z}{\epsilon_o}, \qquad (10.3)$$

where ϵ_o is the permittivity, q is the charge per ion ($q = -e$ for an electron), and n_z the distributed ion density. The boundary conditions are $E = -\nabla V = E_o$ at infinity and $E = -Ze/4\pi\epsilon_o a^2$ for Z charges ($Z > 0$ for positive charges and $Z < 0$ for negative charges) on the surface at a given time, ϵ_o is the permittivity of free space. It is readily shown that at any point on the sphere,

$$E_a = 3E_o \cos\theta - \frac{Ze}{4\pi\epsilon_o a^2}, \qquad (10.4)$$

where θ is the azimuthal angle in the spherical coordinate.

Field Charging—For particle radius a much larger than the mean free paths of the ions ($a \gg 1\ \mu$), the random motion of the ions needs not be considered, and the total electric flux ψ entering the sphere is given by

$$\psi = \int_0^\pi 4\pi\epsilon_o E_a 2\pi a^2 \sin\theta\, d\theta = 12\pi\epsilon_o a^2 E_o\left(1 - \frac{Ze}{12\pi\epsilon_o E_o a^2}\right)^2. \quad (10.5)$$

At saturation, $\psi = 0$, and

$$Z_s = \frac{12\pi\epsilon_o E_o a^2}{e}.$$ (10.6)

The rate of charging is given by the charging current i,

$$i = \frac{n_z q K \psi}{4\epsilon_0} = \frac{d(Ze)}{dt},$$ (10.7)

where K is the ion mobility. Integration gives

$$-\frac{n_z q K t}{4\epsilon_o} = \frac{\dfrac{Z}{Z_s}}{1 - \dfrac{Z}{Z_s}}.$$ (10.8)

White [W16] showed that for $n_z = 5 \times 10^{14}$ m^{-3}, $K = -2.2$ (cm/sec)/(v/cm); and $q = -e$, the time to reach $Z/Z_s = \frac{1}{2}$ is 2 millisec. When applied to dielectric particles, Equation (10.6) is modified to

$$Z_s = \frac{12\pi\epsilon_o E_o a^2 \left(1 + 2\dfrac{\epsilon_r - 1}{\epsilon_r + 2}\right)}{q},$$ (10.9)

where ϵ_r is the dielectric constant, $\epsilon_r = \epsilon/\epsilon_o$, ϵ is the permittivity of the material.

Charging by Diffusion in an Electric Field—For a radius a of the order of 0.5 μ or less, random motion of ions must be accounted for and the contribution of external electric field becomes less significant. Studies were made by Arendt and Kallmann [A13], White [W17], Penney and Lynch [P9], and Murphy, Adler, and Penney [M53]. The method of the latter is discussed here.

A spherical particle of radius a is introduced into a region of unipolar ions of given density n_{zo} and electric field E_o. It acquires charge due to ions striking the particle. As its charge begins to build up, its repelling force redistributes the ions in the vicinity. For the application of the kinetic theory, we refer to the coordinate system as shown in Fig. 10.2. For number density n_z of ions and mean free path Λ, the number of ions which have a collision in an infinitesimal volume dV per unit time with a speed between v and $v + dv$ after the collision is $n_z(v/\Lambda)f(v)\,dv\,dV$; $f(v)$ being the distribution function of speed v and n_z the local ion concentration. The rate at which these ions arrive at area dA from dV at P is $n_z(v/\Lambda)f(v)\,dv(dA\cos\theta_R/4\pi r^2)\,dV$ [K13, W17]. Since the number of molecules heading to dA is attenuated by $e^{-r/\Lambda}$

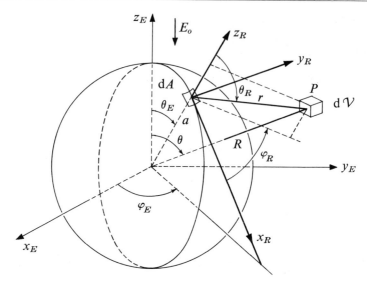

Figure 10.2 Coordinate systems for ions at point P in volume dV heading for area dA on the sphere [M53].

by collision, and as the sphere becomes charged to the same signs as the incident ion, the ion must have a minimum kinetic energy $\frac{1}{2}mv_c^2$ to overcome the opposing field around the charged solid. The rate of arrival at dA from dV is given by

$$\left.\frac{dn}{dt}\right|_{dA\,dV} = \frac{n_z\,dV\,dA\cos\theta_R}{4\pi r^2}e^{-r/\Lambda}\int_{v_c}^{\infty}\frac{v}{\Lambda}f(v)\,dv. \tag{10.10}$$

Integrating over the entire volume (r from 0 to ∞, θ_R from 0 to $\pi/2$, and ϕ_R from 0 to 2π),

$$\left.\frac{dn}{dt}\right|_{dA} = \frac{dA}{4\pi}\int_0^{\infty}dr\int_0^{\pi/2}d\theta_R\sin\theta_R\int_0^{2\pi}d\phi\,n_z$$

$$\times\,e^{-r/\Lambda}\int_{v_c}^{\infty}\frac{v}{\Lambda}f(v)\,dv. \tag{10.11}$$

For ions with a Maxwellian distribution in speed,

$$\int_{v_c}^{\infty}vf(v)\,dv = 4\pi\int_{v_c}^{\infty}\left(\frac{m_z}{2\pi kT}\right)^{3/2}v^3\exp\left(-\frac{m_zv^2}{2kT}\right)dv, \tag{10.12}$$

where m_z is the mass of an ion, k the Boltzmann constant, and T the absolute temperature of the system. v_c is given by

$$\psi^* = \frac{m_zv_c^2}{2kT} = \frac{eV_a}{kT} - \frac{eV_p}{kT}, \tag{10.13}$$

where V_a is the potential at dA, and V_p that at P. Equation (10.12) gives, for mean speed $\bar{v} = \sqrt{8kT/\pi m_z}$,

$$\int_{v_c}^{\infty} vf(v)\, dv = \bar{v}(1 + \psi^*) \exp(-\psi^*) \quad \text{for } \psi^* > 0 \atop = \bar{v} \qquad\qquad\qquad\qquad \text{for } \psi^* < 0} . \tag{10.14}$$

The factor $(1 + \psi^*)e^{-\psi^*}$ is seen to be the fraction of ions which have had a collision at P and have sufficient kinetic energy to reach the sphere.

With uniform external field E_o, from solving Eq. (10.3), the region outside the sphere has a potential [S92] of

$$V = E_o \cos\theta_E \left[R - \frac{a^3}{R^2}\frac{\epsilon_r - 1}{\epsilon_r + 2} \right]. \tag{10.15}$$

Since the potential due to the charge on the sphere is $V = Ze/R$, the potential of the ion is

$$\frac{eV_p}{kT} = \frac{Ze^2}{4\pi\epsilon_o akT}\frac{a}{R} + \frac{eE_o a}{kT}\left[\frac{R}{a} - \frac{\epsilon_r - 1}{\epsilon_r + 2}\frac{a^2}{R^2} \right] \cos\theta_E . \tag{10.16}$$

Denote N_{et} as the electrothermo number; that is, the ratio of electrostatic to thermal energy, or

$$(N_{et})_p = \frac{Ze^2}{4\pi\epsilon_o akT} \equiv \alpha$$

$$(N_{et})_E = \frac{eE_o a}{kT} , \tag{10.17}$$

where subscripts p and E are for particle and external field, respectively; we then have

$$\frac{eV_p}{kT} = \alpha\frac{a}{R} + (N_{et})_E\left[\frac{R}{a} - \frac{\epsilon_r - 1}{\epsilon_r + 2}\frac{a^2}{R^2} \right] \cos\theta_E , \tag{10.18}$$

and

$$\frac{eV_a}{kT} = \alpha + (N_{et})_E\left[1 - \frac{\epsilon_r - 1}{\epsilon_r + 2} \right] \cos\theta_E . \tag{10.19}$$

In the above the ions are assumed to be positively charged; for negative ions, the sign of e should be changed to negative. It is seen that α or $(N_{et})_p$ will be unchanged but $(N_{et})_E$ should be changed to $-(N_{et})_E$.

For positive ions, the nature of the solution varies from the vicinities of $\theta_E = 0$, $\theta_E = \pi$, and $\theta_E = \pi/2$. Relative to $\theta_E = 0$, $\psi^* < 0$, and charging rate is increased by increase in E_o. Around $\theta_E = \pi$, $\psi^* > 0$, the charging rate is reduced by increase in E_o. Near $\theta_E = \pi/2$, ψ^* may be negative for

$\pi/2 < \phi_R < 3\pi/2$, while for $3\pi/2 < \phi_R < \pi/2$, ψ^* is always positive. The local field also changes the ion-density distribution. Jost [J22] gave

$$\nabla^2 n_z + \nabla \psi^* \cdot \nabla n_z = 0, \tag{10.20}$$

with the boundary conditions $R \to \infty$, all θ, $n_z \to n_{zo}$; at $R^* = R/a = 1$, $(\partial n_z/\partial R^*) + (\partial \psi^*/\partial R^*) n_z = 0$.

With n_z determined from Eq. (10.20), the total charging rate is given by

$$\frac{dZ}{dt} = \int_A \frac{1}{dA} \frac{dn}{dt} \, dA = 2\pi a^2 \int_0^\pi d\theta_E \sin \theta_E \left(\frac{1}{dA} \frac{dn}{dt} \Big|_{dA} \right). \tag{10.21}$$

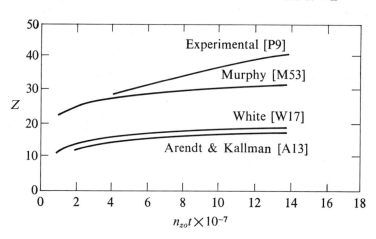

Figure 10.3 Comparison of theories of charge collection to experimental results [M53]. $a = 0.15 \, \mu$, $E_o = 2.65$ kv/cm, $\epsilon_r = 7.2$, (positive corona).

Since $dA = a^2 \sin \theta_E \, d\theta_E \, d\phi_E$, analytical solution of Eq. (10.20) with ψ^* given by Eq. (10.13) is not available; a numerical solution was given in detail by Murphy [M52]. His computations of dioctylpthalate smoke ($\epsilon_r = 7.2$) is shown in Fig. 10.3, in comparison with experimental results and other methods of computations.

Simple cases are the cases of $a \gg \Lambda$, and of $E_o = 0$. When $a \gg \Lambda$, ψ^* approaches zero, and

$$\frac{dn}{dt} \Big|_{dA} = \frac{\bar{v} \, dA}{4} n_{za},$$

where n_{za} is the ion density at $r = a$. Denote $\tau = a\bar{v}e^2 n_{zo}t/4\epsilon_o kT$, and the total charging rate is given by

$$\frac{d\alpha}{d\tau} = \frac{1}{2n_{zo}} \int_0^\pi d\theta_E \sin \theta_E n_{za}, \tag{10.22}$$

which is the average value of n_{za} over the surface of the particle in the gaseous phase, thus reverting the case of simple field charging.

The case of $E_o = 0$ is extremely simple when applied to unipolar ions. The results given by Murphy, Adler, and Penney [M53] are shown in Fig. 10.4 for various ratios of a/Λ. The basic relations will be clarified later when considering the simultaneous presence of ions and electrons.

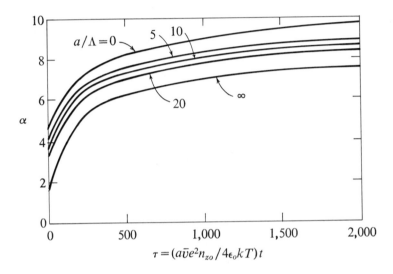

$$\tau = (a\bar{v}e^2 n_{zo}/4\epsilon_o kT)t$$

Figure 10.4 Particle charge in the absence of external field for various ratios of particle radius a and mean free path (λ) [M53].

Scattering of Electrons and Ions—The problem of interaction of a spherical particle with a slightly ionized gas was treated by Rosen [R32] and Dimick and Soo [D30]. The latter extended the method of Murphy, Adler, and Penney [M53] for the case of zero external field to interaction with an ionized gas with presence of ions of both signs.

Since the electrons have a higher velocity than the positive ions by virtue of their small mass, the particle tends to assume a negative charge. It is seen that the cases in Eq. (10.14) now represent the integrated distribution for electrons for $\psi^* > 0$, while $\psi^* < 0$ applies to positive ions. For a gas with a low degree of ionization the ion-gas atom and electron-gas atom collisions will dominate over the electron-ion collisions by roughly the ratio of the neutral gas atoms to the positive ion density. As a first approximation the interaction of the incident ions and electrons can be neglected. The additional assumption is made that there is 100 per cent attachment of all electrons and ions arriving at the particle surface, since image forces between the ion and the surface will come into play when the ion approaches closely to the surface of the solid.

Combining Eqs. (10.11) and (10.14) for electrons of density n_{eo} at a large distance away from the particle, and integrating over ϕ_R, we have for the electrons,

$$
\begin{aligned}
\frac{dn_e}{dt}\bigg|_{dA} = \tfrac{1}{2}dAn_{eo}\bar{v}_e\bigg\{ & [1+\alpha]\tfrac{1}{2}\exp(-\alpha) \\
& - \alpha\exp(-\alpha)\int_0^\infty dr\,\frac{1}{\Lambda_e}\exp\left(\frac{-r}{\Lambda_e}\right)\int_0^{\pi/2}\frac{d\theta_R\sin\theta_R\cos\theta_R}{R}\bigg\},
\end{aligned}\quad(10.23)
$$

where R is given in accordance with Fig. 10.2 as $R = (r^2 + a^2 + 2ra\cos\theta_R)^{1/2}$. Similar treatment of the equation for the ions gives

$$
\begin{aligned}
\frac{dn_i}{dt}\bigg|_{dA} = \tfrac{1}{2}dAn_{io}\bar{v}_i\int_0^\infty dr\,\frac{1}{\Lambda_i}\exp\left(\frac{-r}{\Lambda_i}\right) \\
\times \int_0^{\pi/2}d\theta_R\sin\theta_R\cos\theta_R\exp(-\alpha).
\end{aligned}\quad(10.24)
$$

For the equilibrium situation, equating Eqs. (10.23) and (10.24) and setting $x = \cos\theta_R$ give

$$
\frac{n_{eo}}{n_{io}} = \left(\frac{T_i m_e}{T_e m_i}\right)^{1/2}\frac{\exp\alpha\int_0^\infty\exp\left(\frac{-r}{\Lambda_i}\right)\left(\frac{dr}{\Lambda_i}\right)\int_0^1 x\,dx\exp\left[\dfrac{\alpha a}{(r^2+a^2+2arx)^{1/2}}\right]}{\tfrac{1}{2}(1+\alpha)-\alpha\int_0^\infty\exp\left(\frac{-r}{\Lambda_e}\right)\left(\frac{dr}{\Lambda_e}\right)\int_0^1\dfrac{x\,dx}{(r^2+a^2+\alpha arx)^{1/2}}},
$$
$$(10.25)$$

subject to the condition that

$$
n_{eo} + n_z = n_{io}, \qquad (10.26)
$$

an average particle-charge density related to the charge Z on each particle by

$$
n_z = n_p Z, \qquad (10.27)
$$

where n_p is the number density of the dispersed solids. To use the summation of one-particle interactions with the ionized gas to represent the behavior of the dispersed solids requires that the interparticle spacing be larger than an equivalent Debye shielding distance [L10] for the solids $\Lambda_D = (\epsilon_o kT/n_{eo}e^2)^{1/2}$. This limits the particle densities to approximately $n_p = (2\Lambda_D)^{-3}$.

The integrals with respect to dx in Eq. (10.27) can be attempted directly, or carried out by expanding $(1/R)$ in Legendre polynomials [J1] and the integrals over the Legendre polynomials can be evaluated by use of Rodrigue's formula; Eq. (10.27) becomes, for $r' = r/a$,

$$\frac{n_{eo}}{n_{io}} = \left(\frac{T_i m_e}{T_e m_i}\right)^{1/2} \exp(\alpha)$$

$$\times \left\{ 1 + 2a\alpha \sum_{l=0}^{\infty} \frac{(-1)^{l+1}}{2^l l!} \left[\int_{\infty}^{1} \frac{\exp\left(\frac{-r'a}{\Lambda_i}\right) r'^l \, dr'}{\left(\frac{\Lambda_i}{a}\right)} \right. \right.$$

$$\left. + \int_{1}^{\infty} \frac{\exp\left(\frac{-r'a}{\Lambda_i}\right) dr}{\left(\frac{\Lambda_i}{a}\right) r'^{l+1}} \right] \left[\int_{0}^{1} \frac{d^l (x^2 - 1)^l}{dx^l} x \, dx \right] \right\}$$

$$\div \left\{ 1 + \alpha - 2a\alpha \sum_{l=0}^{\infty} \frac{(-1)^{l+1}}{2^l l!} \left[\int_{0}^{1} \frac{\exp\left(\frac{-r'a}{\Lambda_e}\right) r'^l \, dr'}{\left(\frac{\Lambda_e}{a}\right)} \right. \right.$$

$$\left. + \int_{1}^{\infty} \frac{\exp\left(\frac{-r'a}{\Lambda_e}\right) dr'}{\left(\frac{\Lambda_e}{a}\right)(-r')^{l+1}} \right] \left[\int_{0}^{1} \frac{d^l (x^2 - 1)^l}{dx^l} x \, dx \right] \right\}, \qquad (10.28)$$

which can be evaluated numerically.

With extensive approximations Eq. (10.28) can be reduced to the result given by Rosen [R32]. We assume $T_i = T_e$ and neglect all other terms of the denominator except the 1. Replacing $(a^2 + r^2 + 2arx)^{-1/2}$ by $1/a$, and $r \ll \Lambda$, we have

$$\frac{dn_e}{dt}\bigg|_{dA} = \left(\frac{8kT}{\pi m_e}\right)^{1/2} n_{eo} \exp(\alpha)$$

$$\frac{dn_i}{dt}\bigg|_{dA} = \left(\frac{8kT}{\pi m_i}\right)^{1/2} n_{io} \exp(-\alpha), \qquad (10.29)$$

regardless of sign of α, and

$$\frac{n_{eo}}{n_{io}} = \left(\frac{m_e}{m_i}\right)^{1/2} \exp(2\alpha) \sim \left(\frac{m_e}{m_i}\right)^{1/2} e^{\alpha}(1 + \alpha). \qquad (10.30)$$

Using $n_{eo} + Zn_p = n_{io}$ and setting

$$\chi = \frac{e^2 n_{io}}{4\pi\epsilon_o akT},$$

with $(m_e/m_i)^{1/2} \ll 1$ so $n_{eo} \ll n_{io}$ if χ/n_p is small compared to 1 (i.e., when n_p is large, n_{io} is small and a is large), when (n_{eo}/n_{io}) is small, Eq. (10.28) becomes

$$\frac{n_{eo}}{n_{io}} = \left(\frac{m_e}{m_i}\right)^{1/2}\left(1 + \frac{\chi}{n_p}\right)e^{\chi/n_p} \sim \left(\frac{m_e}{m_i}\right)^{1/2}\left(1 + \frac{2\chi}{n_p}\right), \qquad (10.31)$$

as given by Rosen [R32]. The calculation of more accurate values by use of Eq. (10.28) has to include many terms around a to insure convergence.

Another aspect of charge collection of interest is the interaction of a space craft with the ionosphere. Davis and Harris [D14] computed the ion trajectories around a charged satellite in the ionosphere, neglecting the earth's magnetic field, with the solution of Poisson's equation for satellites in numbers (10, 25, etc.) of Debye length. Drag on a charged satellite was studied by Jastrow and Pearse [J4], and Wyatt [W32].

Stability of a Charged Droplet—Charge collection of a liquid droplet follows similar relations as a solid sphere except when its deformability (Chap. 3) comes into play. It is seen that if a small droplet carries two charges, repulsive force would give an ellipsoid as a stable shape rather than the sphere, due to surface tension. Stability of a charged droplet was studied first by Rayleigh [S94] and recently by Ailam and Gallily [A4], who showed that stable shape of prolate or oblate ellipsoid exists for ratios of electrostatic energy to surface energy, $N_{es} = 2(q^2/2\epsilon_o a)/4\pi a^2\sigma$, σ is the surface tension, greater than 4. As another dimensionless number, we may denote N_{es} as electrosurface number.

10.3 Colloidal Propulsion

In an intense electric field, electrical atomization (Sec. 3.8) of dielectric liquids produces charged colloidal particles. Schultz and Branson [S17] showed that a dielectric liquid of very low vapor pressure, such as dioctyl-phthalate oil (Octoil) could be dispersed electrostatically as a charged colloid spray in high vacuum. This is done by feeding oil to a needle point or knife edge at up to +20 kv potential. In the survey of Schultz and Wiech [S18], it was indicated that the electrostatic pressure P_e which acts to expand and shatter the liquid is given by [A2, S43]:

$$P_e = \epsilon_o \frac{E^2}{2}\left[(\epsilon_r - 1)^2 + (\epsilon_r - 1) - \bar{\rho}\frac{d\epsilon_r}{d\bar{\rho}}\right],$$

where P_e is normal to the radius of curvature of the liquid surface (dyne/cm²); E is the field strength in the interior of the liquid, just below the transition layer, ϵ_r is the dielectric constant of the liquid of density $\bar{\rho}$. In the transition layer, the dielectric constant changes continuously from the normal liquid value ϵ_r to $\epsilon_r = 1$ at the interface with vacuum. At the liquid surface $E = E_0$ and $\epsilon_r = E_0/E$; thus

$$P_e = \epsilon_o \frac{E_o^2}{2}\left[\frac{\epsilon_r - 1}{\epsilon_r} - \frac{\bar{\rho}}{\epsilon_r^2}\frac{d\epsilon_r}{d\bar{\rho}}\right] \equiv \epsilon_o\frac{E_o^2}{2}f(\epsilon_r,\bar{\rho}),$$

Henriquez [H31] showed that for nonpolar unassociated liquids $f(\epsilon_r,\bar{\rho}) \sim$ 0.55 and nearly 1 for highly associated liquids. The charge-to-mass ratio was estimated to be

$$\left(\frac{q}{m}\right)_{max} \sim \left[\frac{2\epsilon_o\tau}{f(\epsilon_r,\bar{\rho})r^2\bar{\rho}^2}\right]^{\frac{1}{2}} \times 10^{-6}\ \text{coulomb/kg},$$

where r is the radius of curvature of the liquid meniscus at the instant of dispersion, τ is the tensile strength of the liquid in dynes per square centimeter and is related to surface tension of the liquid σ and molecular radius r_m according to: $\tau \sim 2\sigma/r_m$.

For an estimation of the propulsion parameters, the maximum space-charge-limited current density J in a charged colloid beam is given by the Childs-Langmuir equation as [C33]

$$J = \frac{4\sqrt{2}}{9}\epsilon_o\left(\frac{q}{m}\right)^{\frac{1}{2}}\frac{V_{ag}^{\frac{3}{2}}}{l_{ag}^2}$$

$$= 9.30 \times 10^{-8}\left(\frac{q}{m}\right)^{\frac{1}{2}}V_{ag}^{\frac{3}{2}}l_{ag}^{-2}\ \text{amp/ft}^2,$$

where V_{ag} is the potential difference between the charged colloid source and the accelerating grid in volts, l_{ag} is the distance between the colloid source and the accelerating grid in inches. The net accelerating voltage ΔV required to achieve a desired specific impulse I_{sp} of the exhaust particle beam according to Newton's law:

$$\Delta V = \frac{I_{sp}^2}{2.09 \times 10^{-2}}\left(\frac{q}{m}\right)\ \text{volt},$$

with current requirement given by JA approximately; A is the cross-sectional area of the beam. Extensive experimental studies were also made by Hendricks [H30].

10.4 Charging by Thermionic Emission

Ionization of solid particles at high temperatures was considered by Einbinder [E5] and Smith [S41] and Arshinov and Musin [A15], who used the analogy of ionization of a gas. Soo [S55] studied the interaction between thermionic emission from solid particles and space charges of the phases in a gas-solid suspension. In conformity with other methods of charging particulate matters, this reaction is called thermal electrification. It was shown that at magnitudes of temperatures of 10^3 °K ionization of the gas may become negligible, and thermionic emission as opposed by space charges is the major mechanism, and the time to reach equilibrium is extremely short.

When applied to a charged spherical particle of radius a surrounded by an ionized gas, Poisson's equation becomes

$$\nabla^2 V = \frac{1}{r^2} \frac{d}{dr} r^2 \frac{dV}{dr} = -\frac{e}{\epsilon_0}(n_e - n_z). \tag{10.32}$$

Integration gives the potential at r

$$V(r) = \frac{Ze}{4\pi\epsilon_0 a}\left(1 - \frac{a}{r}\right) + \frac{e}{\epsilon_0 r}\int_a^r (n_e - n_z)r^2 \, dr$$

$$- \frac{e}{\epsilon_0}\int_a^r (n_e - n_z)r \, dr, \tag{10.33}$$

where the first term on the right-hand side is due to charge Z ($Z > 0$ for positive charge) of the particle, the second term is due to shielding by the net charge density within radius r, and the third term is due to image charge effect of these surrounding charges. Thus an electron, say, several diameters ($2a$) away from the solid particles is not necessarily a free electron in the sense of ionization of a gas due to the potential of the particle charge.

Equilibrium in Thermal Electrification of a Single Particle—Consider a static system of a single particle in a finite volume of radius R, since equilibrium is unobtainable when a solid particle of given temperature T in an infinite medium due to continuous thermionic emission. When it is in a finite volume, at equilibrium it is as likely for an electron to move away from the field of a solid particle-charge cloud assembly as it is for it to be attracted toward it. We further take the inside wall of the container as a pure geometric surface, and we neglect any evaporation of the solid material. Overall charge neutrality gives

$$Z = 4\pi \int_a^R (n_e - n_z)r^2 \, dr, \tag{10.34}$$

or the net excess in n_e in the container is that due to thermionic emission. It is noted that the empirical value of the work function φ or potential for thermionic emission originates from image charge and includes the effect of polarization at the surface atoms and surface irregularities. Therefore, instead of computation from the surface of the solid with electron concentration n_{es}, the concentration of electrons immediately outside the surface is taken, or

$$n_{ea} = n_{es} \exp\left(\frac{-\varphi}{kT}\right), \tag{10.35}$$

since φ is experimentally determined, encompassing all the above effects. Consistently, we denote Eq. (10.33) in the form

$$V(r) = V_1(r) - \frac{\varphi}{e}, \tag{10.36}$$

where

$$V_1(r) = \frac{Ze}{4\pi\epsilon_0 a}\left(1 - \frac{a}{r}\right) + \frac{e}{\epsilon_0 r}\int_a^r (n_e - n_z)r^2 \, dr, \tag{10.37}$$

and, assuming Maxwellian velocity distribution of these electrons, their density is given by [K13]

$$n_e(r) = n_{ea} \exp\left(\frac{-eV_1}{kT}\right). \tag{10.38}$$

For convenience in the derivation, we denote $r^* = r/a$, and

$$\rho = 4\pi \int_1^{r^*} \frac{(n_e - n_z)r^{*2} \, dr^*}{n_{ea}} = \frac{N_e - N_z}{n_{ea}a^3}, \tag{10.39}$$

where n_z is the ion density at r^*; n_z is produced by gas atoms only; N_e and N_z are the total number of electrons and ions inside radius r^*, and

$$\rho_R = 4\pi \int_1^{R^*} \frac{(n_e - n_z)r^{*2} \, dr^*}{n_{ea}} = \frac{Z}{n_{ea}a^3}, \tag{10.40}$$

where $R^* = R/a$, and $\rho^* = \rho/\rho_R$. Equation (10.39) gives

$$\frac{n_e - n_z}{n_{ea}} = \frac{\rho_R \dfrac{d\rho^*}{dr^*}}{4\pi r^{*2}}. \tag{10.41}$$

Various parts of Eq. (10.41) can be dealt with according to the following considerations:

(a) The total charge on a solid particle is given by

$$Z = \frac{4\pi a^3}{3}(n_{cs} - n_{es}), \tag{10.42}$$

where n_{cs} is the density of conduction electrons in the solid prior to thermionic emission (or when the solid particle is grounded). Combining Eqs. (10.42), (10.35), and (10.40) gives

$$\frac{4\pi}{\rho_R}\alpha = (\beta_s - 3\alpha)\exp\left[\frac{-\varphi}{kT}\right],\tag{10.43}$$

where $\beta_s = n_{cs}e^2a^2/\epsilon_o kT$, and

$$n_{ea} = \left[n_{cs} - \frac{3Z_p}{4\pi a^3}\right]\exp\left[\frac{-\varphi}{kT}\right].\tag{10.44}$$

(b) n_e and n_z are related by ionization equilibrium at R where $V = 0$ and $dV/dr = 0$, and

$$\frac{n}{n_{eR}n_{zR}} = \frac{PK_p}{n_{eR} + n_{zR} + n},\tag{10.45}$$

where n is the neutral atoms left at the equilibrium condition, $n_{zR} = n_z(R)$, $n_{eR} = n_e(R)$, P is the pressure, K_p is the equilibrium constant, and $n + n_{zR} = n_o$, the original number of gas atoms per unit volume. We get

$$n_{zR} = \frac{n_o(n_{eR} + n_o)}{[n_{eR}(PK_p + 1) + n_o]}$$

$$\sim \frac{n_o^2}{n_{eR}PK_p + n_o}.\tag{10.46}$$

The latter approximation is for $PK_p \gg 1$, $n_o \gg n_{eR}$, and [L10]

$$PK_p = \frac{g}{2g_z}\left(\frac{2\pi m_e kT}{h^2}\right)^{-3/2}(n_o + n_{eR})\exp\left(\frac{I}{kT}\right),$$

where g and g_z are the statistical weights of the ground states of the atom and the ion, I is the ionization potential of the first degree of ionization. The extension to higher degrees of ionization is a matter of detail.

(c) Since there is no net loss of electrons, Eq. (10.38) gives

$$n_e = n_{ea}\exp\left[\frac{-\alpha + \alpha(1 - \rho^*)}{r^*}\right],\tag{10.47}$$

and

$$n_{eR} = n_{ea}\exp(-\alpha)\tag{10.48}$$

$$n_z = n_{zR}\exp\left[\frac{-\alpha(1 - \rho^*)}{r^*}\right],\tag{10.49}$$

for singly charged ions and

$$n_{za} = n_{zR}\exp(-\alpha).\tag{10.50}$$

From Eqs. (10.44) and (10.46), for $\beta_o = n_o e^2 a^2 / \epsilon_o kT$, we get

$$\frac{n_{ea}}{n_{zR}} = \left(\frac{\beta_s}{\beta_o}\right)^2 \exp\left[-\frac{2\varphi}{kT} - \alpha\right] PK_p + \frac{\beta_s}{\beta_o} \exp\left[\frac{-\varphi}{kT}\right]. \quad (10.51)$$

Substitution of Eqs. (10.43) and (10.51) into Eq. (10.41) gives

$$\frac{d\rho^*}{r^{*2}\,dr^*} = \frac{\beta_s A}{\alpha} \exp\left[\frac{-\alpha + \alpha(1 - \rho^*)}{r^*}\right]$$

$$- \frac{\beta_o}{\alpha} \exp\left[\frac{-\alpha(1 - \rho^*)}{r^*}\right] [B \exp(-\alpha) + 1], \quad (10.52)$$

where

$$A = \exp\left(\frac{-\varphi}{kT}\right),$$

and

$$B = n_{cs} \exp\left(\frac{I}{kT} - \frac{\varphi}{kT}\right) \frac{g}{2g_z} \left(\frac{2\pi m_e kT}{h^2}\right)^{3/2},$$

with the boundary conditions: $r^* = 1$, $\rho^* = 0$; $r^* = R^*$, $\rho^* = 1$.

Integration of Eq. (10.52) with a trial value of α to satisfy the boundary condition and to get equilibrium value of α is straightforward. It is noted that at $T = 0[10^3]$, the second term on the right-hand side of Eq. (10.52) is extremely small.

As an example, we take a 1μ zirconia [C33] particle in argon of $n_o = 10^{20}/\text{m}^3$, $R^* = 10$, all at 3000°K (this approximates a gas-solid suspension of $n_p = 2 \times 10^{15}/\text{m}^3$). $\varphi = 3.4$ ev, $I = 15.756$ ev [L10], $g_z = 6$, $g = 1$. Here we have $A = 2.04 \times 10^{-6}$, $B = 2.66 \times 10^{18}$. Integration by trial values of α gives $\alpha = 2.27$ and $Z_p = 206$, $n_{ea} = 4.62 \times 10^{18}/\text{m}^3$, $n_{eR} = 4.76 \times 10^{17}/\text{m}^3$, while $n_{zR} \sim 10^{-20}/\text{m}^3$ (that is, negligible effect of ionization of the gas. Without the solid particle, $n_z = n_e = 1.8 \times 10^{-5}/\text{m}^3$). The distributions are shown in Fig. 10.5. Since the extent of ionization is extremely small, Fig. 10.5 also applies to the case of a finite vacuum. The curves include the total electrons included in r^* around a solid particle, $\rho^* = N_e/Z$; the distribution with respect to the radius, $d\rho^*/dr^* = d(N_e/Z_p)/dr^*$; the potential distribution, $V^* = 4\pi\epsilon_o aV/Ze$; the field, $dV^*/dr^* = d(4\pi\epsilon_o a^2 V/Ze)/dr$; the density, $n^* = n_e/n_{ea}$.

It is seen that the solid particle is surrounded by an electron cloud of diminishing density, bounded by the distributed potential. Ionization of this system occurs when part of the electron cloud is set free (moved to infinity theoretically). This can be accomplished by an external electric field greater than dV/dr at a given radius, by a magnetic field to produce spin of electrons around the solid particle and the attendant drift, or by scattering of gas atoms such as in a turbulent suspension. In general, thermal electrification is not

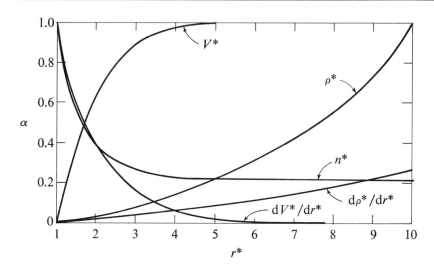

Figure 10.5 Distributions around a solid particle in argon $R^* = 10$ (1 micron zirconia particle at 3000°K, $n_o = 10^{20}/m^3$, $Z_p = 206$, $\alpha = 2.27$).

identical to ionization. From the trend in Fig. 10.5 it is seen that more than 80 per cent of the bounded electrons can be set free by disturbances such as turbulence.

It is noted that n_{cs} can be determined from the Richardson-Dushman equation for thermionic current density J_e:

$$J_e = A_o T^2 \exp\left(-\frac{\varphi}{kT}\right), \qquad (10.53)$$

a relation which is applicable even with the presence of the gaseous phase because: (a) at the temperature level of interest, surface adsorption of an inert gaseous phase is negligible [E22]; (b) the temperature level of interest is too low for secondary emission by collisions of electrons and ions to take place [C33]. The experimental coefficient A_o [C33] is, in turn, related to the conduction electron concentration (for average reflectivity $\bar{r}$ of the surface for electrons)

$$n_{cs} = \frac{A_o T^2}{e} \bigg/ \left(\frac{kT}{2\pi m_e}\right)^{1/2} (1 - \bar{r}), \qquad (10.54)$$

by equating the thermionic current density J_e to free-electron current density; and, further, it can be shown that, for nonmetal or metal with a surface layer, Schottky's modification may be expressed as [T16]:

$$A_o T^2 = e(2n_b)^{1/2}\left(\frac{2\pi m_e kT}{h^2}\right)^{1/4}\frac{kT}{h}(1 - \bar{r})\exp\left(\frac{-\Delta\epsilon}{2kT}\right) \qquad (10.55)$$

where n_b is the total electron concentration in the solid, $\Delta\epsilon$ is the energy gap from the conduction band. When $\Delta\epsilon = 0$ and $n_b = 2(2\pi m_e k T/h^2)^{3/2}$ from equation of thermionic current density to that of emitted electrons, A_o reduces to its value for an "ideal metal," $4\pi em_e k^2/h^3$ [S59].

Rate of Electrification—The rate of electrification before equilibrium is reached can be determined from the electrons at a finite rate in analogy to the loss of planetary atmosphere, with velocity v_c at the surface of the solid particle given by $mv_c^2/2 = Z_p e^2/4\pi\epsilon_o a$. The maximum rate of escape per unit area is given [K13] by:

$$\dot{n}_{ec} = \frac{2}{\pi^{1/2}} n_{ea} \left[\frac{m_e}{(2kT)^{1/2}} \right]^3$$

$$\times \int_{v_c}^{\infty} v^3 \exp \frac{-m_e v^2}{2kT} \, dv \int_0^{\pi/2} \sin\theta \cos\theta \, d\theta$$

$$= n_{ea} \left(\frac{kT}{2\pi m_e} \right)^{1/2} (1 + \alpha) \exp(-\alpha). \tag{10.56}$$

The rate of thermal electrification is therefore

$$\frac{dZ_p}{dt} = 4\pi a^2 \dot{n}_{ec}$$

$$= \frac{4\pi\epsilon_o T}{e^2} (\beta_s - 3\alpha) \exp\left[-\left(\frac{\varphi}{kT}\right) - \alpha \right]$$

$$\times 1 + \alpha \left(\frac{kT}{2\pi m_e} \right)^{1/2}, \tag{10.57}$$

or,

$$\frac{d\alpha}{dt^*} = (\beta_s - 3\alpha)(1 + \alpha) \frac{\exp(-\alpha)}{\beta_s}, \tag{10.58}$$

where $t^* = \beta_s (kT/2\pi m_e a^2)^{1/2} \exp(-\varphi/kT)t$. Integration of Eq. (10.58) gives

$$t^* = \left(\frac{\beta_s}{\beta_s + 3\alpha} \right) \left[\exp(-1) \int_1^{(1+\alpha)} \frac{\exp(y)}{y} \, dy - \exp\left(\frac{\beta_s}{3} \right) \int_{-\beta_s/3}^{-(\beta_s/3)+\alpha} \frac{\exp(y)}{y} \, dy \right]. \tag{10.59}$$

In the case of a metal at $T = 3000°K$, $\beta_s \sim 7 \times 10^6$. β_s is slightly smaller for insulators, but, in general, $\beta_s \gg 1$. Hence, Eq. (10.56) reduces to

$$t^* \sim \exp(-1) \int_1^{(1+\alpha)} \frac{\exp(y)}{y} \, dy. \tag{10.60}$$

Equation (10.60) is plotted as shown in Fig. 10.6. The value of t^* for a metal is given by: $t^* = t \exp(-\varphi/kT) \times (4\pi m_e k T e^2 a/\epsilon_o h^3)$. At 3000°K and $\varphi \sim$ 3.5 ev, $t^* = 5 \times 10^{10}t$. Figure 10.6 shows that the initial stage of thermal electrification occurs at an extremely fast rate. In the above example, the value of $t^* \sim 5 \times 10^{10}t$. However, it is interesting to note that it takes 10^{10^6} sec for a 1 μ metallic particle to lose 90 per cent of its electrons in an infinite vacuum. The fraction of electron loss is given by $3\alpha/\beta_s$.

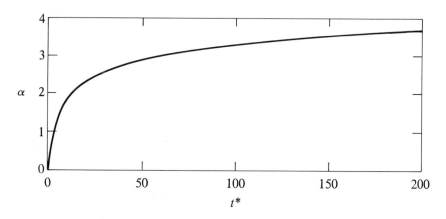

Figure 10.6 Thermal electrification as a rate process.

It is also interesting to determine the heat removed from the solid particle due to thermal electrification, in addition to other energy transports. Where there is no loss of energy due to convection and radiation, each electron emitted requires an excitation of φ ev. The temperature change of a solid particle due to emission is given by

$$m_p c_p \frac{dT}{dt} = -\varphi \frac{dZ_p}{dt}$$

$$= -\frac{4\pi\epsilon_o a k \varphi}{e^3} \frac{d(\alpha T)}{dt}, \qquad (10.61)$$

where m_p is the mass of the solid particle and c_p is its specific heat. Equation (10.61) integrates to, for change from State 1 to State 2,

$$T_2(\alpha_2 + K^*) = T_1(\alpha_1 + K^*), \qquad (10.62)$$

where $K^* = (m_p c_p e^2/4\pi\epsilon_o a k \varphi) = (e^2 a^2 c_p \bar{\rho}_p/3\epsilon_o k \varphi)$, where $\bar{\rho}_p$ is the density of the solid material. For most solids, $K^* \sim 10^8$, hence, the temperature drop due to thermal electrification alone is negligible within the time of most experiments. Equation (10.62) may be considered as the adiabatic equation of thermal electrification.

Studies on charging of solid particles and ionization by thermionic as well as photoemissions were made by Sodha [S45, S46], following the approach of Einbinder [E5] and according to kinetic theory, but the space-charge effect was neglected by Sodha.

10.5 Interaction of Solid Particles with an Ionized Gas

The problems of attenuation of radio waves by combustion product of a metallized propellant rocket and the concentration of ash particles in a combustion magnetohydrodynamic generator led to studies of interactions of solid particles in a suspension in an ionized gas by Soo [S54, S55], and Soo and Dimick [S64].

When applied to a uniform gas-solid suspension of n_p solid particles per unit volume, the volume ratio of gas to solid is $(R^{*3} - 1)$. For a solid of density $\bar{\rho}_p$ and particle cloud density ρ_p,

$$R^{*3} \sim \frac{\bar{\rho}_p}{\rho_p} \tag{10.63}$$

The mass ratio of solid to gas (subscript g) is

$$\frac{M_p}{M_g} \sim \frac{\bar{\rho}_p}{\rho_g R^{*3}}. \tag{10.64}$$

The above applies to a uniform suspension for large R^* without external field or turbulent field.

In a turbulent gas-solid suspension, a sufficient amount of emitted electrons becomes free due to scattering. The field around a solid particle has to be dealt with statistically, based on average free-electron density n_e, given by

$$n_e = n_{es} \exp\left[\frac{-\varphi_e}{kT}\right], \tag{10.65}$$

where φ_e is the equivalent thermionic potential energy. Summing over a field which is much greater than each solid particle-electron cloud system [L10],

$$\varphi_e = \varphi + \frac{Z_p e^2}{4\pi r} + \int_{\text{volume}} \sum \frac{n_s e^2}{4\pi\epsilon_o r_s} \, d(\text{volume})$$

$$\sim \varphi + \frac{Z_p e^2}{4\pi\epsilon_o r} \exp\left(\frac{-r}{R_o}\right) \sim \varphi + \frac{Z_p e^2}{4\pi\epsilon_o a}, \tag{10.66}$$

where n_s is the space-charge density at r_s from the solid particle under consideration, and R_o is the Debye-Hückel length given by summing over locations i, or

$$R_o^2 = \frac{\epsilon_o \left(\sum_i n_{pi} Z_{pi} \right)^{-1} kT}{e^2} \gtrless (n_p)^{-\frac{2}{3}}. \tag{10.67}$$

In the study by Soo and Dimick [S64], the case in which substantial extent of ionization may occur among the gaseous atoms of a gas-solid suspension was considered. At equilibrium, the condition of charge neutrality gives, for nonreactive solid particles in an inert gas:

$$n_e = n_z + Z n_p, \tag{10.68}$$

where n_e and n_z are electron and ion concentration (per unit volume) in the gaseous phase respectively. Ionization equilibrium in the gaseous phase gives [S55]

$$n_e n_z \simeq \frac{n^2}{P K_p}, \tag{10.69}$$

for low extent of ionization (say, less than 1 per cent), where n is the concentration of neutral atoms, P the pressure and K_p the equilibrium constant; taking first-degree ionization only for the present,

$$n_e n_z \simeq n \frac{2 g_z}{g} \left(\frac{2 \pi m_e kT}{h^2} \right)^{\frac{3}{2}} \exp \left(\frac{-I}{kT} \right), \tag{10.70}$$

where g, g_z are the statistical weights of the atom and ion respectively, h is the Planck constant, m_e is the electronic mass, I is the ionization potential of first-degree ionization.

Equilibrium between the phases is reached when there is no net gain or loss of charge due to random motion. At the surface of the solid particle, the number of ions diffusing toward the solid particle per unit time, $\dot{N}_z$, is equal to that of electrons diffusing toward the particle, $\dot{N}_e$, minus that of electrons leaving by thermionic emission, or, from Eqs. (10.53), (10.65), and (10.66),

$$\dot{N}_e - \frac{4 \pi a^2 A T^2}{e} \exp \left(\frac{-\varphi}{kT} \right) = \dot{N}_z, \tag{10.71}$$

where, with consistent degree of approximation,

$$\dot{N}_e = 2 a^2 n_e \left(\frac{2 \pi kT}{m_e} \right)^{\frac{1}{2}} \exp \alpha \tag{10.72}$$

$$\dot{N}_z = 2 a^2 n_z \left(\frac{2 \pi kT}{m_z} \right)^{\frac{1}{2}} \exp (-\alpha), \tag{10.73}$$

(m_z being the mass of an ion); $\alpha < 0$ for negatively charged solid particles, according to Eq. (10.29). Equations (10.72) and (10.73) apply to all values of α. Substitution of these relations into Eq. (10.71) gives

$$n_e \exp \alpha - \frac{2m_e \pi A T^2}{e} (2\pi m_e kT)^{-\frac{1}{2}} \exp \left(\frac{-\varphi}{kT}\right) = \left(\frac{m_e}{m_z}\right)^{\frac{1}{2}} n_z \exp(-\alpha).$$

$$(10.74)$$

The equilibrium value of α is given, by eliminating n_e and n_z from Eq. (10.68), (10.70), and (10.74) to be

$$\frac{\left[B - \left(\dfrac{m_e}{m_z}\right)^{\frac{1}{2}} \alpha \exp(-\alpha)\right][B - \alpha \exp \alpha]}{4\left(\dfrac{m_e}{m_z}\right)^{\frac{1}{2}} \sinh^2 \left[\alpha + \frac{1}{4} \ln \left(\dfrac{m_z}{m_e}\right)\right]} = K,$$

$$(10.75)$$

where the parameters B and K are given by

$$B = 2\pi m_e e A T^2 \frac{\exp\left(-\dfrac{\varphi}{kT}\right)}{(2\pi m_e kT)^{\frac{1}{2}} 4\pi \epsilon_o a k T n_p}$$

$$= (1 - \bar{r}) \frac{n_{cs} e^2}{4\pi \epsilon_o a k T n_p} \exp\left(\frac{-\varphi}{kT}\right)$$

$$K = n e^4 \frac{2g_z}{g} \left(\frac{2\pi m_e kT}{h^2}\right)^{\frac{3}{2}} \frac{\exp\left(-\dfrac{I}{kT}\right)}{(4\pi \epsilon_o a k T n_p)^2}$$

$$= \left(\frac{n_{cs} e^2}{4\pi \epsilon_o a k T n_p}\right)^2 \left(\frac{n}{n_{cs}}\right)^2 \frac{2g_z}{g} \left[\frac{\left(\dfrac{2\pi m_e kT}{h^2}\right)^{\frac{3}{2}}}{n}\right] \exp\left(\frac{-I}{kT}\right).$$

Equation (10.75) reduces for $K = 0$ to the case of negligible ionization in the gaseous phase. The parameter K relates the competition between thermionic emission and collection of electrons from thermal ionization of the gas by the electrostatic capacitance of the solid particles in the nature of a floating probe [B16].

Equation (10.75), in general, gives α as a multivalued function for given B and K. However, the only values of α which are physically significant are those giving positive (or zero) values of n_e and n_i; that is, α's are restricted to those giving

$$n_e = \frac{\dfrac{n_p 4\pi \epsilon_o a k T}{e^2} \left[B - \left(\dfrac{m_e}{m_z}\right)^{\frac{1}{2}} \alpha \exp(-\alpha)\right]}{\left[\exp \alpha - \left(\dfrac{m_e}{m_z}\right)^{\frac{1}{2}} \exp(-\alpha)\right]} \geqslant 0,$$

$$(10.76)$$

and

$$n_z = \frac{\dfrac{n_p 4\pi\epsilon_o a k T}{e^2}(B - \alpha \exp \alpha)}{\left[\exp \alpha - \left(\dfrac{m_e}{m_z}\right)^{\frac{1}{2}} \exp(-\alpha)\right]} \geqslant 0. \tag{10.77}$$

Thus, for given B and K, α is unique. Another asymptotic condition for α is that

$$\sinh\left[\alpha + \tfrac{1}{4}\ln\left(\frac{m_z}{m_e}\right)\right] > 0. \tag{10.78}$$

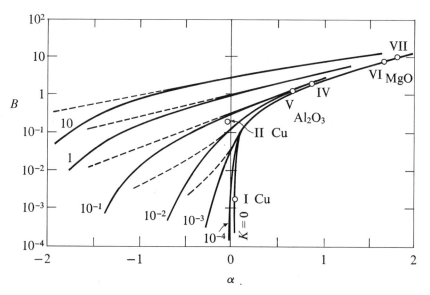

Figure 10.7 Equilibrium of ionization of a gas (argon)—solid suspension (circles show asymptotic states of experiments with various solids; dashed lines for each value of K give the limit of $m_e/m_z = 0$ for any gas).

Therefore, the maximum negative charge that can be collected (besides the limits for electric breakdown [C33]) by a solid particle is

$$\alpha > -\tfrac{1}{4}\ln\left(\frac{m_z}{m_e}\right), \tag{10.79}$$

a condition limited by the rates of collision even in the absence of thermionic emission. The relation between α, B, and K for argon is shown in Fig. 10.7, which gives the trend for all gases. In this case, the value of m_z and m_e for argon give $\alpha > -2.8$ as the limit α for electron collection (the lowest is $\alpha > -0.94$ for hydrogen atoms). Figure 10.7 shows that for $K = 0$, the solid particles can only become positively charged [S55], and this case gives the maximum value of α possible for given B. At higher values of K, depending on its relation to B, the solid particles can become positively or negatively charged (electrons are then effectively collected by solid particles). It is seen that solid particles tend to become negatively charged with combination of low ionization potential of the gas and high thermionic potential of the solid. The circles in Fig. 10.7 are approximate asymptotic states of the experiments given below. The dashed lines for each value of K in Fig. 10.7 give the limit for any gas which gives heavy ions ($m_e/m_z \cong 0$). It is seen that in the range of α near and above 0, the value of m_e/m_z does not affect the relation between α, B, and K.

It is seen that for $Z = 0$, $n_e = n_z$, $n_e \gg (m_e/m_z)^{1/2} n_z$, and $\bar{r} \sim 0$. Equation (10.74) when substituted into Eq. (10.70) gives

$$\frac{n_z}{n} = \frac{g_z}{g} \exp \left[\frac{-(I - \varphi)}{kT} \right], \tag{10.80}$$

the equation for surface ionization of an ideal metal given by Langmuir and Kingdom [R9] as a reduced form of Eq. (10.75). The same condition, when applied to Eq. (10.71), gives

$$\frac{n_z}{n} = 2 \left(\frac{g_z}{g} \right) \left(\frac{2\pi m_e kT}{h^2} \right)^{3/4} (2n_b)^{-1/2} \exp \left[\frac{-\left(I - \varphi - \dfrac{\Delta\epsilon}{2} \right)}{kT} \right], \tag{10.81}$$

showing that oxides, for instance, can be more effective in producing surface ionization than metals [S59].

Experimental Study—The simplest model for ionization and recombination processes is an inert gas. However, measurable extent of equilibrium thermal ionization cannot be maintained in an inert gas at a temperature level of 3000°K and moderate pressures of tens of millimeters of Hg. Therefore, experimental study by Soo and Dimick [S64] was made with an arc flame of argon undergoing nonequilibrium recombination with or without addition of various solid particles. This is also a realistic model for the recombining jet of a rocket after rapid expansion through a nozzle.

Experiments were carried out with a subsonic arc-heated jet of argon (99.996 per cent pure) with total temperatures ranging from 1000°K to 3000°K in a plenum chamber into which the arc-heated jet and solid particles were delivered. When solid particles were not introduced, the conveyance gas (also argon) stream is maintained so that a total argon flow rate of 25.6 g/min is maintained in all tests. The power input to the arc ranged from 0.5 to 5.0 kw, 15 to 24 v at 30 to 210 amp. With the $\frac{1}{4}$-in. sharp-pointed tungsten cathode, no erosion of the tip was noticeable over the test range. Metered feed rates of solid particles ranged from 0.08 to 4.5 g/min with an S. S. White dental unit. Particle sizes were nearly 10 μ for copper and alumina and nearly 2 μ for magnesia. A subsonic jet was produced by blowing down from the plenum chamber through a ¼-in. diameter orifice into a vacuum duct (3 in. diameter, 12 in. long, Vicor glass) at 40 to 90 mm Hg, connected to a vacuum tank and pump system.

Measurements of charge density were made in terms of the saturation current of a rugged (to withstand the blast of solid particles and their coating action) double probe with water-cooled copper electrodes of ¾ in. diameter with 3-mm gap (potential difference was around 3 v). Measured current ranges from 0.001 to 1.0 ma were obtained with a Keithley electrometer. The probe faces were installed parallel to the direction of the jet to minimize coating by the solid material. The probe traverse in position was converted to the time of progression of the jet by measurement of the jet velocity by a total head probe and gas temperature by a thermocouple probe. These probes were traversed along the axis of the jet. The temperature of the solid particles was measured with a pyrometer.

Due to the necessary ruggedness of the probes, only one of the probes (electric, pitot, and thermocouple) can be accommodated during each run.

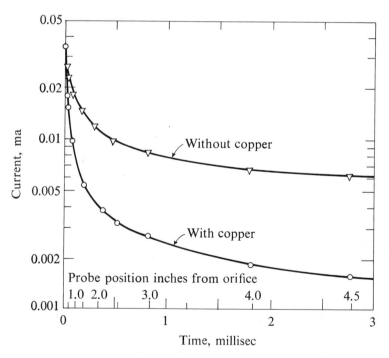

Figure 10.8 Effect of copper particles in the recombination of argon.

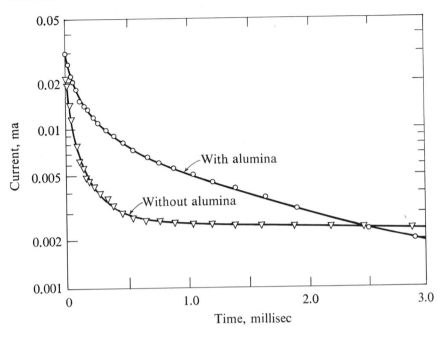

Figure 10.9 Effect of alumina particles on the recombination of argon.

Frequent cleaning of the experimental system was made necessary by the effective coating of the plasma-sprayed solids [G43].

Typical experimental results are shown in Figs. 10.8 and 10.9, with probe current vs. time, t (probe position in inches from the orifice of the jet is included in Fig. 10.8). Along this time scale, recombination took place in the ionized gas with or without addition of solid particles.

For the simple situation of an ionized gas without particles the recombination rate constant k_r is defined according to [L55]:

$$\frac{dn_e}{dt} = -k_r n_e n_z = -k_r n_e^2 . \tag{10.82}$$

The effect of ambipolar diffusivity is negligible for pressure above 10 mm Hg. Integrating Eq. (10.82) gives

$$k_r = \frac{\dfrac{1}{n_e} - \dfrac{1}{n_{eo}}}{t - t_o}, \tag{10.83}$$

where subscript o denotes the initial time taken in the experiment. In terms of current, i, for the curves without solid particles such as in Figs. 10.8 and 10.9, taking $n_e \cong n_z$ and expressing

$$\frac{di}{dt} = -a_2 i^2,$$ (10.84)

we get

$$a_2 = \frac{\dfrac{1}{i} - \dfrac{1}{i_o}}{t - t_o},$$ (10.85)

which gives k_r for a known relation between i and n_e. With the approximation according to Talbot [T1],

$$i_z = \frac{A_p n_z e \bar{v}_z}{4},$$ (10.86)

where A_p is the area of the probe face and $\bar{v}_z$ the average thermal velocity of the ions. Since $n_e \sim n_z$ between the probes, we have

$$a_2 \sim \frac{4k_r}{eA_p \bar{v}_z},$$ (10.87)

for $\bar{v}_z = \sqrt{8kT/\pi m_z}$, we get for the experiments without solid particles, recombination coefficients as given in Table 10.1. The data in Table 10.1 of k_r for given P and n_e compares favorably with data assembled by Loeb [L55] and Bates [B24].

TABLE 10.1

RECOMBINATION OF ARGON WITHOUT SOLID PARTICLES [S64]

Case	I	III	IV	V	VI	VII
T_{total}, °K	2000	3000	2400	1100	2700	2800
T_g, °K	800	1300	900	600	1200	1200
P, mm Hg	45	60	45	48	93	130
$\dot{m}_g$, g/min	25.6	25.6	25.6	48	33.1	33.1
Power input, kw	2.25	4	2.95	1	3.4	3.7
n_g/cm³	6.0×10^{17}	4.9×10^{17}	5.3×10^{17}	8.0×10^{17}	7.5×10^{17}	1.05×10^{18}
n_{eo}/cm³	3.0×10^{10}	4.3×10^{9}	5.4×10^{8}	3.2×10^{9}	1.3×10^{10}	2.5×10^{9}
v_o, m/sec	312	368	330	250	356	360
a_2	34.0	117	370	3300	292	850*
k_r, cm³/sec	1.4×10^{-7}	7.3×10^{-7}	2.3×10^{-6}	2.1×10^{-5}	1.8×10^{-6}	5.3×10^{-6}

* For all a_2, i in milliamperes, t in milliseconds.

When applied to the cases with solid particles (Cu, Al_2O_3, MgO), the variation of probe current i with time t in the form of a polynomial was postulated according to

$$\frac{di}{dt} = a_0 - a_1 i - a_2 i^2. \tag{10.88}$$

The physical meaning of this approximation is that

(a) a_0 corresponds to the generation of current or charge carriers in the medium between the electrodes. This can arise due to thermionic emission from the solid particles, ionization of the vapor of the solid phase, or impurities on the solid particles.

(b) a_1 corresponds to a recombination with the solid particles by three-body collisions. The current i is first-order here, since the high electrical conductivity of a solid at high temperatures permits deionization through alternate collisions of the ions and electrons with the solids.

(c) a_2 has a similar meaning as before. It may include recombination of the ionized vapor of the solid phase together with three-body recombination with the atoms or molecules of the solid phase if we take the concentration of the atoms or molecules of the solid phase as constant.

The above is necessarily a simplification of the real events. However, it serves to generalize the fact that copper particles increase the overall rate of recombination (Cases I and III), while Al_2O_3 and MgO decrease the overall rate of recombination (Cases IV, V, VI, and VII). The results of these computations are given in Table 10.2.

TABLE 10.2

RECOMBINATION OF ARGON WITH INJECTION OF VARIOUS SOLID MATERIALS [S64]

Case	I	III	IV	V	VI	VII
Solid	Copper	Copper	Al_2O_3	Al_2O_3	MgO	MgO
Size, μ	10	10	10	10	2	2
$\dot{m}_p$, gm/min	4.52	4.52	2	2	0.08	0.08
n_{eo}	5.6×10^{10}	6.5×10^9	1.6×10^9	3.3×10^{10}	1.3×10^{10}	1.6×10^9
a_0	-0.48		0.0054	0.0027	0.0033	0.0012*
a_1	-11.1		1.24	0.67		
a_2	25	416	99	160	4.4	29*
Initial particle temperature, °K	1350	1500	1200	1000	1500	1500
Estimated:						
k_r, cm³/sec	7.6×10^{-7}	2.6×10^{-6}	6.2×10^{-7}	3.0×10^{-6}	1.3×10^{-7}	1.5×10^{-6}
% evaporated	0.2	0.2	0.01	0.01	0.03	0.03
k_1, l/sec			2.5×10^{-3}	0.88×10^{-3}		
n_p, /cm³			1.5×10^3	2.4×10^3	1.7×10^4	1.3×10^4
$4\pi a^2 n_p$, m²/m³			0.47	0.76	0.86	0.65

* For all a_0, a_1, a_2, i in milliamperes, t in milliseconds.

It is noted that for the curves with copper particles (Fig. 10.9), the increase of the recombination rate may be attributed to the vapor phase of the copper and the solid surfaces.

For MgO and Al_2O_3, k_r decreases from the no-particle case by approximately an order of magnitude. This may be attributed to the scattering by the ions by positively charged solid particles. The coefficient a_1 for MgO has a small negative value. Corresponding to a_1, we may denote the surface recombination coefficient as

$$k_1 = \frac{a_1 \times 10^{-3}}{4\pi a^2 n}, \frac{1}{\sec}, \tag{10.89}$$

for a total particle surface area $4\pi a^2 n_p$ (in m^2).

From the data given in Table 10.2, estimated limiting values (based on the initial condition of the jet) of α, B, and K for various experiments are shown in Fig. 10.7. The cases of copper were computed from the ionization potential of its vapor, which is present in substantial amounts (this changes the negative limit of α in Fig. 10.7 to -2.9, but the modification of curves in Fig. 10.7 at the range of α of our interest is small). The copper particles, with a high thermionic potential of the solid ($\varphi = 4.38$ ev) and low ionization potential of their vapor ($I = 7.68$ ev) tend to become negatively charged or uncharged, thus enhancing recombination of argon ions ($I = 15.756$ ev) at its surface. The oxides, due to negligible evaporation, become positively charged ($\varphi_{MgO} = 3.19$ ev, $\varphi_{Al_2O_3} = 3.77$ ev), and thus scatter the ions of argon and reduce its recombination rate. The increased rate at later times (Fig. 10.9) was due to cooling of solid particles.

Therefore, if the solid particles were initially uncharged as in the above experiments (charging due to wall impact in the feeder is negligible), metals would be more effective in collecting free electrons. The really effective way of removing free electrons is by introducing significantly charged solid particles.

Further details on the probe theory as applied to a system including solid particles and an ionized gas were given by Dimick [D29]. Johnson and Bullock [J15] gave further details on the Debye shielding distance and a critical temperature at which the sheath changes from that of ions to that of electrons, confirming the above results [S64].

Collection of Electrons—When positively charged solid particles of initial charge Z_i are introduced into an ionized gas of ion concentration n_I (equal to initial electron concentration n_{ei} for ionization given by $M \rightleftharpoons M^+ + e$), the final concentration of electrons is

$$n_e = n_p(Z - Z_i) + n_I, \tag{10.90}$$

and

$$Z_i = v_p(n_{cs} - n_{esi}). \tag{10.91}$$

Substitution of Eqs. (10.65), (10.66), and (10.91) into Eq. (10.90) gives

$$n_e \sim \left(n_{cs} - \frac{n_I}{n_p v_p} - \frac{Z_i}{v_p} \right)$$

$$\times \exp \left[-\frac{\varphi}{kT} - \frac{e^2}{4\pi\epsilon_0 akT} \left(Z_i - \frac{n_I - n_e}{n_p} \right) \right]. \qquad (10.92)$$

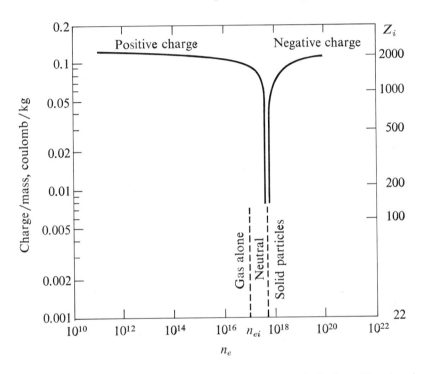

Figure 10.10 Effect of initial charge of solid particles on an ionized gas (data based on example of constant temperature of 3000°K, $n_{ei} = 10^{17}/m^3$, 1-μ zirconia particles, $n_p = 10^{15}/m^3$, charged to Z_{pi}.

Equation (10.92) gives for n_{ei} of $10^{17}/m^3$ at 3000°K with the insulator particles in the example of p. 429 charged to 2000 holes each initially, a reduction of n_e to $10^{14}/m^3$. Due to thermionic emission, when the particles are neutral initially, the free-electron concentration usually tends to be elevated; initially negatively charged particles tend to raise the free-electron concentration further (Fig. 10.10). The time required in this example depends on the rate of distribution of solid particles. Electrostatic dispersion from 1 cm to 1 m takes 10^{-5} sec as shown by Soo [S55].

An experimental study of collection of electrons by solid particles (iron, alumina) was made by Soo and Dimick [S63]. The effect of injection of solid particles into a glow discharge in a blow down system is shown in Fig. 10.11, indicating that collection of electrons by alumina particles was sufficient to quench a glow discharge.

The charge buildup on solid-propellant rockets as the cause of flame-burst mechanism was studied by Fristrom, Oyhus, and Albrecht [F32]. They

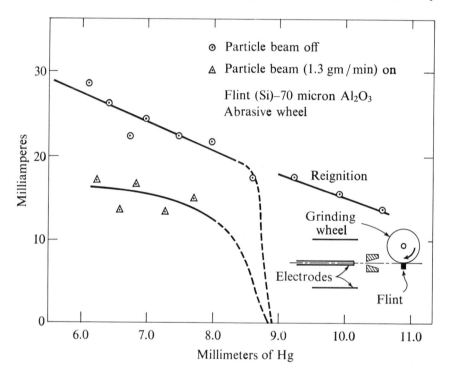

Figure 10.11 Decrease in discharge current due to injection of solid particles.

showed that a solid-propellant rocket may act as a Van de Graaff generator due to charge buildup through the ejection of charged carbon and alumina particles in the rocket exhaust. It was shown that such charge buildup may lead to a potential of 10^6 v.

The effect of solid particles on the electron concentration was shown by Balwanz [B12], who showed that addition of aluminum to a fuel may raise the electron concentration by 1 to 2 orders of magnitude. Chemical non-equilibrium effects in thermal arc jet propulsion was studied by Mironer and Macomber [M38]. It is also expected that thermal electrification plays an important part in the combustion of solid fuel in a gas at high temperature. An extensive study on the experimental nature of combustion of metals was given by Fassel, Papp, Hildenbrand, and Sernka [F7].

Heat transfer between an ionized gas and entrained particles was studied by Engelke [E14].

10.6 Mobility and Electrical Conductivity

The response of droplets and particles to electric fields is measured by their mobility. From the point of view of electrical control of various combustion processes, Gugan, Lawton, and Weinberg [G49] studied the mobility of charged molecular clusters, droplets, and particles. Their survey indicated that sufficient data have been assembled for ions such as given in the treatise by Loeb [L55]. For small particles such that small ion mobility applies, White [W17] gave the mobility as

$$K_p = \frac{0.235 \left[\dfrac{\mathcal{M} + \mathcal{M}_i}{\mathcal{M}_i}\right]^{0.5} \bar{\rho}_o}{[(\epsilon_{ro} - 1)\mathcal{M}]^{0.5}\bar{\rho}}, \tag{10.93}$$

where $\mathcal{M}$ and $\mathcal{M}_i$ are the molecular weights of the gas and the ion respectively, ϵ_{ro} is the dielectric constant, and $\bar{\rho}_o$ is the density of the gas at 0°C and 1 atm, and $\bar{\rho}$ is the density of the gas. For large ions, the Langevin equation gives [L55]:

$$K_p = 0.815 \frac{q\Lambda}{\mathcal{M}\sqrt{\langle v^2 \rangle}} \left[\frac{\mathcal{M}_i + \mathcal{M}}{\mathcal{M}_i}\right]^{0.5}, \tag{10.94}$$

where q is the ionic charge, Λ is the ionic mean free path, and $\sqrt{\langle v^2 \rangle}$ is the root-mean-square velocity of the gas molecule.

For still larger particles, the drag force (Sec. 2.1) on the particle is to be equated to the force due to electric field, or

$$\mathscr{F} = EeZ. \tag{10.95}$$

This consideration gives

$$K_p = \frac{eZ}{6\pi\mu a}, \tag{10.96}$$

for the Stokes regime, and

$$K_p \cong a^{-1}\left(\frac{eZ}{0.22\pi\bar{\rho}E}\right)^{0.5}, \tag{10.97}$$

for the Newton regime. It is seen that Z itself is, in general, a function of the electric field present (Sec. 10.2), thus the mobility is dependent on electric field, as outlined by Gugan, Lawton, and Weinberg [G49].

The electrical conductivity of a suspension with thermal electrification was investigated by Soo [S55]. The mixture consisted of charged solid particles (of micron or submicron range), electrons (due to thermal electrification alone), and the gas atoms of the suspending gas. It was seen that the cross section for collision between electrons (subscript e below) and charged solid particles (subscripts p below) with coulomb interaction far exceeded that between, say, helium atoms (subscript a) and electrons interacting with an inverse fifth power relation. Due to large Debye shielding distance in this case, combination of effects of diffuse scattering and space charge led to lower electrical conductivity than in an ionized gas of similar electron concentration.

The method of calculation of electrical conductivity of a gas consisting of ions, electrons and atoms as presented in Ref. [C18] and reduced by Cann [C2] can be simplified for the present approximation as

$$\sigma_e = \frac{3}{16}\left(\frac{2\pi}{m_e kT}\right)^{1/2}\frac{e^2}{q_{ep}}, \qquad (10.98)$$

where the reference cross section q_{ep} is given by

$$q_{ep} = \pi\left(\frac{e^2 Z}{8\pi kT\epsilon_0}\right)^2 \ln\,(\alpha_d)_{ep}, \qquad (10.99)$$

and the cutoff parameter in coulomb interactions is given by

$$(\alpha_d)_{ep} = 1 + 4\left(\frac{12\pi\epsilon_0 kT}{Ze^2}\right)^2\left(\frac{\epsilon_0 kT}{2e^2 n_e}\right). \qquad (10.100)$$

Thus, for $0.1\ \mu$ zirconia particles at $10^{18}/m^3$ in helium at $3000°K$ and 1 atm $(3 \times 10^{24}/m^3)$ with $n_e = 10^{19}/m^3$, the electrical conductivity of the mixture is 2.8 mho/m and is nearly independent of the pressure of the suspending gas. This is in comparison to a combustion gas at $3000°K$ seeded with, say, 1 per cent potassium, whose electrical conductivity is nearly 60 mho/m at 1 atm [D19], but is reduced considerably as the pressure increases. For the electron concentration of the gas-solid mixture as given in Fig. 10.7 for $K = 0$ at different temperatures, curve A in Fig. 10.12 was calculated. From the point of view of coulomb scattering of electrons by solid particles alone, a large reference cross section suggests higher electrical conductivity as the charge on solid particles decreases. In general,

$$\sigma_e \propto \frac{T^{3/2}}{n_e}, \qquad (10.101)$$

and

$$n_e \propto T^{\alpha'}. \qquad (10.102)$$

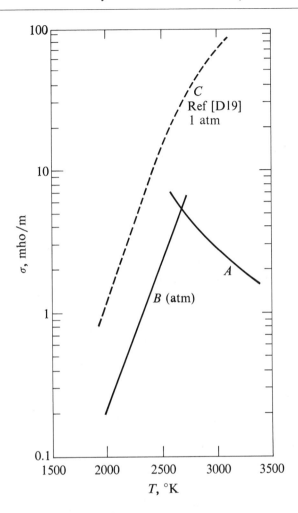

Figure 10.12 Electrical conductivity due to thermal electrification and comparison to combustion gas seeded with potassium.

In the case illustrated, $\alpha' > \frac{3}{2}$, and therefore the electrical conductivity increases with decrease in temperature from the range considered.

However, for the given pressure of the suspending gas, as the influence of coulomb scattering decreases, the elastic scattering of gas atoms becomes more significant. The electrical conductivity may then be approximated by

$$\sigma_e = \frac{n_e e^2}{kT} D_{ea},$$ (10.103)

with diffusivity D_{ea} given by

$$D_{ea} \sim \sqrt{\frac{8kT}{\pi m_e}} \Lambda_{ea}.$$ (10.104)

Equation (10.103) gives the electrical conductivity as shown by curve B in Fig. 10.12. This suggests an optimum electrical conductivity in a medium due to thermal electrification at an intermediate temperature below the boiling point of the solid particles.

It is known that in an electric field E a spherical dielectric particle such as zirconia will polarize with the surface charge density of $3\epsilon_o E \cos \theta$ where θ is measured from the direction of the field [J1]. It can be shown that for a 0.1-μ particle, the chance of polarization with one electron is no more than 10^{-4} for a field of 100 v/m, while for the example of 0.1-μ zirconia, the total charge is 10 holes per particle (or a charge to mass ratio of 0.32 coulomb/kg); therefore, no significant effect on thermal electrification can be expected from polarization of solid particles.

For submicron particles in a high-temperature medium, one can also expect sufficient partition of energy in the rotational degrees of freedom. For 0.1 μ zirconia particles at 3000°K the mass is 5×10^{-8} kg and the moment of inertia amounts to $\frac{1}{2} \times 10^{-32}$ kg-m^2; the root-mean-square angular velocity $\sqrt{\langle \omega^2 \rangle}$ amounts to 3×10^6 rad/sec for each degree of freedom (partition of mean translational energy gives rise to a velocity of no more than 10^{-1} m/sec). The energy of the solid is still due to its temperature; its ratio to that of kinetic partition is $m_p N_o / \mathscr{M}$, where m_p is the mass of each particle, N_o is the Avogadro number, $\mathscr{M}$ is the molecular weight (this ratio is 2.5×10^7 for 0.1-μ zirconia particles). The rotational random motion further eliminates the effect of polarization of a particle in a field.

It is seen that thermal electrification alone does not give rise to high electrical conductivity. Measurements on non-equilibrium electrical and thermal conductivities of suspensions were made by Wu [W34].

Magneto-Gas Dynamic Relations—Due to extremely high heat-transfer coefficient of a gas-solid suspension by large radiative transfer at high temperatures, the possibility of using a gas-solid system for MHD energy conversion with, for instance, nuclear heating is worth considering (Sec. 5.6). The relatively low electrical conductivity of, for instance, a helium-zirconia mixture may be remedied by seeding with cesium so that the electrical conductivity will be at the same level as shown by curve C of Fig. 10.12. This is important because the power density P of MHD conversion is given [D19] by

$$P = \sigma_e E(uB - E),$$ (10.105)

where u is the flow velocity, B and E the magnetic field and the electric field respectively, and the vectors of u, B, and E are orthogonal.

Much slower temperature drop of fluid is expected when compared to helium alone seeded with cesium, thus, nearly constant conductivity can be maintained over relatively long sections of an MHD generator using the gas-solid system.

When applied to one-dimensional analysis of MHD of a conductive gas-solid suspension in the *E-B* field, the two-phase gas dynamic equations (7.34) and (7.33) should be replaced by

$$\frac{d}{dx^*}\left[T^* + u^{*2} + m_p^* \frac{c_p}{c} T_p^* + \dot{m}_p^* u_p^{*2}\right] = -H^*(u^* - I^*)A^* \tag{10.106}$$

$$\frac{dP^*}{P^*} + \frac{c}{\bar{R}} \frac{du^{*2}}{T^*} + \frac{\dot{m}_p^* c u^*}{\bar{R} u_p^*} \frac{du_p^{*2}}{T^*} + \frac{c}{\bar{R}} \frac{H^*}{I^*} (u^* - I^*)\,dx^* = 0, \tag{10.107}$$

where

$$H^* = \frac{\bar{R}L\sigma_e E B}{cP_o} \tag{10.108}$$

$$I^* = \frac{E}{B\sqrt{2cT_o}}, \tag{10.109}$$

and

$$P^* = \frac{P}{P_o}$$

$$H^*(u^* - I^*) = P \frac{\bar{R}L}{cP_o\sqrt{2cT_o}} \tag{10.110}$$

is the dimensionless power density.

It is expected that solid particles such as due to ash or soot from combustion or deliberately introduced particles of controlled size contribute favorably to MHD generation. Presence of solid particles in plasma MHD accelerators in general would reduce the performance of such thrust-producing devices.

Interaction of Solid Particles with an Electrolyte—Interaction of solid particles with the conductivity of an electrolyte has been applied in the determination of size of solid particles. The Coulter principle [U3] utilizes the change of resistance ($\Delta \mathcal{R}$) of an electrolyte solution between two electrodes across an aperture of area A when a solid particle is drawn through this aperture by the electrolyte. For a solid particle of volume v_p, equivalent conductivity σ_p, and projected area A_p to A of aperture, particle dimension ratio x_p (= length parallel to aperture axis/diameter of equivalent sphere), and conductivity of electrolyte σ_o, the change of resistance is given by

$$\Delta \mathcal{R} = \frac{v_p}{\sigma_o A^2}\left[\frac{1}{1 - \frac{\sigma_p}{\sigma_o}} - \frac{A_p}{x_p A}\right]^{-1}. \tag{10.111}$$

10.7 Collection and Coalescence

Numerous investigations have been made on the Cottrell precipitator and resin-wool charged filter. Based on fundamental principles of electrostatics, Kraemer and Johnstone [K34] formulated the mechanics of deposition of charged aerosols on collecting surfaces. Neglecting the inertia force, the equation of motion in Sec. 5.2 is modified to

$$0 = F(\mathbf{u} - \mathbf{u}_p) - \frac{\mathscr{F}_e}{m_p}, \tag{10.112}$$

where $\mathscr{F}_e$ is the electrical force. For a system of bodies $j = 1, 2, \ldots, n$, including the collector ($j = 1$) and the particles $(2, \ldots, n)$, each with charge Q_j and at potential V_j, the work done by the electrical force $\mathscr{F}_{ej}$ over displacement $\delta \mathbf{r}_j$ is given by

$$-\sum \mathscr{F}_{ej} \delta \mathbf{r}_j + \sum V_j \delta Q_j = \tfrac{1}{2}\delta \sum Q_j V_j, \tag{10.113}$$

or

$$\mathscr{F}_{ei} = \frac{1}{2} \sum_{j=1}^{n} V_j \frac{\partial Q_j}{\partial \mathbf{r}_i} - \frac{1}{2} \sum_{j=1}^{n} Q_j \frac{\partial V_j}{\partial \mathbf{r}_i}. \tag{10.114}$$

The potentials and charges on conductors or widely separated dielectric bodies are related by

$$V_j = \sum_k p_{jk} Q_k, \tag{10.115}$$

where p_{jk} is the coefficient of potential depending on geometry. As an example, for the case in which collector and particles are all insulated from ground, $Q_j = \text{constant}$,

$$\mathscr{F}_{ei} = -\frac{1}{2} \sum_j Q_j \frac{\partial V_j}{\partial \mathbf{r}_i} = -\frac{1}{2} \sum_j \sum_k Q_j Q_k \frac{\partial p_{jk}}{\partial \mathbf{r}_i}. \tag{10.116}$$

Since p_{jk} is independent of the charges or potential, they can be determined by assuming only one body in the system to be electrified. The effect of surrounding uncharged bodies is given by the Debye equation [D17] for the pseudo-dielectric constant, ϵ_r', of a medium consisting of conducting uncharged spheres of number density n_p suspended in a gas:

$$\frac{\epsilon_r' - 1}{\epsilon_r' + 2} = \frac{4\pi}{3} n_p a^3. \tag{10.117}$$

The surrounding uncharged spheres will not have any appreciable effect on the potentials and forces if $\epsilon_r' \sim 1$, or $n_p a^3 \ll 1$.

When $j = 1, 2$ only, Maxwell [M17] gave for two conducting spheres of radii R_c (collector) and a (aerosol),

$$
\left.
\begin{aligned}
p_{11} &= \frac{1}{4\pi\epsilon_o R_c} - \frac{a^3}{4\pi\epsilon_o r_{12}^4} - \frac{a^5}{4\pi\epsilon_o r_{12}^6} - \cdots \\[2mm]
p_{12} &= \frac{1}{4\pi\epsilon_o r_{12}} + \frac{R_c^3 a^3}{2\pi\epsilon_o r_{12}^7} \\[2mm]
p_{22} &= \frac{1}{2\pi\epsilon_o a} - \frac{R_c^3}{4\pi\epsilon_o r_{12}^4} - \frac{R_c^5}{4\pi\epsilon_o r_{12}^6} - \cdots
\end{aligned}
\right\}, \qquad (10.118)
$$

when $R_c \gg a$,

$$
p_{11} \sim \frac{1}{4\pi\epsilon_o R_c}, \qquad \frac{dp_{11}}{dr_{12}} = \frac{a^3}{\pi\epsilon_o r_{12}^5} \qquad (10.119)
$$

$$
p_{12} \sim \frac{1}{4\pi\epsilon_o r_{12}}, \qquad \frac{dp_{12}}{dr_{11}} = -\frac{1}{4\pi\epsilon_o r_{12}^2}. \qquad (10.120)
$$

If the aerosol particle is a dielectric material [B48],

$$
\frac{dp_{11}}{dr_{12}} = \left(\frac{\epsilon_r - 1}{\epsilon_r + 2}\right) \frac{a^3}{\pi\epsilon_o r_{12}^5}. \qquad (10.121)
$$

The coefficient p_{12} cannot be simplified where r_{12} is small; that is, when the aerosol is close to the surface of the collector, expressing in the form

$$
p_{22} = \left\{ \frac{1}{4\pi\epsilon_o}\left(\frac{1}{a} + \frac{1}{R_c}\right) + \frac{R_c}{4\pi\epsilon_o r_{12}^2} - \frac{r_{12}^2}{4\pi\epsilon_o R_c (r_{12}^2 - R_c^2)} \right\}. \qquad (10.122)
$$

Taking the collector to be a conductor or having large ϵ_r, and

$$
\frac{dp_{22}}{dr_{12}} = \left\{ -\frac{R_c}{2\pi\epsilon_o r_{12}^3} + \frac{R_c r_{12}}{4\pi\epsilon_o (r_{12}^2 - R_c^2)^2} \right\}. \qquad (10.123)
$$

For $j > 2$, denote γ as the angle between r_{12} and r_{2j}

$$
p_{2j} = \frac{1}{4\pi\epsilon_o r_{2j}}; \qquad \frac{dp_{2j}}{dr_{12}} = -\frac{\cos\gamma}{4\pi\epsilon_o r_{2j}^2}. \qquad (10.124)
$$

For sufficiently low concentration,

$$
p_{ij} = \frac{1}{4\pi\epsilon_o a}, \qquad \frac{dp_{ij}}{dr_{12}} = \left(\frac{\epsilon_r - 1}{\epsilon_r + 2}\right) \frac{8a^3 \cos\gamma}{3\pi\epsilon_o r_{2j}^5}. \qquad (10.125)
$$

All other p_{ij} for $i \neq j \neq 2$ vanish because r_{ij} are invariant during displacement of aerosol 2.

For the case of spherical collector with constant charge, we now have

$$\mathscr{F}_{2e} = -\left(\frac{\epsilon_r - 1}{\epsilon_r + 2}\right)\frac{a^3 Q_1^2}{2\pi\epsilon_0 r_{12}^5} + \frac{Q_1 Q_2}{4\pi\epsilon_0 r_{12}^2}$$

$$+ Q_2^2\left(\frac{R_c}{4\pi\epsilon_0 r_{12}^3} - \frac{R_c r_{12}}{4\pi\epsilon_0 (r_{12}^2 - R_c^2)^2}\right) - \frac{Q_2^2 R_c^3 n_p}{3\epsilon_r r_{12}^2}. \quad (10.126)$$

For spherical collector at constant potential,

$$\mathscr{F}_{2e} = -\left(\frac{\epsilon_r - 1}{\epsilon_r + 2}\right)\frac{8V_1^2 R_c^2 \pi\epsilon_0 a^3}{r_{12}^5} + \frac{V_1 Q_2 R_c}{r_{12}^2}$$

$$+ Q_2^2\left(\frac{R_c}{4\pi\epsilon_0 r_{12}^3} - \frac{R_c r_{12}}{4\pi\epsilon_0 (r_{12}^2 - R_c^2)^2}\right)$$

$$- \frac{Q_2^2 R_c^3 n_p}{3\epsilon_r r_{12}^2} - \frac{Q_2^2 R_c^2 \pi n_p R^2}{4\pi\epsilon_0 r_{12}^2}, \quad (10.127)$$

where R is the radius of the cloud of aerosols surrounding the collector. Writing Eq. (10.112) in the form

$$\mathbf{u}_p = \mathbf{u} + \frac{\mathscr{F}_e}{m_p F}, \quad (10.128)$$

and applying the relation for F in rarefied gas (small aerosols) or $F = 6\pi\bar{\mu}a/m_p C$, C is the Cunningham correction factor and $C = 1 + 0.8 \times 10^{-5} \Lambda/a$. In spherical coordinates with axial symmetry,

$$u_{pr} = \frac{dr}{dt} = u_r + \frac{C\mathscr{F}_{er}}{6\pi\bar{\mu}a} \quad (10.129)$$

$$u_{p\theta} = r\frac{d\theta}{dt} = u_\theta + \frac{C\mathscr{F}_{e\theta}}{6\pi\bar{\mu}a}, \quad (10.130)$$

where r is the radial coordinate and θ the azimuthal angle.

In terms of dimensionless variables $r^* = r/R_c$, $t^* = tv_0/R_c$, where v_0 is the free-stream velocity of the aerosols. Equations (10.129) and (10.130), on substitution of Eq. (10.126) or Eq. (10.127), become, for velocity field of u given by potential-flow theory:

$$\left.\begin{aligned}
\frac{dr^*}{dt^*} &= (1 - r^{*-3})\cos\theta - (N_{ev})_I r^{*-5} + [(N_{ev})_E - (N_{ev})_S \\
&\quad - (N_{ev})_G]r^{*-2} + (N_{ev})_M[r^{*-3} - r^*(r^{*2} - 1)^{-2}] \\
\frac{d\theta}{dt^*} &= -(r^{*-1} + \tfrac{1}{2}r^{*-4})\sin\theta
\end{aligned}\right\} \quad (10.131)$$

and, for viscous flow (Stokes),

$$
\left.\begin{aligned}
\frac{dr^*}{dt^*} &= (1 - \tfrac{3}{2}r^{*-1} + \tfrac{1}{2}r^{*-3})\cos\theta - (N_{\mathrm{ev}})_I r^{*-5} \\
&\quad + [(N_{\mathrm{ev}})_E - (N_{\mathrm{ev}})_S - (N_{\mathrm{ev}})_G]r^{*-2} + (N_{\mathrm{ev}})_M[r^{*-3} - r^*(r^{*2} - 1)^{-2}] \\
\frac{d\theta}{dt^*} &= -(r^{*-1} - \tfrac{3}{4}r^{*-2} - \tfrac{1}{4}r^{*-4})\sin\theta
\end{aligned}\right\}
$$

$$(10.132)$$

The dimensionless parameters which may be called electroviscous numbers: $(N_{\mathrm{ev}})_M$, $(N_{\mathrm{ev}})_S$, $(N_{\mathrm{ev}})_G$, $(N_{\mathrm{ev}})_I$, and $(N_{\mathrm{ev}})_E$ for a spherical collector are, for aerosol charge $Q_2 = q$, the ratio of image force to viscous force:

$$
(N_{\mathrm{ev}})_M = \frac{Cq^2}{24\pi^2\epsilon_0\bar{\mu}v_o a R_c^2}.
$$

The ratio of space-charge force to viscous force is

$$
(N_{\mathrm{ev}})_S = \frac{Cq^2 R_c n_p}{18\pi\epsilon_0\bar{\mu}a v_o}.
$$

The ratio of force due to induced charge for collector at constant voltage to viscous force is

$$
(N_{\mathrm{ev}})_G = \frac{Cq^2 n_p R_c^2}{24\pi\epsilon_0\bar{\mu}v_o a}.
$$

The ratio of image force to viscous force is

$$
(N_{\mathrm{ev}})_I = \frac{Ca^2 Q_1^2}{12\pi^2\epsilon_0\bar{\mu}v_o R_c^5}\left(\frac{\epsilon_r - 1}{\epsilon_r + 2}\right) \qquad \text{for the collector at constant charge}
$$

$$
= \frac{4C\epsilon_0 V_1^2 a^2}{3\bar{\mu}v_o R_c^3}\left(\frac{\epsilon_r - 1}{\epsilon_r + 2}\right) \qquad \text{for the collector at constant voltage.}
$$

The ratio of coulombic force to viscous force is

$$
(N_{\mathrm{ev}})_E = \frac{CqQ_1}{24\pi^2\epsilon_0\bar{\mu}v_o a R_c^2} \qquad \text{for the collector at constant charge}
$$

$$
= \frac{CqV_1}{6\pi\bar{\mu}v_o a R_c} \qquad \text{for the collector at constant voltage.}
$$

All these parameters serve an analogous purpose as the inertia parameter in Eq. (5.20).

Kraemer and Johnstone [K34] made extensive computations for a number of combinations of (N_{ev})'s and carried out experiments with impaction of dioctyl phthalate aerosol. Their results are summarized in Fig. 10.13, giving the collection efficiency or fraction of impaction as defined in Sec. 5.2. In

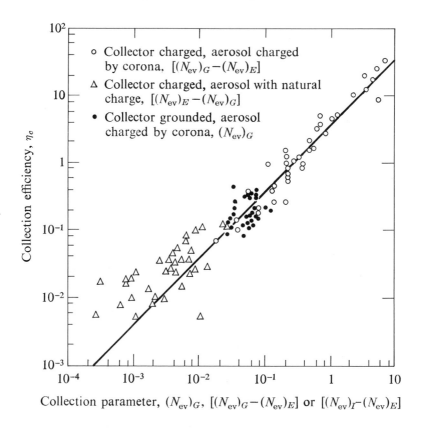

Figure 10.13 Collection of dioctyl phthalate aerosol particles on spherical collector [K34].

Fig. 10.13, $(N_{ev})_G$ applies to the case of the aerosols charged and the collector grounded; $[(N_{ev})_G - (N_{ev})_E]$ applies the case with the aerosols charged, but the collector is held at constant charge or potential; $[(N_{ev})_I - (N_{ev})_E]$ applies to the case where only the collector is charged or held at a constant potential.

Dawkins [D16] extended Kraemer's work to electrostatic collection by a cylindrical collector. Natanson [N1] reviewed the work of others and presented equations for collection of aerosol particles by electrical forces. Goyer,

Gruen, and La Mer [G36], Rossano and Silverman [R37] and Silverman, Conners, and Anderson [S34] have experimentally investigated the effect of charge on filtration efficiency. Gillespie [G18] presented a filtration equation which combines electrical and mechanical forces. Krasnogorskaya [K36] analyzed the role of electric forces in the formation of atmospheric precipitation.

Collection of a charged gas-bourne particle by a single uncharged cylindrical collector was studied by Whitby, Lundgren, and Jordan [W15, L62]. They provided data on the relationship between a filter's single-fiber collection efficiency and a dimensionless image force-drag force parameter.

TABLE 10.3

RANGE OF EXPERIMENTS OF WHITBY, LUNDGREN, AND JORDAN [W15]

Variable	$1\ \mu$	$0.1\ \mu$
Filter-face velocity v_o, fps	4.4 to 160	4.4 to 80
Aerosol median charge q_p, electron/particle	-300 to $+320$	0 to $+6$
Aerosol concentration n_p, particle/cm³	30 to 120	4×10^3 to 6×10^5
Charged aerosol penetration P (ratio)	0.005 to 0.71	0.38 to 0.89
Filter-fiber diameter $2R_c$, microns	10 to 43	10 to 43
Image-force parameter $(N_{ev})_M$	10^{-4} to 3×10^{-2}	2×10^{-6} to 2×10^{-4}
Single-fiber efficiency η_c	0.001 to 0.3	0.003 to 0.05
N_{Re}	0.01 to 1.0	0.04 to 1.0

Aerosol collection due to image force (charged particle and neutral fiber) was measured using test aerosols of 0.1 and 1 μ diameter, deliberately charged to various degrees. Two differential aerosol generators were used to generate test aerosols. Solid 1-μ (mass median diameter, "mmd") particles having a geometric standard deviation σ_g of 1.09 were generated with a spinning-disk generator from 4 parts methylene blue dye and 1 part uranine dye dissolved in a denatured alcohol-demineralized water solution. Solid 0.1-μ mmd particles having σ_g of 1.28 were generated with a British collision atomizer followed by a special impactor and by nebulizing and evaporating a mixture of 1 part methylene blue and 1 part uranine dye dissolved in demineralized water. Samples were collected using low pressure impactor technique followed by electron microscopy [L62]. The range of their experiments is given in Table 10.3.

Neutral aerosol particles were charged in a corona charger of the type developed by Langer and Radnik [L13]. The aerosol is charged by passing through the corona emanating from a 3-mil platinum wire. The resulting particle charges are listed in Table 10.4.

The aerosol charge q and charge uniformity, or geometric standard deviation σ_{gq}, were determined by an aerosol charge spectrometer [L61], in which a thin filament of charged aerosol was injected into a laminar flow field between two parallel collector plates maintained at equal but opposite potentials, variable from 0 to $\pm 10^4$ v. Charged particles were deflected in the electric field and precipitated onto the collector plates. The charge distribution was calculated from the particle distribution in the plates and an afterfilter.

TABLE 10.4

PARTICLE CHARGE MEASURED BY WHITBY, LUNDGREN, AND JORDAN [W15]

	Case 1	Case 2	Case 3	Case 4
a	1.0	1.0	1.0	0.1
q, electron/particle	+320	+150	+90	+6
σ_{gq}	1.18	1.38	1.36	1.26

Naturally occurring charge on 1-μ diameter

$\qquad q = -300$ electron/particle, $\qquad \sigma_{gq} = 1.5$

Neutralized, 1 μ diameter

90%	< -6 electrons/particle
10%	> -6 electrons/particle

Neutralized 0.1 diameter

25%	-1 electron/particle
30%	$+1$ electron/particle
45%	0 electron/particle

The single-fiber efficiency, η_c, is defined as the ratio of

$$\left(\frac{\text{Flow stream area}}{\text{Projected filter area}} \right)$$

both normal to the direction of free-stream flow. For projected fiber diameter $2R_c$, the fraction of aerosol removed per unit flow area is $2\eta_c R_c L$, for total fiber length L per unit filter-face area. L was obtained for measured fiber diameter, fiber density, and fiber weight per unit area. For n layers (n large) aerosol penetration through each layer is

$$P_c = 1 - \eta_c(2R_c)\frac{L}{n}, \tag{10.133}$$

where

$$L = \frac{w}{\pi \rho_{\text{filter}} R_c^2} \quad \text{cm/cm}^2, \tag{10.134}$$

w is the weight per unit filter area, and ρ_{filter} the density of filter material. Alternatively

$$P_c = \exp\left(-2\eta_c R_c L\right), \tag{10.135}$$

single-fiber efficiency is

$$\eta_c = -\frac{\ln P_c}{2R_c L}. \tag{10.136}$$

The image-force parameter, $(N_{\text{ev}})_M$ representing the attractive force between a charged aerosol particle and its image in the collecting fiber, was given by Kraemer [K34] as

$$(N_{\text{ev}})_M = \left(\frac{\epsilon_r - 1}{\epsilon_r + 1}\right)\frac{q^2}{48\pi^2\epsilon_o R_c^2\bar{\mu}(2a)v_o}, \tag{10.137}$$

when ϵ_r is the dielectric constant of the cylinder.

The Natanson's [N1] equation for single-fiber collection efficiency with uncharged cylinder is

$$\eta_T = \left[\left(\frac{\epsilon_r - 1}{\epsilon_r + 1}\right)\frac{q^2}{12\pi^2(2 - \ln N_{\text{Re}})\bar{\mu}(2a)\epsilon_o R_c^2 v_o}\right]^{\frac{1}{2}}. \tag{10.138}$$

From experimental results,

$$\eta \cong 1.5(N_{\text{evM}})^{\frac{1}{2}}. \tag{10.139}$$

Collision efficiency of cloud droplets was also determined by Lindblad and Semonin [L45]. Using the flow field around a sphere derived by Proudman and Pearson [P32], who combined the Stokes' solution with the Oseen's solution, and treating the potential field E outside the spheres as uniform, they solved the problem of interaction of two droplets of radii a_1, a_2 as due to dipoles of moment $p = a^3 E$ oriented in the direction of the applied field. Thus

$$\mathscr{F}_{er} = \frac{p_1 p_2}{r^4}\left(1 - 3\cos\alpha\right) \tag{10.140}$$

$$\mathscr{F}_{e\theta} = \frac{6p_1 p_2}{r^4}\sin\alpha\cos\alpha, \tag{10.141}$$

where α is the angle between the dipole moment p and the radius vector r. They also included the inertia effect such that Eq. (10.112) now reads

$$\frac{d\mathbf{u}_p}{dt} = F(\mathbf{u} - \mathbf{u}_p) - \frac{\mathscr{F}_e}{m_p}. \tag{10.142}$$

They solved the problem numerically.

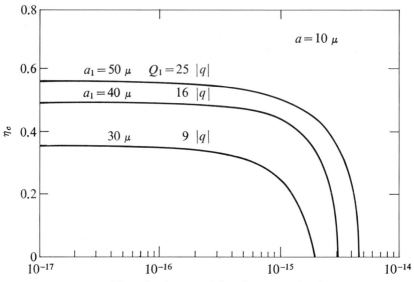

Electric charge of droplet, q, coulomb

(a) Charges of similar sign

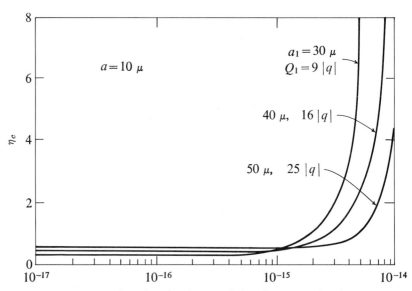

Negative electric charge of droplet, q, coulomb

(b) Charges of opposite sign

Figure 10.14 Typical collision efficiencies of charged droplets [P26].

Plumlee [P26] took into consideration the inertia forces, viscous flow field, and distribution of surface-charge density of interacting droplets, as well as external electric field. A set of his results is shown in Fig. 10.14, illustrating the collision efficiency between charged droplets. The choice of charges in Fig. 10.14, for instance, follows the relation of charge being proportional to the square of droplet radius suggested by Gunn [G51] and Eq. (10.6).

Coalescence—The fact that coalescence of raindrops is basically due to electric charges was suggested by Rayleigh [S94]. It is also well known that collision of droplets does not necessarily lead to coalescence. An extensive survey of studies was given by Plumlee [P26]. The rates of coalescence of oil drops in water and water drops in oil and the effect of chemical additives were measured by Cockbain and McRoberts [C34]. The main factor affecting the stability was shown to be the resistance to wetting of absorbed film by the particulate phase. Gillespie and Rideal [G19] showed that a film was formed between the drop and the interface which drained unevenly. The thickness of the air gap separating the colliding surfaces was measured by light-interference patterns by Prokhorov [P31], who showed that at 100 per cent relative humidity the surfaces coalesce readily. Charles and Mason [C19] found a decrease in droplet stability with a decrease in temperature and a decrease with an applied electrostatic field. Berg, Fernish, and Gaukler [B33] photographed two liquid drops pressed together. The time for coalescence was found to decrease with an increase in an electric potential applied between the drops. Plumlee [P26] showed from motion-picture records that the coalescence time for 2-mm drops varies as the inverse of their potential difference, φ_o. For the model of two drops with flat deformations, the ratio of the separation of the surface at coalescence, $2h$, to the separation at the start of the deformation, $2h_o$, is given by

$$\frac{h_1}{h_0} = \exp\left(-k_c\varphi_o^{7/4}\right), \tag{10.143}$$

where k_c is a constant. This dependence was shown to be due to the influence of the electrostatic force on the growth of perturbation on the surfaces of the liquid, which affects the probability of coalescence at a given separation. Other factors studied were collision velocity, air pressure, and charge transfer.

The influence of charges on the adhesion of particles to surfaces was discussed in a survey by Corn [C41].

Electrostatic deposition has been used in a number of processes. Reif [R7] described the process of applying dry coatings on paper by charging powderous coating material and depositing by image charge, and electrostatic coating of ceramics on metal with electrostatic deposition with potential and charge produced by corona wires. Xerography utilizes deposition of powder on an electrostatic image on an insulating photoconductive surface by exposure of the uniformly charged layer to light [D27]. A technique of electrostatic seed sorting was reported by Tombs [T40].

10.8 Dynamics of a Cloud of Charged Particles

As in Chap. 6, we shall now treat the problem of a cloud of electrically charged particles from the point of view of a continuum [S57].

Contributions of charges on the solid particles (in a neutral gas or vacuum) to the dynamics of a gas-solid suspension will include elementary relations of electrostatics and electrodynamics.

The forces and moments acting on a solid particle consist of those due to the net charge, electric dipole (permanent or induced dipoles, depending on the material) in the electric field due to the charged particles and external field, and magnetic dipole in the induced magnetic field. Neglecting effects of magnetic dipoles, the force $\mathscr{F}$ acting on a solid particle is given by

$$\mathscr{F} = q(\mathbf{E} + \mathbf{v} \times \mathbf{B}) + \nabla(\mathbf{p} \cdot \mathbf{E}), \tag{10.144}$$

where q is the charge, $\mathbf{E}$ is the electric intensity, $\mathbf{v}$ is the velocity, and $\mathbf{p}$ is the dipole moment. The contribution due to electric dipoles is small in the cases under consideration.

Let us consider a large number of uniformly charged solid particles emerging from a spherically symmetrical density distribution with the external constraint, which initially kept the particles within a radius R_0, suddenly removed. We ask for the spreading of the solid particles and its physical effects. For the sake of simplicity, we further assume that the particles are released in a vacuum.

Using the Lagrangian frame of reference, the momentum balance gives, in the r-direction,

$$m \frac{dv}{dt} = qE + \frac{\partial}{\partial r}(pE), \tag{10.145}$$

where

$$E = \frac{1}{4\pi\epsilon_o r^2} \int_0^r 4\pi r'^2 n_{pq}\, dr' = \frac{(q/m)}{4\pi\epsilon_o r^2} M_r \tag{10.146}$$

for

$$M_r = \int_0^r 4\pi\rho_p r'^2\, dr' \tag{10.147}$$

and

$$p = v_p P = \left(\frac{m}{\bar{\rho}_p}\right)\frac{3(\epsilon_r - 1)}{(\epsilon_r + 2)}\epsilon_o E, \tag{10.148}$$

where v_p is the volume of a solid particle, P is the polarization, ρ_p is the density of the solid material, ϵ_r is the dielectric constant, and velocity v is in the r direction. Equation (10.145), together with initial conditions, gives the complete solution. The simplicity of the chosen system makes the solution possible by expressing

$$v = \frac{dr}{dt} \tag{10.149}$$

Substitution into Eq. (10.145) gives, for a particle initially at radius R,

$$v\frac{dv}{dr} = \frac{1}{\epsilon_o}\left(\frac{q}{m}\right)^2\frac{M_R}{4\pi r^2} - \frac{12}{\bar{\rho}_p\epsilon_o}\frac{(\epsilon_r - 1)}{(\epsilon_r + 2)}\left(\frac{q}{m}\right)^2\frac{M_R^2}{(4\pi)^2 r^5}, \tag{10.150}$$

where $M_R = M_r(R)$ at $t = 0$, where $v = 0$. It is seen that the dipole effect is due to the gradient of electric intensity which, in this case, produces a deceleration. The ratio of the force due to dipole $\mathscr{F}_d$ to that due to electrostatic repulsion, $\mathscr{F}_e$, is

$$\frac{\mathscr{F}_d}{\mathscr{F}_e} = \frac{12}{\bar{\rho}_p}\frac{(\epsilon_r - 1)}{(\epsilon_r + 2)}\frac{M_R}{4\pi r^3}, \tag{10.151}$$

which for uniform distribution within $r = R$ is

$$\frac{\mathscr{F}_d}{\mathscr{F}_e} = \frac{4(\epsilon_r - 1)}{(\epsilon_r + 2)}\frac{\rho_p}{\bar{\rho}_p}. \tag{10.152}$$

Which gives for very low dielectric constant ($\epsilon \gtrsim 1$), $\mathscr{F}_d/\mathscr{F}_e \sim \frac{4}{3}(\epsilon_r - 1)\rho_p/\bar{\rho}_p$ and for very high dielectric constant $\mathscr{F}_d/\mathscr{F}_e \sim 4\rho_p/\bar{\rho}_p$, where $\rho_p/\bar{\rho}_p = \phi$ of the particulate system. Therefore, for a dilute particulate system, the dipole effect due to self-field is negligible. It could be significant, however, as a source of instability in a fluidized bed (Sec. 9.4). In this case, integration after nondimensionalizing gives, for a particle at radius R initially,

$$\frac{2\pi\epsilon_o R}{M_R(q/m)^2}v^2 = v^{*2} = \left(\frac{dr^*}{dt^*}\right)^2 = \left(1 - \frac{1}{r^*}\right), \tag{10.153}$$

where $r^* = r/R$. Further integration gives, for $t^* = t\sqrt{M_R(q/m)^2/2\pi\epsilon_o R^3}$, and $r^* = 1$ at $t^* = 0$,

$$t^* = \sqrt{r^*(r^* - 1)} + \ln[\sqrt{r^*} + \sqrt{r^* - 1}]. \tag{10.154}$$

Equations (10.153) and (10.154) give the position and velocity at given time t^* of each particle initially at radius R. Each particle reaches an asymptotic velocity of $\sqrt{M_R(q/m)^2/2\pi\epsilon_o R}$ at infinity.

The density distribution can be visualized as follows: If the initial density distribution is such that we have a uniform sphere, the above relations show that the cloud expands uniformly, giving a uniform distribution all the time and, finally, the radius of the system expands at a constant speed. If the initial distribution is uniform in a spherical shell, the result of its expansion is a uniform hollow sphere with the inside radius preserved and outer radius as given by Eq. (10.154). Because the collision among the particles does not occur in this system, final density distribution can be obtained from the initial density distribution by superposition.

Because of the spherical symmetry the Maxwell electromagnetic equations give [J1], for magnetic induction $\mathbf{B} = 0$,

$$\nabla \cdot \mathbf{J} = -\frac{\partial}{\partial t} \nabla \cdot \mathbf{D} = -\frac{\partial}{\partial t} \rho_e , \qquad (10.155)$$

which is none other than the continuity equation of the cloud of solid particles; $\mathbf{D}$ is the electric displacement. The electromagnetic energy [P1] of this system is just the electrostatic energy. An energy balance of the system and the surroundings shows that the decrease in the electromagnetic energy as the whole system expands gives rise to an increase in kinetic energy of the particles. The system therefore suffers no loss via electromagnetic waves. The Poynting flux of the electromagnetic radiation given by $\mathbf{E} \times \mathbf{H}$ is zero. This case involving spherical symmetry is the only situation in which there is no electromagnetic radiation.

Next, we take an axisymmetric system with charged particles moving axially (in the z-direction) at velocity v_z initially constrained within radius R_0, and then the radial constraint is removed at $t = 0$. The field at radius r is equal to that due to a line source along the axis of linear charge density, λ_e, where

$$\lambda_e = 2\pi \int_0^r \rho_e r \, dr = \left(\frac{q}{m}\right) \int_0^R \rho_p r \, dr$$

$$= \left(\frac{q}{m}\right) M_r'(R) = \left(\frac{q}{m}\right) M_R' , \qquad (10.156)$$

where M_r' is the mass of particles per unit axial length within the radius R. The field at radius R gives the acceleration due to electrostatic repulsion from the core:

$$\frac{dv_r}{dt} = \frac{d^2 r}{dt^2} = \frac{1}{\epsilon_o} \left(\frac{q}{m}\right)^2 \frac{M_r'}{r} . \qquad (10.157)$$

The ratio of the force due to dipole to that due to electrostatic repulsion is now $[3(\epsilon_r - 1)/(\epsilon_r + 2)](M_r'/\pi r^2 \rho_p)(\rho_p/\bar{\rho}_p)$ and the dipole effect due to self-field is again negligible for dilute suspensions.

Equation (10.157) shows that in the absence of turbulence and other field forces, a charged gas-solid suspension in a pipe will eventually settle at the wall by the electrostatic force.

Because of axial velocity, a magnetic field is induced in the θ-direction [S76]. The radial force on a particle amounts to

$$\frac{1}{\mu_m} \frac{1}{r} \frac{\partial}{\partial r}(rB_\theta) = \mathbf{J} = n_p q v_z = \rho_p\left(\frac{q}{m}\right)v_z . \tag{10.158}$$

For constant ρ_p, and inside of radius r, we have

$$B_\theta = \frac{\mu_m \mathbf{J} r}{2}, \tag{10.159}$$

where μ_m is the permeability of the particle field. The equation of motion of the particles at radius r in the radial direction at a steady state is given by

$$\rho_p v_r \frac{dv_r}{dr} = -\mathbf{J}B_\theta + n_p q E_r = -\mu_m \mathbf{J}^2 \frac{r}{2} + \rho_p^2\left(\frac{q}{m}\right)^2 \frac{r}{2\epsilon_o}, \tag{10.160}$$

that is, the particles driven by electrostatic field are slowed down by the induced magnetic field depending on the mass flow, $\rho_p v_z$. The $\mathbf{J}^2$ term is similar to the magnetic pinch in a plasma. Integration of Eq. (10.160) shows that, for $\mathbf{J}$ given by Eq. (10.160), the electrostatic repulsion is eliminated by the induced magnetic field only when

$$v_z^2 = \frac{1}{\mu_m \epsilon_o} . \tag{10.161}$$

Since $1/\mu_m \epsilon_o$ is the square of the speed of light, we see that the electrostatic repulsion is canceled only when the axial velocity is that of light in the medium under consideration. Therefore, the self-pinch effect on a charged gas-solid suspension is usually negligible.

To calculate the behavior of this system as the outer boundary of particles expands without constraint, Eqs. (10.160) and (10.156) give

$$v_r \frac{dv_r}{dr} = \left(\frac{q}{m}\right)^2 \frac{M'_R}{4\pi\epsilon_o r} - \mu_m \rho_p\left(\frac{q}{m}\right)^2 v_z^2 \frac{r}{2}, \tag{10.162}$$

which integrates to, as a particle changes its radical position,

$$v_r^2 = \left(\frac{q}{m}\right)^2 \frac{M'_R}{2\pi\epsilon_o}\left[\ln\frac{R'}{R} - \mu_m\epsilon_o v_z^2\right]. \tag{10.163}$$

Equation (10.163) gives the change in the total kinetic energy per unit length

$$\int \frac{v_r^2}{2} 2\pi R\, dR\rho_{po} = \left(\frac{q}{m}\right)^2 \frac{M^2}{8\pi\epsilon_o}\left[\ln\frac{R'_0}{R_0} - \mu_m\epsilon_o v_z^2\right]. \tag{10.164}$$

The electromagnetic energy per unit length $\dot{m}$ inside of R is

$$U = \frac{1}{2} \int_0^R (\epsilon_o E_r^2 + \mu_m H_\theta^2) \, dr$$

$$= \frac{1}{16\pi} \left(\frac{q}{m}\right)^2 M_R'^2 (1 + \mu_m \epsilon_o v_z^2), \qquad (10.165)$$

for a uniform density of the solid particles to begin with, since ρ_p is always uniform, for the same reason as in the spherical system. Thus, the total electromagnetic energy is constant inside the radius R_0'. The acceleration of the particles is, therefore, due to the decrease of electromagnetic energy outside the system. In this case the Poynting flux, $\mathbf{s}$, in energy per unit area per unit time points to the downstream of the cylindrical system,

$$\mathbf{s} = \mathbf{E} \times \mathbf{H} = \left(\frac{q}{m}\right)^2 M'^2 \frac{v_z}{(2\pi)^2 \epsilon_o} \left(\frac{R}{R_0}\right)^2 \frac{1}{R_0^2}. \qquad (10.166)$$

The total axial flux of energy is now

$$S = \int_A \mathbf{s} \, dA' = \left(\frac{q}{m}\right)^2 M'^2 \frac{v_z}{8\pi\epsilon_o}, \qquad (10.167)$$

in energy per unit time.

Turbulent Flow of a Charged Gas-Solid Suspension—One situation of interest consists of a gas-solid suspension flowing through a pipe. If the pipe is a conductor or a uniformly charged insulator, the Gauss law says that there is no electric field inside of the pipe due to the wall. If the particles are uniformly charged and axisymmetrically distributed over the pipe, the particle will eventually settle at the wall if there is no fluid turbulence. Equation (10.157) shows that for small glass beads in atmospheric air at a loading of 1 kg of solid per kilogram of air, the acceleration amounts to, at radius 1 cm from the axis, 10 times that due to gravity, even for a charge-to-mass ratio of 0.002 coulomb per kg. The radial component of turbulent intensity of particles, according to the approximation of Soo [S48], will be to the order of 10 sq m/sec² for 100 μ particles. This effect can overshadow completely that due to gravity on a gas-solid suspension in a horizontal pipe. This furnishes one possible explanation for the large difference between transverse and longitudinal intensities of particles in Sec. 2.8. Density distribution as determined by Soo [S53] may attribute its drift velocity mainly to electric charges on the particles also.

In dealing with a turbulent suspension of charged solid particles in a gas flowing in a cylindrical pipe of a conductor, the inside wall of the pipe forms a closed equipotential surface, regardless of its charge. The particles will be driven toward the wall by mutual repulsion; a sustained gas-solid suspension will have to be due to turbulent diffusion from the wall. Effect of nonuniform charges on the wall may, however, show up in the case of a pipe of insulating materials.

In dealing with the fully developed turbulent pipe flow of a suspension, the concentration distribution of solid particles is given [S71, S72] by

$$\frac{1}{r}\frac{\partial}{\partial r} Dr \frac{\partial \rho_p}{\partial r} = \frac{d\rho_p}{dt}. \tag{10.168}$$

for charged particles, Eq. (10.160) gives

$$v_r \frac{dv_r}{dr} = \left(\frac{q}{m}\right)^2 \frac{\int_0^r \rho_p 2\pi r'\, dr'}{4\pi\epsilon_o r} - \mu_m \rho_p \left(\frac{q}{m}\right)^2 v_z^2 \frac{r}{2}. \tag{10.169}$$

The last term due to induced magnetic field is negligible. If we take the distribution as determined by Soo [S53] where a drift velocity was recognized, but its source was unspecified:

$$\rho_p = \rho_{po} + (\rho_{pw} - \rho_{po})\left(\frac{r}{R}\right)^\alpha, \tag{10.170}$$

where subscript o denotes the center and w denotes the wall of the pipe ($r = R$). Equation (10.169) gives a drift velocity:

$$v_r = \left(\frac{q}{m}\right)\frac{1}{\sqrt{4\pi\epsilon_o}}\left(\frac{r}{R}\right)\sqrt{\rho_{po}\pi R^2}\left[1 + \left(\frac{\rho_{pw} - \rho_{po}}{\rho_{po}}\right)\frac{2}{(\alpha+2)^2}\left(\frac{r}{R}\right)^\alpha\right]^{\frac{1}{2}}. \tag{10.171}$$

Since the drift and diffusion occur at steady state, Eq. (10.168) can be approximated by

$$\frac{1}{r}\frac{d}{dr} D_p r \frac{d\rho_p}{dr} = v_r \frac{d\rho_p}{dr}. \tag{10.172}$$

Solution in a closed form is feasible by expanding v_r given by Eq. (10.171) as:

$$v_r = \frac{q}{m}\left(\frac{\rho_{po}}{2\epsilon_o}\right)^{\frac{1}{2}} r\left[1 + 2B\left(\frac{r}{R}\right)^\alpha - 2B^2\left(\frac{r}{R}\right)^{2\alpha} + \cdots\right], \tag{10.173}$$

where

$$B = \frac{2(\rho_{pw} - \rho_{po})}{\rho_{po}(\alpha+2)^2}. \tag{10.174}$$

Integrating Eq. (10.172) from 0 to r gives

$$D_p r \frac{d\rho_p}{dr} = \left(\frac{q}{m}\right)\sqrt{\frac{\rho_{po}}{2\epsilon_o}} R\alpha(\rho_{pw} - \rho_{po})\left[\frac{R}{\alpha+2}\left(\frac{r}{R}\right)^{\alpha+2}\right.$$
$$\left. + \frac{2BR}{2\alpha+2}\left(\frac{r}{R}\right)^{2\alpha+2} - \frac{2B^2R}{3\alpha+2}\left(\frac{r}{R}\right)^{3\alpha+2} + \cdots\right]. \tag{10.175}$$

Since the concentration profile is well defined by the power-law relation in Eq. (10.170), its concentration gradient at the wall is given for $r = R$, $D_p = D_{pw}$, and

$$\frac{d\rho_p}{dr} = \frac{\alpha(\rho_{pw} - \rho_{po})}{R},$$ (10.176)

thus the exponent α in Eq. (10.170) can be determined from measurement of $d\rho_p/dr$. The particle diffusivity at the wall can be determined from

$$\left(\frac{q}{m}\right)\sqrt{\frac{\rho_{po}}{2\epsilon_o}}\frac{R^2}{D_{pw}} = \left[\frac{1}{\alpha + 2} + \frac{B}{\alpha + 1} - \frac{2B^2}{3\alpha + 2} + \cdots\right]^{-1},$$ (10.177)

$\rho_{po} \sim 1.67\dot{m}_p/\pi R^2 V_o$ ($\dot{m}_p$ is the solid-flow rate, V_o is the fluid velocity at the center of the pipe), $\rho_{pw} \sim 2.4\dot{m}_p/\pi R^2 V_o$, $\partial\rho_p/\partial r^*]_{r=R} = (0.04/0.233)\dot{m}_p/\pi R^2 V_o$; we get from Eq. (10.177). Further, with $\dot{m}_p = 1.24 \times 10^{-2}$ kg/sec, $V_o = 30$ m/sec, and $D_{pw} = 2.7 \times 10^{-4}$ sq. m/sec, we get, from Eq. (10.177):

$$\frac{q}{m} = 4 \times 10^{-6} \text{ coulomb/kg},$$

showing that even a very small charge would have a pronounced effect on concentration distribution.

This is the basis of evaluation of pipe flow in Sec. 4.5. It is noted that

$$N_{ev} = \left(\frac{q}{m}\right)\sqrt{\frac{\rho_{po}}{2\epsilon_o}}\frac{R^2}{D_p},$$

is the ratio of electrostatic force to turbulent forces, which we shall call the turbulent electroviscous number.

Singh [S37] further considered the effects of rotation, magnetic field and compressibility on the disturbances produced by the slow oscillation of a conducting sphere in a conducting viscous medium, and the attendant modification of the drag coefficient.

10.9 Electrohydrodynamic Flow

Extensive details of the performance of electrostatic precipitators are presented in the treatise by White [W16] and Rose and Wood [R26]. In the following, only the fundamental aspects of electrohydrodynamic flow will be explored. It is also intended to identify similarity relations in this type of flow to serve as reference to model studies such as the ones made by Sproull [S77].

The basic formulation of flow of a gas with space charge (electrohydrodynamics) was in studies by Stuetzer [S96]. Space-charge flow with various boundary configurations was made by Lockwood and Hamza [L54], extending from earlier efforts of Langmuir and Blodgett [L15]. Motion of charged aerosol particles in relation to surfaces has also been utilized as basic methods for analyzing particle size [D6, L47] as well as electrostatic precipitation [K34]. In all these studies, theoretical analysis includes that of single particles under viscous drag [D6, L47]; as a stream of microscopic particles with electrostatic field only [L54, L15]; or numerical summation of discrete particles in a hydrodynamic potential flow field [K34]. In the study by Soo [S58, S60], continuing from the previous section, study concerned motion of a cloud of charged solid particles suspended in a gas, with continuum approximation.

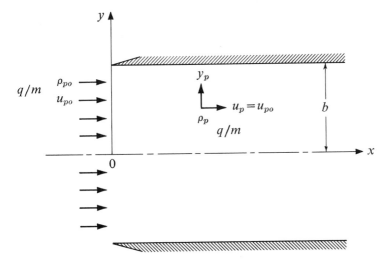

Figure 10.15 Flow of a uniformly charged cloud of solid particles into a channel. (The walls are grounded conductors.)

The significance of the effect of electric charge on solid particles (even for very small charge-to-mass ratio) in gas-solid flow was discussed in Sec. 4.5. The effect is felt even when a short flow length is involved, such as in a nozzle handling gas-solid flow (Sec. 8.5).

Flow into a Channel—To illustrate the application of the basic relations to an electrohydrodynamic flow system of charged solid particles into a grounded channel with low particle concentration (below, say, 0.25 kg/m^3), we consider the following problem, where the basic equations in Chap. 6 are simplified from consideration of two-dimensional motion in an electric field ($i = 1, 2$); fluid motion not strongly affected by particle motion; and one partical size ($s = 1$). We consider the case of slug flow of a cloud of charged solid particles with uniform longitudinal (x-direction) velocity u_o of the fluid into a two-dimensional channel of width $2b$ with grounded conducting walls as shown in Fig. 10.15. Viscous force encountered by particles drifting toward the walls (at velocity v in the y-direction) is taken into account. In this case, the electrostatic forces acting on the particle cloud are entirely due to image charge of the conducting wall and the space charge of the cloud.

At the inlet into the channel, the density of the solid particles is uniform (ρ_{po}). The collision of particles with the wall is taken to be inelastic for the present solution. Taking the range where u is nearly constant; that is, before the hydrodynamic boundary layer has developed significantly (hence the y-component of fluid velocity is zero), the equation of motion in the x-direction gives, for $x' = x/u_o$,

$$\left(\frac{q}{m}\right)E_x = \frac{\partial u}{\partial x'} + v\left(\frac{\partial u}{\partial y}\right) = 0, \tag{10.178}$$

where (q/m) is the charge-to-mass ratio of the cloud, E_x is the electric field in the x-direction. The continuity equation now takes the form

$$\frac{\partial \rho_p}{\partial x'} + \frac{\partial \rho_p v}{\partial y} = 0, \tag{10.179}$$

where ρ_p varies due to drift of solid particles.

The equation of motion in the y-direction is

$$\frac{\partial v}{\partial x'} + v\frac{\partial v}{\partial y} = \frac{q}{m}E_y + F(-v), \tag{10.180}$$

where E_y is the electric field in the y-direction and $F = 6\pi a\bar{\mu}/m$, the time constant of viscous drag based on Stokes' law; a is the radius of the particle, m is its mass. Since $E_x = 0$, the electric field is given by Poisson's equation in the form

$$\frac{\partial E_y}{\partial y} = \frac{q}{m}\frac{\rho_p}{\epsilon_o}, \tag{10.181}$$

where ϵ_o is the permittivity. The initial conditions are: $x = 0$, $v = 0$, and $x = 0$, $y = 0$, $\partial v/\partial y = 0$, with the leading edge effect neglected (see Sec. 10.10).

Equations (10.179) to (10.181) can be solved simultaneously to determine the variation of particle concentration ρ_p due to collection at the walls, and variation in v and E_y due to space charge. Solution is accomplished by introducing a stream function ψ such that

$$\rho_p = -\frac{\partial \psi}{\partial y}, \qquad \rho_p v = \frac{\partial \psi}{\partial x'}, \tag{10.182}$$

which satisfies Eq. (10.179); and, replacing the independent variables (x',y) by (x',ψ), we reduce Eq. (10.180) to

$$\frac{\partial v}{\partial x'} = \frac{q}{m}E_y - Fv,$$

or

$$\frac{\partial}{\partial x'}(ve^{Fx'}) = \frac{q}{m}E_y e^{Fx'}, \qquad (10.183)$$

and Eq. (10.181) to

$$-\frac{\partial E_y}{\partial \psi} = \frac{\left(\dfrac{q}{m}\right)}{\epsilon_o}. \qquad (10.184)$$

Elimination of E_y between Eqs. (10.183) and (10.184) gives

$$\frac{\partial^2}{\partial x' \, \partial \psi}(ve^{Fx'}) = -\left(\frac{q}{m}\right)^2 \epsilon_o^{-1} e^{Fx'}, \qquad (10.185)$$

which has the particular solution

$$v = -\psi\left(\frac{q}{m}\right)^2 \epsilon_o^{-1}\frac{(1 - e^{-Fx'})}{F}. \qquad (10.186)$$

Substitution of Eq. (10.186) with Eq. (10.182) into Eq. (10.179) with

$$\left.\begin{aligned}
\rho^* &= \frac{\rho_p}{\rho_{po}} \\[2mm]
x^{*2} &= \tfrac{1}{2}\left[1 + \frac{u_o}{Fx}e^{-Fx/u_o}\right]\left[\left(\frac{q}{m}\right)^2\frac{\rho_{po}}{\epsilon_o u_o^2}b^2\right]\frac{u_o}{Fb}\frac{x}{b} \\[2mm]
y^* &= \frac{y}{b}
\end{aligned}\right\} \qquad (10.187)$$

gives

$$\frac{\partial \rho^*}{\partial(x^{*2})} + \frac{\partial}{\partial y^*}\left(\rho^*\int \rho^* \, dy^*\right) = 0, \qquad (10.188)$$

giving the distribution of cloud density from a perturbation solution,

$$\rho^* = (1 + x^{*2})^{-1} + y^{*2}(1 + x^{*2})^{-4} + \cdots, \qquad (10.189)$$

the stream function or mass distribution,

$$-\psi = \int_0^y \rho \, dy$$

$$= \rho_{po}b\left\{y^*(1 + x^{*2})^{-1} + \frac{y^{*2}}{3}[1 - (1 + x^{*2})^{-4}] + \cdots\right\}, \qquad (10.190)$$

and the drift-velocity distribution:

$$\frac{v}{u_o} = \left(\frac{u_o}{Fb}\right)[1 - e^{-(Fb/u_o)(x/b)}]\left(\frac{q}{m}\right)^2\left(\frac{\rho_{po}b^2}{\epsilon_o u_o^2}\right)$$

$$\times \left\{y^*(1 + x^{*2})^{-1} + \frac{y^{*2}}{3}[1 - (1 + x^{*2})^{-4}] + \cdots\right\}. \quad (10.191)$$

These relations are shown in Fig. 10.16. The amount collected is shown between the streamline marked 1.0 and the wall in Fig. 10.16a.

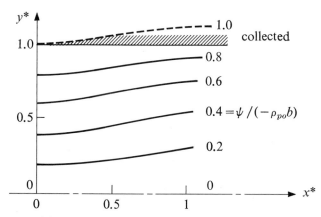

(a) Streamlines of cloud of solid particles

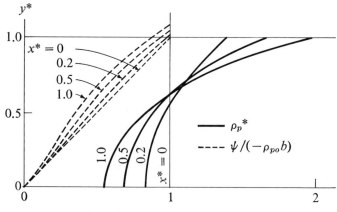

(b) Distribution of concentration and stream function

Figure 10.16 Behavior of slug flow of a charged cloud of solid particles into a two-dimensional channel.

It is noted that

$$\left(\frac{q}{m}\right)^2 \frac{\rho_{po}b^2}{\epsilon_o u_o^2} = (N_{\text{Re}})_{eb}^{-1},\tag{10.192}$$

where $(N_{\text{Re}})_{eb}$ is the "electric Reynolds number" defined by Stuetzer [S96] and is the ratio of inertia force of the solid particle to the electrostatic force, and

$$\frac{u_o}{Fb} = (N_m)_b ,\tag{10.193}$$

is the "gas-solid momentum number" based on dimension b. Expressing it another way, part of the coefficient of Eq. (10.191) can be rewritten as

$$N_m(N_{\text{Re}})_{eb}^{-1} = \frac{u_o}{Fb}\left(\frac{q}{m}\right)^2\left(\frac{\rho_{po}b^2}{\epsilon_o u_o^2}\right) = \left[\frac{\rho_{po}}{4\pi\epsilon_o}\left(\frac{q}{m}\right)^2\frac{b^4\rho^2}{\bar{\mu}^2}\right]\left[\frac{8\pi}{9}\frac{a^2}{b^2}\frac{\bar{\rho}_p}{\bar{\rho}}\right]\left[\frac{\bar{\mu}}{\bar{\rho}u_o b}\right]$$

$$= (N_{\text{ev}})^2\left[\frac{8\pi}{9}\frac{a^2}{b^2}\frac{\bar{\rho}_p}{\bar{\rho}}\right](N_{\text{Re}})_b^{-1},\tag{10.194}$$

where N_{ev} is the "electroviscous number," the ratio of electrostatic (space charge) force to viscous force of the fluid, and $(N_{\text{Re}})_b$ is the Reynolds number of the channel; the bracketed term represents the ratio of cross sections of a particle and the duct, and the density ratio of solid material and the gas. It is seen that scaling and simulation [W16] can be carried out primarily in terms of the above products rather than individual dimensionless quantities (for small particles with large F, the exponential term in Eq. (10.191) approaches zero for finite values of x).

The collision rate per unit area of the channel wall is given by the product $[\rho_p v]_w$ at $y^* = 1$. Equation (10.182) gives

$$[\rho_p v]_w = \left[\frac{\partial \psi}{\partial x'}\right]_{y^*=1} = \tfrac{1}{2}\rho_{po}u_o(N_{\text{Re}})_{eb}^{-1}N_m[1 - e^{-Fx/u_o}]$$

$$\times \left\{\frac{1}{(1 + x^{*2})^2} - \frac{4}{3(1 + x^{*2})^5} + \cdots\right\}.\tag{10.195}$$

It is also seen that $\rho_p v = 0$ at $x = 0$ (the inlet), and the initial rate of increase of $[\rho_p v]_w$ is given by

$$\frac{\partial \rho_p v}{\partial x'}\bigg]_{x=0} = \rho_{po}u_o(N_{\text{Re}})_{eb}^{-1},\tag{10.196}$$

regardless of the value of N_m. These results are plotted as shown in Fig. 10.17 for $(N_{\text{Re}})_{eb} = 10^{-2}$ and $N_m = 10^{-2}$ and 10^{-3}, noting that for $\rho_{po} \sim 0.5$ kg/m³ ($\sim$200 grains/ft³), $b = 0.02$ m, $u_o = 2$ m/sec, $q/m = 3 \times 10^{-3}$ coulomb/kg,

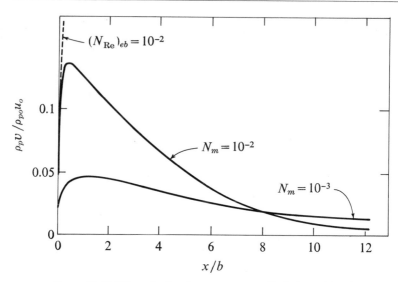

Figure 10.17 Dimensionless impact rate at wall of channel in Fig. 10.15.

$(N_{\mathrm{Re}})_{eb} \sim 0.02$ for 1-μ particles of specific gravity of 2.5 in air at room condition; $F \sim 10^5$ sec^{-1} for $b = 0.02$ m and $u_o = 2$ m/sec, giving $E_{(y=b)} \sim 2.5 \times 10^5$ v/m and $N_m = 10^{-3}$. The corresponding flow Reynolds number $(N_{\mathrm{Re}})_b$ is 2560, $N_{ev} = 2900$ for $(8\pi/9)(a^2/b^2)(\bar{\rho}_p/\rho)$ of 1.53×10^{-5}. Figure 10.17 shows that with higher flow velocity (turbulent flow), to a limit to be determined, the collection rate per unit area could be higher than proportionate to the low velocity (laminar) flow. Extension of basic relations for the study of turbulent flow remains to be thoroughly carried out.

For a particle cloud of a range of size distribution, the above should be modified according to the basic equations, but the above transformation will not be applicable because of multiplicity of streamlines and mutually self-consistent field. Numerical solution, however, is feasible. A curve such as those shown in Fig. 10.17 will be obtained for each narrow size range; summation gives the total accumulation. This will give proportionately greater amounts of large particles near the entrance than in the entering suspension, a fact that is well known [W16] but can now be computed rigorously.

A turbulent mixing theory of flow through an electrostatic precipitator was presented by Williams and Jackson [W27].

Although in most applications, turbulent flow of suspensions, or particle-induced turbulence in the fluid phase (such as in a fluidized bed) is encountered, laminar-flow systems were illustrated because they lend themselves to rigorous mathematical solution. A feasible method for calculating a laminar-flow system can be extended to a turbulent flow system with minimal logical empiricism as shown in the case of a single-phase fluid. An immediate instance here is the generalization in terms of electroviscous number when applied to a turbulent suspension, as in Sec. 10.7.

The electric Reynolds number and electroviscous numbers are in the form for self field of a cloud of charged particles. For given characteristic electric field E_o, they take the following form, for example:

$$(N_{\mathrm{Re}})_{eb} = \frac{_o u_o^2}{E_o(q/m)b} \tag{10.197}$$

and

$$(N_{\mathrm{ev}})_b = \left[\frac{E_o(q/m)}{\bar{\mu}^2} \, b^3 \bar{\rho}^2 \right]^{\frac{1}{2}}. \tag{10.198}$$

10.10 Effect of Electrostatic Forces on Boundary-Layer Motion

Extending the computation of boundary layer in Sec. 8.3, p. 324 the perturbation of electrostatic forces in the laminar boundary-layer motion was treated by Soo [S58]. It is important that we specifically want to consider only the case where electrostatic forces are small enough compared to hydrodynamic forces such that the former contribute as "perturbations." If the prescription is reversed, the "boundary-layer" approximation has to be completely abandoned because coulomb forces act over large distances.

Consider a relatively general situation of flow of a suspension with uniformly charged (q per particle) solid particles of uniform size of mass m per particle over a flat plate which is also charged and is a conductor, as shown in Fig. 10.18a. Equation (8.32) now takes the form

$$\rho \left[u \frac{\partial u}{\partial x} + v \frac{\partial u}{\partial y} \right] = -\frac{\partial P}{\partial x} + F\rho_p(u - u_p) + \frac{\partial}{\partial y} \bar{\mu} \frac{\partial u}{\partial y} + E_x \rho_p \frac{q}{m}, \tag{10.199}$$

where E_x is the electric field in the x-direction. Equation (8.33), p. 324 becomes

$$u_p \frac{\partial u_p}{\partial x} + v_p \frac{\partial u_p}{\partial y} = F(u - u_p) + E_x \frac{q}{m}. \tag{10.200}$$

The dipole forces are neglected because we restrict ourselves to only a light suspension—small ρ_p, in Eq. (10.151). Although the sharp leading edge as required by hydrodynamic simplifications will make dipole forces felt, it constitutes a singularity when dealing with electrostatic effects. The electric potential V is given by Poisson's equation [P1]

$$\frac{\partial^2 V}{\partial x^2} + \frac{\partial^2 V}{\partial y^2} = \frac{-\rho_p(q/m)}{\epsilon_o}, \tag{10.201}$$

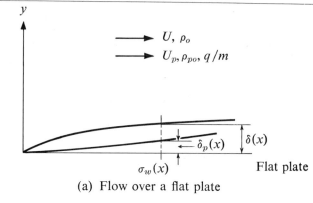

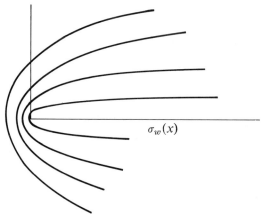

(a) Flow over a flat plate

(b) Potential distribution due to
charged flat plate [P1]

Figure 10.18 Flow of a charged gas-solid suspension over a flat-plate conductor.

which has the solution in the form

$$V = V_w + V_p,$$ (10.202)

where V_w is the potential due to the charged plate and V_p is the potential due to the particle cloud. For a thin sheet of a conductor, V_w is given by [P1]

$$\alpha^2 y^2 = 4V_w^2(\alpha x + V_w^2).$$ (10.203)

Since the conductor constitutes an equipotential surface, its surface charge density σ_w is given by

$$\sigma_w = -\frac{\epsilon_o}{2}\sqrt{\frac{\alpha}{x}}.$$ (10.204)

with a singularity at the leading edge. The potential distribution is shown in Fig. 10.18b, and the electric field due to the conductor is given by

$$E_{xw} = \frac{\partial V_w}{\partial x} = \frac{\alpha V_w}{2(\alpha x + 2V_w^2)}$$

$$= \frac{1}{2}\sqrt{\frac{\alpha}{2}} \frac{[\sqrt{x^2 + y^2} - x]^{\frac{1}{2}}}{\sqrt{x^2 + y^2}} \tag{10.205}$$

$$E_{yw} = \frac{\partial V_w}{\partial y} = \frac{\alpha y^2 V_w}{4V_w^4 + \alpha^2 y^2}. \tag{10.206}$$

For the present two-dimensional system, the potential V_p due to the cloud of charged solid particles of density ρ_p is given by

$$V_p = (2\pi\epsilon_o)^{-1}\frac{q}{m}\int_x\int_y \rho_p(x',y') \ln|r - r'|^{-1} dx' dy', \tag{10.207}$$

integrated over the whole region where

$$r - r' = [(x - x')^2 + (y - y')^2]^{\frac{1}{2}}. \tag{10.208}$$

We should not visualize the charged particle cloud as extending to infinity in the y-direction, in which case the integral would not converge. The field due to the cloud of charged particles is given by

$$E_{xp} = -\frac{\partial V_p}{\partial x}$$

$$= (2\pi\epsilon_o)^{-1}\frac{q}{m}\int_x\int_y \rho_p(x',y')(x - x')|r - r'|^{-2} dx' dy' \tag{10.209}$$

$$E_{yp} = \frac{\partial V_p}{\partial y}$$

$$= (2\pi\epsilon_o)^{-1}\frac{q}{m}\int_x\int_y \rho_p(x', y')(y - y')|r - r'|^{-2} dx' dy'. \tag{10.210}$$

The effect of electrostatic forces on the solid particles with the boundary-layer thickness δ_{p1} is given by the integral

$$I = \frac{q}{m}\int_0^{\delta_{p1}} E_x\rho_p \, dy$$

$$= \frac{q}{m}\frac{1}{2}\sqrt{\frac{\alpha}{2}}\rho_{po}\int_0^{\delta_{p1}} \frac{\rho_p}{\rho_{po}} \frac{[\sqrt{x^2 + y^2} - x]^{\frac{1}{2}}}{\sqrt{x^2 + y^2}} dy$$

$$- \left(\frac{q}{m}\right)^2 \frac{\rho_{po}^2}{4\pi\epsilon_o}\int_0^{\delta_{p1}}\int_0^x\int_0^y \frac{\rho_p(x,y)}{\rho_{po}} \frac{\rho_p(x', y')}{\rho_{po}} \frac{(x - x')}{|r - r'|^2} dx' dy' dy. \tag{10.211}$$

The integration is obviously very tedious; a first-order approximation is

$$I \cong \left\{ \frac{1}{2} \sqrt{\frac{\alpha}{2}} \, \rho_{po} \left(\frac{q}{m} \right) \frac{\sqrt{2}}{4} \frac{\delta_{p1}^2}{x^{3/2}} - \frac{\rho_{po}^2}{4\pi\epsilon_o} \left(\frac{q}{m} \right)^2 \frac{5}{8} \delta_{p1}^2 \right\} \left[1 + 0 \left(\frac{\delta^2}{x^2} \right) \right], \quad (10.212)$$

and Eq. (8.71) takes the form, for $x^* = Fx/U$,

$$x^* \frac{d\delta_{p1}}{dx'} + \delta_{p1} \sim \delta x^* + \frac{1}{4} \frac{\sqrt{\alpha}}{U^2} \left(\frac{q}{m} \right) \frac{\delta_{p1}^2}{x'^{3/2}} \left(\frac{F}{U} \right)^{1/2} - \frac{\rho_{po}}{4\pi\epsilon_o} \left(\frac{q}{m} \right)^2 \frac{\delta_{p1}^2}{UF} \left(\frac{5}{8} \right)$$

$$\equiv 2 \sqrt{\frac{3\bar{\nu}x^*}{F}} \, x^* + \beta_1 \delta_{p1}^2 x^{*-3/2} - \beta_2 \delta_{p1}^2 , \quad (10.213)$$

which accounts for the modification of δ_{p1} due to electrostatic effects. Equation (10.213) shows that for a positively charged plate and positively charged solid particles the second term on the right-hand side gives an increase in δ_{p1} from that given by Eq. (8.72) due to repulsion, but the last term in the right-hand side is always due to attraction by the image charge.

Since we have restricted ourselves to the situation where the electrostatic effects constitute a matter of perturbation, we postulate a solution to Eq. (10.213) in the form

$$\delta_{p1} = \delta_{1p}^{(0)} + \beta_1 \delta_{p1}^{(1)} + \beta_2 \delta_{p1}^{(1')}. \quad (10.214)$$

The first-order perturbation gives

$$\delta_{p1} = \frac{2}{5} \delta x^* + \frac{1}{2} \frac{\sqrt{\alpha}}{U^2} \frac{q}{m} \left(\frac{F}{U} \right)^{1/2} \frac{\bar{\nu}}{F} x^{*3/2} - \frac{\rho_{po}}{10\pi\epsilon_o} \left(\frac{q}{m} \right) \frac{\bar{\nu}}{UF^2} x^{*3}, \quad (10.215)$$

where the first term on the right-hand side is due to viscous force, the second term due to electric field of the plate interacting with viscous force, and the third term is due to electric image force interacting with viscous force. Comparison of the first term and the second term shows that the contribution of the electric field of the plate is insignificant if

$$(N_{\mathrm{Re}})_x^{1/2} = \sqrt{\frac{Ux}{\bar{\nu}}} \gg \frac{5}{4\sqrt{3}} \frac{\sigma_w x}{\epsilon_o U^2} \frac{q}{m} = \frac{5}{4\sqrt{3}} (N_{\mathrm{Re}})_{ewx}^{-1}, \quad (10.216)$$

where subscript *ewx* denotes electric Reynolds number due to plate based on dimension x, while comparison shows that the effect of the image force is small if

$$(N_{\mathrm{Re}})_x^{1/2} = \sqrt{\frac{Ux}{\bar{\nu}}} \gg \frac{1}{2\sqrt{3}} \frac{\rho_{po}}{4\pi\epsilon_o} \left(\frac{q}{m} \right)^2 \frac{x^2}{U^2} = \frac{1}{2\sqrt{3}} (N_{\mathrm{Re}})_{epx}^{-1}. \quad (10.217)$$

It is noted that while the effect of the charge on the plate depends on the signs of charges of the plate and the cloud of particles, the image force always constitutes an attraction. In general, Eqs. (10.216) and (10.217) show that for the electrostatic effect to be small,

$$(N_{\mathrm{Re}})_x^{\frac{1}{2}} \gg (N_{\mathrm{Re}})_{ex}^{-1}, \tag{10.218}$$

noting that large electrostatic charge gives rise to small $(N_{\mathrm{Re}})_{ex}$. A better way to visualize the situation is to define the characteristic interacting parameter in terms of a ratio of electrostatic force to viscous force, which we might call an "electroviscous number" (N_{ev}) such that

$$(N_{\mathrm{ev}})_{wx} = \sqrt{\frac{\sigma_w x q}{\epsilon_o m}} \frac{x}{\bar{\nu}} \tag{10.219}$$

$$(N_{\mathrm{ev}})_{pw} = \sqrt{\frac{\rho_{po}}{4\pi\epsilon_o} \frac{q}{m} \frac{x^2}{\bar{\nu}}}. \tag{10.220}$$

Then Eqs. (10.217) and (10.218) take the form

$$(N_{\mathrm{Re}})_x^{\frac{5}{2}} \gg (N_{\mathrm{ev}})_{wx}^2, \tag{10.221}$$

and

$$(N_{\mathrm{Re}})_x^{\frac{5}{2}} \gg (N_{\mathrm{ev}})_{px}^2, \tag{10.222}$$

or, in general,

$$(N_{\mathrm{Re}})_x \gg (N_{\mathrm{ev}})_x, \tag{10.223}$$

for negligible effect of electric charges. The magnitude of events can be seen by considering these cases:

Case I: $\bar{\nu} = 10^{-5}$ m²/sec, $\rho_{po} = 1$ kg/m³, $q/m = 10^{-4}$ coulomb/kg, $U = 100$ m/sec, $(N_{\mathrm{ev}})_{px} \sim 10^6 x^2$, $(N_{\mathrm{Re}})_x \sim 10^7 x$, which means that the image charge effect (for grounded plate) is small only near the leading edge.

Case II: $\bar{\nu} = 10^{-5}$ m²/sec, $q/m = 10^{-4}$ coulomb/kg, $U = 100$ m/sec, $E_y|_{y=0} = 10^6$ v/m at $x = 0.01$ m, $\sigma = 10^6 \epsilon_o$, $(N_{\mathrm{ev}})_{wx} \sim 10^4$, $(N_{\mathrm{Re}})_x \sim 10^5$. It is seen that in neither case is the electrostatic effect small. For an uncharged plate, the image charge would give rise to collection patterns such that the concentration is high on the downstream side. For a plate charged to the opposite sign, collection will tend toward the leading edge. The modification on boundary-layer thickness will follow a similar trend. With the plate charged to the same sign, the boundary layer could exhibit a lower concentration at the wall.

SUMMARY OF BASIC CONCEPTS

Triboelectric Effect—Wilcke (1757) [M40]

Atmospheric Dust Charging—Rudger (1912) [R46]

Corona Charging—Arendt and Kallman (1926) [A13]

Charged Droplet—Rayleigh (1910) [S94]

Charging by Thermionic Effect—(1963) [S55]

Impaction of Charged Cloud—Kraemer and Johnstone (1955) [K34]

Interaction of Dipole Attraction and Electrostatic Repulsion—(1964) [S57]

Interaction of Diffusion and Electrostatic Effect—(1964) [S72]

Similar Solution for Electrohydrodynamic Flow—(1965) [S60]

REFERENCES

A

1. W. T. ABEL, D. E. BLUMAN, and J. P. O'LEARY, ASME Paper 63-WA-210 (1963).
2. M. ABRAHAM and R. BECKER, "Classical Theory of Electricity and Magnetism" (2 ed.), Hafner, New York (1949), 100.
3. F. AHLBORN, Z. Tech. Physik, 12, 483–491 (1931).
4. G. AILAM and I. GALLILY, Phys. Fluids, 5, 575 (1962).
5. C. W. ALBRIGHT, J. H. HOLDEN, H. P. SIMONS, and L. D. SCHMIDT, Ind. Eng. Chem., 43, 1837 (1951).
6. L. ALDERS, "Liquid-Liquid Extraction," Elsevier, New York (1955).
7. L. G. ALEXANDER, T. BARON, and E. W. COMINGS, U. of Illinois Engineering Experiment Station Report No. 413 (1953).
8. L. G. ALEXANDER and C. L. COLDREN, Ind. Eng. Chem., 43, 1325 (1951).
9. D. ALTMAN and J. M. CURTIS, "Combustion Processes," "High Speed Aerodynamics and Jet Propulsion," Princeton U.P., Princeton, N.J., Sec. C, Vol. II (1956).
10. N. R. AMUNDSON and R. ARIS, "Proceedings of Symposium on Interaction between Fluids and Particles," Institute of Chemical Engineers, London (1962), p. 176.
11. H. C. ANDERSEN and L. H. BELZ, J. Electrochem. Soc., 100, 240 (1953).
12. A. G. ANDERSON, "Handbook of Fluid Dynamics" (V. Streeter, ed.), McGraw-Hill (1961), Sec. 18.
13. P. ARENDT and H. KALLMANN, Z. Phys., 35, 421 (1926).
14. J. H. ARNOLD, Trans. Am. Inst. Chem. Engrs., 40, 361 (1944).
15. A. A. ARSHINOV and A. K. MUSIN, Soviet Phys., 3, 99, 588 (1958).

B

1. R. A. BAGNOLD, Brit. J. App. Phys., 2, 29 (1951).
2. R. A. BAGNOLD, Proc. Roy. Soc. (London), 225A, 49 (1954).
3. R. A. BAGNOLD, Proc. Inst. Civil Engrs., III, 4, 1174 (1955).
4. R. A. BAGNOLD, Phil. Trans. Roy. Soc. (London), 249A, 235 (1956).
5. R. A. BAGNOLD, Phil. Trans., 249, 235 (1957).
6. W. S. BAILEY, E. N. NILSON, R. A. SERRA, and T. F. ZUPNIK, ARS J., 31, 793 (1961).
7. R. M. L. BAKER, Jr., and A. F. CHARWAT, Phys. Fluids, 1, 73 (1958).
8. P. J. BAKKAR and P. M. HEERTJEN, Brit. Chem. Eng., 3, 240 (1958).
9. L. V. BALDWIN and W. R. MICKELSON, Proc. Am. Soc. Civil Engrs., 88, EM2, 37 (1962).
10. L. V. BALDWIN, V. A. SANDBORN, and J. C. LAURENCE, J. Heat Transfer, Trans. ASME, 82, 77 (1960).
11. L. V. BALDWIN and T. J. WALSH, A.I.Ch.E. J., 7, 53 (1961).

12. W. W. BALWANZ, "Proceedings of 10th Symposium (International) on Combustion" (1964), p. 685.
13. J. R. BANISTER, "Fall of Small Particles in the Upper Atmosphere," Sandia Corp. Tech. Memo. 18–59 (51) (1959).
14. J. R. BANISTER and H. L. DAVIS, *Phys. Fluids*, *5* (2), 136 (1962).
15. S. G. BANKOFF and R. D. MIKESELL, *Chem. Eng. Progr. Symp. Ser.*, *55*:29, 95 (1959).
16. R. L. BARGER, NASA TN D-740, p. 12 (1961).
17. J. J. BARKER and R. E. TREYBAL, 41st A.I.Ch.E. Meeting, Paper No. 29, St. Paul, Minn. (1959).
18. W. BARTH, *Chemie-Ing. Techn.*, *30*, 171 (1958); *32*, 164 (1960).
19. M. S. BARTLETT, "An Introduction to Stochastic Processes," Cambridge U.P., London (1955).
20. D. R. BARTZ, *Jet Propulsion*, *1*, 27 (1957).
21. A. B. BASSET, "Hydrodynamics," Deighton, Bell, Cambridge, 1888; Dover, New York (1961), p. 270.
22. B. A. BATCH, J. DALMON, and E. T. HIGNETT, "An Electrostatic Probe for Measuring the Particle Flux in Two-Phase Flow," Central Electricity Research Laboratories Note RD/L/N115/63, England (1963).
23. G. K. BATCHELOR, *Proc. Cambridge Phil. Soc.*, *43*, 533 (1949).
24. D. R. BATES, "Atomic and Molecular Processes," Academic, New York (1962), p. 267.
25. P. K. BAUMGARTEN and R. L. PIGFORD, *A.I.Ch.E. J.*, *6*, 115 (1960).
26. H. A. BECKER, *Chem. Eng. Sci.*, *13*, 245 (1961).
27. H. A. BECKER, R. E. ROSENSWEIG, and J. R. GWOZDZ, "Turbulent Dispersion in Pipe Flow," Fuels Research Lab., M.I.T. Rept. AFC RL-63-727 (1963).
28. H. A. BECKER and H. R. SALLANS, *Chem. Eng. Sci.*, *13* (3), 97 (1961).
29. W. J. BEEK, "Proceedings of Symposium on Interaction between Fluids and Particles," Institute of Chemical Engineers, London (1962), p. 163.
30. D. H. BELDEN and L. S. KASSEL, *Ind. Eng. Chem.*, *40*, 1174 (1949).
31. M. W. BENJAMIN and J. G. MILLER, *Trans. ASME*, *64*, 657 (1942).
32. T. B. BENJAMIN, *J. Fluid Mech.*, *6*, 161 (1959).
33. T. G. O. BERG, G. C. FERNISH, and T. A. GAUKLER, *J. Atmospheric Sci.*, *20*, 153 (1963).
34. W. BESANT, "Hydrostatics and Hydrodynamics," Cambridge U.P., London (1859).
35. H. BIEBER and E. L. GADEN, Jr., Paper at 46th A.I.Ch.E. Meeting, Los Angeles, Calif. (1962).
36. E. C. BINGHAM, "Fluidity and Plasticity," McGraw-Hill, New York (1922).
37. A. M. BINNIE and T. R. GREEN, *Proc. Roy. Soc.* (London), *181*, 134 (1942).
38. R. B. BIRD, W. E. STUART, and E. N. LIGHTFOOT, "Transport Phenomena," Wiley, New York (1960), p. 101.
39. G. BIRKHOFF, R. S. MARGULIES, and W. A. HORNUNG, *Phys. Fluids*, *1*, 201 (1958).
40. D. C. BLANCHARD, Woods Hole Oceanographic Inst., Woods Hole, Mass., Tech. Report, Ref. *54–27* (1954).

41. N. S. BLATCH, *Trans. Am. Soc. Civil Eng.*, *57*, 400 (1906).
42. H. H. BLEICH, *Jet Propulsion*, *26*, 958 (1956).
43. W. R. BLEVIN and W. J. BROWN, *J. Opt. Soc. Am.*, *51*, 975 (1961).
44. A. J. BOBKOWICZ and W. H. GAUVIN, *Can. J. Chem. Eng.*, *43*, 87, April (1965).
45. E. G. BOGT and R. R. WHITE, *Ind. Eng. Chem.*, *40*, 1731 (1948).
46. J. A. BOLT, T. A. BOYLE, and W. MIRSKY, "The Evaporation and Burning of Liquid Fuel Drops," WADC TR 54-390 (1954).
47. F. BOSNJAKOVIC, *Tech. Mech. and Thermo.*, *1*:10, 358 (1930).
48. C. J. BOTTAKER, "Theory of Electric Polarization," Elsevier, New York (1952), pp. 102, 126.
49. W. T. BOTTOMLEY, *Trans. North-East Coast Inst. Engrs. Shipbldrs.*, *53*, 65 (1936).
50. J. BOUSSINESQ, *Compt. Rend.*, *156*, 1124; *157*, 313 (1913); *Bull. Nat. Res. Council*, No. 84 (1932).
51. F. P. BOWDEN and D. TABOR, "The Friction and Lubrication of Solids," Clarendon, Oxford (1950), pp. 302, 307.
52. C. W. BOWMAN, D. M. WARD, A. I. JOHNSON, and O. TRASS, *Can. J. Chem. Eng.*, *39*, 1, 9–13 (1961).
53. R. S. BRADLEY, *Phil. Mag.*, *13*, 853 (1932).
54. R. S. BRADLEY, *Trans. Faraday Soc.*, *32*, 1088 (1936).
55. H. L. BRANDT and B. M. JOHNSON, *A.I.Ch.E. J.*, *9*, 771 (1963).
56. L. BREIMAN, "Theory of Heat and Mass Transfer from a Slowly Moving Sphere to the Surrounding Medium," Rept. No. 2F-2, Norman Bridger Lab., Calif. Inst. of Tech., Pasadena, Calif. (1952).
57. H. BRENNER, *Chem. Eng. Sci.*, *19*, 599 (1964).
58. H. BRENNER, *J. Fluid Mech.*, *12*, 35 (1962).
59. H. BRENNER, *J. Colloid Sci.*, *20*, 104 (1963).
60. H. BRENNER and J. HAPPEL, *J. Fluid Mech.*, *4*, 195 (1958).
61. A. G. BRIDGE, L. LAPIDUS, and J. C. ELGIN, *A.I.Ch.E. J.*, *10* (6), 819 (1964).
62. B. BROWN, "Particle Velocity Lag in Metalized Propellants," Preprint 1607-61, ARS Solid Propellant Rocket Conference (1961).
63. B. BROWN and K. P. MCARTY, "Proceedings of the Eighth Symposium (International) on Combustion," Williams and Wilkins, Baltimore (1962), p. 814.
64. J. A. BROWNING, *Am. Chem. Soc. Advances in Chemistry Series*, No. 20, 136 (1958).
65. J. A. BROWNING and W. G. KRALL, "Fifth Symposium on Combustion," Reinhold, New York (1955), p. 159.
66. C. BRUINZEEL, G. H. REMAN, and E. T. VAN DER LAAN, "Proceedings of Symposium on Interaction between Fluids and Particles," Institute of Chemical Engineers, London (1962), p. 120.
67. R. J. BRUN, W. LEWIS, P. PERKINS, and J. SERAFINI, NACA Rept. No. 1215 (1955).
68. R. J. BRUN and H. H. MERGLER, NACA TN 2904 (1953).
69. S. BRUNAUER, "The Adsorption of Gases and Vapors," Princeton U.P., Princeton, N.J. (1943).
70. J. H. BURGOYNE and J. J. COHEN, *Colloid Sci.*, *8*, 364–366 (June, 1953).
71. J. H. BURGOYNE and L. COHEN, *Proc. Roy. Soc.*, *225*, 375 (1954).

72. S. P. Burks and W. S. Plummer, *Ind. Eng. Chem.*, *20*, 1200 (1928).
73. N. L. Byzova and V. A. Nesterov, *J. Acoust.* (USSR) *5*, 419 (1960).

C

1. R. D. Cadle, "Particle Size," Reinhold, New York (1965).
2. G. L. Cann, "Energy Transfer Processes in a Partially Ionized Gas," Memo No. 61, Calif. Institute of Technology, Army Ordinance Contracts, DA-04-495-Orb-1960 and 3231 (1961).
3. D. J. Carlson, *ARS J.*, *32*, 1107–1109 (1962).
4. D. J. Carlson, "Temperature, Its Measurement and Control in Science and Industry," Reinhold, New York, V. 3, Part II (1962).
5. P. C. Carman, *Trans. Instn. Chem. Engrs.*, *15*, 150 (1937).
6. P. C. Carman, "The Flow of Gases through Porous Media," Butterworth, London (1956).
7. G. F. Carrier, *J. Fluid Mech.*, *4* (4), 376 (1958).
8. E. L. Carstensen and L. L. Foldy, *J. Acoust. Soc. Am.*, *19*, 481 (1947).
9. H. M. Cassel and I. Liebman, *Combustion and Flame*, *3*, 467 (1959).
10. R. A. Castleman, *J. Res. Nat. Bur. Std.*, *6*, 369 (1931).
11. W. Cawood, *Trans. Faraday Soc.*, *32*, 1068 (1936).
12. R. D. Cess, "Proceedings Third Int. Heat Transfer Conf.," *5*, 154 (1966).
13. S. Chandrasekhar, *Rev. Modern Phys.*, *15*, 1 (1943).
14. S. Chandrasekhar, "Radiative Transfer," Dover, New York (1960).
15. B. T. Chao, *Phys. Fluids*, *5*, 69 (1962).
16. B. T. Chao, *Osterreichisches Ingenieur-Archiv*, *18*, 1/2, 7 (1964).
17. D. R. Chapman and R. H. Kester, NACA TN 3097 (1954).
18. S. Chapman and T. G. Cowling, "The Mathematical Theory of Non-Uniform Gases," Cambridge U.P., London (1958).
19. G. E. Charles and S. G. Mason, *J. Colloid Sci.*, *15*, 105 (1960).
20. N. Chien, *Trans. Am. Soc. Civil Eng.*, *121*, 833 (1956).
21. E. G. Chilton, F. M. Sauer, and R. E. Lundberg, "Proceedings of Multi-Phase Flow Symposium," ASME (1963), p. 35.
22. J. H. Chin, C. M. Sliepcevich, and M. Tribus, *J. of Phys. Chem.*, *59*, 841, 845 (1955).
23. P. R. Choudhury and W. F. Stevens, Princeton U. Project SQUID Report TN NTI-2-M (1955).
24. P. R. Choudhury, Hughes Aircraft Co., Report SSD3418R (1963).
25. V. T. Chow, "Handbook of Applied Hydrology," McGraw-Hill, New York (1964), p. 17.
26. F. C. Chromey, *J. Opt. Soc. Am.*, *50*, 7 (1960).
27. B. T. Chu and J. C. F. Chow, AIAA Paper 65-8 (1965).
28. C. M. Chu, C. C. Clark, and S. W. Churchill, "Table of Angular Distribution Coefficients for Light-Scattering by Spheres," Univ. of Michigan Press (1957).
29. J. C. Chu, "Fluidization" (D. F. Othmer, ed.), Reinhold, New York (1956), p. 20.

30. J. C. CHU, J. KALIL, and W. A. WETTEROTH, *Chem. Eng. Progr.*, *49*, 141 (1953).
31. B. J. CLARK, NASA TN-D-2424 (1964).
32. R. H. CLARK, D. E. CHARLES, J. F. RICHARDSON, and D. M. NEWITT, *Trans. Instn. Chem. Engrs.*, *30*, 209 (1952).
33. J. D. COBINE, "Gaseous Conductors," Dover, New York (1958).
34. E. G. COCKBAIN and T. S. MCROBERTS, *J. Colloid Sci.*, *8*, 440 (1953).
35. K. P. COFFIN, "Fifth Symposium (International) on Combustion," Reinhold, New York (1955), p. 267.
36. K. P. COFFIN and R. S. BROKAW, NACA TN 3929 (1957).
37. R. E. COLLINS, "Flow of Fluids through Porous Materials," Reinhold, New York (1961).
38. E. W. COMINGS, C. H. ADAMS, and E. D. SHIPPEE, *Ind. Eng. Chem.*, *40*, 74 (1949).
39. J. E. COPPAGE and A. L. LONDON, *Chem. Eng. Progr.*, *52* (2), 57 (1956).
40. P. D. COPPOCK and G. T. MEIKLEJOHN, *Trans. Instn. Chem. Engrs.* (London), *28*, 52 (1950).
41. M. CORN, *J. Air Pollution Control Assoc.*, *11* (11) 523; *11* (12), 566 (1961).
42. S. CORRSIN, *J. Appl. Phys.*, *23*, 113 (1952).
43. S. CORRSIN and J. LUMLEY, *Appl. Sci. Res.*, *6A*, 114 (1956).
44. A. E. CRAWFORD, *J. Acoust. Soc. Am.*, *27*, 176 (1955).
45. C. T. CROWE, J. A. NICHOLLS, and R. B. MORRISON, "Ninth International Symposium on Combustion," Academic, New York (1963), p. 395.
46. G. T. CSANADY, *J. Atmospheric Sci.*, *20*, 201 (1963).
47. J. CUEILLERON and N. SCARTAZZINI, *Compt. Rend.*, *228*, 489 (1949).
48. F. E. C. CULICK, *Phys. Fluids*, *7*, 1898 (1964).

D

1. J. W. DAILY and G. BUGLIARELLO, *Ind. Eng. Chem.*, *51*, 887 (1959).
2. J. M. DALLAVALLE, "Micrometrics," Pitman, New York (1943).
3. J. M. DALLAVALLE, J. P. MCBRIDE, V. D. ALLRED, and E. V. JONES, Rept. ORNL-2565, Oak Ridge Nat. Lab., USAEC (1958).
4. J. M. DALLAVALLE, C. ORR, Jr., and H. G. BLOCKER, *Ind. Eng. Chem.*, *43*, 1377-80 (1951).
5. C. DALTON, J. L. SCHWEPPE, and L. O. BILLIG, ASME Paper No. 64-WA/HT-27 (1964).
6. J. H. DANIEL and F. S. BRACKETT, *J. Appl. Phys.*, *22*, 542 (1951).
7. R. DARRAS, P. BAQUE, and D. LECLERCQ, *Compt. Rend.*, *249*, 1647 (1959).
8. W. DASKIN, "Proceedings of Fourth Midwestern Conference on Fluid Mechanics," Purdue University (1956), p. 329.
9. R. L. DATTA, D. H. NAPIER, and D. M. NEWITT, *Trans. Instn. Chem. Engrs.* (London), *28*, 14 (1950).
10. J. F. DAVIDSON, *Trans. Instn. Chem. Engrs.*, *39*, 230 (1961).
11. J. F. DAVIDSON and D. HARRISON, "Fluidized Particles," Cambridge U.P., London (1963).
12. C. N. DAVIES, *Proc. Inst. Mech. Eng.*, *1B*, 185 (1952).
13. R. M. DAVIES and G. I. TAYLOR, *Proc. Roy. Soc.*, *A200*, 375 (1950).

14. A. H. DAVIS and I. HARRIS, NASA TN D-704 (1961).
15. N. DAVIS and E. G. THURSTON, *J. Acoust. Soc. Am.*, *22*, 20 (1950).
16. G. S. DAWKINS, Tech. Rept. No. 15, Engineering Experiment Station, U. of Illinois, Urbana, Ill. (1958).
17. P. DEBYE, "Polar Molecules," Dover, New York (1945).
18. S. R. DE GROOT and P. MAZUR, "Non-Equilibrium Thermodynamics," Interscience, New York (1962).
19. R. G. DEISSLER, NASA TN D-680 (1961).
20. K. J. DE JUHASZ, *Trans. Am. Soc. Mech. Engrs.*, *OGP-53-5* (1931).
21. J. W. DELAPLAINE, *A.I.Ch.E. J.*, *2*, 127 (1956).
22. F. DeMARIA and J. E. LONGFIELD, *Chem. Eng. Progr. Symp. Ser.*, "Fluidization" (F. A. Zenz, ed.) *58* (38), 16 (1962).
23. R. T. DERBYSHIRE, G. E. HEWITT, and B. NICHOLLS, "X-Radiography of Two-Phase Gas-Liquid Flow," AERE-M-1321, Harwell, England (1964).
24. P. DERGARABEDIAN, *J. Appl. Mech.*, *20*, 537 (1953).
25. P. DERGARABEDIAN, *J. Fluid Mech.*, *9*, 39 (1960).
26. R. DE SALINS, *Compt. Rend.*, *234*, 2437 (1952).
27. J. H. DESSAUER, G. R. MOTT, and H. BOGDONOFF, *Photographic Engineering*, *6*, 250 (1955).
28. P. L. P. DILLON and L. E. LINE, Jr., *Jet Propulsion*, *26*, 1091 (1956).
29. R. C. DIMICK, "An Experimental Study of Deionization in Gas Containing Solid and Liquid Impurities," Ph.D. Thesis, U. of Illinois, Urbana, Ill. (1964).
30. R. C. DIMICK and S. L. SOO, *Phys. Fluids*, *7*, 1638 (1964).
31. I. D. DOIG and G. H. ROPER, *Austral. J. Chem. Eng.*, 9 (Jan.); 9 (Feb.) (1963).
32. J. L. DOOB, "Stochastic Processes," Wiley, New York (1953).
33. R. G. DORSCH, P. G. SAPER, and C. F. KADOW, NACA TN 3587 (1955).
34. W. L. DOYLE, J. B. CONWAY, and A. V. GROSSE, *J. Inorg. Nucl. Chem.*, *6*, 138 (1958).
35. A. W. DOYLE, B. V. MOKLER, R. R. PERRON, and A. D. LITTLE, "New Means of Fuel Atomization," American Petroleum Institute, Pub. No. 1701, New York (1962).
36. R. M. DRAKE, Jr., *J. Heat Transfer, Trans. ASME*, *83*, 170 (1961).
37. R. M. DRAKE, Jr., and G. H. BACKER, *Trans. ASME, J. Basic Eng.*, *74*, 1241 (1952).
38. K. M. DUFF, "Condensation of Carbon Dioxide in Supersonic Nozzles," Gas Turbine Lab. Report 76, M.I.T., Cambridge, Mass. (1964); also with P. G. HILL, "Proceedings 1964 Heat Transfer and Fluid Mechanics Institute" (Ed. M. A. Saad and J. A. Miller), Stanford University Press (1966), p. 268.
39. A. E. DUKLER, M. WICKS III, and R. G. CLEVELAND, *A.I.Ch.E. J.*, *10*, 38 (1964); *10*, 45 (1964); also "Proceedings Third Int. Heat Transfer Conf.", *5*, 39 (1966).
40. J. A. MUFFIE and W. R. MARSHALL, Jr., *Chem. Eng. Progr.*, *49*, 417; 480 (1953).
41. R. DURAND, "Proceedings of Minnesota Hydraulics Convention," Part I (1953), pp. 89–103.
42. E. J. DURBIN, NACA TN 2441 (1951).
43. J. L. DUSSOURD and A. H. SHAPIRO, "A Deceleration Probe for Measuring

Stagnation Pressure and Velocity of a Particle Laden Gas Stream," Heat Transfer and Fluid Mechanics Institute, Univ. of Calif. (1955).

44. V. D. DUNSKY, S. S. ZABRODSKY, and A. I. TAMARIN, "Proceedings Third Int. Heat Transfer Conf.," *4*, 293 (1966).

E

1. E. R. G. ECKERT and R. M. DRAKE, Jr., "Heat and Mass Transfer," McGraw-Hill, New York (1959).
2. R. B. EDELMAN and D. H. KIELY, Aerodynamics Research Rept. No. 188, NOLTR 62-202 (1962).
3. R. B. EDELMAN and H. ROSENBAUM, AIAA Paper 65-7 (1965).
4. R. EICHHORN and S. SMALL, *J. Fluid Mech.*, *20* (3), 513 (1964).
5. H. EINBINDER, *J. Chem. Phys.*, *26*, 948 (1957).
6. A. EINSTEIN, *Ann. Phys.*, Leipzig, *19*, 289 (1906).
7. A. EINSTEIN, "The Theory of Brownian Movement," Dover, New York (1956).
8. J. C. ELGIN and H. C. FOUST, *Ind. Eng. Chem.*, *42*, 1127 (1950).
9. M. E. ELLION, "A Study of the Mechanism of Boiling Heat Transfer," Jet Propulsion Lab. Report, Memo 20-88, Calif. Institute of Technology, Pasadena, Calif. (1954).
10. S. R. M. ELLIS and M. J. F. KELLY, "Proceedings of Symposium on Interaction between Fluids and Particles," Institute of Chemical Engineers, London (1962), p. 107.
11. I. T. ELPERIN, I. A. LEPESHINSKY, and L. L. PAVLOVSKY, Second All Soviet Union Heat Transfer Conf., Minsk, B.S.S.R., USSR, Paper No. 5-23 (1965).
12. M. M. E. WAHIL, O. A. UYEHARA, and P. S. MYERS, NACA TN 3179 (1953).
13. E. R. ELZINGA, Jr., and J. T. BANCHERO, *A.I.Ch.E. J.*, *7*, 394 (1961).
14. J. L. ENGELKE, "Heat Transfer to Particles in the Plasma Flame," 46th National Convention, A.I.Ch.E. (1962).
15. P. S. EPSTEIN, *Phys. Rev.*, *23*, 710 (1924).
16. P. S. EPSTEIN, *Z. Phys.*, *54*, 537 (1929).
17. P. S. EPSTEIN and R. R. CARHART, *J. Acoust. Soc. Am.*, *25*, 553 (1953).
18. D. ERGUN, *Chem. Eng. Progr.*, *48*, 89 (1952).
19. D. ERGUN and A. A. ORNING, *Ind. Eng. Chem.*, *41*, 1179 (1949).
20. A. J. ERICKSON, "A Theoretical and Experimental Investigation of the Aerothermopressor Process," Report, Gas Turbine Lab., M.I.T., Cambridge, Mass. (1958).
21. H. ERKKU, "Radiant Heat Exchange in Gas Filled Slabs and Cylinders," Sc.D. Dissertation, M.I.T., Cambridge, Mass. (1959).
22. G. ERLICH, "1961 Trans. of 8th Vacuum Symposium and 2nd International Congress," Pergamon, New York (1962), p. 126.
23. R. H. ESSENHIGH, *J. Inst. Fuel*, London, 239 (1961).
24. R. H. ESSENHIGH and J. B. HOWARD, AIAA Paper, 65-57 (1965).
25. L. B. EVANS, S. W. CHURCHILL, and C. M. CHU, ASME Paper No. 64-WA/HT-36 (1964).

26. U. R. EVANS, "The Corrosion and Oxidation of Metals," St. Martin's, New York (1960).
27. G. H. EWING, ASME Paper 64-WA/PID-7 (1964).

F

1. A. FAGE and F. C. JOHANSEN, *Proc. Roy. Soc.* (London), *116A*, 170 (1927).
2. J. FANUCCI and H. LEW, General Electric Report TIS59SD380 (1959).
3. L. FARBAR, *Ind. Eng. Chem.*, *21*, 1184 (1949).
4. L. FARBAR and C. A. DEPEW, *Ind. Eng. Chem. Fundamentals*, *2* (2), 130 (1963).
5. L. FARBAR and M. J. MORLEY, *Ind. Eng. Chem.*, *49*, 1143 (1957).
6. I. FARO, T. R. SMALL, and F. K. HILL, *J. Appl. Phys.*, *34*, 40 (1952).
7. W. M. FASSEL, C. A. PAPP, D. L. HILDENBRAND, and R. P. SERNKA, *Solid Propellant Rocket Res.*, ARS. Series, *1*, 259 (1960).
8. H. L. FEIN, AIAA Paper 65-10 (1965).
9. J. R. FERRON and C. C. WATSON, "Fluidization" (F. A. Zenz, ed.), *Chem. Eng. Progr. Symp.* Series *58* (38), 79 (1962).
10. F. FISNER, *3rd International Congr. Appl. Mech.*, Stockholm, 1930.
11. L. W. FLORSCHUETZ, "On the Mechanics of Vapor Bubble Collapse," Ph.D. Thesis, Mech. Eng., U. of Illinois, Urbana, Ill. (1963).
12. N. L. FOEKING, "Pneumatic Conveying in Small Pipes," Ph.D. Thesis, Cornell U., Ithaca, N.Y. (1951).
13. L. FONDA and H. HERNE, "Aerodynamic Capture of Particles," Pergamon, New York (1960), p. 26.
14. O. L. FORGACS, A. A. ROBERTSON, and S. G. MASON, "Fundamentals of Paper-Making Fibres," Brit. Paper and Board Maker's Assoc., Kenley, Surrey, England, p. 447 (1958).
15. W. FORSTALL and A. H. SHAPIRO, *J. Appl. Mech.*, *17*, 399 (1950); *18*, 219 (1951).
16. H. K. FORSTER, *J. Appl. Phys.*, *25*, 1067 (1954).
17. H. K. FORSTER, *A.I.Ch.E. J.*, *3*, 535 (1957).
18. K. E. FORSTER, *Phys. Fluids*, *4*, 448 (1961).
19. H. K. FORSTER and N. ZUBER, *J. Appl. Phys.*, *25*, 474 (1954).
20. P. J. FORSTER, *Combustion and Flame*, *7*, 227 (1963).
21. G. FRANCIS, "Ionization Phenomena in Gases," Butterworth, London (1960).
22. J. FRENKEL, "Kinetic Theory of Liquids," Oxford U.P. (1946); Dover, New York (1955).
23. F. N. FRENKIEL, NASA TM 1436 (1958).
24. S. K. FRIEDLANDER, *A.I.Ch.E. J.*, *3*, 43 (1957).
25. S. K. FRIEDLANDER, *A.I.Ch.E. J.*, *3*, 381 (1957).
26. S. K. FRIEDLANDER, *ARS J.*, *29*, 296 (1959).
27. S. K. FRIEDLANDER, *Phys. Fluids*, *3*, 693 (1960); also *J. Atm. Sci.*, *22*, 571, 577 (1965).
28. S. K. FRIEDLANDER, *ARS J.*, *31*, 96 (1961).
29. R. FRIEDMAN and A. MAČEK, *Combustion and Flame*, *6*, 9 (1962).
30. R. FRIEDMAN and A. MAČEK, "Ninth Symposium (International) on Combustion," (1962), p. 703.

31. H. L. FRISCH, *J. Chem. Phys.*, *22*, 123 (1954).
32. R. M. FRISTROM, F. A. OYHUS, and G. H. ALBRECHT, *ARS J.*, *32*, 1729 (1962).
33. N. FROESSLING, *Gerlands Beitraze zur Geophysik*, *52*, 170 (1938).
34. N. FUCHS, NACA TM 1160 (1947).
35. N. FUCHS, "Evaporation and Droplet Growth in Gaseous Media," Sec. 2, Pergamon, New York (1959).
36. N. FUCHS, "The Mechanics of Aerosols," Macmillan, New York (1964).
37. N. FUCHS and I. PETRJANOFF, *Nature*, *139*, 111 (1937).
38. R. D. FULMER and D. P. WIRTZ, AIAA Paper 65-11 (1965).

G

1. C. A. GALLAER and J. W. SCHINDELER, *J. Air Pollution Control Assoc.*, *13* (12), 574 (1963).
2. B. GAL-OR and W. RESNICK, *Chem. Eng. Sci.*, *19*, 653 (1964).
3. R. GANS, *Ann. Phys.*, *86*, 628 (1928).
4. F. R. GARBIS and R. A. BAKHTIONZIN, *Soviet J. Atomic Energy* (English Translation, *11* (5), 378 (1962).
5. F. H. GARNER and D. HAMMERTON, *Chem. Eng. Sci.*, *3*, 1 (1954).
6. F. H. GARNER and A. H. P. SKELLAND, *Trans. Instn. Chem. Eng.*, *29*, 315 (1951).
7. J. GASTERSTAEDT, *V.D.I. Forschungs Arbeiten*, 265 (1924).
8. W. H. GAUVIN, *Can. J. Chem.*, *7*, 48 (1955).
9. W. H. GAUVIN and J. DLOUHY, *Municipal Utilities Magazine*, *96*, 17 (1958).
10. W. H. GAUVIN and J. J. O. GRAVEL, "Proceedings of Symposium on Interaction between Fluids and Particles," Institute of Chemical Engineers, London (1962), p. 250.
11. J. M. GEIST, J. L. YORK, and G. G. BROWN, *Ind. Eng. Chem.*, *43*, 1371-3 (1951).
12. H. G. GIBSON, W. T. ABEL, and G. E. FASCHING, "Proc. Multi-Phase Flow Symposium," ASME (1963), p. 49.
13. W. H. GIEDT, *J. Aerospace Sci.*, *18*, 725 (1951).
14. E. GIFFEN and A. MURASZEN, "Atomization of Liquid Fuels," Chapman and Hall, London (1953).
15. M. GILBERT, H. N. HOWARD, and B. L. HICKS, NACA TN 1078 (1946).
16. S. GILL, *Proc. Cambridge Phil. Soc.*, *47*, 96 (1951).
17. G. R. GILLESPIE, U. of Illinois Engineering Station Technical Report 9, Urbana, Ill. (1953).
18. T. GILLESPIE, *J. Colloid Sci.*, *10*, 299 (1955).
19. T. GILLESPIE and E. K. RIDEAL, *Trans. Faraday Soc.*, *52*, 173 (1955).
20. E. R. GILLILAND, *Ind. Eng. Chem.*, *44*, 218 (1952).
21. E. R. GILLILAND and E. A. MASON, *Ind. Eng. Chem.*, *41*, 1191 (1949).
22. P. E. GLASER, "Proceedings of International Heat Transfer Conference" (1961), p. 829.
23. I. GLASSMAN, *Jet Propulsion*, *27*, 542 (May 1957).
24. S. GLASSTONE, K. J. LAIDLER, and H. EYRING, "The Theory of Rate Processes," McGraw-Hill, New York (1941).
25. R. D. GLAUZ, *ARS J.*, *32*, 773 (1962).
26. G. A. E. GODSAVE, "The Burning of Single Drops of Fuel: Part I and II,"

National Gas Turbine Establishment Report Nos. R 66 (1950), and R 87 (1951), Ministry of Supply, TPA3/TTB (London).

27. E. J. GOHR, "Fluidization" (D. F. Othmer, ed.), Reinhold, New York (1956), p. 102.

28. L. J. GOLDBERG, H. M. S. WATKINS, E. E. BAERKE, and M. A. CHATIGNY, *J. Hygiene, 56* (1958).

29. V. GOLDSCHMIDT, "Two-Phase Flow in a Two-Dimensional Jet," Ph.D. Thesis, Syracuse U., Syracuse, N.Y. (1965).

30. H. L. GOLDSMITH and S. G. MASON, *J. Colloid Sci., 17*, 448 (1962).

31. M. GOLDSMITH and S. S. PENNER, *Jet Propulsion, 24*, 245 (1954).

32. M. GOLDSMITH and C. K. PERKINS, "Experiments on the Burning of Single Drops of Fuel in Oxygen-Inert Gas Mixtures," Jet Propulsion Lab. Technical Report No. 4 (1954).

33. H. GOLDSTEIN, "Classical Mechanics," Addison-Wesley, Cambridge, Mass. (1950), p. 58.

34. S. GOLDSTEIN, "Modern Developments in Fluid Dynamics," Clarendon, Oxford (1938), pp. 83, 492.

35. S. W. GOUSE, Jr., and G. A. BROWN, ASME Paper No. 64-WA/FE-35 (1964).

36. G. G. GOYER, R. GRUEN, and V. K. LaMER, *J. Phys. Chem., 58*, 137 (1954).

37. K. D. GRANZOW, *Phys. Fluids, 5* (2), 142 (1962).

38. H. L. GREEN and W. R. LANE, "Particle Clouds, Dusts, Smokes and Mists," E. and F. N. Spon Ltd., London (1957).

39. P. GRIFFITH, *Trans. ASME, 80*, 721 (1958).

40. P. GRIFFITH, ASME Paper 64-WA/HT-43 (1964).

41. P. GRIFFITH and G. B. WALLIS, *Trans. ASME, J. Heat Transfer, 83C*, 307 (1961).

42. R. M. GRIFFITH, *Chem. Eng. Sci., 12*, 198 (1960).

43. S. J. GRISAFFE and W. A. SPITZIG, NASA TN D-1705 (1963).

44. A. V. GROSSE, "High Temperature, A Tool of the Future," Stanford Res. Inst., (1956), p. 59.

45. A. V. GROSSE and J. B. CONWAY, *Ind. Eng. Chem., 50*, 663 (1958).

46. U. GROSSMANN, *Chem. Ing. Tech., 28*, 107 (1956).

47. G. W. GROVIER, B. W. RADFORD, and S. C. DUNN, *Can. J. Chem. Eng., 35*, 58 (1957).

48. F. T. GUCKER, Jr., "Air Pollution," McGraw-Hill, New York (1952).

49. K. GUGAN, J. LAWTON, and F. J. WEINBERG, "Proceedings of 10th Symposium (International) on Combustion" (1964), p. 709.

50. R. D. GUMPRECHT and C. M. SLIEPCEVICH, *J. Phys. Chem., 57*, 90 (1953).

51. R. GUNN, *J. Geophys. Rev., 54*, 57 (1949).

52. F. C. GUNTHER, Jet Propulsion Lab. Progress Report 4-75, Calif. Institute of Technology, Pasadena, Calif. (1950).

53. F. C. GUNTHER and F. KREITH, Jet Propulsion Lab. Progress Report 4-120, Calif. Institute of Technology, Pasadena, Calif. (1950).

H

1. W. L. HABERMAN and R. K. MORTON, David Taylor Model Basin Report 802 (1953).

2. W. L. HABERMAN and R. K. MORTON, *Trans. Am. Soc. Civil Engrs.*, *121*, 227 (1956).

3. J. HADAMARD, *Compt. Rend.*, *152*, 1735 (1911).

4. W. W. HAGERTY, U.S. Air Force Tech. Rept. 6067 (1952).

5. A. R. HALL and J. DIEDERICHSEN, "Fourth Symposium on Combustion," Williams and Wilkins, Baltimore (1953), p. 837.

6. E. A. N. HALTSROM, "Design of Experimental Apparatus for the Study of Two-Phase Flow in Circular Straight Pipe," M.S. Thesis, Princeton U., Princeton, N.J. (1953).

7. D. HAMMERTON and F. H. GARNER, *Trans. Instn. Chem. Eng.* (London), *32* (Supplement) S-18 (1954).

8. G. W. HANCHER and S. JURY, *Chem. Eng. Progr. Symp. Ser.*, *55* (24), 87 (1959).

9. T. J. HANRATTY, G. A. LATINEN, and R. H. WILHELM, *A.I.Ch.E. J.*, *2*, 372 (1956).

10. A. R. HANSON, "Proceedings of 2nd Midwestern Conference of Fluid Mechanics," Ohio State University, Columbus, O. (1952), p. 415.

11. J. HAPPEL and H. BRENNER, "Low Reynolds Number Hydrodynamics," Prentice-Hall, Englewood Cliffs, N.J. (1965).

12. J. K. HARDY, NACA, ARR 4111 (1944).

13. O. H. HARIU and M. C. MOLSTAD, *Ind. Eng. Chem.*, *41*, 1148 (1949).

14. W. G. HARLAND, Shirley Inst. Mem., *28*, 111; *J. Text. Inst.*, *46*, T472 (1955).

15. D. B. HARMON, Jr., *J. Franklin Inst.*, *259*, 519 (1955).

16. G. J. HARPER, A. M. HOOD, and J. D. MORTON, *J. Hygiene*, *56*, 364 (1958).

17. L. S. HARRIS, *J. Air Pollution Control Assoc.*, *13*, 613 (1963).

18. D. HARRISON and L. S. LEUNG, "Proceedings of Symposium on Interaction between Fluids and Particles," Institute of Chemical Engineers, London (1962), p. 127.

19. P. L. HARRISON, "Seventh International Symposium on Combustion," Butterworth, London (1959), p. 913.

20. P. L. HARRISON and A. D. YOLTE, *Proc. Roy. Soc.* (London), *A261*, 357 (1961).

21. G. K. HARTMAN and A. B. FOCKE, *Phys. Rev.*, *57*, 221 (1940).

22. I. HARTMENN, *Ind. Eng. Chem.*, *40*, 752 (1948).

23. R. A. HARTUNIAN and W. R. SEARS, *J. Fluid Mech.*, *3*, 27 (1957).

24. F. W. HARTWIG, *J. Am. Rocket Soc.*, *23*, 242 (1953).

25. H. A. HASSAN, *AIAA J.*, *2*, 395 (1964).

26. H. M. HAWKINS, Y. S. TANG, J. H. GARY, and A. O. WIKMAN, "A Special Analytical Study of Heat Transfer Phenomena with Clouds of Small Particles in Air at High Temperatures," Univ. of Florida Eng. and Ind. Experiment Station Rept. (1950).

27. I. HAYAKAWA, *J. Air Pollution Control Assoc.*, *12* (6), 265 (1962).

28. L. J. HELLINCKX, "Proceedings of Symposium on Interaction between Fluids and Particles," Institute of Chemical Engineers, London (1962), p. 72.

29. F. HELML and J. A. SCHEDLING, *Staub 25*, 155-7 (1951).

30. C. D. HENDRICKS, Jr., "Charged Droplet Experiments," 2nd AFOSR Symposium on Advanced Propulsion Concepts, Boston, Mass. (1959).

31. P. C. HENRIQUEZ, *Rev. Trav. Chim.*, *54*, 574 (1935).

32. C. E. HERMANCE, R. SHINNER, A. ACZARRAGA, L. KURYLKO, J. WENOGRAD, and M. SUMMERFIELD, AIAA Paper 65-59 (1965).

33. H. HERNE, *Int. J. Air Pollution*, *3*, 26 (1960).
34. J. HERSHKOWITZ, F. SCHWARTZ, and J. V. R. KAUFMAN, "Eighth Int. Symposium on Combustion," Williams and Wilkins, Baltimore (1960), p. 720.
35. G. HETTNER, *Z. Phys.*, *37*, 179 (1926).
36. G. H. HIGGINBOTHAM, D. R. OLIVER, and S. G. WARD, *Brit. J. Appl. Phys.*, *7*, 372 (1958).
37. D. L. HINKLE, C. ORR, and J. M. DALLAVALLE, *J. Colloid Sci.*, *9*, 70 (1955).
38. C. N. HINSHELWOOD, "The Structure of Physical Chemistry," Clarendon, Oxford (1951).
39. J. O. HINZE, *Appl. Sci. Res.*, *A1*, 263, 273 (1949).
40. J. O. HINZE, *A.I.Ch.E. J.*, *1*, 289 (1955).
41. J. O. HINZE, "Turbulence," McGraw-Hill, New York (1959).
42. J. O. HINZE, *Appl. Sci. Res.*, *A1*, 273 (1959).
43. J. O. HINZE, *Appl. Sci. Res.*, *A11*, 33 (1962).
44. J. O. HIRSCHFELDER, C. F. CURTISS, and R. B. BIRD, "Molecular Theory of Gases and Liquids," Wiley, New York (1954).
45. R. HIRSCHKRON and F. F. EHRICH, ASME Paper 64-WA/FE-30 (1964).
46. A. W. HIXSON and S. J. BAUM, *Ind. Eng. Chem.*, *36*, 528 (1944).
47. A. W. HIXSON and E. L. GADEN, Jr., *Ind. Eng. Chem.*, *42*, 1792 (1950).
48. B. HODKINSON, *Engineering*, *143*, 629 (1937).
49. S. A. HOENIG, *J. Appl. Phys.*, *28*, 1218 (1957).
50. S. F. HOERNER, "Fluid Dynamic Drag," Horner, Midland Park, N.J. (1958), pp. 3–8.
51. R. F. HOGLUND, *ARS J.*, *32*, 662 (1962).
52. G. J. HOOYMAN, "Thermodynamics of Irreversible Processes in Rotating Systems," Ph.D. Thesis, U. of Leiden, Netherlands (1955).
53. E. R. HOSLER, A.I.Ch.E. Preprint No. 10, 6th National Heat Transfer Conference, Boston, Mass. (1963).
54. I. C. HOTTEL, G. C. WILLIAMS, and H. C. SIMPSON, "Fifth Symposium on Combustion," Reinhold, New York (1955), p. 101.
55. H. G. HOUGHTON, *Physics*, *4*, 413 (1933).
56. L. HOWARTH, *Proc. Cambridge Phil. Soc.*, *34*, 185 (1938).
57. L. HOWARTH, *Proc. Roy. Soc.* (London), *A154*, 3 (1936).
58. J. T. HOWE, NASA TR R-95 (1961).
59. J. T. HOWE, NASA TN D-1031 (1961).
60. N. T. HSU, K. SATO, and B. H. SAGE, *Ind. Eng. Chem.*, *46*, 870 (1954).
61. S. HU and R. C. KINTNER, *A.I.Ch.E. J.*, *1*, 42 (1955).
62. F. C. HUBER and E. E. REID, *Ind. Eng. Chem.*, *18*, 535 (1926).
63. T. F. HUETER and R. H. BOLT, "Sonics," Wiley, New York (1955), p. 418.
64. R. R. HUGHES, *Ind. Eng. Chem.*, *49*, 947 (1957).
65. R. R. HUGHES and E. R. GILLILAND, *Chem. Eng. Progr.*, *48*, 497 (1952).
66. J. A. HULTBERG, "Numerical Solution to the Flow of a Gas-Solid Suspension through a Nozzle," Project SQUID Report ILL-17-R (AD 604 107), Univ. of Virginia, Charlottesville, Va. (1964).
67. J. A. HULTBERG, "Flow of a Gas-Solid Suspension through a Nozzle," Ph.D. Thesis, U. of Illinois, Urbana, Ill. (1964).

68. J. A. HULTBERG and S. L. SOO, *Astronautica Acta, 11* (3) 207 (1965).
69. G. A. HUGHMARK, *Ind. Eng. Chem. Fund.*, *4*, 361 (1965).

I

1. E. H. IMMERGUT and F. R. EIRICH, *Ind. Eng. Chem.*, *45*, 2500 (1953).
2. R. D. INGEBO, NACA TN 2368 (1951).
3. R. D. INGEBO, NACA TN 3265 (1954).
4. R. D. INGEBO, NACA TN 3762 (1956).
5. A. T. IPPEN and F. RAICHLEN, *Proc. Am. Soc. Civil Engrs.*, *83*, HY5, 1392 (1957).
6. S. IRMAY, *Trans. ASME, J. Basic Eng.*, *82*, 961 (1960).
7. T. F. IRVINE, Jr., ASME Paper 58-A-155 (1958).
8. H. S. ISBIN and G. R. GAVALAS, "Two-Phase Flow Through an Aperture," Heat Transfer and Fluid Mechanics Institute, U. of Washington, Seattle, W. (1962).
9. H. S. ISBIN, J. E. MOY, and A. J. R. DA CRUZ, *A.I.Ch.E. J.*, *2*, 361 (1957).
10. K. ITO, "On Stochastic Differential Equations," *American Math Soc. Memoir*, No. 4 (1956).

J

1. J. D. JACKSON, "Electrodynamics," Wiley, New York (1962), p. 46.
2. M. JAKOB, "Heat Transfer," I and II, Wiley, New York (1949).
3. H. A. JANSSEN, *Z. ver. Deut. Ing.*, *39*, 1045 (1895).
4. R. JASTROW and C. A. PEARSE, *J. Geophys. Res.*, *62* (3), 413 (1957).
5. K. O. L. F. JAYAWEERA and B. J. MASON, *J. Fluid Mech.*, *22*, 709 (1965).
6. G. B. JEFFERY, *Proc. Roy. Soc.* (London), *A102*, 161 (1922).
7. R. C. JEFFREY and J. R. A. PEARSON, *J. Fluid Mech.*, *22*, 721 (1965).
8. V. G. JENSON, *Proc. Roy. Soc.* (London), *A249*, 346 (1959).
9. A. W. JENIKE and R. T. SHIELD, *J. Appl. Mech.*, *26*, *Trans. ASME, 81E*, 559 (1961).
10. G. JEPSON, A. POLL and W. SMITH, *Trans. Instn. Chem. Engrs.*, *41*, 207 (1963).
11. P. JOERG and B. L. McFARLAND, "Radiation Effects in Rocket Nozzles," Aerojet-General Corp., Report No. S62-245 (1962).
12. J. R. JOHANSON, *J. Appl. Mech.*, *31*, *Trans. ASME, 86E*, 499 (1965).
13. J. R. JOHANSON, *Trans. Soc. Min. Eng.*, *232*, 69 (1965).
14. A. I. JOHNSON and L. BRAIDA, *Can. J. Chem. Eng.*, *35*, 165 (1957).
15. C. C. JOHNSON and C. K. BULLOCK, *J. Appl. Phys.*, *35*, 2804 (1964).
16. H. A. JOHNSON, *Trans. ASME*, *77*, 1257 (1955).
17. I. JOHNSON and V. K. LA MER, *J. Am. Chem. Soc.*, *69*, 1184–92 (1947).
18. H. F. JOHNSTONE, R. B. FIELD, and M. C. TASSLER, *Ind. Eng. Chem.*, *46*, 1601 (1954).
19. H. F. JOHNSTONE, R. L. PIGFORD, and J. H. CHAPIN, *Trans. A.I.Ch.E.*, *37*, 95 (1941).
20. S. J. R. JONES and W. SMITH, "Proceedings of Symposium on Interaction between Fluids and Particles," Institute of Chemical Engineers, London, (1962), p. 190.

21. D. D. JOSEPH and L. N. TAO, *ZAMM*, *44* (8/9) 361 (1964).
22. W. JOST, "Diffusion in Solids, Liquids, and Gases," Academic, New York (1952), p. 46.
23. J. R. JOYCE, *J. Inst. Fuel*, *26*, 200 (1953).

K

1. H. KADA and T. J. HANRATTY, *A.I.Ch.E. J.*, *6*, 624 (1960).
2. J. KAMPÉ DE FERIET, *Ann. Soc. Sci. Bruxelles*, *I-59*, 145 (1939).
3. T. W. KAO, *Phys. Fluids*, *8*, 812 (1965).
4. N. S. KAPANY, "Fiber Optics," Parts 1–6, *J. Optical Soc. Am.*, *47*, 413 (1957); *47*, 423 (1957); *47*, 494 (1957); *49*, 779 (1959); *49*, 770 (1959); *47*, 1109 (1959).
5. A. KARMIS, H. L. GOLDSMITH, and S. G. MASON, *Nature*, *200*, 159 (1963).
6. H. B. KARPLUS, "The Velocity of Sound in a Liquid Containing Gas Bubbles," AEC Rept. No. COO-248 (1958).
7. L. L. KAVANAU, *Trans. ASME*, *77*, 617 (1955).
8. M. J. KAWAJUTI, *J. Phys. Soc.* (*Japan*), *10*, 694 (1955).
9. B. H. KAYE and R. P. BOARDMAN, "Proceedings of Symposium on Interaction between Fluids and Particles," Institute of Chemical Engineers, London (1962), p. 17.
10. B. H. KAYE and R. DAVIS, "Proceedings of Symposium on Interaction between Fluids and Particles," Institute of Chemical Engineers, London (1962), p. 22.
11. C. H. KEITH, A. B. ARONS, Ref. No. *53-48*, Woods Hole Oceanographic Inst., Woods Hole, Mass. (1953).
12. E. N. KEMLE, M. H. LAJOY, and E. N. KEMLER, Jr., General Mills, Inc., Rept. 1233, Project 8-2402 (1953).
13. E. H. KENNARD, "Kinetic Theory of Gases," McGraw-Hill, New York (1938).
14. D. A. KENNEDY, "Some Measurements of the Dispersion of Spheres in a Turbulent Flow," Ph.D. Thesis, Johns Hopkins U., Baltimore (1965).
15. J. F. KENNEDY, *J. Fluid Mech.*, *16*, 521 (1963).
16. K. N. KETTENRING, E. L. MANDERFIELD, and J. M. SMITH, *Chem. Eng. Progr.*, *46*, 139 (1950).
17. B. KIVEL, ASME Paper 61-WA-264 (1961).
18. P. S. KLEBANOFF, NACA Report 1247 (1955).
19. J. R. KLIEGEL, "Proceedings of Ninth Symposium (International) on Combustion," Butterworth, London (1962), p. 811.
20. J. R. KLIEGEL, "One-Dimensional Flow of a Gas-Particle System," Space Technology Lab. Report (1961).
21. J. R. KLIEGEL and G. R. NICKERSON, Report Space Technology Lab., Paper No. 1713-61, Am. Rocket Soc. Meeting (1961).
22. R. T. KNAPP and A. HOLLANDER, *Trans. ASME*, *70*, 419 (1948).
23. J. G. KNUDSEN and D. L. KATZ, "Fluid Dynamics and Heat Transfer," McGraw-Hill, New York (1958).
24. V. O. KNUDSEN, J. V. WILSON, and N. S. ANDERSON, *J. Acoust. Soc. Am.*, *20*, 849 (1948).

25. H. Komoda, *Japan Soc. Aerospace Eng.*, 274–279 (1957).
26. M. C. Kordecki and C. Orr, *A.M.A. Arch. Env. Health*, *1*, 1 (1960).
27. A. H. Korn, *Chem. Eng.*, *47* (3), 108 (1950).
28. H. H. Korst, "Proceedings of the Symposium on Single and Multi-Component Flow Processes" (R. L. Peskin and C. F. Chen, eds.), Eng. Res. Pub. No. 43, Rutgers U. (1965), p. 71.
29. S. I. Kosterin, *Izvestia Akad. Nauk*, 12 (1949).
30. V. Kourganoff, "Basic Methods in Transfer Problems," Clarendon Press, Oxford (1952).
31. L. S. G. Kovasznay, "Technique for the Optical Measurement of Turbulence in High Speed Flow," Heat Transfer and Fluid Mechanics Institute, Berkeley, Calif. (1949).
32. L. S. G. Kovasznay and A. Arman, *Rev. Sci. Instr.*, *28*, 793 (1957).
33. R. H. Kraichman, *Phys. Fluids*, *7* (1), 142 (1964).
34. H. R. Kraemer and H. F. Johnstone, *Ind. Eng. Chem.*, *47*, 2426 (1955).
35. H. Kramers, M. D. Westermann, J. H. DeGroot, and F. A. A. Dupont, "Proceedings of Symposium on Interaction between Fluids and Particles," Institute of Chemical Engineers, London (1962), p. 114.
36. N. V. Krasnogorskaya, "Problems of Atmosphere and Space Electricity" (S. C. Coroniti, ed.), Elsevier, New York (1965), p. 178.
37. M. Kremmer and O. Okurounmu, Gas Turbine Lab. Rept. No. 79, M.I.T., Cambridge, Mass. (1965).
38. A. R. Kriebel, *Trans. ASME, J. Basic Eng.*, *83*, 333 (1961).
39. A. R. Kriebel, ASME Paper 63-WA-13 (1963).
40. I. M. Krieger and T. J. Dougherty, *Trans. Soc. Rheology*, *3*, 133 (1959).
41. R. Kronig and J. Bruijsten, *J. Appl. Sci. Res.*, *A2*, 439 (1951).
42. M. A. Krzywoblocki, *Jet Propulsion*, *26*, 760 (1956).
43. O. Kubaschewski and B. E. Hopkins, "Oxidation of Metals and Alloys," Butterworth, London (1953).
44. A. A. Kudirka, R. J. Grosh, and P. W. McFadden, *Ind. Eng. Chem. Fundamentals*, *4*, 339 (1965).
45. S. Kumaga, and H. Isoda, "Fifth Symposium on Combustion," Reinhold, New York (1955), p. 190.
46. G. J. Kynch, *Trans. Faraday Soc.*, *48*, 166 (1952).

L

1. D. T. Lacey, J. H. Bowen, and K. S. Basden, *Ind. Eng. Chem. Fundamentals*, *4*, 275 (1965).
2. S. Lafazan and B. Siegel, "Ablative Thrust Chambers for Space Application," A.I.Ch.E. 46th National Meeting (1962).
3. T. J. Laidler and E. G. Richardson, *J. Acoust. Soc. Am.*, *9*, 217 (1938).
4. A. D. K. Laird, T. I. Sun, and J. Wing, ASME Paper 63-WA-242 (1963).
5. H. Lamb, "Hydrodynamics," Dover, New York (1932).
6. V. K. La Mer, "Air Pollution," McGraw-Hill, New York (1952).
7. V. K. La Mer and S. Hochberg, *Chem. Revs.*, *44*, 341 (1949).

8. R. B. Lancashire, E. A. Lezberg, and J. F. Morris, *Ind. Eng. Chem.*, *52*, 44 (1960).

9. H. Landahl and K. Hermann, *J. Colloid Sci.*, *4*, 103 (1949).

10. L. D. Landau and E. M. Lifschitz, "Statistical Physics," Addison-Wesley, Reading, Mass. (1958), p. 322.

11. W. R. Lane, *Ind. Eng. Chem.*, *43*, 1312 (1951).

12. R. J. Lang, *J. Acoust. Soc. Am.*, *34*, 6 (1962).

13. G. Langer and J. L. Radnik, *J. Appl. Phys.*, *32*, 955 (1961).

14. I. Langmuir, *Phys. Rev.*, *12*, 368 (1918).

15. I. Langmuir and K. Blodgett, *Phys. Rev.*, Ser. 2, *24*, 49 (1924).

16. I. Langmuir and K. Blodgett, "Mathematical Investigation of Water Droplet Trajectories," General Electric Research Lab., Rept. RL-225, 1944–5; *J. Meteorol.*, *5*, 175 (1948).

17. L. Lapidus and J. C. Elgin, *A.I.Ch.E. J.*, *3*, 63 (1957).

18. L. Lapidus, J. A. Quinn, and J. C. Elgin, *A.I.Ch.E. J.*, *7*, 260 (1961).

19. C. E. Lapple and C. B. Shepherd, *Ind. Eng. Chem.*, *32*, 605 (1940).

20. M. G. Larian, "Fundamentals of Chemical Engineering Operations," Prentice-Hall, Englewood Cliffs, N.J. (1958).

21. B. K. Larkin and S. W. Churchill, *A.I.Ch.E. J.*, *5*, 467 (1959).

22. J. Laufer, NACA Report 1053 (1951).

23. J. Laufer, NACA TN 2954 (1953).

24. J. Laufer, NACA TR 1174 (1954).

25. M. R. L'Ecuyur and S. N. B. Murthy, NASA TN D-2547 (1965).

26. P. G. Ledig and E. R. Weaver, *J. Am. Chem. Soc.*, *46*, 650 (1924); *Ind. Eng. Chem.*, *15*, 931 (1923).

27. D. W. Lee, NACA Rept. 425 (1932).

28. D. W. Lee and R. C. Spencer, NACA TN 424 (1932).

29. G. Lee and W. H. Gauvin, *Tappi*, *41*, 110 (1958).

30. G. Lee and W. H. Gauvin, *Canadian Oil and Gas Ind.*, *12*, 64 (1959).

31. S. Leliavsky, "An Introduction to Fluvial Hydraulics," Constable, London (1955).

32. M. Leva, "Fluidization," McGraw-Hill, New York (1959).

33. M. Leva, "Proceedings of Symposium on Interaction between Fluids and Particles," Institute of Chemical Engineers, London (1962), p. 143.

34. O. Levenspiel, *Ind. Eng. Chem.*, *51*, 787 (1959).

35. V. G. Levich, "Physicochemical Hydrodynamics," Prentice-Hall, Englewood Cliffs, N.J. (1962), p. 209.

36. C. H. Lewis, Jr., E. E. Petersen, A. Acrivos, and S. C. Tao, "A Study of Solid Particle Distribution in a Gas-Solid Jet," presented at ACS Symposium (1961).

37. H. E. Lewis, D. G. Edwards, M. J. Goglia, R. I. Rice, and L. W. Smith, *Ind. Eng. Chem.*, *40*, 67 (1948).

38. W. K. Lewis, E. R. Gilliland, and W. C. Bauer, *Ind. Eng. Chem.*, *41*, 1104 (1949).

39. W. K. Lewis, E. R. Gilliland, and H. Girouard, "Fluidization" (F. A. Zenz, ed.), *Chem. Eng. Progr. Symp. Ser.*, *58* (38), 87 (1962).

40. W. K. LEWIS, E. R. GILLILAND, and P. M. LANG, "Fluidization" (F. A. Zenz, ed.), *Chem. Eng. Progr. Symp. Ser.*, *58* (38), 65 (1962).
41. L. LICHTENSTEIN, "Vorlesungen uber einige Klassen Nichtlinearen Integral-gleichungen und Integro-Differential Gleichungen," Berlin, pp. 30–46 (1931).
42. L. LIEBERMANN, *J. Appl. Phys.*, *28*, 205 (1957).
43. M. J. LIGHTHILL, *J. Fluid Mech.*, *2*, 493 (1957).
44. C. C. LIN, *Proc. N.A.S.*, *46* (1960).
45. N. R. LINDBLAD and R. G. SEMONIN, *J. Geophys. Res.*, *68*, 1051 (1963).
46. D. L. LINNING, *Inst. of Mech. Engrs. (London), Proc.* (B), *1B* (2) (1952).
47. W. N. LIPSCOMB, T. R. RUBIN, and J. H. STURDIVANT, *J. Appl. Phys.*, *18*, 72 (1947).
48. G. LITTAYE, *Compt. Rend.*, *217*, 340 (1943).
49. F. E. LITTMAN, F. M. CHURCH, and E. M. KINDERMAN, *J. Less-Common Metals*, *3*, 367, 379 (1961).
50. H. LITTMAN, *A.I.Ch.E. J.*, *10*, 924 (1964).
51. V. C. LIU, *J. Meteorol.*, *13*, 399 (1956).
52. V. C. LIU, S. C. PANG, and H. JEW, *Phys. Fluids*, *8*, 788 (1965).
53. R. W. LOCKHART and R. D. MARTINELLI, *Chem. Eng. Progr.*, *45*, 39 (1949).
54. D. L. LOCKWOOD and V. HAMZA, NASA TN D-1461 (1962).
55. L. B. LOEB, "Basic Processes of Gaseous Electronics," U. of Calif. Press, Berkeley (1955), pp. 421, 478, 560.
56. H. A. LORENTZ, "The Theory of Electrons," Dover, New York (1915), p. 147.
57. T. J. LOVE, Jr., "An Investigation of Radiant Heat Transfer in Absorbing, Emitting, and Scattering Media," Ph.D. Thesis, Purdue Univ.; Report ARL-63-3, Aeronautical Research Lab., Office of Aerospace Research, USAF (1963).
58. T. J. LOVE, Jr., and R. J. GROSH, *Trans. ASME, J. Heat Transfer*, *87c*, 161 (1964).
59. J. L. LUMLEY, "Some Problems Connected with the Motion of Small Particles in Turbulent Fluid," Ph.D. Thesis, Johns Hopkins U. (1957).
60. J. L. LUMLEY, *J. Math. Phys.*, *3* (2), 309 (1962).
61. D. A. LUNDGREN, M.S. Thesis, U. of Minnesota (1962).
62. D. A. LUNDGREN and K. T. WHITBY, "Effect of Particle Electrostatic Charge on Filtration by Fibruous Filters," *Ind. Eng. Chem. Process Design Develop.* (1965).
63. F. E. LUTHER and R. E. PATERSON, "Electrostatic Atomization Testing Facility," Calif. Res. Corp. Report, June 6 (1961).

M

1. D. K. C. MACDONALD, "Thermoelectricity," Wiley, New York (1962).
2. E. M. MACK and R. E. MARRINER, *Chem. Eng. Progr.*, *45*, 545 (1949).
3. C. A. MADONNA and R. F. LAMA, *A.I.Ch.E. J.*, *4*, 497 (1958).
4. A. D. MANDE and R. L. WHITMORE, *Brit. J. Appl. Phys.*, *7*, 98 (1956).
5. N. MANSON, F. FERRIÉ, and R. KLING, *J. Soc. Ing. Automobile*, *25*, 191–195 (August, 1952).
6. F. E. MARBLE, *AIAA Journal*, *1*, 2793 (1963).
7. F. E. MARBLE, *Phys. Fluids*, *7*, 1270 (1964).

8. F. E. Marble, "Combustion and Propulsion," 5th AGARDograph Colloquium, Pergamon (1963), p. 175.

9. E. K. Marchildon, "Shape, Turbulence and Acceleration Effects on the Dynamics of Particle-Fluid Systems," Ph.D. Thesis, McGill U., Montreal, Canada (1965).

10. E. K. Marchildon, A. Clamen, and W. H. Gauvin, *Phys. Fluids, 7*, 2018 (1964).

11. E. K. Marchildon, A. Clamen, and W. H. Gauvin, *Can. J. Chem. Eng., 42*, 178 (1964).

12. T. J. Marshall, "Proceedings of Symposium on Interaction between Fluids and Particles," Institute of Chemical Engineers, London (1962), p. 299.

13. W. R. Marshall, Jr., *Chem. Eng. Progr. Monograph Ser., 50*, No. 2 (1954).

14. S. W. Martin, "Symposium in Particle Size Measurement," American Society for Testing Materials, New York (1941).

15. B. J. Mason, "The Physics of Clouds," Oxford, London (1957), p. 369.

16. K. B. Mathur and P. E. Gishler, *A.I.Ch.E. J., 1*, 152 (1955).

17. J. C. Maxwell, "A Treatise on Electricity and Magnetism," Vol. 1, p. 231, Clarendon, Oxford (1904).

18. W. G. May and F. R. Rossell, "High Pressure Fluidization," Paper presented at North New Jersey Section, ACS Meeting (1954).

19. W. H. McAdams, "Heat Transmission" (3rd ed.), McGraw-Hill, New York (1954).

20. C. W. McCracken and W. M. Alexander, NASA TN D-1174 (1961).

21. T. K. McCubbin, Jr., *J. Acoust. Soc. Am., 25*, 1013 (1953).

22. L. K. McCune and R. H. Wilhelm, *Ind. Eng. Chem., 41*, 1124 (1949).

23. D. A. McDonald, "Blood Flow in Arteries," Arnold, London (1960).

24. K. W. McHenry and R. H. Wilhelm, *A.I.Ch.E. J., 3*, 83 (1957).

25. H. K. McMillan, W. E. Fontain, and J. B. Chaddock, ASME Paper No. 64-WA/FE-4 (1964).

26. A. B. Metzner and M. Whitlock, *Trans. Soc. Rheol., 2*, 239 (1958).

27. D. H. Michael, *J. Fluid Mech., 18*, 19 (1964).

28. W. R. Mickelson, NACA TN 3570 (1955).

29. H. S. Mickley and C. A. Trilling, *Ind. Eng. Chem., 43*, 1220 (1951).

30. C. C. Miesse, American Rocket Society Ninth Annual Meeting, Paper 167-54 (1951).

31. C. C. Miesse, Conference on Atomization, Sprays, and Droplets, Northwestern University, Sept. 24–25 (1953).

32. C. C. Miesse, *Ind. Eng. Chem., 47*, 1690 (1955).

33. C. C. Miesse, "Fifth Symposium on Combustion," Reinhold, New York (1955), p. 190.

34. G. D. Miles, L. Shedlovsky, and J. J. Ross, *J. Phys. Chem., 49*, 93 (1945).

35. R. A. Millikan, *Phys. Rev., 22*, 1 (1923).

36. L. M. Milne-Thomson, "Theoretical Hydrodynamics," (4th ed.), Macmillan, New York (1960), p. 554.

37. K. Min, B. T. Chao, and M. E. Wyman, *Rev. Sci. Instr., 34*, 529 (1963).

38. A. Mironer and H. Macomber, Paper 2355-62, ARS Meeting (1962).

39. A. R. MITCHELL and J. W. CRAGGS, *Math Tables and Other Aids to Computation*, 7, 127 (1953).
40. D. J. MONTGOMERY, *Solid State Physics*, 9, 139 (1959).
41. M. J. MOONEY, *J. Rheol.*, 2, 210 (1931).
42. D. W. MOORE, *J. Fluid Mech.*, 23 (4), 749 (1966).
43. D. W. MOORE, *J. Fluid Mech.*, 6, 113 (1959).
44. J. H. MORGENTHALER, ARS Preprint 1715-61 (1961).
45. G. MORRELL, NASA TN D-677 (1961).
46. G. MORRELL, "Eighth International Symposium on Combustion," Williams and Wilkins, Baltimore (1960), p. 1059.
47. P. M. MORSE and H. FESHBACH, "Methods of Theoretical Physics," McGraw-Hill, New York (1953), pp. 180, 784, 785.
48. K. H. MUELLER, *Jet Propulsion*, 25, 468 (1955).
49. R. A. MUGELE and H. D. EVANS, *Ind. Eng. Chem.*, 43, 1317 (1951).
50. J. W. MULLIN and C. R. TRELEAVEN, "Proceedings of Symposium on Interaction between Fluids and Particles," Institute of Chemical Engineers, London (1962), p. 201.
51. B. P. MULLINS, *Fuel*, 32, 211 (1953).
52. A. T. MURPHY, "Changing of Fine Particles by Random Motion of Ions in an Electric Field," Ph.D. Thesis, Carnegie Institute of Technology, Pittsburgh, Pa. (1956).
53. A. T. MURPHY, F. T. ADLER, and G. W. PENNEY, *AIEE Trans.*, 78, 318 (1959).
54. G. MURPHY, D. F. YOUNG, and R. J. BURIAN, US AEC Rept. No. ISC-a474 (1954).
55. J. D. MURRAY, *J. Fluid Mech.*, 21, 465 (1965).
56. J. D. MURRAY, *J. Fluid Mech.*, 22, 57 (1965).

N

1. G. L. NATANSON, *Proc. Acad. Sci. USSR, Phys. Chem. Section*, 112, 95 (1957).
2. N. K. NAYYAR and G. S. MURTY, *Proc. Physical. Soc.* (London) (1960).
3. L. W. NEEDHAM and N. W. HILL, *Fuel in Science and Practice*, 26, 101 (1947).
4. D. W. NETZER, Report No. TM-62-3, Jet Propulsion Center, Purdue Univ., Lafayette, Ind. (1962).
5. J. L. NEURINGER and R. E. ROSENSWEIG, *Phys. Fluids*, 7, 1927 (1964).
6. D. M. NEWITT, J. F. RICHARDSON, and C. A. SHOOK, "Proc. Symposium on Interaction between Fluids and Particles," Institute of Chemical Engrs, London (1962), p. 87.
7. T. NISHIHARA, T. KORI, and T. YOSHIZUMI, *Chem. Engr.* (Japan), 17, 347–50 (1953).
8. N. NISHIWAKI, "Fifth Symposium on Combustion," Reinhold, New York (1955), p. 148.
9. I. NISHIWAKI, "Brief Survey on Growth and Collapse of Steam Bubbles," AEC Report No. TID-11060 (1960).
10. I. NISHIWAKI, and L. A. KLEIN, "Condensation of Steam in Steam-Air Bubbles Immersed in Water," AEC Report No. TID-6520 (1960),

11. S. Nukiyama and Y. Tanasawa, *Trans. Soc. Mech. Engrs.* (Japan), *5*, 68 (1939).

O

1. M. P. O'Brien and J. E. Gosline, *Ind. Engr. Chem.*, *27*, 1436 (1935).
2. W. Ohnesorge, *J. Roy. Aeronaut. Soc.*, *58*, 78 (1944).
3. R. B. Olney, *A.I.Ch.E. J.*, *10* (6), 827 (1964).
4. W. T. Olson, *ARS J.*, *32*, 672 (1962).
5. J. C. Orcutt, J. F. Davidson and R. L. Pigford, "Fluidization," (F. A. Zenz, ed.), *Chem. Eng. Prog. Symp. Ser.*, *58* (38), 1 (1962).
6. C. Orr and J. M. Dallavalle, "Fine Particle Measurement," Macmillan, New York (1959).
7. S. Ostrach and D. G. McConnel, AIAA Paper 65–132 (1965).
8. K. Oswatitsch, *ZAMM*, *22*, 1 (1942).
9. D. F. Othmer, "Fluidization," Reinhold, New York (1956).
10. P. R. Owen, Proceedings of B. C. U. R. A. Conference at Leatherhead, Surrey, England, "Aerodynamic Capture of Particles" (E. G. Richardson ed.), Macmillan, New York (1960).

P

1. L. Page, "Introduction to Theoretical Physics," Van Nostrand, Princeton (1952).
2. G. N. Patterson, "Molecular Flow of Gases," Wiley, New York (1956).
3. R. E. Pattle, *Trans. Instn. Chem. Engrs.* (London), *28*, 27 (1950).
4. K. W. Pearce, "Proceedings of Symposium on Interaction between Fluids and Particles," Institute of Chemical Engineers, London (1962), p. 30.
5. T. Pearcy and B. McHugh, *Phil. Mag.*, *46*, 783 (1955).
6. R. B. Penndorf, "Research on Aerosol Scattering in the Infra-Red-Scattering Coefficients for Absorbing and Non-Absorbing Aerosols," Scientific Rept. No. 3, AVCO Corp. Tech. Rept. RAD-TR-60–27 (1960).
7. S. S. Penner, *J. Am. Rocket Soc.*, *23*, 85 (1953).
8. S. S. Penner, "Chemical Reactions in Flow Systems," Butterworth, London (1955).
9. G. W. Penney and R. D. Lynch, *AIEE Trans.*, *76*, 294 (1957).
10. M. Perlmutter and R. Siegel, *Trans. ASME*, Ser. C, *84*, 301 (1962).
11. M. Perlmutter and R. Siegel, *Trans. ASME*, Ser. C, *85*, 55 (1963).
12. F. Perrin, *J. Phys. Radium*, *5*, 497 (1934); *7*, 1 (1936).
13. R. L. Peskin, "Particle-Particle and Particle-Fluid Interaction in Two-Phase Turbulent Flow," Proceedings of Heat Transfer and Fluid Mechanics Institute, Stanford U.P., Stanford, Calif. (1960)
14. R. L. Peskin, "Some Effects of Particle-Particle and Particle-Fluid Interactions in Two-Phase Flow Systems," Ph.D. Thesis, Princeton University, Princeton, N.J. (1959).
15. R. L. Peskin, "The Diffusivity of Small Suspended Particles in Turbulent Fluids," presented at the National Meeting A.I.Ch.E., Baltimore (1962).
16. R. L. Peskin and H. A. Dwyer, ASME Paper 65-WA/FE-24 (1965).

17. R. L. Peskin and J. P. Lawler, *ASHRAE Trans.*, *69*, 293 (1963).
18. R. L. Peskin and R. J. Raco, *J. Acoust. Soc. Am.*, *35*, 1378 (1963).
19. R. L. Peskin, H. W. Wise, and W. A. Rosser, Jr., "Burning Rate and Ignition of Liquid-Fuel Drops," American Petroleum Institute Conference Paper CP 64-7 (1964).
20. O. Pinkus, *Trans. ASME, J. Appl. Mech.*, 425 (1952).
21. M. S. Plesset, *J. Appl. Mech.*, *16*, 277 (1949).
22. M. S. Plesset and D. Y. Hsieh, *Phys. Fluids*, *3*, 882 (1960),
23. M. S. Plesset and S. A. Zwick, *J. Appl. Phys.*, *23*, 95 (1952).
24. M. S. Plesset and S. A. Zwick, *J. Appl. Phys.*, *25*, 493 (1954).
25. M. S. Plesset and S. A. Zwick, *J. Math. and Phys.*, *33*, 309 (1955).
26. H. R. Plumlee, "Effects of Electrostatic Forces on Drop Collision and Coalescence in Air," Dept. of Electrical Engineering Report No. CPRL-8-64, U. of Illinois, Urbana, Ill. (1964).
27. L. A. Povinelli, NASA TN D-1438 (1962).
28. H. R. C. Pratt, F. R. Dell, R. Gaylor, I. Jones, and J. B. Lewis, *Trans. Instn. Chem. Engrs.*, *29*, 89 (1951).
29. H. R. C. Pratt, R. Gaylor, N. W. Roberts, R. Murdock, and J. D. Thornton, *Trans. Inst. Chem. Engrs.*, *31*, 69 (1953).
30. R. P. Probert, *Phil. Mag.*, *37*, 94 (1946).
31. P. S. Prokhorov, *Trans. Faraday Soc.*, *18*, 41 (1954).
32. I. Proudman and J. R. A. Pearson, *J. Fluid. Mech.*, *2*, 237 (1957).
33. B. B. Pruden and N. Epstein, *Chem. Eng. Sci.*, *14*, 696 (1964).
34. S. Prager, *Phy. Fluids*, *4*, 1477 (1961).

R

1. W. D. Rannie, "Perturbation Analysis of One-Dimensional Heterogeneous Flow in Rocket Nozzles," Conference on Propellants, Combustion and Liquid Rockets, Am. Rocket Soc., Palm Beach, Fla., April (1961).
2. W. E. Ranz, ASME Paper No. 54-A-143 (1954).
3. W. E. Ranz, "On Sprays and Spraying," Engineering Research Bulletin No. 65, Penn. State Univ., University Park, Pa. (1956).
4. W. E. Ranz and W. R. Marshall, *Chem. Eng. Progr.*, *48*, 147, 173 (1952).
5. W. E. Ranz and J. B. Wong, *Arch. Ind. Hyg. and Occupational Med.*, *5*, 464–77 (1952); *Ind. Eng. Chem.*, *44*, 1371 (1952).
6. D. J. Rasbash, "Proceedings of Symposium on Interaction between Fluids and Particles," Institute of Chemical Engineers, London (1962), p. 217.
7. R. B. Reif, *Tappi*, *38*, 607 (1955).
8. R. B. Reif, *Ceramic Age*, *79*, 40 (1963).
9. A. L. Reimann, "Thermionic Emission," Wiley, New York (1934), p. 298.
10. H. Reuter, "Proceedings of Symposium on Interaction between Fluids and Particles," Institute of Chemical Engineers, London (1962), p. 165.
11. A. J. Reynolds, *J. Fluid Mech.*, *22*, 113 (1965).
12. W. C. Reynolds, NASA TN D-182 (1959).
13. S. O. Rice, *Bell System Tech. J.*, *23*, 24 (1944).

14. E. G. RICHARDSON, "Ultrasonic Physics," (A. E. Brown, ed.) Chaps. 4, 8, Elsevier, New York (1962), p. 259, 272.
15. E. G. RICHARDSON and E. TYLER, *Proc. Phys. Soc.*, *45*, 142 (1933).
16. J. F. RICHARDSON and M. McLEMAN, *Trans. Instn. Chem. Engrs.*, *38*, 257 (1960).
17. J. F. RICHARDSON and J. SZEKELY, *Trans. Instn. Chem. Engrs.*, *39*, 212 (1961).
18. J. F. RICHARDSON and W. N. ZAKI, *Trans. Instn. Chem. Engrs.*, *32*, 35 (1954).
19. K. RIETEMA, "Proceedings of Symposium on Interaction between Fluids and Particles," Institute of Chemical Engineers, London (1962), p. 275.
20. K. RIETEMA and C. O. VERNER, "Cyclones in Industry," Elsevier, New York (1961).
21. A. RIEZ, *Arkiv. f. Math. Astr. Och. Fys.*, *20*, IV (1943).
22. R. G. RIGGS and S. W. CHURCHILL, *A.I.Ch.E. J.*, *10* (6), 810 (1964).
23. W. H. ROBBINS, NASA TN D-586 (1961).
24. W. H. M. ROBINS, "Proceedings of Symposium on Interaction between Fluids and Particles," Institute of Chemical Engineers, London (1962), p. 26.
25. S. I. RUBINOW and J. B. KELLER, *J. Fluid Mech.*, *11*, 447 (1961).
26. H. E. ROSE and A. J. WOOD, "An Introduction to Electrostatic Precipitation in Theory and Practice," Constable, London (1956).
27. W. M. ROHSENOW and H. Y. CHOI, "Heat, Mass and Momentum Transfer," Prentice-Hall, Englewood Cliffs, N. J. (1961).
28. P. S. ROLLER, U. S. Bureau of Mines, Tech. Paper 490 (1931).
29. M. J. ROMANELLI, "Mathematical Method of Digital Computers" (A. Ralston and H. S. Wilf, eds.) Wiley, New York (1960), p. 110.
30. J. B. ROMERO and L. N. JOHANSON, "Fluidization" (F. A. Zenz, ed.), *Chem. Eng. Progr. Symp. Ser.*, *58* (38), 28 (1962).
31. H. E. ROSE and H. E. BARNACLE, *The Engineer*, 898, 939 (1957).
32. G. ROSEN, *Phys. Fluids*, *5*, 737 (1962),
33. M. D. ROSENBERG, "Gaseous-Type Cavitation in Liquids," ONR Report Proj. NR-348-903, Acoust. Res. Lab., Harvard U., Cambridge, Mass. (1956).
34. B. ROSENBERG, David Taylor Model Basin Report 727 (1953).
35. P. ROSENBLATT and V. LaMER, *Phys. Rev.*, *70*, 385 (1946).
36. R. E. ROSENSWEIG, H. C. HOTTEL, and G. C. WILLIAMS, *Chem. Eng. Sci.*, *15*, 111 (1961).
37. A. J. ROSSANO, Jr., and L. SILVERMAN, A.E.C. NYO-1954, Air Cleaning Laboratory, Harvard School of Public Health (1955).
38. S. ROSSELAND, "Astrophysik auf Atom-Theoretischer Grundlage," Springer-Verlag, Berlin, pp. 41–44 (1931).
39. P. N. ROWE, "Fluidization" (F. A. Zenz, ed.), *Chem. Eng. Progr. Symp. Ser.*, *58* (38), 42 (1962).
40. P. N. ROWE, "Proceedings of Fluidization Symposium of the Society of the Chemical Industry," London (1963), p. 15.
41. P. N. ROWE, *Chem. Eng. Progr.*, *60*, 75 (1964).
42. P. N. ROWE and B. A. PARTRIDGE, "Proceedings of Symposium on Interaction between Fluids and Particles," Institute of Chemical Engineers, London (1962), p. 135.
43. P. N. ROWE and B. A. PARTRIDGE, *Chem. Eng. Sci.*, *18*, 511 (1963).

44. P. N. Rowe, B. A. Partridge, and E. Lyall, *Chem. Eng. Sci.*, *19*, 973 (1964).
45. S. R. Rubinowitz, *Ann. Physik*, *62*, 695 (1920).
46. W. A. D. Rudger, *Phil. Mag.*, *23*, 852 (1912).
47. W. A. D. Rudger, *Phil. Mag.*, *25*, 481 (1913).
48. G. Rudinger, "Proceedings of Multi-Phase Flow Symposium," ASME (1963), pp. 55–61.
49. G. Rudinger, *Phys. Fluids*, *7*, 658 (1964).
50. G. Rudinger, AIAA Paper 65–9 (1965).
51. G. Rudinger and A. Chang, *Phys. Fluids*, *7*, 1747 (1964).
52. D. Rush and W. Forstall, Jr., "Apparatus for the Determination of the Concentration of Helium in Air by the Thermal Conductivity Method," Meteor Internal Report No. 4, Gas Turbine Laboratory, M.I.T., Cambridge, Mass. (1947).
53. W. Rybczynski, *Bull. Acad. Sci.* (Cracovie), Ser. A, 40 (1911).

S

1. P. G. Saffman, *J. Fluid Mech.*, *13*, 120 (1962).
2. P. G. Saffman, *J. Fluid Mech.*, *22*, 385 (1965).
3. J. J. Salomone and M. Newmann, *Ind. Eng. Chem.*, *47*, 283 (1955).
4. F. M. Sauer, *J. Aerospace Sci.*, *18*, 5 (1951).
5. H. Sauerwein and F. E. Fendell, *Phys. Fluids*, *8*, 1564 (1965).
6. S. Sauer, NACA TN-147 (1957).
7. P. Savic and J. W. Gosnell, *Can. J. Chem. Engr.*, *40*, 238 (1962).
8. S. M. Scala, "Proceedings of 10th International Aeronautical Congress," Springer-Verlag, Vienna (1959).
9. S. M. Scala, *J. Aerospace Sci.*, *27* (1), (1960).
10. H. Scartazzini, *Compt. Rend.*, *230*, 97 (1950).
11. S. A. Schaaf and P. L. Chambre, "Flow of Rarefield Gas," in "Fundamentals of Gas Dynamics" (H. W. Emmons, ed.), Princeton U.P., Princeton, N.J. (1958).
12. A. E. Scheidegger, "The Physics of Flow through Porous Media," Macmillan, New York (1957).
13. H. Schlichting, "Boundary Layer Theory," McGraw-Hill, New York (1960).
14. D. C. Schluderberg, "The Application of Gas-Ceramic Mixtures to Nuclear Power," Rept. No. CF 55-8-199 ORSORT, AEC (1955).
15. J. Schmiedel, *Physik. Z.*, *29*, 593 (1928).
16. W. R. Schowalter and H. F. Johnstone, *A.I.Ch.E. J.*, *6*, 648 (1960).
17. R. D. Schultz and L. K. Branson, "The Colloidal Rocket," 2nd AFOSR Symposium on Advanced Propulsion Concepts, Boston, Mass.; Tech. Memo TM-836, ARPA Contract AF 49(638)-656; Aerojet General Corp., Azusa, Calif. (1959).
18. R. D. Schultz and R. E. Wiech, Jr., "Advanced Propulsion Techniques" (S. S. Penner, ed.), AGARD Combustion and Propulsion Panel, Pergamon, N.Y. (1961), p. 98.
19. L. E. Scriven, *Chem. Eng. Sci.*, *10*, 1 (1959).

20. G. Segré and A. Silberberg, *Nature, 189,* 209 (1961); *J. Fluid Mech., 14,* 115, 136 (1962).
21. J. R. Sellars, M. Tribus, and J. S. Klein, *Trans. ASME, 78,* 441 (1956).
22. K. T. Semrau, *J. Air. Pollution Control Assoc., 13,* 587 (1963).
23. J. Serafini, NACA Rept. No. 1159 (1954).
24. C. J. T. Sewell, *Phil. Trans. Roy. Soc.* (London), *A120,* 239 (1910).
25. A. H. Shapiro, "Dynamics and Thermodynamics of Compressible Fluid Flow," Ronald, New York (1953).
26. Sharples Corp., *Chem. Process., 16,* 180, October (1953).
27. J. Shen and J. M. Smith, *Ind. Eng. Chem. Fundamentals, 4,* 293 (1965).
28. L. B. Shepherd and C. E. Lapple, *Ind. Eng. Chem., 32,* 605 (1940).
29. W. R. Sherman, *A.I.Ch.E. J., 10* (6), 855 (1964).
30. T. K. Sherwood and D. S. Maisel, *Chem. Eng. Progr., 46,* 131, 172 (1950).
31. T. K. Sherwood and R. L. Pigford, "Absorption and Extraction," McGraw-Hill, New York (1952), p. 237.
32. W. W. Shuster and P. Kisliak, *Chem. Eng. Progr., 48,* 455 (1952).
33. R. S. Silver and J. A. Mitchell, *Trans. of the North-East Coast Inst. of Engrs. and Shipbuilders, 62,* 47 (1945).
34. L. Silverman, E. W. Conners, Jr., and D. M. Anderson, A.E.C. NYO-4610, Air Cleaning Laboratory, Harvard School of Public Health (1956).
35. C. G. Sinclair, "Proceedings of Symposium on Interaction between Fluids and Particles," Institute of Chemical Engineers, London (1962), p. 78.
36. D. Sinclair, "Handbook of Aerosols," U.S. Atomic Energy Commission, Washington, D.C. (1950).
37. M. P. Singh, *Phys. Fluids, 8,* 797 (1965).
38. R. E. Singleton, *ZAMP, 16* (4) 421 (1965).
39. J. C. Slattery, *A.I.Ch.E. J., 10* (6), 817 (1964).
40. C. A. Sleicher and M. Tribus, *Trans. ASME, 79,* 789 (1957).
41. F. T. Smith, *Proc. of Third Conference on Carbon,* 419 (1957).
42. M. Smoluchowski, *Z. Phys. Chem., 92,* 151 (1917).
43. W. R. Smythe, "Static and Dynamic Electricity," McGraw-Hill, New York (1939).
44. I. N. Snedden, "Fourier Transforms," McGraw-Hill, New York (1951), p. 7.
45. M. S. Sodha, *Brit. J. Appl. Phys., 14,* 172 (1963).
46. M. S. Sodha, C. J. Palumbo, and J. T. Daley, *Brit. J. Appl. Phys., 14,* 916 (1963).
47. S. L. Soo, *Trans. ASME, 74,* 879 (1952).
48. S. L. Soo, *Chem. Eng. Sci., 5,* 57 (1956).
49. S. L. Soo, *J. Acoust. Soc. Am., 32,* 943 (1960).
50. S. L. Soo, *A.I.Ch.E. J., 7,* 384 (1961).
51. S. L. Soo, "Analytical Thermodynamics," Prentice-Hall, Englewood Cliffs, N.J. (1962).
52. S. L. Soo, "Proceedings of Symposium on Interaction between Fluids and Particles," Institute of Chemical Engineers, London (1962), p. 50.
53. S. L. Soo, *Ind. Eng. Chem. Fundamentals, 1,* 33 (1962).
54. S. L. Soo, *Phys. Fluids, 6,* 145 (1963).

55. S. L. Soo, *J. Appl. Phys. 34*, 1689 (1963).
56. S. L. Soo, *Phys. Fluids, 7*, 1883 (1964).
57. S. L. Soo, *Ind. Eng. Chem. Fundamentals, 3*, 75 (1964).
58. S. L. Soo, "Gas-Solid Flow," Proc. of Symposium on Single and Multi-Component Flow Processes" (R. L. Peskin and C. F. Chen, eds.), Engineering Res. Pub. No. 45, Rutgers U., New Brunswick, N.J. (1965), p. 1.
59. S. L. Soo, *Proceedings of Symposium on High Temperature Conversion of Heat to Electricity.* Argonne National Laboratory-University of Arizona, ANL-TID-7687, p. 200 (1964).
60. S. L. Soo, *Ind. Eng. Chem. Fundamentals, 4*, 426 (1965).
61. S. L. Soo, "Fluid Dynamics of Multiphase System," Paper No. 36E, A.I.Ch.E Conference, Dallas, Texas (1966).
62. S. L. Soo, *Astronautica Acta, 11*, 422 (1965); also *Appl. Mech. Rev., 19*, item 2637 (1966).
63. S. L. Soo and R. C. Dimick, "Proceedings of Multi-Phase Flow Symposium," ASME (1963), p. 43.
64. S. L. Soo and R. C. Dimick, "Proceedings of 10th Symposium (International) on Combustion" (1964), p. 699.
65. S. L. Soo and H. K. Ihrig, Jr., "Proceedings of Gas Dynamics Symposium," Northwestern University (1956), p. 35.
66. S. L. Soo, H. K. Ihrig, Jr., and A. F. El Kouh, *Trans. ASME, J. Basic Eng., 82D* (3), 609 (1960).
67. S. L. Soo and R. L. Peskin, "Statistical Distribution of Solid Phase in Two-Phase Turbulent Motion," Project SQUID Tech. Report PR-80-R (ONR), Princeton U., Princeton, N.J. (1958).
68. S. L. Soo and J. A. Regalbuto, *Can. J. Chem. Eng., 38* (5), 160 (1960).
69. S. L. Soo and C. L. Tien, *J. Appl. Mech., Trans. ASME, 27*, 5 (1960).
70. S. L. Soo, C. L. Tien, and V. Kadambi, *Rev. Sci. Inst., 30*, 821 (1959).
71. S. L. Soo and G. J. Trezek, *Ind. Eng. Chem. Fundamentals, 5*, 388 (1966).
72. S. L. Soo, G. J. Trezek, R. C. Dimick, and G. F. Hohnstreiter, *Ind. Eng. Chem. Fundamentals, 3*, 98 (1964).
73. D. B. Spalding, *Fuel, 29*, 25 (1950); *32*, 169 (1953).
74. D. B. Spalding, *Aeronaut. Quart., 10*, 1 (1959).
75. K. E. Spells and S. Bokowski, *Trans. Instn. Chem. Engrs.* (London), *28*, 38 (1950).
76. L. Spitzer, "Physics of Fully Ionized Gases," Interscience, New York (1956).
77. W. T. Sproull, *J. Air Pollution Control Assoc., 10*, 307 (1960).
78. W. T. Sproull, *Nature, 190* (4780), 976 (1961).
79. J. R. Stalder and D. Jukoff, *J. Aerospace Sçi., 15*, 381 (1948).
80. Standards of Hydraulic Institute, Data Section, p. 3–12 (1951).
81. T. V. Starkey, *Brit. J. Appl. Phys., 6*, 34 (1955).
82. T. V. Starkey, V. A. Hewlett, J. H. A. Roberts, and R. E. James, *Brit. J. Appl. Phys., 12*, (10), 545 (1961).
83. T. V. Starkey and R. E. James, *Nature, 178*, 207 (1956).
84. E. S. Starkman, V. E. Schrock, K. F. Neusen, and D. J. Maneely, ASME Paper No. 63-AHGT-4 (1963).

85. L. Steg and H. Lew, "Hypersonic Ablation," General Electric Rept. R62SD 55. Presented at AGARD Hypersonic Conference TCEA, April (1962).
86. H. H. Steinour, *Ind. Eng. Chem.*, *36*, 618, 840, 901 (1944).
87. A. J. Stepanoff, *Mech. Eng.*, *86*, 29 (1964).
88. H. G. Stever, "High Speed Aerodynamics and Jet Propulsion" (Fundamentals of Gas Dynamics, Vol. 3), Princeton U.P. (1958), pp. 526–573.
89. I. H. Stockel, "Fluidization" (F. A. Zenz, ed.), *Chem. Eng. Progr. Symp. Ser.*, *58* (38), 106 (1962).
90. A. Stodola, "Steam and Gas Turbines," McGraw-Hill, New York, 1927, pp. 117–128, 1034–1073.
91. G. G. Stokes, "Mathematical and Physical Papers," Vol. 3, p. 55, Cambridge U.P. (1891).
92. J. A. Stratton, "Electromagnetic Theory," McGraw-Hill, New York (1952), p. 205.
93. J. Strong, "Concepts of Classical Optics," Appendix N from N.S. Kapany, "Fiber Optics," Freeman, San Francisco (1958).
94. J. W. Strutt (Lord Rayleigh), "Theory of Sound," Dover, New York (1929).
95. J. W. Strutt (Lord Rayleigh), *Phil. Mag.*, *34*, 94 (1917).
96. O. M. Stuetzer, *Phys. Fluids*, *5*, 534 (1962).
97. S. L. Sullivan, B. W. Hardy, and C. D. Holland, *A.I.Ch.E. J.*, *10* (6), 848 (1964).
98. M. Summerfield (ed.), "Solid Propellant Rocket Research," Academic, New York (1960).
99. G. W. Sutton, *Jet Propulsion*, *29* (2), 136 (1958).
100. G. W. Sutton, "Proceedings of Seventh Int. Combustion Symposium," Butterworth's Sci. Publication (London), 539 (1958).
101. G. W. Sutton, *J. Aerospace Sci.*, *27* (5), 375 (1960).
102. R. T. Swann and J. South, NASA TN D-741 (1961).
103. J. B. Sykes, Monthly Notes, *Royal Astronomical Soc.*, *111* (1951).
104. J. Szekely, "Proceedings of Symposium on Interaction between Fluids and Particles," Institute of Chemical Engineers, London (1962), p. 197.

T

1. L. Talbot, *Phys. Fluids*, *3*, 289 (1960).
2. Y. Tanasawa, "Applied Mechanics," Hottorie Service Foundation and Japan Science Foundation (1940).
3. S. Taneda, "Experimental Investigation of the Wake behind a Sphere at Low Reynolds Numbers," Reports of Research Institute for Applied Mechanics, IV, 99–105 (1956).
4. R. F. Tangren, C. H. Dodge, and H. S. Seifert, *J. Appl. Phys.*, *20*, 637 (1949).
5. G. I. Taylor, *Proc. London Math. Soc.*, *20*, 196 (1922).
6. G. I. Taylor, *Proc. Roy. Soc.* (London), *151A*, 421 (1935).
7. G. I. Taylor, *Proc. Roy. Soc.* (London), *164A*, 476 (1937).
8. G. I. Taylor, *Proc. Roy. Soc.* (London), *A201*, 192 (1950).
9. G. I. Taylor, *Proc. Roy. Soc.* (London), *A223*, 446 (1954).
10. G. I. Taylor, "The Shape and Acceleration of a Drop in a High Speed Air

Stream," Ptn/6600/5278/49, Chemical Defense Experimental Establishment (Gt. Britain), (1956).

11. G. I. TAYLOR, *Proc. Roy. Soc.*, *A138*, 41 (1932).
12. G. I. TAYLOR, *Proc. Roy. Soc.*, *A226*, 34 (1954).
13. T. D. TAYLOR, "Theoretical Analysis of Heat, Mass, and Momentum Transfer at Low Reynolds Numbers," Ph.D. Thesis, U. of Calif., Berkeley, Calif. (1962).
14. T. D. TAYLOR and A. ACRIVOS, *J. Fluid Mech.*, *18*, 466 (1964).
15. C. M. TCHEN, Dissertation, Delft, Martinus Nijhoff, The Hague (1947).
16. D. TER HAAR, "Statistical Mechanics," Rinehart, New York (1956), p. 245.
17. A. J. TER LINDEN, *Proc. Inst. Mech. Engrs.*, *160*, 233 (1949).
18. N. J. THEMELIS and W. H. GAUVIN, *A.I.Ch.E. J.*, *8*, 437 (1962).
19. N. J. THEMELIS and W. H. GAUVIN, *Trans. Am. Inst. Min (Metall.) Engrs.*, *65*, 225 (1962).
20. H. THOMANN, "Influence of Condensation of Water Vapor in Wind Tunnels on Heat Transfer and Recovery Temperature," Heat Transfer and Fluid Mechanics Institute (1962); also *Phys. Fluids*, *9*, 897 (1966).
21. D. G. THOMAS, *A.I.Ch.E. J.*, *6* (4) 631) 1960).
22. D. G. THOMAS, *A.I.Ch.E. J.*, *7*, 423 (1961).
23. D. G. THOMAS, *A.I.Ch.E. J.*, *7*, 431 (1961).
24. D. G. THOMAS, *Chem. Eng. Progr. Symp. Ser.*, *57*, 182 (1961).
25. D. G. THOMAS, *A.I.Ch.E. J.*, *8* (2) 266 (1962).
26. D. G. THOMAS, *Progress in International Research in Thermodynamics and Transport Properties*, ASME, 704 (1962).
27. D. G. THOMAS, *A.I.Ch.E. J.*, *8*, 373 (1962).
28. D. G. THOMAS, *Progress in International Research in Thermodynamics and Transport Properties*, ASME, 669 (1962).
29. D. G. THOMAS, *A.I.Ch.E. J.*, *9*, 310 (1963).
30. M. W. THRING, P. J. FOSTER, I. A. McGRATH, and J. S. ASHTON, "Proceedings of Internal Heat Transfer Conference" (1961); and C. R. HOWARTH, "Proc. Third Int. Heat Transfer Conf.," *5*, 122; *5*, 101 (1966).
31. C. L. TIEN, "Transport Processes in Two-Phase Turbulent Flow," Ph.D. Thesis, Princeton U., Princeton, N.J. (1959).
32. C. L. TIEN, *Trans. ASME, J. Heat Transfer*, *83C*, 183 (1961).
33. C. L. TIEN and M. M. ABU-ROMIA, *J. Spacecraft and Rockets*, *1* (4), 433 (1964).
34. C. L. TIEN and R. GREIF, *Int. J. Heat Mass Transfer*, *7*, 1145 (1964).
35. C. L. TIEN and V. QUAN, ASME Paper 62-HT-15 (1962).
36. S. TIMOSHENKO, "Theory of Elasticity," McGraw-Hill, New York (1934), p. 339.
37. F. E. TIPPETS, ASME Paper 63-WA-162 (1963).
38. E. C. TITCHMARSH, *Proc. London Math. Soc.*, *23*, 23 (1925).
39. W. TOLLMIEN, *ZAMM*, *6*, 468 (1906) ; NACA TM 1085 (1945).
40. D. M. TOMBS, "Seed Sorting," La Physique des Forces Electrostatiques, Centre National de la Recherche Scientifique, Paris (1961), p. 392.
41. R. D. TOOMEY and H. F. JOHNSTONE, *Chem. Eng. Progr.*, *a48*, 220 (1952).
42. R. D. TOOMEY and H. F. JOHNSTONE, *Chem. Eng. Progr. Symp. Ser.*, *49*, 51 (1953).
43. B. TOPLEY and R. WHYTHAN-GRAY, *Phil. Mag.*, *4*, 873 (1927).
44. J. E. C. TOPPS, *J. Inst. Petrol.*, *37*, 535 (1951).

45. L. B. TOROBIN and W. H. GAUVIN, *Can. J. Chem. Eng.*, *37*, 129, 167 (1959); *38*, 142, 189 (1960); *39* (1961).
46. L. K. TOWER, NACA RM E-57 C 11 (1957).
47. W. L. TOWLE and T. K. SHERWOOD, *Ind. Eng. Chem.*, *31*, 457 (1939).
48. H. C. H. TOWNEND, *Proc. Roy. Soc.* (London), *145*, 180 (1934).
49. A. A. TOWNSEND, *Proc. Roy. Soc.* (London), *224A*, 487 (1954).
50. M. TRIBUS and A. GUIBERT, *J. Aerospace Sci.*, *19*, 391 (1952).
51. M. TRIBUS, J. S. KLEIN, and J. REMBOWSKI, "A Method for Calculating the Rate of Evaporation and the Change in Drop Size Distribution for Pure Sprays Injected into Unsaturated Air," Univ. of Mich. Eng. Research Inst. Report, USAF WADC Contract No. AF 18-(600)-51 (1952).
52. F. G. TRICOMI, "Integral Equations," Interscience, New York (1957).
53. I. P. TROTTER, Jr., "Point Studies of Mean Flow Properties in Vertical Gas-Solids Transport Systems," 28th Annual Chem. Eng. Symposium on Dynamics of Multi-Phase Systems (1961).
54. C. TRUESDELL, *Lincei-Rend. Sc. fiz. mat. and nat.*, *22*, 158 (1957); also with R. TOUPIN, "The Classical Field Theories," Part 1 (1960), p. 469, 707; with W. NOLL, "The Nonlinear Field Theories of Mechanics," Part 3 (1965), p. 537; both of v. 3, "Handbuch der physik (S. Flugge, ed.).
55. H. S. TSIEN, *Quart. Appl. Math.*, *1*, 130 (1943).
56. E. TYLER, *London Phil. Mag.*, *16*, 504 (1933).
57. G. J. TREZEK, "Fully Developed and Accelerating Particulate Flow in Circular Ducts," Ph. D. Thesis, U. of Illinois, June, 1966.
58. G. J. TREZEK and S. L. SOO, "Proceedings 1966 Heat Transfer and Fluid Mech. Inst." (M. A. Saad and J. A. Miller) Stanford University Press (1966), p. 148.

U

1. M. S. UBEROI and L. S. G. KOVASZNAY, *J. Appl. Phys.*, *26*, 1, 19 (1955).
2. T. UEMATO, O. MUNEKAZI, and T. FUZISAWA, *Japan. Soc. Mech. Engrs. J.*, *5*, 470 (1962).
3. O. A. ULLRICH, "Size Analysis of Fine Particles and Results Obtained with an Electrical Sensing-Zone Particle Analyzer," Paper presented at the Instrument Society of America Conference, New York (Sept. 26 1960).
4. U.S. Air Force, "Handbook of Geophysica", Macmillan, New York (1960).
5. R. J. URICK, *J. Acoust. Soc. Am.* 20, 283 (1948).

V

1. J. J. VAN DEEMTER and E. T. VAN DER LAAN, *Appl. Sci. Res.*, *A10*, 102 (1961).
2. B. G. VAN DER HEGGE ZIJNEN, *Appl. Sci. Res.*, *A7*, 205 (1958).
3. H. C. VAN DE HULST, "Light Scattering by Small Particles," Wiley, New York (1957).
4. H. VAN DER KOLK, "Cyclones in Industry," (K. Rietema and C. O. Verner, eds.), Elsevier, Amsterdam (1961), pp. 77–85.
5. V. VANEČEK, R. DRBOHLAV, M. MARKVART, "Proceedings of Symposium on Interaction between Fluids and Particles," Institute of Chemical Engineers, London (1962), p. 232.

6. D. W. VAN KREVELEN and P. J. HOFTIJZER, *Chem. Eng. Prog.*, *46*, 29 (1950).

7. D. VAN ZOONEN, "Proceedings of Symposium on Interaction between Fluids and particles," Institute of Chemical Engineers, London (1962), p. 64.

8. I. E. VAS, E. M. MURMAN, and S. M. BOGDONOFF, AIAA Paper 65–51 (1965).

9. H. VERSCHOOR, *Trans. Inst. Chem. Engrs.* (London), *28*, 52 (1950).

10. R. VISKANTA and R. J. GROSH, "Heat Transfer by Simultaneous Conduction and Radiation in an Absorbing Medium," ASME Paper No. 60-RT-23 (1960).

11. R. VISKANTA and R. J. GROSH, *Trans. ASME J. Heat Transfer*, *84C*, 63 (1961).

12. R. VISKANTA and R. J. GROSH, *Int. J. Heat Mass Transfer*, *5*, 795 (1962).

13. R. E. VOLLRATH, *Phys. Rev.*, *42*, 298 (1932).

14. M. S. VOLYNSKII, *Doklady Akad. Nauk* (USSR), *62*, 301 (1948).

15. T. VON KÁRMÁN, *J. Aeronaut. Sci.*, *1*, 1 (1934).

16. B. VONNEGUT and R. L. NEUBAUER, *J. Colloid Sci.*, *7*, 616 (1952).

17. B. VONNEGUT and R. L. NEUBAUER, *Anal. Chem.*, *24*, 1000 (1952).

W

1. S. WAKIYA, *J. Phys. Soc. Japan*, *8*, 254 (1955).

2. L. WALDMANN, *Z. Naturforsch.*, *14a*, 589 (1959).

3. G. B. WALLIS, "Some Hydrodynamic Aspects of Two-Phase Flow and Boiling," International Heat Transfer Conference, Boulder, Colo. (1961).

4. G. B. WALLIS, "Proceedings of Symposium on Interaction between Fluids and Particles," Institute of Chemical Engineers, London (1962), p. 9.

5. W. H. WALTON and W. C. PREWETT, *Proc. Phys. Soc.* (London) *52B*, 341 (1949).

6. W. H. WALTON and A. WOOLCOCK, "Aerodynamic Capture of Particles," Pergamon, New York (1960), p. 129.

7. W. W. WAMSLEY and L. N. JOHANSON, *Chem. Eng. Prog.*, *50*, 347 (1954).

8. V. W. WEEKMAN, Jr., and J. E. MYERS, *A.I.Ch.E. J.*, *10* (6), 951 (1964).

9. P. P. WEGENER and A. A. POURING, *Phys. Fluids*, *7*, 352 (1964).

10. N. WIENER, *Acta Math.*, *55*, 117 (1930).

11. W. E. WELSH, Jr., and A. B. WITTE, "A Comparison of Analytical and Experimental Local Heat Fluxes in Liquid-Propellant Rocket Thrust Chambers," ASME Paper 61-AV-59, Presented at Aviation Conference, Los Angeles, Calif. (1961).

12. C. Y. WEN and H. P. SIMONS, *A.I.Ch.E. J.*, *5*, 263 (1959).

13. L. WENDER and G. T. COOPER, A.I.Ch.E. Paper No. 57-HT-31 (1957).

14. J. W. WESTWATER, Advances in Chemical Engineering (T. B. Drew and J. W. Hoopes, Jr., eds.), *1*, 2, Academic, New York (1956).

15. K. T. WHITBY, D. A. LUNDGREN, and R. C. JORDAN, Tech. Rept. No. 13, Mech. Eng. Dept., U. of Minnesota (1961).

16. H. J. White, "Industrial Electrostatic Precipitation," Addison-Wesley, Reading, Mass. (1963).

17. H. J. WHITE, *AIEE Trans.*, *70*, 1189 (1951).

18. V. E. WHITMAN, *Phys. Rev.*, *28*, 1287 (1926).

19. D. J. WILEN, "Magnetic Field Interactions with a Moving Metal Slug," B.S. Thesis, M.I.T., Cambridge, Mass. (1961).

20. R. H. WILHELM and M. KWAUK, *Chem. Eng. Progr.*, *44*, 201 (1948).
21. R. H. WILHELM and W. J. RICE, *A.I.Ch.E. J.*, *4*, 423 (1958).
22. R. H. WILHELM and S. VALENTINE, *Ind. Eng. Chem.*, *43*, 1199 (1951).
23. F. A. WILLIAMS, *Phys. Fluids*, *1*, 541 (1958).
24. F. A. WILLIAMS, "Eighth International Symposium on Combustion," Williams and Wilkins, Baltimore (1961), p. 50.
25. F. A. WILLIAMS, "ARS Progress Series in Astronautics and Rocketry," Academic, New York (1961).
26. F. A. WILLIAMS, S. S. PENNER, G. GILL, and E. F. ECKEL, *Combustion and Flame*, *3*, 355 (1959).
27. J. C. WILLIAMS and R. JACKSON, "Proceedings of Symposium on Interaction between Fluids and Particles, Institute of Chemical Engineers, London (1962), p. 282.
28. W. W. WILLMARTH and H. T. NAGAMATSU, *J. Appl. Phys.*, *23*, 1089 (1952).
29. H. WISE, J. LORELL, and B. J. WOOD, "Fifth Symposium on Combustion," Reinhold, New York (1955), p. 132.
30. H. G. WOLFHARD and W. G. PARKER, *Proc. Phys. Soc.* (London), *62B*, 523 (1949).
31. J. R. WROBEL and H. N. McMANUS, Jr., *Developments in Mechanics*, *1*, 578 (1961).
32. P. J. WYATT, *J. Geophys. Res.*, *65*, 1673 (1960).
33. R. WYNKOOP and R. H. WILHELM, *Chem. Eng. Progr.*, *46*, 300 (1950).
34. C. WU, "Transport Properties of a Partially Ionized Gas-Solid Suspension," Ph.D. Thesis, U. of Illinois (1966).

Y

1. G. YASUI and L. N. JOHANSON, *A.I.Ch.E. J.*, *4*, 445 (1958).
2. H. C. YEH and W. J. YANG, *Phys. Fluids*, *8*, 806 (1965).
3. J. L. YORK and H. E. STUBBS, *Trans. ASME*, *74*, 1157 (1952).
4. J. L. YORK, H. E. STUBBS, and M. R. TEK, *Trans. ASME*, *75*, 1279 (1953).
5. T. YUGE, *J. Heat Transfer, Trans. ASME*, *82*, 214 (1960).

Z

1. F. A. ZENZ, *Ind. Eng. Chem.*, *41*, 2801 (1949).
2. F. A. ZENZ, "Fluidization" (D. F. Othmer, ed.) Reinhold, New York (1956), p. 77.
3. F. A. ZENZ, *Petrol. Refiner*, *36*, 173 (1957).
4. F. A. ZENZ, *Ind. Eng. Chem. Fundamentals*, *3* (1) 65 (1964).
5. F. A. ZENZ and D. F. OTHMER, "Fluidization and Fluid-Particle Systems," Reinhold, New York (1960).
6. J. ZIEREP, *Z. f. Flugwiss*, *3*, 22 (1953).
7. J. W. ZINK and L. P. Delsasso, *J. Acoust. Soc. Am.*, *30*, 765 (1958).
8. N. ZUBER, *Int. J. Heat Mass Transfer*, *2*, 83 (1961).
9. S. A. Zwick, "The Growth and Collapse of Vapor Bubbles," Hydrodynamics Lab. Report No. 21–19, Calif. Institute of Technology, Pasadena, Calif. (1954).
10. S. A. ZWICK, *Phys. Fluids*, *3*, 685 (1960).

SUBJECT INDEX

509

AUTHOR INDEX